PRINCIPLES OF
PLANT PATHOLOGY

PRINCIPLES OF PLANT PATHOLOGY

S. A. J. TARR, Ph. D., D. Sc.
Reader in Plant Pathology, The Department of Biological Sciences, University of Exeter

WINCHESTER PRESS
NEW YORK

First published 1972

Published by
WINCHESTER PRESS
460 Park Avenue
New York   10022

Library of Congress catalog card no. 71–189145

ISBN   0 87691 069 X

Printed in Great Britain by
Butler and Tanner Ltd, Frome and London

Contents

Preface

This book is an attempt to provide a reasonably comprehensive account of plant pathology for students wishing to specialize in the subject, and for those other students who wish to obtain a background of plant pathology. The emphasis throughout is on principles, with references to sources of more detailed information where necessary. Since plant diseases caused by fungi have been more intensively studied than those due to any other single cause, the subject is discussed mainly with reference to fungal plant pathogens but reference is made to other groups of plant pathogens where appropriate. Although viruses cause many important plant diseases a detailed treatment of this group is precluded by limitations of space; fortunately several excellent books on plant viruses have been published in recent years.

Different plant pathologists have different ideas as to the form a book on plant pathology should take. After considerable thought I have adopted a fairly conventional plan in which two introductory chapters are followed by chapters on the main causes of disease in plants, the interaction of plant and pathogen, the interaction of populations of plants and pathogens as influenced by the environment, and the control of plant diseases. A brief chapter on plant injury due to insects, nematodes, mites and other animals has been included because, in my view, a wider approach to plant damage whether due to pathogens, pests or non-parasitic agents is desirable. The book ends with a chapter on sources of information on plant diseases. It would be unrealistic to suppose that the text is free from errors and notification of any errors or omissions will be appreciated.

I should like to thank Dr G. C. Ainsworth for contributing Chapter 2, Professor S. D. Garrett, FRS for checking Chapter 8, Mr H. G. Morgan (Chapter 9), Dr G. G. Pritchard (Chapter 3) and Miss S. M. Robb (Chapter 4). My thanks are also due to the authors and publishers who have allowed me to reproduce figures and tables from books and published papers, as acknowledged. I am greatly indebted to Miss M. A. Turner who took many of the original photographs, and to Dr J. E. Crosse (Figs. 6.2, 6.3, 6.4), Miss S. M. Robb (Fig. 4.7), Mr P. S. Rattan (Figs. 17.2, 26.2) and Professor J. Webster (Fig. 17.3) who very kindly allowed me to use photographs in their possession.

The Hatherly Biological Laboratories S. A. J. TARR
University of Exeter May 1972
Devonshire

To N.P.T. and G.P.T.

1 Introduction : general concepts

The precise scope of plant pathology (phytopathology), the study of disease in plants, is difficult to define. Plant pathology is concerned with all aspects of plant disease and thus has a much wider content than human pathology which is only one of the many aspects of disease in man including hygiene, public health, immunology, preventive medicine and therapy to mention but a few. This situation has arisen largely because much more effort has been directed towards investigating human diseases, for it is natural that man should seek to cure his own ills rather than those of plants. It is only within comparatively recent years that plant pathologists have begun to specialize in individual aspects of disease in plants, whereas those concerned with human diseases have done so for much longer. Considerable progress has been made in many aspects of plant pathology in the past 25 years or so. The literature is extensive and ever-increasing, so much so that it is becoming difficult to keep abreast of it, and pathologists are specializing in particular aspects of the subject.

The fields in which notable advances have been made include the interaction of plant and pathogen at the chemical, molecular and genetical level (still not well understood), the study of plant viruses and root diseases, the chemistry of fungitoxicity, and the mathematical analysis of the development and spread of pathogens within crops as related to meteorological and other factors. On the practical side can be mentioned the production of more effective crop protection chemicals, especially systemic ones, and improved equipment for applying them, the breeding of disease resistant varieties of plants, and the beginnings of international cooperation in the study and control of plant pathogens.

'Disease' is sometimes used in a very wide sense to include all types of plant injury whether caused by fungi, bacteria, parasitic angiosperms, viruses, mycoplasmata, non-parasitic agents, insects, mites, nematodes or other animals. There is some logic in this but it is difficult for any one person to have an adequate knowledge of all these agents, and in practice injury caused by pests – insects, mites, nematodes and other animals – is generally investigated by the entomologist and nematologist. The other disease inciting agents mentioned above remain the province of the plant pathologist, although there is an increasing tendency for virologists and bacteriologists to deal with virus and bacterial diseases of plants, respectively. Nevertheless, it is extremely useful for anyone concerned with plant diseases to have a working knowledge of the kind of plant injury that pests cause and of the relationships between pests and disease inciting organisms (pathogens). There are interesting parallels in the reactions of plants to pathogens, to pests and to mechanical and chemical injury, parallels which are likely to shed light on the fundamental nature of plant injury. On the more practical side plant pathologists working with plants in the field or glasshouse will certainly encounter pest damage and should be able to recognize it as such.

A wider approach to plant injury, whether caused by pathogens, viruses, non-parasitic agents, pests or weeds has much to commend it, particularly in developing countries where the need to reduce plant injury, however caused, is often urgent. The trend towards this wider outlook on plant disease is reflected in the increased attention now being paid to methods of simultaneously controlling pathogens and pests, for example by combined fungicide-insecticide treatment of the sowing seed, and by soil fumigation which controls pathogens, nematodes and weeds. Plant pathology, thus enlarged, would comprise a number of branches each with its own specialists: thus there would be specialists in virus diseases, specialists in nematode diseases, and also specialists in the disorders of particular crop plants or groups of crop plants. The scope and organization of plant pathology would thus become comparable with that of human medicine.

Terminology

Each science has its own terms and concepts. Some of those used by plant pathologists have been borrowed from human pathology, cannot be precisely defined and are used loosely and in different ways by different workers. Attempts have been made to rationalize their meanings, as in the lists of definitions compiled in the U.S.A. (Anon., 1940), Britain (Anon., 1950) and more recently in the Netherlands (Anon., 1968a), and by Robinson (1969) for terms used in disease resistance. These lists emphasize the ambiguous nature of such terms as 'virulence' and conclude that they should not be used, but they do not suggest more satisfactory substitutes. This lack of a standardized and generally accepted terminology is a serious problem in plant pathology and generates much confusion. It should be borne in mind when considering the explanations of some of the more widely used terms and concepts of plant pathology briefly outlined below. Other terms are explained as they occur, and a knowledge of biological terms in general use is assumed.

Disease, pathogen, parasite, virulence, aggressiveness

Although familiar, **disease** is difficult to define with precision, as discussed above. It involves harmful physiological changes in the plant and is considered further elsewhere (p. 18). It may be caused by non-parasitic agents such as adverse soil conditions and is then sometimes described as a **disorder**, or it may be caused by a pathogen – indeed some would restrict its application to infectious diseases caused by living organisms and viruses. In a literal sense a **pathogen** is any agent which causes damage, but the term is generally used to denote living organisms, especially fungi and bacteria, which attack plants. Most, but not all, pathogens are also **parasites** in that they derive the materials they need for growth from a living plant, the **host** or **suscept,** as distinct from **saprophytes** (**saprobes**) which derive these materials from dead organic matter. Parasites may be **obligate** in that they are restricted to living tissue (also known as **biotrophs**) or **facultative** – able to colonize living or dead tissue. Obligate is also used to denote those parasites which have not been grown in axenic culture, that is, free from any other organism. **Necrotrophs** (**perthophytes**) grow on dead tissue which they have previously killed, as discussed elsewhere (p. 186). There are also a few non-parasitic pathogens which injure the plant by producing substances toxic (**phytotoxic**) to it before invading it. The position of viruses is anomalous and they are best regarded separately: they cannot be regarded as living organisms but they do act as pathogens in that they cause disease. Neither can they logically be regarded as parasites since they are not organisms.

Virulence and **aggressiveness** are ambiguous terms not infrequently confused with **pathogenicity,** the ability to cause disease. Virulence has been used as a measure or degree of pathogenicity in the sense that a pathogen may comprise several strains (races) of varying virulence, some of which may be **avirulent** (**non-virulent**). It has recently been used to denote qualitative rather than quantitative differences in pathogenicity, strains differing in virulence when they attack different varieties of the host plant. Virulence is an extremely ambiguous word and wherever possible should be avoided. Aggressiveness is equally ambiguous and has been used by Gaumann (1950) to describe the capacity of a parasite to invade and grow in its host plant and to reproduce on or in it. In this sense high aggressiveness can be combined with low pathogenicity, as in some obligate parasites which invade the plant efficiently but cause only minimal damage to it, at least in the early stages of attack. Aggressiveness is also used as a measure of pathogenicity.

It is evident that there is considerable confusion as to the meanings of these terms and Gaumann (1950, p. 177) concludes: 'The ambiguity in the use of all these terms is itself a reflection of the endless diversity of the parasitic life, which can never be completely covered by any single term. The choice of the most felicitous turn of phrase to convey the facts of each particular case must therefore always be left to the discretion of the individual.'

Immune, resistant, susceptible, tolerant, symptomless carriers, hypersensitivity

These terms are generally used to describe the reactions of plants to disease inciting agents, although some workers restrict their application to diseases caused by pathogens. **Immune** means exempt from infection – the establishment of a parasitic relationship between two organisms – and in this sense is an absolute quality. **Resistance** and **susceptibility** are measures of the extent to which the plant is damaged by the pathogen or, more often, the extent to which the plant prevents the entry or subsequent growth of the pathogen within its tissues. High resistance (low susceptibility) approaches immunity, and between it and high susceptibility are varying degrees of resistance or susceptibility.

Resistance has been classified as **horizontal** (uniform) when it is evenly spread against all races of a pathogen, or as **vertical** (differential) when it is effective against some races of the pathogen but not against others. It may be **polygenic** (determined by many genes), **oligogenic** (several genes) or **monogenic** (one gene). The genes involved may be **major** or **minor** with respect to their effectiveness in conferring resistance. Two other terms are relevant here. **Tolerant** plants offer little resistance to the pathogen but, although infected, are only slightly affected in that the symptoms – the visible reaction of the plant to the pathogen – are relatively mild. The extreme of tolerance is shown by **symptomless carriers** in which the disease inciting agent (usually a virus) is present but causes no symptoms. **Hypersensitive** plants develop minute necrotic flecks or spots resulting from rapid death of the cells in the vicinity of the invading pathogen (the **infection court**), so that the progress of the latter is halted although it does not necessarily die immediately. Hypersensitivity thus confers high resistance and is sometimes used in the sense of immunity.

Entry, infection, symptoms

Under suitable conditions the **entry** (**penetration**) of a pathogen into a susceptible plant is followed by **infection** in which a parasitic relationship between the two organisms is established. In highly resistant or immune plants, penetration may occur but not infection. Infection is followed by **colonization** in which the pathogen advances through the tissues of the host to varying extents. Colonization may be limited, as in self-limiting lesions, or a considerable area of tissue may be invaded by the pathogen. In **systemic infections** the pathogen spreads through the plant to varying extents, often seeming to have little adverse effect on the tissues through which it grows or is transported.

Diseased plants show several visible **symptoms,** known collectively as the **syndrome,** by which the disease is recognized and after which it is named. The most important types of symptoms are (1) **necrosis** (death) of the infected tissue; (2) increased cell division (**hyperplasia**) and/or increase in cell size (**hypertrophy**), leading to overgrowths such as galls, tumours and witch's brooms: hypertrophy is also used in a general sense to denote increased size of an organ; (3) reduced growth (**hypoplasia**) or stunting of the infected plant or organ: chlorosis, the failure of chlorophyll development, is regarded by some as a form of hypoplasia.

Fungitoxic, fungicidal, fungistatic

These words describe agents which adversely affect fungi. **Fungitoxic (antifungal)** substances are harmful to fungi and include **fungicides** which kill fungi, and **fungistats** which prevent their growth as long as fungus and fungistat are in contact; similarly **bactericides** and **bacteristats** in respect of bacteria. Fungistatic and fungicidal are relative terms, and a fungistat may be fungicidal if present in a sufficiently high concentration.

Symbiosis, mutualism, antagonism, synergism

Symbiosis, the living together of unlike organisms, includes parasitism if the host remains alive. More often it is used to describe associations in which there is a considerable degree of tolerance between the organisms involved (**mutualism**). This is in contrast to **antagonism (antibiosis)** in which one organism is injured by another, especially when the antagonist exerts its harmful effects by secreting toxic substances (**antibiotics**). **Synergism** occurs when the combined effect of two organisms acting together is greater than the sum of the two separate effects. It is similarly used in respect of fungicides.

Significance of plant diseases and pests

The importance of minimizing the heavy crop losses due to diseases and pests in a world in which starvation and malnutrition are widespread is self-evident. Such losses are often high in agriculturally underdeveloped regions where measures to control diseases and pests are rarely applied to peasant food crops although they may be applied to plantation crops grown for export. Sometimes, because of their rapidly increasing population, such areas are often those least able to afford any reduction in their food supplies, and under these conditions crop failure, whatever the cause, is likely to have disastrous consequences. This problem will continue and intensify for many years to come.

Control of diseases and pests is only one of the ways of increasing crop yields. Others include use of fertilizers, cultivation of higher yielding varieties of crop plants, and improved crop husbandry. The processing of natural vegetation into acceptable food is a promising approach, and other ways of producing the basic food needed by man will no doubt be developed. The problem is often one of distribution rather than production, in that surplus grain may be destroyed in one country while people starve in another. Until distribution of food can be rationalized on a world basis attention must be directed to increasing crop yields and food production in areas where they are low. In some cases these increases will need to be combined with voluntary measures to restrict population increases, but effective control of plant pathogens and pests would augment enormously food production in many parts of the world. Thus, the crop loss caused by smuts and witchweed (*Striga* spp.) to sorghum in Africa is estimated at some 9% – about one million tonnes of grain, enough to feed more than $5\frac{1}{2}$ million people for a year (Vallega and Chiarappa, 1964).

The disastrous effects of such diseases as black stem rust of wheat (*Puccinia graminis f. sp. tritici*), potato blight (*Phytophthora infestans*), rice blast (*Pyricularia oryzae*), coffee rust (*Hemileia vastatrix*), and the diseases of cacao caused by the swollen shoot complex of viruses are well known and have been graphically described by Large (1940), Klinkowski (1970) and Carefoot and Sprott (1969). These are spectacular diseases which have had great social and economic consequences, but it should not be forgotten that there are many other diseases which, although less spectacular, are a steady and ever-present drain on crop yields.

Precise knowledge of the losses caused by pathogens and pests on a world or regional basis is lacking, and the numerous estimates are of varying degrees of credibility. An exhaustive analysis of the crop losses in major world crops has been carried out by Cramer (1967), while losses due to diseases in the former British colonies are estimated by Padwick (1956) to have been 20–30% for cacao, cotton, wheat, potato and tobacco, and about 12% for all the crops considered. Insect pests probably caused similar losses so that a total of some 20% yield loss due to diseases and pests seems likely and this is probably a conservative estimate. Detailed estimates of crop losses and costs of disease control in California, U.S.A., in 1963 have been published (Anon., 1965); losses averaged about 10%, worth about 264 million dollars, for all crops – equivalent to nearly 400,000 'lost' hectares. Control measures cost some 60 million dollars, a total of about 324 million dollars debitable to plant diseases in that year. A general account of crop losses caused by plant diseases is given by McClellan *et al.* (1964).

It is often said that crop losses due to diseases, pests and weeds in agriculturally advanced countries amount to about 10–20% annually, and this is probably as good an estimate as any. In less developed areas the losses are almost certainly greater, sometimes much greater, as those who have seen the devastation not infrequently wrought by diseases and pests in such areas can testify. In addition there is a growing awareness that even in agriculturally advanced countries the full yield potential of crop plants is rarely, if ever, realized. Apparently minor pathogens and pests probably cause greater losses than is at present appreciated, especially those which attack the roots of plants.

Content and arrangement of the text

There is much more information on those plant diseases caused by fungi than on those caused by other groups of pathogens and, for this reason, the principles of plant pathology are discussed here chiefly with reference to fungi, with reference to other disease inciting agents where appropriate. Plant viruses (and *Mycoplasma*-like organisms) have been studied more intensively in recent years but limitations of space preclude a detailed account of this important group. Bacterial diseases of plants are treated in less detail because – with some notable individual exceptions – they are less important than fungal and virus diseases, and this applies also to the plant diseases caused by parasitic flowering plants.

A short chapter on the more important pests which attack plants, and on the relationships between pests and pathogens, is included because, as discussed above, I feel that plant pathologists should know something about all agents which damage plants. There is a separate chapter on root diseases since these show special, interesting features often related to the fact that roots live in soil, a medium biologically and chemically more complex than the air which surrounds the shoots of plants.

The study of plant diseases can be divided into four interrelated aspects: the causes of disease (aetiology); interaction of plant and pathogen (including pathogenesis, the development of disease in the plant); interaction of populations of plants and pathogens and environment (epidemiology); and control of plant diseases. This is a convenient arrangement if not followed too rigidly, and is adopted in this book after the present introductory chapter and the historical introduction to plant pathology contributed by Dr G. C. Ainsworth.

2 Historical introduction to plant pathology

G. C. Ainsworth

Plant diseases are older than agriculture and since biblical times there has been speculation on their cause, cure, and prevention. As an applied scientific discipline, however, plant pathology only began to emerge towards the end of the eighteenth century and this brief survey is confined to the past 250 years. Whetzel (1919) in his useful *Outline of the History of Plant Pathology*, divided the eighteenth and nineteenth centuries into the Zallingerian, Ungerian, Kühnian, and Millardetian Periods (after the names of dominant workers) and from 1906 as the Present Era. Large (1940) in his most readable *Advance of the Fungi*, illustrated the development of plant pathology by considering a succession of typical diseases such as potato blight, vine mildew, wheat bunt, club root of crucifers, and coffee rust. Other patterns are discernible. The nineteenth century is characteristically the age of the pathogen when the pathogenicity, first of fungi, then of bacteria, and at the turn of the century of viruses, was recognized and studies were made of the development and life histories of pathogens for their own sake. Geographically, plant pathology was of European origin; towards the end of the nineteenth century emphasis shifted to North America, where the U.S.A. is still in the van of progress, but after the two World Wars – particularly after the Second – the spread of research on plant pathology became worldwide.

Fragmentation is yet another tendency. In the early nineteenth century, as evidenced by the Reverend Miles Joseph Berkeley's famous series of articles in the *Gardeners' Chronicle* (Berkeley, 1854–57), 'vegetable pathology' included a consideration of plants in a state of health and all types of disorders, whether of parasitic or non-parasitic origin or caused by insects or other pests. Subsequently, in many countries animal pests have been relegated to entomologists (with the notable exception of plant pathogenic nematodes which often fall to the plant pathologist) and thus plant pathology has not the comprehensiveness of medical or veterinary science which are its equivalents. This is possibly one reason why plant pathology or 'plant health' has never attracted the degree of public attention given to medicine and veterinary science. Another reason – as mentioned in Chapter 1 – is that man has always shown more concern for his own health and that of his animals than for that of his plants. As in medicine, there is the inevitable increase in specialization within plant pathology, and host-pathogen systems and other topics are taken over as 'models' for academic research by workers who may never have seen a diseased plant in the field. This is all to the good: knowledge is increased. But it must be remembered that a feedback to plant pathology is not inevitable, and the right end of plant pathology is the prevention and cure of disorders of plants.

Pathogenicity

Fungi

The concept of pathogenicity, which is fundamental to plant pathology, evolved slowly and was on the whole accepted with difficulty. Robert Hooke (1635–1703) who in his *Micrographia*, 1665, was the first to illustrate in detail a microscopic fungus which attacked plants, believed rose rust (*Phragmidium mucronatum*) (figure 2.1) to be derived from putrified host

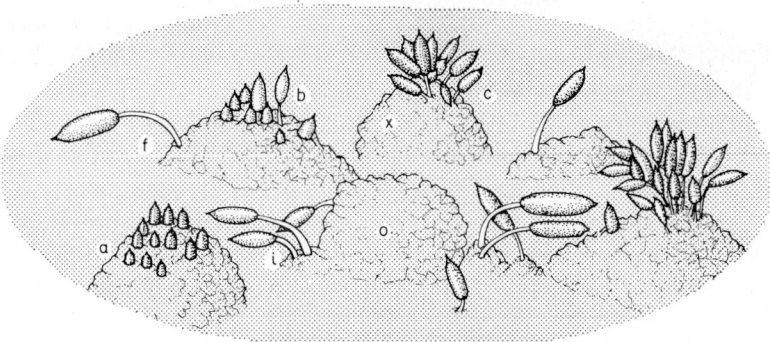

Figure 2.1   The first illustration of a plant parasitic fungus, believed to be *Phragmidium mucronatum* (rose rust), as seen by Hooke in 1665.

tissue (Hooke, 1665). Although the idea of spontaneous generation persisted for almost another 2 centuries this view did not prevent the making of correct recommendations for the control of disease. For example, the Reverend Stephen Hales (1667–1761) in his *Vegetable Statics*, 1727, (Hales, 1727) regarded 'moldy fen' (or mildew) of hops to be derived from the corruption of the stagnating sap resulting from reduced transpiration in damp weather, but 'because the small seeds of the quick growing mold . . . are blown over the whole ground', he asked 'might it not then be advisable to burn the fenny hop-vines as soon as the hops are picked, in the hopes thereby to destroy some of the mold?' Two years later, in 1729, the Italian

Pier Antonio Micheli (1679–1737) in *Nova Plantarum Genera* (Micheli, 1729) described the cultural experiments by which he demonstrated that several common moulds were distinct entities. The significance of these results, however, like that of so many of Micheli's acute observations, was not appreciated at the time. It was Spallanzani at the end of the century and Tyndall and Pasteur some 50 years later who finally disproved spontaneous generation, while as a parallel development the identities of different microfungi were generally recognized even if their association with disease was often considered to be a secondary (saprobic) rather than a primary (parasitic) relationship.

Cereal rusts

Rust of cereals was known to the Romans, but it was not until 1767 that Felice Fontana (1730–1805) described and illustrated as 'black rust' and 'red rust' the teliospores and urediospores of *Puccinia graminis*, the cause of stem rust of wheat (Fontana, 1767). Fontana did not recognize a connexion between the two states, but he did recognize the rusts as parasitic plants responsible for the disease. By 1805 Joseph Banks (1743–1820) in his well known and frequently quoted pamphlet (Banks, 1805) was cautiously expressing his opinion that the two spore states were of one rust and he also drew attention to the association of barberry plants with wheat rust. He considered it 'notorious' that barberry was subject to attack by a 'yellow parasitic fungus' and suggested that the parasitic fungus of barberry and that of wheat were one and the same species. Unknown to Banks, experimental evidence for this view had been obtained the previous year by his fellow countryman Thomas Andrew Knight (1759–1838) who infected wheat plants with stem rust by brushing them with a branch of rust-diseased barberry which had been damped with water (Ramsbottom, 1912). Similar, but more comprehensive experiments were made independently in Denmark in 1816 by Niels Pedersen Scholer (1772–1851), but orthodoxy was not convinced (Lind, 1913) and heteroecism in *P. graminis* was not generally accepted until after de Bary (1865, 1866).

Cereal smuts

Smuts of cereals, and wheat bunt (*Tilletia caries*) in particular, also have a long history, outstanding contributions to the elucidation of the aetiology of bunt having been made by two Frenchmen. In 1775 M. Tillet (1714–91), Master of the Mint at Troyes, concluded from a series of experiments, both well designed and executed, that the disease resulted from the contamination of the seed with bunt dust (Tillet, 1755; Wehnelt, 1937) but it was left to Bénédict Prévost (1755–1819) to prove the mycotic nature of the infection. Over a 10 year period Prévost made an outstanding and comprehensive study which showed the bunt dust to be fungus spores, whose germination he recorded. He also discovered copper to be toxic to spores and recommended a copper sulphate steep as a preventive seed treatment. *The Memoir* (Prévost, 1807) in which he recorded his findings and set out his conclusions is a landmark not only for plant pathology but for micro-biology and for biology in general.

Potato blight

In the 1830's the Italian Agostino Bassi (1773–1856) demonstrated that the muscardine disease of silkworms was caused by the fungus now known as *Beauveria bassiana* (Bassi, 1835), and a few years later David Gruby (1810–1898) elucidated the mycotic nature of thrush and ringworm in man (Zakon and Benedek, 1944). Evidence was thus available that fungi are able to cause disease in plants, animals, and man. When, however, potato blight swept through Europe in the 1840's, resulting in the Irish famine (Woodham-Smith, 1962; Bourke, 1964) its aetiology was the subject of long and heated controversy (see Large, 1940) and only slowly did the view gain ground that the mould associated with the affected potatoes was the cause and not the result of the disease. It was de Bary (1861, 1863) who finally established beyond criticism that *Phytophthora infestans* was the causal agent of potato blight.

Among many other examples of economically important fungal diseases of plants subsequently described, powdery mildew (*Uncinula necator*) and downy mildew (*Plasmopara viticola*) of the grapevine were major con-tributory factors in establishing both the pathogenicity of fungi and the economic importance of plant diseases.

Bacteria

The American Thomas J. Burrill (1839–1916) of the University of Illinois was the first to describe a bacterial disease of plants when in 1878–1884 he showed that fireblight of pears and apples was caused by the bacterium now known as *Erwinia amylovora* (Elliott, 1930). Shortly after-wards Jan Hendrik Wakker (1859–1927) independently showed that yellow disease of hyacinths was also caused by a bacterium (*Xanthomonas hyacinthi*). However, the early work on plant pathogenic bacteria and the establishment of their study as an important branch of plant pathology will always be associated with the name of Erwin Frink Smith (1854–1927) who, for most of his working life, was on the staff of the United States Department of Agriculture. Erwin Smith is especially noted for his studies on crown gall and for the texts (Smith, 1905–14, 1920) in which he sum-marized work by himself and others in this field. He is also still remembered for his controversy with the German bacteriologist Alfred Fischer (1858–1913) who denied that bacteria were a primary cause of disease in plants.

Viruses

Virus diseases of plants have a long history. Among the many diseases of unknown cause, potato leaf roll, as 'leaf curl', gave concern in the second half of the eighteenth century and 'broken tulips' were illustrated by painters 200 years before that. There are also several eighteenth-century records of transmission of leaf mottling of jasmin and passion flower by grafting. In 1886 Adolf Mayer (b. 1843), the German director of the Agricultural Experiment Station at Wageningen, Netherlands, introduced the term 'mosaic' and showed that tobacco mosaic was infectious (Mayer, 1886). In 1892 the Russian Dmitrii Ivanowski showed that tobacco mosaic virus passed a bacteria-proof filter (Ivanowski, 1892), and 6 years later M. W. Beijerinck (1851–1931), the distinguished Dutch microbiologist, introduced the concept that tobacco mosaic was a 'contagious living fluid' (Beijernick, 1898).

During the present century the study of virus diseases has been one of the most actively developing branches of plant pathology, and viruses now rank second in importance to fungi as agents of plant disease. Publications on virus diseases of plants account for approximately 20% of the annual literature (Ainsworth, 1964). For further details regarding the development of plant virology the historical review by Corbett (1964) should be consulted.

Textbooks

General texts

Books devoted to plant diseases began to appear towards the end of the eighteenth century, and were characterized by a taxonomic approach. Disorders of plants were grouped into classes and genera, and even particularized as species, and following medical practice, these various symptomatological categories were dignified by Latin names. Two of the best known works of the period are the Latin dissertation by J. B. Zallinger (1731–85) (Zallinger, 1773) and the monograph by the Italian F. Ré (1763–1817) (Ré, 1807). It was still generally held that any fungi associated with disease were derived from diseased plant tissue and this autogenic hypothesis was given detailed expression by the German Franz Unger (1800–70) as late as 1833 in his *Die Exantheme der Pflanzen* (Unger, 1833). Berkeley's series of 173 articles on vegetable pathology in the *Gardeners' Chronicle* for 1854–57 (Berkeley, 1854–57), although never published in book form, can perhaps be noted here for they mark a watershed between the old and the new. While a generic classification of disease was adopted, Berkeley believed fungi to be a primary cause of plant disease and his approach, in what is his major contribution to plant pathology, was both broadly based and detailed.

Berkeley was basically a mycologist, and during the next 50 years other leading mycologists – particularly Anton de Bary and O. Brefeld in Germany, the two Tulasne brothers in France, and M. S. Woronin in Russia – by deepening knowledge of parasitic fungi greatly influenced the approach to plant disease.

Julius Kühn (1825–1910), an experienced practical agriculturist who became professor of agriculture at the University of Halle, can be considered the first plant pathologist and his famous textbook (Kühn, 1858) set a new and high standard. During the next 40 years plant pathology was dominated by German textbooks, including those by E. Hallier (1831–1904) (Hallier, 1868), O. Kirschner (1851–1925) (Kirschner, 1890), Karl von Tubeuf (1862–1941) (Tubeuf, 1895), and A. B. Frank (1839–1900) (Frank, 1895–96). Special mention must be made of the textbooks by P. C. M. Sorauer (1838–1916) the first edition of which appeared in one volume in 1874 (Sorauer, 1874). Subsequently, a second edition appeared in two volumes, a third in three, and today Sorauer's *Handbuch*, which covers both pests and diseases, is a standard reference work of half a dozen volumes which are periodically updated.

At the turn of the century comparable texts began to appear in other countries. For example, in France there were those by E. E. Prillieux (1829–1915) (Prillieux, 1895–97) and E. G. Delacroix (1858–1907) (Delacroix, 1902, 1908) and George Massee's (1850–1917) *Text-book of Plant Disease* in England (Massee, 1899). At this time there was, however, a shift of geographical emphasis and the excellent *Fungous Diseases of Plants* by B. M. Duggar (1872–1956) of Cornell University published in 1906 (Duggar, 1906) marked the beginning of the dominance of English language textbooks on plant pathology of United States origin as instanced by those of F. D. Heald (1872–1954) whose books (Heald, 1926, 1937) were much appreciated by students.

Delacroix, in a posthumous work completed by A. Maublanc (1880–1958), wrote on tropical plant pathology (Delacroix, 1911) as did E. J. Butler (1874–1943) in his classical text (Butler, 1918) based on his work and experience in India. Later, Butler began a single volume general text which was completed after his death by S. G. Jones (Butler and Jones, 1949). This marks the end of an era. The literature on phytopathology is now so extensive and diverse that, as in so many branches of science, recourse is having to be made to multi-author syntheses of progress, as for example the three-volume work edited by Horsfall and Dimond (1959–60).

Special texts

There have been special texts on bacterial diseases since those of Erwin Smith – for example, those of Elliott (1931) and Dowson (1887–1963) (1949) – while virus diseases have been treated in several works of which two – for which several editions have been called – are K. M. Smith's text dealing with specific diseases (K. M. Smith, 1937) and F. C. Bawden's more general account of plant viruses (Bawden, 1939). Mycological books dealing with rusts, smuts, and other fungi causing diseases of plants are too numerous to catalogue here.

Practising plant pathologists usually specialize in the diseases of certain crops or groups of crops and create a need for monographs on the pathology of special crops. The name of Robert Hartig (1839–1901) is associated with the development of the pathology of forest trees (Hartig, 1882) and Sorauer wrote the first monograph on diseases of fruit trees (Sorauer, 1879).

In conclusion it may be noted that the pattern of general texts has usually been determined by the pathogens – viruses, bacteria, fungi, diseases caused by the last being arranged according to the prevailing mycological classification. In monographs on particular crops, however, it has frequently been more convenient to group the diseases according to the parts of the host plant chiefly affected.

Control

Chemicals

Many nutritional disorders of plants can be remedied by the application of chemicals. Appropriate treatment with fertilizers or the macronutrients required for plant growth is usually designed by the agriculturist or horticulturist, but deficiency diseases, disorders typically caused by the lack of such elements as boron, iron, magnesium, and manganese which are needed in fairly small amounts (the so-called trace elements) commonly fall within the plant pathologist's province. Usually, the control of plant disease by chemicals is thought of as the eradication or the prevention of infection of pathogens by the application of chemicals toxic to the pathogens, and here, comment will be restricted to these practices.

For centuries treatment with diverse substances has been advocated against diseases and pests of plants, but most of these panaceas were of little use. Of the three elements sulphur, copper, and mercury, compounds of which have been most widely used as fungicides during the present century, sulphur has the longest history – one that can be traced back to classical times. A landmark in the use of sulphur was the introduction in 1802 by William Forsyth (1737–1804), gardener to George III, of lime sulphur for the control of mildew on fruit trees. Aqueous suspensions of flowers of sulphur were also first used about that time against fungal diseases.

The toxicity of copper to fungi had been noted by Prévost (1807) and others but the turning point not only in the use of copper but in the use of chemicals to control plant disease in general was the introduction by P. M. A. Millardet (1838–1902) of the copper-lime complex known as Bordeaux mixture for the control of downy mildew (*Plasmopara viticola*) which was then ravaging French vineyards (Millardet, 1885). It was soon discovered that Bordeaux mixture was equally effective against potato blight and for the next 50 years Bordeaux mixture was used more than any other fungicide against a wide range of diseases in all parts of the world. Its supplementation by 'fixed copper' compounds and by the wide range of organic fungicides and other compounds and formulations now available has been well and concisely summarized in the historical review by McCallan (1967). It is perhaps of interest to recall that apart from the limited use of streptomycin against certain bacterial diseases, in marked contrast to their use in human and animal medicine, antibiotics have made a negligible contribution to the control of plant disease.

Resistant varieties

That different species or varieties (cultivars) of plants show differences in disease incidence has long been noticed. R. Austen (d. 1676) recorded that 'Crab trees . . . are usually free from canker' (Austen, 1657) and there are several other similar references to such differences in the literature of the next 200 years. During the opening years of the twentieth century the American W. A. Orton (1877–1930) broke new ground by the introduction of crop varieties resistant to *Fusarium* (Whetzel, 1919), and the rediscovery of Mendel's results led Rowland H. Biffen (1874–1949) at Cambridge, England, to investigate the inheritance of susceptibility and resistance in wheat varieties to yellow rust (*Puccinia striiformis*). He was able to demonstrate that these characters showed the Mendelian pattern of inheritance (Biffen, 1904, 1907) and this finding helped to put on a firm basis the breeding for resistance not only of cereals to rust but also of many other plants. Plant breeders today make one of the major and most satisfactory contributions to the control of plant disease.

Legislation

Pests and diseases of plants respect no boundaries and the control of a disease of major economic importance is thus usually a social problem, the solution of which frequently requires legal sanctions. The earliest legislation against plant disease related to the destruction of barberry plants in attempts to prevent the rusting of wheat. The first such law was introduced in Rouen, France, in 1660, long before the connexion between barberry and wheat rust was understood, and during the next century similar laws were passed in the New England states of North America. (The Massachusetts Barberry Law of 1775 is reprinted in Plowright (1889)). Towards the end of the nineteenth century Boards or Departments of Agriculture began to be set up by governments, and thus plant disease became a matter for continuous government scrutiny and action, the latter being of two main types: first, measures designed to control the spread and if possible the eradication of a disease recently introduced or recognized in the country; second, prevention of the introduction of potentially serious pathogens from other countries.

In Great Britain a Board of Agriculture was instituted in 1889 but it was not until 1907 under the Destructive Insects and Pests Act that the Board was empowered to deal with both insect pests and fungal diseases by the issue of Orders. The first Orders against diseases were against American gooseberry mildew (*Sphaerotheca mors-uvae*), which in 1900 had been recorded for the first time in Europe, and wart disease of potatoes (*Synchytrium endobioticum*). The latter was brought under control by the 1930's as a direct result of this official action which required the reporting of outbreaks and enforced the use of resistant varieties in areas where the disease had occurred. The resistant stocks were officially tested and certified, thus providing an early example of officially guaranteed propagating material. There are now in Great Britain schemes for the certification of seed potatoes, strawberries and other soft fruits, tree fruits, and hops. The earliest official control of the quality of propagating material was the testing of seed for purity, germinability, and freedom from disease, and the International Seed Testing Association was formed for the exchange of information in this field and for the standardization of seed testing methods.

Since 1942 the Ministry of Agriculture has had a voluntary Agricultural Chemicals Approval Scheme whereby consumers are offered guidance on the reliability of a wide range of products for controlling pests and diseases.

The exclusion of disease is typically legislated against by the complete or partial embargo of plant material from other countries or by the importation under licence of material certified as healthy by the exporting country; but even such material may be required to be grown in quarantine until proved free from disease. The National Quarantine Act of 1912 initiated such action by the U.S.A.

Recently, it has been recognized that even national legislation is not sufficient and that international cooperation in devising regulations for the movement of plants and plant products about the world is most desirable. The Food and Agriculture Organization of the United Nations (FAO) has a Plant Protection Branch with both Near and Far East Regional Offices, and in 1951 FAO adapted the earlier text of the 1929 Plant Protection Convention of the International Institute of Agriculture, Rome. The present convention has fifty signatory nations each of which undertakes to organize a Plant Protection Service to supervise the phytosanitary control of plant imports and the organization of phytosanitary control within the country. There are also various regional international organizations including the European and Mediterranean Plant Protection Organization (EPPO) and others for Central and South America, South-East Asia, and the Pacific Region. Africa is covered by the Inter-African Phytosanitary Commission (IAPSC) which, begun in 1954 for Africa south of the Sahara, now attempts the coordination of plant disease legislation for the whole of Africa.

Further details of the history of plant pathology in Great Britain are given by Marsh (1968) and Ainsworth (1969).

3 The causes of plant diseases: non-parasitic agents

There is no entirely satisfactory definition of disease. It has been defined as harmful deviation from normal functioning of physiological processes (Anon., 1950), a definition which has the merit of emphasizing the dynamic nature of disease as a reaction between the plant and the causal agent of the disease. It also makes the point that disease involves abnormal physiological changes which result in the visible changes by which we recognize the disease, and that diseases adversely affect the plant. These aspects are discussed by Stakman and Harrar (1957) who define a plant disease as 'a physiological disorder or structural abnormality that is deleterious to the plant or to any of its parts or products, or that reduces their economic value', that is including deterioration of harvested plant products such as timber. It is important to distinguish between the disease, for example potato blight, and the causal agent (*Phytophthora infestans*), and between injury (usually a sudden short-lived act) and disease which is a more prolonged process – transient as opposed to continuous irritation (Horsfall and Dimond, 1959). There is, however, growing evidence that the response of plants to physical or chemical injury resembles in some respects their response to at least some pathogens (p. 248) so that similar symptoms can and do result from dissimilar agents.

It is customary and convenient to distinguish between diseases due to non-parasitic (inanimate or non-transmissible) causes and those due to parasitic (animate or transmissible) agents. Apart from viruses, this seems a reasonable distinction provided it is appreciated that there is often a close connexion between injury and pathogens, as in wound-pathogens or, for example, the colonization of frost damaged tissue by secondary invaders which aggravate the damage.

Plant damage caused by pests (insects, mites, nematodes and so on) is not usually the concern of the plant pathologist, but he occasionally has to deal with it and a working knowledge of these pests is therefore useful. Pests are not uncommonly associated with virus, bacterial and fungal pathogens as disseminators, inoculating agents, or providers of the initial injury through which the pathogen invades the plant. In some cases the relationship may be a more or less obligate one approaching symbiosis. The biological relationship between insects and fungi are diverse and interesting, ranging from entomogenous fungi to termites which cultivate fungi as food in 'fungus gardens'. Similar relationships perhaps hold for nematodes and fungi; some fungi enter roots through lesions caused by nematodes and some are parasitic on nematodes and might be used in their control. The physiological responses of the plant to injury by pests are probably basically similar to its response to pathogens, so that similar symptoms tend to develop.

Diseases due to non-parasitic causes

In a broad sense most of these diseases derive from unfavourable environmental conditions and so do not spread from plant to plant in the field. When the causal factor is corrected or removed the plant recovers although it may meantime have suffered a considerable set-back to growth. Non-parasitic injury can also predispose the plant to attack by pathogens which may be more destructive and more persistent.

Non-parasitic causes of disease include (1) adverse climatic conditions, (2) mechanical and chemical injury, and, (3) adverse soil conditions, the last-named including those caused by deficiency, excess or imbalance of elements essential for normal plant growth (the deficiency and toxicity diseases). It is very doubtful whether plant damage caused, for example, by hail or lightning should be included under disease – it seems more logical to regard it as injury – and similarly for crop failures due to inadequate rainfall. There are many inconsistencies of this sort. Information on diseases of non-parasitic origin is given in many books on plant disease, for example Stakman and Harrar (1957), Walker (1950), Heald (1926), Peace (1962: trees and shrubs), Chester (1947), Boyce (1938: trees).

There are also disturbances of genetical origin, such as chlorosis, spotting and striping of leaves, dwarfing, variegation, abnormal inflorescences (see Meyer, 1966), and others. The symptoms of these conditions can resemble those caused by pathogens but they do not spread from plant to plant and they are likely to be inherited to varying extents. Harmful genetical aberrations tend to die out but others may persist. The causes of some diseases have not been established and these are commonly referred to as being of 'unknown origin' until such time as their nature is elucidated.

Adverse climatic conditions

These include temperature, humidity, light, wind, lightning, hail, sleet, ice, snow, and rain.

Temperature is one of the most important factors affecting the growth and distribution of plants. As would be expected, tropical plants are generally intolerant of low temperatures whereas the reverse applies to many temperate plants. Although some plants are injured by a low but above-freezing temperature, freezing is the major cause of plant injury at low temperatures. If sufficiently severe, freezing brings about the formation of ice crystals in the intercellular spaces and within the cells, resulting in injury to the plasma membrane and often death of the cell with subsequent discoloration. Desiccation and changes in protoplasmic colloids may also be involved and the adverse effects of freezing are not well understood. Young succulent parts of high water content (young leaves, buds, blossom, growing points) are especially susceptible to damage by frost and the affected tissue often becomes somewhat translucent, thereafter turning black and drying up. This tissue is often invaded by opportunist pathogens such as *Botrytis cinerea*. The onset of cold weather in relation to the developmental stage of the plant is important in that a moderate spring frost can severely damage young leaves and blossom, whereas a much harder frost in winter when the plant is dormant may do little harm. Alternate freezing and thawing can damage the inner bark and cambium of some trees and can also cause the soil to contract and expand, thus damaging the roots and sometimes lifting them from the soil, so exposing them to frost damage. Prolonged frost may bring about wilting through immobilization of the soil water due to freezing, and typical drought symptoms are often to be seen on cabbages and other plants during lengthy cold spells in winter. Frost damage can be minimized by covering the plants with straw or paper, by growing them in places least liable to frost, and by artificial warming, but this is possible only in glasshouses or with valuable orchard crops at blossom time.

Excessive heat can also kill plant tissue, especially if the tissue is succulent, but it is difficult to distinguish this from the harmful effects of high light intensity since the two commonly occur together. Temperatures of 40–50°C for any considerable time are likely to injure temperate and warm temperate plants to varying extents depending on their size and age. Seedlings are especially liable to scalding and heat canker because they are without shade and are near the surface of the soil where temperatures may rise to above 50°C on clear sunny days in some areas. Plants differ in their tolerance to heat and some tropical ones tend to survive hot dry weather in a semidormant condition. Leaf scorching can also result from hot, dry winds which also have a desiccating effect on plants. Heat injury to seedlings can sometimes be reduced by crowding, leaving a cover of weeds over the soil, by mulching, or by shading. Scalded and frosted plant tissue is liable to invasion by fungi and bacteria. Resistance of plants to frost, heat and drought seems to be related (see Levitt, 1951).

Light is necessary for development of chlorophyll and inadequate light results in weak, aetiolated, spindly plants which are liable to attack by pathogens. Excessively bright light destroys chlorophyll and can be destructive. According to MacMillan (1918, 1923) sunscald of beans in Colorado is caused by the ultraviolet rays in bright sunlight at high altitude. In addition, the time of flowering of some crop plants is affected by day length (photoperiod).

Humidity affects the rate of transpiration of plants and very dry atmospheric conditions can be injurious, particularly if combined with heat and wind. It also influences the sporulation of fungal pathogens and their invasion of host plants, but generally speaking it is of little importance as a cause of disease in plants.

Other climatic factors which can damage plants include the following. (1) High winds which cause breaking of tree branches, lodging of cereals, and loosening of plants in the soil leading to root damage. Numerous small necrotic spots develop on leaves exposed to high wind carrying particles of sand or soil. (2) Hail and sleet may severely damage foliage, flowers and fruit, particularly the latter, resulting in laceration and decay following attack by secondary invaders. (3) Heavy rain, particularly when combined with high wind, can beat down plants and result in extensive lodging, waterlogging of the soil and leaching of soluble nutrients. (4) Lightning damage to trees is well known but herbs, particularly the more succulent ones, are sometimes affected, the damage taking the form of a roughly circular area of dead plants. Necrosis of the parenchymatous tissue (pith, cortex) frequently occurs, with subsequent decay of the damaged tissue (see Walker, 1950). (5) Accumulation of snow and ice can break the branches of trees, and ice forming in crevices of the bark may cause it to crack open, thus exposing the inner tissues to attack by pathogens. Plants covered by snow may, however, be partially protected from frost.

The physical injury caused by these factors is often aggravated by microorganisms which invade the damaged tissue. Such secondary decay can be reduced by the application of protectant fungicides as soon after the original injury as possible, for example by application of fungicidal paint to places where branches have broken away. Little can be done to prevent these climatic visitations, but it is sometimes possible to minimize their harmful effects by such common-sense methods as planting windbreaks to protects plants in exposed windy places.

Mechanical and chemical injury

Increased use of machines in agriculture and horticulture has inevitably resulted in greater mechanical damage to crops by cultivators, sprayers, harvesters, and others. This paves the way for entry by shoot and root invading parasites, especially if the machines are used inexpertly or carelessly. Mechanical separators and seed drills can damage sowing seed and so bring about reduced emergence and poor stands, the damaged seed being attacked by soilborne pathogens; in fact anything which damages the seed – rough handling, insect attack or unsuitable storage conditions – can have this effect, particularly with soft seed or that having a thin, easily broken seed coat as in some varieties of groundnut. Similar considerations apply to other planting material (tubers, bulbs and so on), and also to stored vegetables and fruit, all of which are likely to decay if bruised or broken.

Chemical injury from faulty application of fungicides, insecticides and, especially, herbicides is also on the increase, and care must be taken to prevent spray drift, for some plants are extremely susceptible to even traces of hormone and other weed killers. Overdoses of pesticides and the application of unsuitable pesticides, such as lime-sulphur on 'sulphur-shy' plants, can also be damaging. Phytotoxic substances are likely to occur in the air of industrial areas where atmospheric pollution is high. These include sulphur dioxide, hydrogen sulphide, coal gas and chlorine. Industrial dust, such as cement dust, may cause plant injury, and 'smog' (smoke and fog) damage is becoming increasingly serious in some highly populated areas. The symptoms of chemical injury generally appear on the leaves, often as a rather indefinite browning, necrosis and eventually shedding.

Smog damage to plants has been investigated by Middleton *et al.* (1950). As described by Rich (1964) the main phytotoxic component of smog is peroxyacetyl nitrate (PAN), a reaction product of ozone and waste hydrocarbons from traffic. Ozone itself is formed by photochemical action of ultraviolet light on exhaust fumes and can reach a sufficient concentration to be phytotoxic. It also results from electrical discharges (lightning) and possibly by the action of ultraviolet light on volatile hydrocarbons produced by large masses of vegetation. Some may perhaps originate from the ozone-rich outer layers of the stratosphere. Ozone damage to plants is reviewed by Rich (1964) who describes the first symptoms as water soaked spots, followed by chlorosis along or between the veins, and eventually necrosis and drying up of affected leaves, which may be shed.

Darley and Middleton (1966) list the principal phytotoxic substances in polluted air as ethylene (causing epinasty and leaf abscission), hydrogen fluoride (marginal and apical browning and necrosis of leaves, leading to tattered margins), nitrogen dioxide (leaf bleaching), ozone (stippling, mottling and chlorosis of leaves), peroxyacyl nitrates (PANs, typical silvering or bronzing of the lower leaf surface), and sulphur dioxide (interveinal chlorosis). Damage to plants by photochemical air pollution is reviewed by Middleton (1961) and Heck (1968). This type of plant damage is likely to become more widespread with increasing industrialization and is already a problem in parts of the U.S.A. On the credit side it may be noted that some pollutants appear to be fungitoxic, and black spot of roses caused by *Diplocarpon rosae* is rarely found in industrial areas where the air contains more than about 100 mg of sulphur dioxide per cubic metre (Saunders, 1966). Other plant pathogens reported to be absent from areas of high atmospheric pollution include *Microsphaera*

Table 1   Principal phytotoxic atmospheric pollutants
[from Saunders, 1970]

(1) Deposited matter
    (a) Dust and grit
    (b) Soot and smoke
(2) Sulphur dioxide
(3) Sulphuric acid droplets
(4) Fluorine and fluorides
(5) Photochemical or oxidant pollutants
    (a) Photochemical smog
    (b) Ozone
    (c) Peroxyacyl nitrates, e.g. peroxyacetyl nitrate (PAN)
    (d) Oxides of nitrogen
    (e) Ethylene
    (f) Aldehydes
(6) Heavy metals, e.g., iron, lead, etc.

alphitoides (oak mildew), several conifer rusts including *Melampsora cerastii* (*Melampsorella caryophyllacearum*), *Phragmidium* spp. and *Puccinia graminis* (black rust of cereals) (Saunders, 1970). The phytotoxicity of various gases likely to be present in the atmosphere is reviewed by Thomas (1951), and the effects of air pollution on plants generally are discussed by Thomas (1961) and Webster (1967). The main phytotoxic atmospheric pollutants are listed in Table 1 from Saunders (1970).

Little is known about the effects of atmospheric pollutants on the metabolic processes of plants. There is evidence that ozone and peroxyacetyl nitrate, both photochemically produced phytotoxicants, adversely affect the semi permeability of the cellular membranes – possibly by reacting with the lipids of cell membranes and also by reducing the ability of the plant to repair the damage (Rich, 1964). These two pollutants are also reported to reduce photosynthesis, to damage chloroplasts, and to interfere with amino acids and enzymes, particularly those dependent on sulphydryl groups for their activity; these aspects are discussed by Duggar and Ting (1970).

Adverse soil conditions

The principal factors involved here are the moisture content, physical structure, aeration, chemical composition, and reaction of the soil. These are closely interrelated and change in one is likely to bring about changes in the others and in the numbers and types of microorganisms present.

Adequate soil moisture is necessary for normal growth but different plant species have greatly different requirements, and a moisture level sufficient for one species may be quite inadequate for another. With rain grown crops not only the amount of rain but also its distribution and form are important. Irregular rain resulting in alternating periods of water-logging and desiccation is likely to weaken the plant and thus render it more susceptible to pathogens, particularly root pathogens, whereas the same amount of rain distributed evenly generally produces vigorous plants less liable to infection.

Excessive soil moisture tends to occur in low lying, poorly drained, clay soil in high rainfall areas. If prolonged, it results in chlorotic, weak, stunted plants with subnormal roots liable to attack by soil fungi, although the latter will probably be discouraged by the anaerobic conditions of waterlogging. Seed sown in waterlogged soil may rot before or after germination. Excessive soil moisture no doubt adversely affects the plant in several ways – through reduced oxygen supply, or by the accumulation of carbon dioxide or other toxic metabolites perhaps produced by anaer-obic soil microorganisms – and the problem is not well understood. It can be reduced by improving the drainage of the soil, by avoiding low lying fields which are liable to flooding, or by adjustment of planting date to avoid heavy rainfall, although the last named is of limited scope. Soil moisture can be regulated in glasshouses and in irrigated crops in arid regions.

Prolonged deficiency of soil moisture results in failure of the seed to germinate, weakening or death of the young seedling before or after emergence, stunted growth, shedding of young flowers and fruits and buds, and premature flowering and senescence. In extreme cases the plant wilts and dies. Drought is generally worst on light, sandy, well drained soils of poor water retaining capacity. Similar damage can result from water shortage in the plant due to root incapacitation by fungi, nematodes, insects or physical damage caused by agricultural implements. Some root rot diseases are encouraged by dry conditions. Temporary wilting can occur in very hot, sunny weather – especially at mid-day – even when there is adequate soil moisture, but the plants normally recover when cooler conditions return.

The physical structure of the soil not only affects its water retaining capacity and aeration but, if sufficiently hard and compact, can retard the growth of roots and so result in stunted plants. Impenetrable 'pans' may form through accumulation and compaction of hard, insoluble particles at a certain level in the soil, thus leading to near-cessation of root development with accompanying die-back of the shoots and sometimes death of the tree. The position of such pans will depend on ploughing depth and the depth to which water penetrates. They can sometimes be broken up by physical means although this will probably involve damage to the roots. Coarse gravel soils may hold insufficient water for most plants except in very wet areas, and under these conditions the soluble nutrients will tend to be leached out. Very heavy soils are likely to be waterlogged in wet weather and more or less impermeable – except for cracking – when dry. These factors will influence the growth of the plant and its liability to infection by pathogens, particularly those attacking its roots. Aeration of soil is greatly influenced by its physical structure and moisture content, and poor aeration is likely to result in stunted, weak plants.

Unsuitable chemical composition or pH of the soil can be damaging to plants. Some plants can withstand considerable alkalinity or acidity, but most grow best around neutrality or slight acidity. An unfavourable pH results in poor growth and sometimes death. It also has indirect effects on the availability of mineral elements in the soil to plant roots, as in calcareous soils where it reduces the availability of iron and manganese (lime induced chlorosis). It is sometimes possible to correct high acidity by addition of lime and, less easily, high alkalinity by addition of sulphur, although this may have phytotoxic effects. The salts responsible for the unfavourable pH can sometimes be washed out by irrigation. The most important diseases caused by unfavourable chemical composition of the soil are the deficiency and toxicity diseases considered below.

Diseases due to deficiency, excess or imbalance of the elements essential to plant growth

In addition to water, oxygen and carbon dioxide, plants require fairly large amounts of nitrogen, smaller quantities of potassium, phosphorus, calcium, magnesium, sulphur and iron, and trace amounts of manganese, zinc, molybdenum, boron, copper, and chlorine. Some plants are also thought to require sodium, silicon, aluminium, gallium or various other elements, and growth may be enhanced by these and others (see Stiles, 1961), but whether they are essential to all plants is uncertain.

Arnon (1950) suggested three criteria for defining an essential element – that the plant cannot complete its life cycle without it, that its effect on the plant is direct, and that its action is specific so that it cannot be replaced by any other element. This last criterion is perhaps too narrow in that the functions of some essential elements can be partly or fully taken over by related ones. Essential elements are perhaps best described as those which function in metabolism whether or not their action is specific ('metabolism nutrients': Nicholas, 1957, 1961).

More refined methods of experimentation might enable this list of essential elements to be extended since some of the supposedly pure salts used in water culture experiments probably contain minute amounts of impurities, and this is also likely to be true of the apparatus and water used. A discussion of non-essential mineral elements is given by Bollard and Butler (1966).

Deficiency, excess or imbalance of essential elements can all be harmful to the plant. Nutrients can only be taken up in certain forms by roots and if present in other forms are not available to the plant unless converted to an available form by microorganisms or other agents. Hence a plant can show deficiency symptoms because the apparently deficient element is present in an unavailable form. Antagonism – the retardation of absorption of one substance by another (for example, potassium by calcium) – can occur, and pH changes may affect the absorption of some elements. Mineral nutrients are normally absorbed from dilute solutions, otherwise there is a danger of phytotoxicity. Deficiencies are to some extent associated with certain types of soil and weather; thus elements present in a highly soluble form are likely to be washed out of sandy soils by heavy rain. Soil microorganisms, particularly bacteria, can affect the availability of nutrients to plants; for example, bacteria which convert manganous into manganic salts are encouraged in alkaline soil and may be involved in lime induced chlorosis since manganic compounds are not readily available to the plant. Microbial conversions probably play an important role in the availability or otherwise of other elements, such as iron, and need further study. The factors affecting availability of micronutrients are discussed by Leeper (1952), and Barber (1968) has reviewed microorganisms in relation to the inorganic nutrition of higher plants.

Deficiency symptoms can appear on almost all parts of the plant and are often characteristic, but in other cases they may be rather indefinite and difficult to identify. They may resemble those due to other non-parasitic agents, fungi, bacteria, insects and (especially) viruses. Somewhat similar symptoms may result from deficiencies of different elements, and deficiency of one element can cause different symptoms in different plants. Symptoms of nitrogen, phosphorus and magnesium deficiency tend to appear on the lower leaves and spread upwards, whereas those of other elements – calcium, copper and boron – spread from the younger to the older parts of plants according to where they are needed. Chlorosis, mottling, abnormal pigmentation, premature senescence, necrosis, die-back, stunting of leaves and roots, distortion, and lodging and tillering of cereals occur in deficiencies of different elements (these are described below), and in a general way the symptoms are related to the function of the element in the plant. Thus, a shortage of iron or magnesium, both necessary for development of chlorophyll, results in chlorosis.

Generally speaking, mineral elements may function in the plant by influencing the osmotic pressure of cells, the pH of cells by perhaps acting as buffers, and the permeability of cytoplasmic membranes. They are also constituents of protoplasm and cell walls, and play an important role in enzyme activity (Hewitt, 1958). The role of mineral elements in plants is discussed by Evans and Sorger (1966), Gauch (1957), Reuther *et al.* (1958: tree crops), Broyer and Stout (1959: macronutrients), Nicholas (1961), Pirson (1955), McElroy and Nason (1954: micronutrients in enzyme systems), Hewitt (1951), Mulder (1950), Steward (1963: inorganic nutrition of plants) and others.

Different species of plants differ considerably in their requirements for, and tolerance to, macronutrients and micronutrients, so that one species may develop conspicuous symptoms of deficiency or toxicity whereas another species in the same patch of soil appears unaffected. Numerous excellent photographs of symptoms on a range of plants will be found in Wallace (1961).

Faulty mineral nutrition can predispose plants to attack by some pathogens and pests. Potato blight (*Phytophthora infestans*) is said to be more severe on plants growing in magnesium deficient soil, and excess of nitrogen (particularly easily available nitrogen) results in 'soft' plants which tend to be more susceptible to pathogens and pests. According to Gerretsen (1937) the grey specks on leaves of manganese deficient oat plants are due to bacterial infection of the roots rather than directly to manganese deficiency, alkaline products of the bacteria perhaps being translocated to the leaves where they cause the typical grey lesions. The resistance of the roots to the bacteria is presumably lower in manganese deficient plants. Such indirect effects can be important in that the damage caused by pathogens and pests to deficient plants may be greater than that due to the deficiency alone.

Diagnosis of deficiency diseases

This can be difficult, particularly if more than one element is deficient or if the syndrome is obscured by damage caused by adverse weather, pathogens or pests. The following are the more important methods used, and a fuller account is given by Wallace (1961). Practical experience is invaluable in diagnosis of mineral deficiencies, and there are many pitfalls which the experienced observer has learnt to avoid.

Symptoms

The effects of each deficiency on the plant under consideration must be known, this knowledge being obtained from the results of systematic sand or water culture experiments carried out under controlled conditions in the laboratory. This method is useful, particularly to experienced observers, but in some plants (notably cereals) the symptoms may not be sufficiently distinctive for reliable identification. The plants may have suffered considerable damage by the time that symptoms become clear enough for diagnostic purposes. It is, however, a rapid method requiring no apparatus or laboratory work, although the latter may be advisable to confirm the diagnosis.

Indicator plants

These are plants which develop pronounced and distinctive symptoms in response to deficiences of specific elements; young oat plants develop grey leaf specks if manganese is deficient. They can be planted in the suspected soil and include various brassicae, sugarbeet, lettuce and others. A list of indicator plants and the deficiency symptoms which they develop is given by Wallace (1961). This is a useful adjunct to diagnosis on symptoms.

Experimental treatment of affected plants

Several trial elements are separately applied to the affected plant by injection into leaves, shoot tips, petioles, and stems or, more often, by spraying over the leaves (see Roach, 1938). Solid salts can be injected into the branches of affected trees. The solutions are best applied to young plants by a sprayer or a watering can with a fairly fine rose. The test solutions should be strong enough to be effective but care must be taken to avoid phytotoxicity; between 0·1 and 1% is often suitable for micronutrients and between 1 and 4% for macronutrients. It may be necessary to use a wetting agent if the leaves of the plant are waxy. Responses from spraying often appear after 1 or 2 weeks or sometimes less. Application of chemicals to the soil is generally less effective and slower as they may not be immediately available to the plant. Selection of trial elements should be based on symptoms or other evidence available. This is a valuable method of diagnosis, especially for deficiencies of elements required only in very small amounts.

Chemical analysis of affected plants

Analysis of comparable leaves of healthy and deficient plants can give useful information. It is essential that the leaves used should be as similar as possible, that is, of similar age, and collected and treated in the same way and at the same time as there may be considerable differences between the chemical composition of young and old leaves of the same plant. More rapid methods of plant analysis have been devised, some based on colour or turbidity tests, and spectrographic methods can be used to detect not only multiple deficiencies but also toxicities. Outfits for plant analysis in the field are available and give quick and reasonably accurate results when properly used. Plant analysis is very useful when used in conjunction with visual diagnosis, and is reviewed by Smith (1962).

Chemical analysis of soil

The results of some analytical methods indicate the amount of a given element in the soil but not necessarily whether it is present in a form available to the plant. Various methods of determining availability have been used, often based on extraction with solutions of neutral salts such as sodium chloride. Soil analysis is useful for phosphorus and potassium, but must be carefully carried out and the results interpreted by experienced workers. Portable soil analysis outfits for field use are sometimes used but full analysis is only possible in the laboratory. This method is particularly useful for detecting deficiencies or toxicities before the crop is sown and should be a routine procedure in the utilization of new land.

Bioassay methods

Aspergillus niger and certain other microorganisms have in recent years been used to estimate minute amounts of magnesium, manganese, copper, zinc and molybdenum and some other elements in soil or plant material. The fungus requires these microelements in small amounts for normal growth in liquid culture, and deficiency will result in reduced or abnormal growth and/or sporulation. A known quantity of the material to be assayed is incorporated in a culture solution containing all the nutrients except that being assayed. The resulting growth of the fungus is estimated by comparison with a standard series of known concentrations of the nutrient. The weight of mycelium, amount of sporulation, type of growth, and other characters give useful information as to possible deficiency in the material assayed; for example, the conidia of *A. niger* tend to be yellow at low copper content but turn brown to black at high concentrations. Bioassay methods of this sort necessitate the use of specially purified glassware, water and chemicals as described by Wallace (1961).

Which of these methods is best used will depend on individual circumstances including the laboratory facilities and trained staff available. It may be advisable to use several methods or to check the results of visual diagnosis by, for example, spraying experiments with the elements thought to be deficient.

Correction of deficiency diseases

When identified, the deficient element or elements can be supplied to the plant in several ways. Macronutrients – nitrogen, phosphorus and potassium (NPK) – are usually applied as fertilizers to the soil in fairly large amounts. Micronutrients are applied in much smaller quantities, kilogrammes per hectare, either mixed with the normal fertilizer or seed or applied directly to the growing plants. This can be done by spraying the plants with a dilute solution of a suitable salt of the deficient element in what is judged from the results of soil or plant analyses to be the required amount. Care must be taken to avoid phytotoxicity due to a too highly concentrated solution or to application at an unfavourable time, for example in bright sunlight. Spraying is especially useful if a quick result is required and with substances which may be immobilized in the soil.

Injection into stems and leaves is sometimes used, especially with trees, and even hammering nails of the deficient element into branches has been effective in some cases. Soil treatment, which renders available nutrients which were previously unavailable, may be possible. In these corrective measures it is important that approximately the right amount of the deficient element be applied and this should previously be estimated or, if this is not possible, should be based on experience and the phytotoxicity of the element which is being supplemented. Too little will be ineffective, too much may damage the plants and upset the balance of nutrients; tolerance to a specific micronutrient differs in different species of plants but many have a narrow tolerance to boron and copper. Tolerance to macronutrients is generally wider and these are of course applied in larger amounts. Foliar application of nutrients to plants is discussed by Boynton (1954), Wittwer and Teubner (1959), and Halliday (1961).

Deficiency of individual elements

Brief notes on the deficiency of individual elements are given below; fuller information can be obtained from Wallace (1961) and Stiles (1961).

Nitrogen

This element occurs in several plant constituents including proteins, amino acids, alkaloids and chlorophyll. Nearly half the weight of dried protoplasm is said to be nitrogenous, and nitrogen is required in considerable quantities by all plants. Some nitrogen compounds are readily translocated from old to young tissue where they are most needed, so that deficiency symptoms appear on the older plant parts, and the growing points are the last to be affected. These symptoms include stunting of roots, shoots and leaves, the latter becoming chlorotic and the older ones developing reddish-purple 'autumnal tints' or being prematurely shed. Buds may die, and flowering and fruiting are reduced so that yields are likely to be poor. Cereals may show reduced tillering and poor yield of grain, while nitrogen deficient fruit trees tend to produce small, hard, highly coloured fruits which keep well (regulation of nitrogen supply can be used to control colour and keeping quality). Nitrogen deficiency is sometimes seen in neglected orchards and fields where heavy weed growth takes up much of nitrogen present in the soil. The addition of large amounts of carbon as organic matter to soil encourages microbial growth which 'locks up' much of the available soil nitrogen and so results in deficiency. Microbiological factors, including the relative numbers and activity of nitrifying and denitrifying bacteria, affect the soil nitrogen content and excessive acidity or waterlogging may reduce nitrification and so cause symptoms of nitrogen deficiency. Continuous cropping without replacement of the nitrogen lost tends to result in nitrogen deficiency unless effective legumes are grown, especially in light, sandy soils lacking organic matter.

Nitrogen deficiency can be corrected by the use of nitrogenous fertilizer, by including legumes in the rotation, and by modifying soil conditions to encourage nitrification and discourage denitrification. In acute cases dilute solutions of nitrogenous compounds such as urea can be sprayed over affected plants, particularly fruit trees and bushes.

Excessive nitrogen can be harmful in that it produces soft, lush plants which are often more susceptible to diseases and pests and which tend to remain in a vegetative condition so that flowering and fruiting are delayed. Cereals may develop long succulent stems which break easily.

Phosphorus

This element takes part in many chemical reactions in the plant and is present in phospholipids, nucleic acids, many coenzymes and nucleoproteins. Phosphates are also thought to act as buffers in maintaining a suitable pH in plant cells. The functions of phosphorus and nitrogen seem to be interrelated and deficiency symptoms of the two elements can be somewhat similar. Phosphorus is involved in nitrogen metabolism and seems to be of particular importance in seeds and seedlings, in root development, and in the ripening of seeds and fruits. Its role in photosynthesis is reviewed by Arnon (1956), and its metabolism by McElroy and Glass (1951, 1952).

Inorganic and organic phosphorus compounds occur in soil but are often insoluble until transformed chemically or microbiologically. Soluble phosphates tend to be in short supply and move only slightly in soil, especially in heavy clay soils or where the iron content is high; they are commonly 'fixed' by calcium in neutral and alkaline soils and by iron and aluminium in acid ones. Symptoms of phosphorus deficiency in many ways resemble those of nitrogen deficiency and include stunting of roots, shoots and leaves, reduced flowering, premature defoliation and reduced yield. The leaves, however, tend to be dull, bluish-green with purplish tints, and in some plants there is a dull bronzing with purple or brown spotting. The leaf margins sometimes have a brown, scorched appearance, and fruits are soft, acid and do not keep well. Symptoms appear first on the older leaves.

Phosphorus deficiency (unavailability) tends to occur in acid soils and in those soils subject to heavy leaching, also in poor clay and ironstone soils. It is corrected by application of a suitable phosphate fertilizer (for example, superphosphate) which should be placed as near the roots of the plants as possible. It is sometimes applied with the sowing seed in the drill. Where phosphorus is unavailable rather than deficient it may be possible to reduce the phosphorus-fixing power of the soil by altering the pH.

Potassium

Soluble, mainly inorganic, potassium salts are present throughout the plant, particularly in young, actively growing plants, but their function is not well understood. They are probably regulatory and possibly involved in protein synthesis and photosynthesis, and as cofactors in enzyme reactions.

Symptoms of potassium deficiency are varied and include dull bluish leaves (sometimes with interveinal chlorosis), tip burn, marginal scorching, brown spotting, and sometimes the leaves tend to curl or roll. Symptoms are most severe on the older leaves. Scorched leaf margins often indicate potassium deficiency but this can be due to deficiency of calcium or phosphorus or to chemical injury, hot dry winds and other causes. Dieback and stunting of the shoots, sometimes accompanied by increased tillering and a lack of flowering stems in cereals, occur in acute deficiencies. There may also be internode shortening and poor root development leading to reduced growth and yields. Potassium deficient trees are liable to develop die-back and may be killed in severe cases.

Potassium deficiency is most prevalent in light, sandy and chalky soils especially where the land has been overcropped without addition of fertilizer. The remedy is to use a suitable crop rotation and a good potash fertilizer; in fact, potassium is normally included in general purpose (NPK) fertilizers. It is possible that sodium can partially replace potassium in the plant but this seems to be true to only a very limited extent. Cotton plants sometimes show symptoms of potash deficiency ('cotton rust'), the leaves developing bronzing and marginal scorching, finally turning reddish-brown and dying. The bolls are small and contain inferior fibres.

Sulphur

Sulphur is a constituent of some amino acids, proteins and vitamins. Its deficiency results in symptoms rather similar to those of nitrogen deficiency – chlorosis, reduced growth and sometimes reddish tinting of the leaves. These symptoms are often but not always more pronounced in young parts of the plant. Sulphur deficiency is not common and most soils, except those which have been severely eroded or leached, apparently contain adequate amounts of sulphur although not all of it may be available to the plant. Certain bacteria can convert sulphur to sulphates and some is no doubt deposited in soil in industrial areas. Tea yellows in Malawi has been attributed to sulphur deficiency and is said to affect tobacco also. In tea the leaves become smaller, rolled, brittle and chlorotic, leading to defoliation and dying back of the branches. Sulphur deficiency is generally corrected by applying sulphur-containing fertilizers such as ammonium sulphate.

Calcium

Much of the calcium in plants occurs in cell walls associated with pectic compounds. It is especially involved at active growing points and is thought to play an essential role in cell division. Possibly, it neutralizes harmful acidic substances produced in the plant. The symptoms of calcium deficiency usually appear at the tips of shoots. Young leaves are often severely distorted and curled with irregular, ragged margins and there may be scorching, spotting and marginal chlorosis. The leaf mesophyll tissue and stems and flower stalks frequently collapse and the growing points may be killed, resulting in die-back. The roots are poorly developed and may appear gelatinous.

Calcium deficiency is likely to occur in soils derived from rocks of low calcium content especially if exposed to leaching, as with light sandy soils. It is commoner in acid soils where the situation may be complicated by manganese and/or aluminium toxicity, and phosphorus deficiency. Calcium deficiency and soil acidity are normally treated by application of lime, sometimes in large quantities.

Withertop of flax in Australia is apparently caused by a temporary calcium deficiency during wet weather, and blossom end rot of tomatoes has also been attributed to this deficiency, although this appears to be a complex condition. Apple trees in the British Isles sometimes show symptoms of calcium deficiency in the form of interveinal and marginal necrosis, which may be preceded by mild chlorosis and purple tinting.

Magnesium

This element forms part of the chlorophyll molecule, takes part in the phosphorus metabolism of plants, and is an activator for some enzymes. Symptoms appear first on the old leaves which commonly develop chlorosis in the form of interveinal mottling ('marbling'). Tinting may also occur and in severe cases there may be extensive defoliation. Deficiency tends to develop at the end of the growing season when it probably causes only minor damage, but it sometimes appears during excessively wet weather when magnesium is washed out of the soil. Prolonged deficiency, as in perennial crops, results in stunted growth and poor yields. Apples and other fruits fail to ripen normally and are small and of poor colour and flavour. Symptoms are varied on different plants and are not always easy to diagnose.

Magnesium deficiency is generally most prevalent in light, acid, sandy soils, especially in wet areas or seasons. It can be brought about by excessive application of potash fertilizers, notably potassium sulphate. The use of artificial fertilizers, many of which lack magnesium, instead of farm-yard manure (which contains it) is likely to result in magnesium deficiency problems. The remedy is to apply occasional dressings of magnesium sulphate or of magnesium limestone instead or ordinary lime. Acute deficiency can usually be cured by foliar spraying with 2% magnesium sulphate solution with a spreader if necessary.

Diseases attributed to magnesium deficiency include 'sand drown' of tobacco which occurs in deep sandy soils along the Atlantic seaboard of the U.S.A.; this is essentially a progressive chlorosis of the leaves from below upwards. Magnesium deficiency is reported to be a major problem with citrus in Florida where extensive chlorosis and defoliation can occur. It has also been reported to increase the susceptibility of plants to some fungal pathogens.

Iron

Formation of chlorophyll is dependent on iron, and some enzymes (for example cytochrome oxidase and catalase) contain this element. Iron is physiologically active in the ferrous state, and ferric salts taken in by the roots are thought to be rapidly reduced, although oxidizing agents (including perhaps manganese) might prevent reduction and so bring about symptoms of iron deficiency (for example manganese induced chlorosis). Conversely, manganese deficiency might bring about chlorosis due to iron toxicity (see Shive, 1941). This view is questioned by Hewitt (1948).

Inadequate iron results in severe chlorosis and since this element is rather immobile in the plant the symptoms are worst on young growth. Although mottling may occur the leaves are often completely yellow and scorching sometimes develops at the tips and margins. Iron deficiency is more frequently met with in fruit plants than in vegetables or cereals, such plants as raspberry, strawberry and apple sometimes being severely affected.

There is adequate iron, chiefly as oxides, for plant growth in most soils, and deficiency can result either from its unavailability or from its immobility within the plant. Iron deficiency is often, if not usually, a condition which can be induced by several factors and may be of complex origin. Deficiency tends to be most prevalent in calcareous or alkaline soils, the conditions being known as lime induced chlorosis, but it can occur in acid soils containing much manganese. It is also reported that high concentrations of zinc, copper, phosphorus and other substances can induce iron deficiency, and deficiencies of calcium, magnesium and potassium can apparently do the same under laboratory conditions. It is clear that the problem of iron deficiency in plants is a very complex one.

For these and other reasons, the addition of iron salts to soils is rarely effective in remedying iron deficiency. Spraying the plants with soluble salts is likely to be more effective but may be phytotoxic. In recent years iron chelates – organic compounds in which the iron is not easily separated from the rest of the molecule – have been used as foliage sprays and also in soil treatment; such chelates are best applied as an injection into the subsoil. Salts such as ferrous sulphate can be injected as solids into stems of iron deficient fruit trees. A cover of vegetation in orchards is said to relieve iron deficiency to some extent, perhaps through acidification of the soil or by production of organic substances which form chelates with the iron compounds present.

Cereals and potatoes appear to be little affected by iron deficiency but fruit trees are generally susceptible. Pineapple yellows in Hawaii is thought to be due to iron deficiency associated with high manganese content of the soil. This is corrected by spraying with ferrous sulphate solution. Iron chlorosis is discussed by Brown (1956) and the role of this element in plant nutrition is reviewed by Price (1968).

Manganese

This element is an activator in some enzyme systems including oxidation-reduction reactions of respiration and photosynthesis and seems in some way to be involved in chlorophyll formation. It is closely associated with iron in the plant and the two elements may show antagonistic effects; for example, high manganese can induce iron deficiency, and *vice versa*. Symptoms of manganese deficiency are varied but usually include chlorosis as flecking, streaking or mottling depending on the plant affected. Growth is stunted, and necrotic areas may develop on the leaves or elsewhere. Root development is often subnormal. Symptoms may first appear on the younger or older parts of the plant, depending on the part involved.

Manganese commonly occurs in soil as oxides and the higher oxides (for example, manganese dioxide) are not easily available to roots. Its availability increases in acid soils and, whereas deficiency tends to develop in alkaline soils, there may be phytotoxicity in acid ones. Certain soil bacteria may be involved in these effects, being favoured in alkaline soils where they convert the manganese into higher oxides largely unavailable to the plant. Availability is also said to be reduced in calcareous peat soils and others with a high content of organic matter but, as with iron, many aspects of manganese deficiency and toxicity remain obscure.

Several destructive diseases caused by manganese deficiency have been described – grey speck of oats, speckled yellows of sugarbeet, pahola blight of sugarcane in Hawaii, frenching of tung (*Aleurites*) in Florida, and marsh spot of peas. The last named is interesting in that although the seeds may be severely affected the parent plants often show only a slight chlorosis. The interior of the seed shows a dark necrotic spot ranging from a small speck to a large brown cavity and the disease tends to occur in low-lying, marshy land, notably Romney Marsh, hence the name.

Copper

The functions of copper in the plant are not well understood but it is present in ascorbic acid oxidase, polyphenol oxidase and several other enzymes. There appears to be some sort of relationship between copper and iron – possibly copper oxidizes ferrous iron to the relatively insoluble ferric form. Copper is highly phytotoxic and only very small amounts are normally present in soil. Deficiency symptoms include stunted leaves, which are often of a bluish-green colour, and development of necrotic areas. Affected cereal leaves show withering, marginal chlorosis and tip necrosis. Heading is considerably reduced and the heads themselves are dwarfed, distorted and with imperfectly developed chlorotic tips ('withertip', 'whiteheads'). Copper deficient fruit trees often die back and develop chlorosis and rosetting.

Copper deficiency tends to occur on reclaimed heath soils, peats, and poor acid sands and gravels. It can also occur in calcareous soils, and liming or a high content of organic matter are reported to reduce its availability. It can often be corrected by application of copper salts to the soil or, better, to the foliage or into the branches of affected trees but care must be taken to avoid phytotoxicity.

An example of copper deficiency is 'reclamation disease' of cereals, typically occurring on reclaimed heath or moorland soils. The plants develop withertip and set little or no seed; the condition is controlled by application of copper sulphate to the soil. Copper deficiency is also responsible for die-back or exanthema of fruit trees (especially citrus) in various parts of the world.

Zinc

Zinc is highly phytotoxic but is present in, or activates, several enzymes in the plant. It is thought to be involved in the synthesis of indole acetic acid, and deficiency can result in abnormal growth of the affected plant.

The first symptoms are generally interveinal chlorosis which may be followed by necrosis and purple pigmentation. Affected leaves are stunted and malformed, the internodes are shortened, and fruiting is greatly reduced. This can lead to rosetting, the development of a rosette of small, stiff leaves. Deficient cereals often show purpling and death of the older leaves. Zinc deficiency appears to have an adverse effect on the chloroplasts, resulting in their localized destruction or inhibition.

Zinc is present in only very small quantities in most soils and deficiency can develop in most of them under certain conditions. The factors affecting its availability to plants are imperfectly understood. Addition of lime and phosphates reduces its availability, and also, probably, organic matter. Prolonged use of zinc-free inorganic fertilizers instead of farmyard manure (which probably contains zinc) is likely to increase the incidence of this deficiency. Application of zinc salts to acid soils may be effective but not so with neutral or alkaline soils, and spraying the deficient plants with zinc sulphate (with or without lime) is preferable whenever possible. Injection of zinc salts into the base of the trunk or driving zinc nails into the wood have also proved effective in some cases. Care must be taken to avoid phytotoxicity.

Diseases thought to be caused by zinc deficiency include mottle leaf (foliocellosis) of citrus which can be very destructive. This is essentially an interveinal chlorosis in which the leaves become smaller and more chlorotic until they are reduced to yellow structures only 2·5 cm or so long. Affected shoots die back and in severe attacks the tree may be killed. The roots are reduced and may have only a few functional rootlets. This condition can be treated by application of zinc sulphate to the soil or, better, as a foliage spray or by placing it in holes bored in the trunk and subsequently sealed. Other fruit trees may be similarly affected, as in little leaf and rosette diseases of apple, pear, plum, grape and others. Pecan rosette, sickle leaf of cacao, bronzing of tung and whip-tip (white bud) of maize are other diseases which have been attributed to zinc deficiency.

Molybdenum

This element seems to be closely involved in the nitrogen metabolism of plants and is necessary for the fixation of nitrogen by nitrogen-fixing bacteria. The enzyme nitrate reductase contains molybdenum, and shortage of this element leads to an accumulation of nitrate in leaves and a reduction in protein synthesis. Deficiency often causes a chlorosis in the form of spotting, mottling, or a general yellowing. Scorching and wilting may follow, and eventually necrosis and abscission of the affected leaves. The leaf tissues may become thin and papery, and development of the lamina may be suppressed as in whiptail of cauliflower. In leguminous plants the nitrogen-fixing root nodule bacteria may fail to develop, thus resulting in symptoms of nitrogen deficiency.

Molybdenum is required in minute amounts – it is said that one part per hundred million will prevent deficiency symptoms appearing on tomato plants in water culture experiments. It is widely distributed in soils and its availability is increased under alkaline conditions, as in liming; high pH may in fact bring about molybdenum toxicity to animals feeding on certain pastures. Cobalt salts are also said to increase its availability. The addition of small amounts of sodium molybdate, sometimes as little as 280 g/ha, to the soil has been reported to correct this deficiency.

Whiptail of cauliflower and other brassicas is apparently caused by molybdenum deficiency. The leaves develop an interveinal chlorosis, the margins become limp and brown, and eventually most of the lamina withers away leaving only the bare midrib with perhaps a few small irregular pieces of lamina attached to it. Yellow spot can cause severe defoliation of citrus trees in Florida, and strap leaf of rozelle (*Hibiscus sabdariffa*) is also attributed to molybdenum deficiency.

Boron

Many roles have been ascribed to boron, including involvement in water uptake by the plant, in carbohydrate and nitrogen metabolism, and in the formation of pectic substances in cell walls. There is also some evidence for relationships between boron, calcium and potassium. Shortage of boron may thus be expected to have varied and severe effects, and this is generally true in that the metabolism of deficient plants appears to be seriously upset and is often accompanied by the collapse of affected tissue.

The first visible symptom of boron deficiency is the death of the apical growing point. Lateral shoots then develop and their growing points die so that the plant becomes stunted and composed of numerous small shoots. Stems and leaves may become thickened, distorted and sometimes brittle. The root system is stunted, and flowering and fruiting are greatly reduced. Spontaneous breakdown of parenchymatous tissue is a characteristic of boron deficiency, particularly in storage organs such as turnips. The pith and epidermis may be affected, resulting in roughened, hollow stems. Leaves are scorched and curled, and fruits are often severely deformed and useless. Boron is widespread in rocks and soils but is not always readily available to roots. It is easily leached from the soil and its availability is reduced by lime, overliming being a common cause of boron deficiency. It is not very mobile in plants and apparently accumulates in leaves where it is in some way 'fixed'. Deficiency symptoms appear first on the younger leaves and it is said that cells of the apical meristem may show deficiency symptoms whilst the lower leaves of the same plant suffer boron toxicity (Meyer, Anderson and Bohning, 1960).

Boron deficiency can sometimes be controlled by adding borax to the soil (a few kg/ha) or by spraying it over deficient plants. It is highly phytotoxic and care must be taken in this respect. It causes several important diseases, especially of vegetables and root crops; cereals seem rarely to show boron deficiency and presumably have only a very low requirement for it. Heart rot of sugarbeet and mangold are widely distributed, especially on alkaline soils and in dry years. The first symptoms are curling and stunting of the young leaves, which may die. The other leaves become similarly affected and the crown of the plant begins to die and decay. Affected leaves often appear scorched and yellow and tend to be prostrate on the soil. The root decays to varying extents and is often invaded by *Phoma betae*. Affected beets have a reduced sugar content and are hollow and brownish. Canker and internal black spot of beetroot is a somewhat similar disease in which hard, black, necrotic masses of tissue develop within the root. In brown heart ('raan') of swedes and turnips the external symptoms are inconspicuous but the affected root shows mottling and discolouration of the vascular tissues. In severe cases all the tissue within the cambium disintegrates, leaving a hollow, worthless turnip.

Boron deficiency causes the development of rather hard, brown patches on the curds of cauliflowers which tend to decay in wet weather. Affected plants have poor root systems and a hollow pith in the stem. Other diseases attributed to boron deficiency include cracked stem of celery, lucerne yellows, internal cork (corky pit) of apple, brown spot of apricot, die-back of raspberries, and top sickness of tobacco. These descriptive names give an idea of the varied diseases caused by deficiency of this element (see Bussler, 1964).

Chlorine

Little is known about the function of this element in plants although chloride is apparently involved in photosynthesis (Losada *et al.* 1961).

Chlorides occur in soil, particularly near the sea, and deficiency is most likely to occur on inland, well drained, sandy soils. In deficient tomato plants the leaflets develop apical wilting and there is a progressive chlorosis followed by bronzing and necrosis. Formation of fruits is reduced. There is little information on deficiency of chlorine in other plants.

Further information on these and other deficiencies can be obtained from Wallace (1961), Stiles (1961: mainly manganese, zinc, boron, copper and molybdenum), Peace (1961: trees and shrubs), Butler and Jones (1949), Lamb *et al.* (1958), Anon. (1957), Fleming (1965: mainly pasture plants), and the extensive '*Bibliography of the Literature on the Mineral Elements*' compiled by the Chilean Nitrate Educational Bureau Inc., New York, Volume I, 1948 and subsequent volumes.

Toxicity diseases

Large amounts of trace elements are phytotoxic and this is particularly true of manganese, zinc, boron and copper as described by Stiles (1961). Apparently non-essential elements such as aluminium and selenium may be present in toxic quantities in some soils. There may be injury to the protoplasm or disruption of enzyme systems resulting in death of the plant, or an excess of one element may lead to deficiency of another with harmful effects on the plant. Excess nitrogen or phosphorus may for example, induce potassium deficiency, and excess potassium may induce magnesium deficiency. The susceptibility of plants to toxicity of this sort depends not only on the element involved but also on the species of plant and such factors as the age and physiological condition of the plant or organ. The effects of excess of manganese, zinc, boron, copper and molybdenum on plants are discussed by Stiles (1961).

The chief symptoms of manganese toxicity are root browning and the development of brownish-purple spots, chlorosis, and marginal necrosis on the leaves. This toxicity usually occurs in acid soils which apparently increase the availability of this element. Some plant species tolerate as much as 50 p.p.m. of manganese whereas others may be injured by 1 p.p.m. or less in water culture experiments. Zinc toxicity induces root browning and chlorosis of the leaves and some plants are killed by 1 p.p.m. or less; different varieties of the same species can differ markedly in their susceptibility to zinc.

Symptoms of boron toxicity include chlorosis and necrosis of the foliage and stunting of the plant; less than 1 p.p.m. can be toxic to some plants. Molybdenum toxicity often causes chlorosis and in some cases development of a golden yellow colour due to the formation of yellow globules of a molybdenum-tannin compound. Aluminium toxicity can occur in acid soils, the roots of affected plants being poorly developed and stubby. Selenium toxicity has also been reported.

Toxicity diseases can sometimes be alleviated by modifying the soil conditions as in reducing the acidity in the case of manganese toxicity. Alkali injury, often caused by high concentrations of sodium salts (mainly chloride, sulphate and carbonate) in the soil, occurs in some areas, particularly arid ones, and can sometimes be corrected by prolonged irrigation. Plants vary a great deal in their alkali tolerance and some, such as sugarbeet, are very tolerant. The physiology of salt tolerance is discussed by Bernstein and Hayward (1958). Toxic elements in soil are discussed by Bear (1957).

Excess or deficiency of certain elements in pasture plants can have adverse effects on the animals which eat them, and several animal diseases of this sort have been reported. They include selenium poisoning of stock in the U.S.A., 'scouring' of cattle attributed to toxic amounts of molybdenum in some clovers and grasses used for forage, and 'pining' disease of sheep possibly due to a shortage of cobalt in the diet, resulting from grazing on cobalt deficient land: these are discussed by Stiles (1961).

4 Viruses and *Mycoplasma*-like organisms as plant pathogens

Symptoms of virus diseases – notably flower-breaking and variegation – have been known for several hundred years, but it is only within the past 70 years or so that viruses have been recognized as causing disease in plants and only within the past 40 years that they have been intensively studied. The number of viruses attacking plants is perhaps about 600 and new ones are still being discovered; precise figures are not available since some viruses exist as a number of strains which, in some cases, have been described as separate viruses. Some diseases, previously ascribed to viruses, are now thought to be due to *Mycoplasma*-like organisms (p. 76).

Plant virus particles ('virions') consist of a single or double strand of nucleic acid surrounded by a protein coat ('capsid'). Most plant viruses contain RNA (ribonucleic acid) but Shepherd *et al.* (1968) report that cauliflower mosaic virus contains DNA (deoxyribonucleic acid). Of the animal and bacterial viruses (bacteriophages) some contain RNA, some DNA, and the virus which attacks the blue-green alga *Plectonema boryanum* is reported to contain DNA (Schneider *et al.*, 1964) and to resemble tailed bacteriophages. Virus particles are individually too small to be seen with the ordinary light microscope and are of various shapes, including long flexuous threads, rigid rods, and icosahedra with twenty sides. There is no completely satisfactory definition of a virus. Bawden (1964) suggests 'sub-microscopic, infective entities that multiply only intracellularly and are potentially pathogenic' and rightly points out that they should not be regarded as either organisms or molecules. Size, as indicated by the passage of viruses through bacterial filters is, however, no longer sufficient to distinguish a virus. Thus viruses and *Mycoplasma* are comparable in size and filterability, the main differences being that viruses contain either RNA or DNA, never both, and can replicate only in a living cell. Multiplication of viruses is imperfectly understood but the metabolism of the infected cell is in some unknown way diverted to the synthesis of further virus particles, this being an essentially different process from reproduction in fungi and bacteria. Further information on these aspects can be obtained from Bald (1966), Bawden (1964), Mundry (1963) and Caspar (1964). The structure of plant viruses is discussed by Knight (1964) and Horne and Wildy (1963).

Effects of viruses on plants

Viruses are similar to obligate parasites in that they cannot be grown on non-living media. They are intimately associated with the host cell and few kill the infected plant although some cause severe distortion and dwarfing. The changes brought about by viruses are discussed here under (1) morphological changes, or symptoms, (2) histological and cytological changes, and (3) metabolic changes, but these are of course interrelated.

Morphological changes

Among the symptoms resulting from virus infection of plants are mosaics and mottles of various types, which may or may not be accompanied by varying amounts of blistering and distortion of the infected leaf (figure 4.1). In extreme cases the leaf may be almost completely chlorotic, as in the diseases known as 'yellows'. There may be extensive thickening of the infected leaf, dwarfing, epinasty, rolling or curling, or a combination of these. Outgrowths (enations) develop in some virus infections and there may be vein-thickening, vein-banding or vein clearing (figures 4.2, 4.3). The leaves are sometimes reduced ('little leaf') or the lamina is greatly suppressed ('fern-leaf', 'shoe string'). In some virus diseases the leaves become stiff or brittle, as in tobacco rattle, so called because they rattle when moved.

Plants infected by some viruses show symptoms on the flowers. These include 'breaking' of the flower colour to give multicoloured flowers (which can be horticulturally valuable) (figure 4.4) and virescence (greening) of the petals (phyllody). Dwarfing of the flowers occurs in many virus diseases but in a few the sepals are enlarged. The flowers are often reduced in number although flowering is said to be stimulated in spike disease of sandal (*Santalum*). Flowering may be premature or delayed, and pollen and/or ovules may fail to function to varying extents. Fruit production is often reduced through premature abscission or sterility, or both. The fruits borne by trees infected by certain viruses tend to be small, of poor quality, and misshapen – blistered, warty, scarred, cracked – and may show intensified or reduced pigmentation, or necrotic lesions or streaks. Their texture may be affected, so that they become corky or woody, and they often ripen unevenly, are of an inferior flavour, and contain a reduced number of seeds.

Some viruses affect the size or growth habit of the plant to varying

(a)

(b)

Figure 4.1 *Primula* plant infected by cucumber mosaic virus; the virus causes (a) stunting of the whole plant and (b) abnormally small, distorted leaves.

(a)   *(b)*

Figure 4.2 Tomato aspermy virus on (*a*) *Hyoscyamus niger* – extreme stunting and distortion of the infected plant; (*b*) *Nicotiana glutinosa* – infected leaves are severely reduced, misshapen and bear enations on their lower surface. Uninfected leaves on the left.

Figure 4.3 Vein clearing and altered leaf shape of honeysuckle infected by (possibly) arabis mosaic virus, a nematode transmitted virus.

Figure 4.4   Carnation flower showing colour breaking caused by virus.

Figure 4.5   *Left:* uninfected tomato plant; *right:* tomato plant infected by tomato aspermy virus which results in severe stunting and distorted growth of the plant.

extents. Elongation or – more often – stunting and rosetting not infrequently occur with some systemic viruses (figure 4.5). Roots may be reduced in plants infected by certain viruses, perhaps resulting from the general unthriftiness of virus infected plants. Growth is sometimes stimulated and gives rise to witch's broom symptoms and overgrowths of various kinds (galls, tumours). Some viruses cause necrosis of tissue at the points of infection (local lesions), or in the phloem or in areas distant from the points of infection (secondary lesions).

From this brief outline, which is far from comprehensive, it is clear that the symptoms of virus diseases in plants are very varied, often severe, and sometimes bizarre, as shown by such descriptions as pea pimple pod, maize wallaby ear, passion fruit woodiness, tomato shoestring, citrus tristeza and others listed by Martyn (1968). Virus symptoms are sometimes so slight as to pass unnoticed except on close examination, and they may disappear under certain environmental conditions such as high temperature or following the application of certain fertilizers (masked symptoms). Some plants can be symptomless carriers in that they contain the virus, often in a transmissible form, but show no outward symptoms. A detailed account of virus symptoms is given by Holmes (1964).

Histological and cytological changes

The symptoms described above are related to underlying histological changes in the plant tissues. Thus, the chlorotic tissue of mottled leaves is generally thinner than the normal green tissue and has shorter palisade cells containing fewer and smaller chloroplasts. Some viruses, often those which cause leaf curling and yellowing, bring about necrosis of the phloem tissue whereas in others necrosis is preceded by tissue proliferation and is perhaps caused by crushing rather than directly by the virus. Necrosis often takes the form of small lesions but is systemic with some viruses. Tobacco rattle virus brings about a systemic necrosis in inoculated tobacco plants, necrotic lesions developing on leaves and stems. This is accompanied by breakdown of the pith and cortex, and the xylem is eventually affected. Some other viruses cause degenerative changes of various sorts but the physiology of these changes remains obscure.

Overgrowths such as those formed in swollen shoot disease of cacao, the elongated leaf galls in Fiji disease of sugarcane, and the leaf enations caused by the cotton leaf curl virus originate in part from increased cambial activity producing extra vascular tissue which may be abnormal in nature. The character of the cells may be changed, palisade tissue being replaced by spongy parenchyma or *vice versa* according to the virus involved. Hypertrophy of cells sometimes occurs. Xylem is generally less affected by virus than is parenchyma or phloem, but tyloses and formation of gum have been described in the xylem of plants infected with some viruses.

These examples illustrate some of the more important histological changes which occur in virus infected plants. Many others could be given and these changes are reflected in the symptoms which appear on the infected plant. The symptoms and histological changes caused by a virus can differ in different plants – tobacco mosaic virus, for example, causes mosaic on *Nicotiana tabacum* and local lesions on *N. glutinosa* (figure 4.6). The histological and morphological changes which develop in virus infected plants are characteristic of the virus–plant combination rather than of the virus alone. Further details concerning the anatomical changes caused by viruses can be obtained from Esau (1967).

Inclusion bodies of various types are formed within cells infected by some viruses. Some of these inclusions, particularly the crystalline ones,

Figure 4.6   Local lesions caused by tobacco mosaic virus on leaves of *Nicotiana glutinosa*.

are apparently clusters of virus particles and are large enough to be seen under the light microscope, whereas X-bodies, as the amorphous inclusions are often termed, are thought to contain varying amounts of virus and are perhaps developmental stages of crystalline inclusion bodies, as discussed by Esau (1967). Inclusion bodies are most numerous in epidermal cells and have been classified by Matsui and Yamaguchi (1966) as X-bodies, crystalline inclusions, intranuclear inclusions, and others; the nature of the two last named is uncertain.

Inclusion bodies have been observed in most of the tissues and organs of infected plants but their distribution is often irregular or localized.

They can be present in infected plants which show no external symptoms, as reported by Robb (1963) for dahlia mosaic virus, and in such cases their presence is a useful indication of a symptomless carrier. The inclusion bodies of dahlia mosaic virus are spherical, highly refractive, and apparently bounded by a membrane which may contain phospholipid (figure 4.7). It is possible that they originate in the nuclei of young tissue

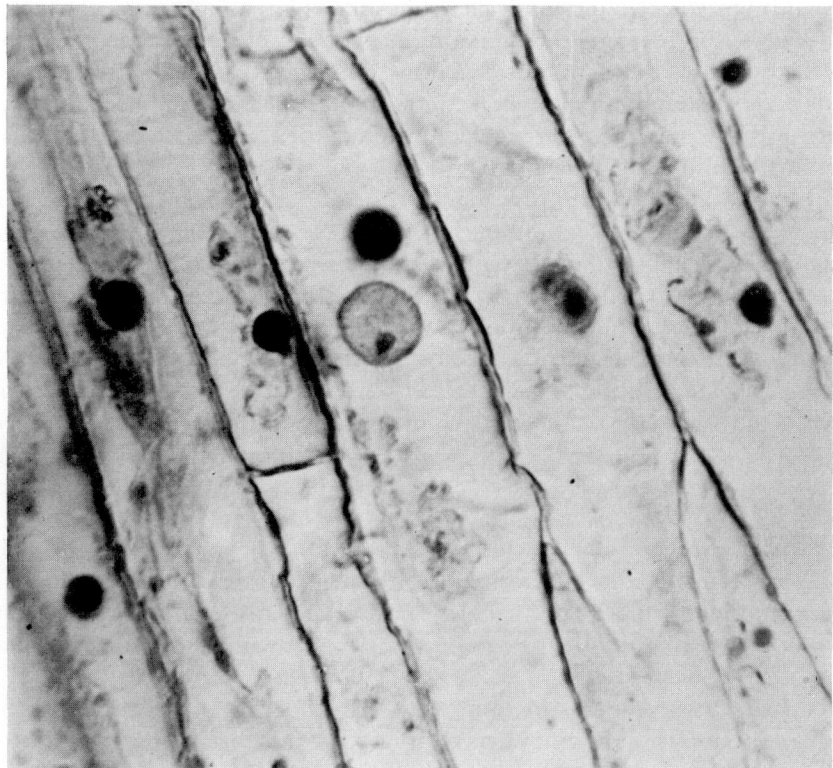

Figure 4.7 Inclusion bodies (the dark spherical bodies, stained with trypan blue) in epidermal cells of dahlia leaf infected by dahlia mosaic virus ($\times$ 1000).

from which they migrate into the cytoplasm and that they are in some way related to virus multiplication (Robb, 1964). The demonstration of inclusion bodies is a rapid and convenient method of diagnosing virus infections but unfortunately their absence is of little significance since they have not been observed in plants infected by some viruses. They have been reported for about fifty viruses and further investigation will no doubt reveal their presence in others. Inclusion bodies are discussed by McWhorter (1965) and by Matsui and Yamaguchi (1966).

There are reports of virus RNA and particles in the nuclei of infected cells, and some visual evidence of their presence in nuclei has been obtained with the electron microscope. It is not surprising that nuclear division may fail or be abnormal in cells infected with certain viruses, as described by Caldwell (1952) and Wilkinson (1953, 1960) in chrysanthemum aspermy virus. The latter author (1960) has described amitotic nuclear division in *Petunia* stem enations caused by this virus, the nuclei elongating, constricting and cleaving into two daughter nuclei. The significance of this is uncertain. Amitotis may be associated with a shortage of RNA and Wilkinson considers that during division of virus infected cells there is competition between the virus particles and the nuclear DNA for the RNA present in the nucleolus. Since the formation of the nuclear spindle in mitosis is dependent on RNA any shortage of the latter could lead to amitotic nuclear division. Other abnormalities shown by virus infected cells included lobing and distortion of the nucleolus which often extends as a finger-like vesicle across the spindle, and spindle breakdown resulting in either scattering of the chromosomes or their failure to separate, the latter leading to the formation of 'giant' nuclei. The sterility of plants infected by certain viruses could perhaps be associated with such nuclear abnormalities. The effects of viruses upon nuclear division in plants have received comparatively little attention and need further investigation.

Metabolic changes

Viruses affect the nucleic acid metabolism of the infected cell, thereby bringing about changes in protein synthesis which in some way result in the formation of more virus. They are not known to contain or produce enzymes or toxins of the type produced by parasitic microorganisms which obtain their nutrients more or less directly from the infected plant. The effects of viruses on the metabolism of the host plant are likely to be indirect in the sense that they derive from this generalized interference with the functioning of the cells in the infected tissue. Some viruses have a profound and very injurious effect on the infected plant, in others the symptoms are relatively slight, and symptomless carriers are not visibly affected although their physiology is no doubt modified.

The symptoms caused by a virus are related to the underlying physiological changes in the infected plant. Mosaic, mottling and yellowing of leaves, leading to reduced photosynthetic efficiency, indicate some sort of interference with chlorophyll. This could be due to its destruction or reduced formation, or to damage to the chloroplasts. Such damage has been described by Carroll and Kosuge (1969) who found that tobacco mosaic virus became systemic in tobacco plants kept at 38°C for 7–8 days after inoculation whereas necrosis developed when such plants were subsequently kept at 21°C for 1–2 days. Chloroplasts in the cells of the necrotic tissue became invested with osmophilic granules, lost much of their plastidial membrane, showed disorganized internal lamellae, and accumulated prominent starch granules. Virus particles were present in the degenerated chloroplasts but were not seen in the earlier stages of degeneration.

Reduced efficiency of chloroplasts has also been reported in virus infected plants and the photochemical activity of chloroplasts from sugar-beet leaves infected by beet yellows virus was only half that of chloroplasts from uninfected leaves (Spikes and Stout, 1955). The changes described above will obviously result in reduced photosynthetic activity of the infected plant but such reduction may perhaps be due to other causes as well, for example to nitrogen deficiency associated with virus multiplication in the tissue, as suggested by Bawden (1964) for tobacco mosaic virus. Farkas and Solymosy (1965) consider that chlorosis may be associated with a deficiency of nutrients in the infected plant due to the competing metabolic pathways of virus synthesis and the normal metabolic processes of the plant. This results in a shift towards increased breakdown processes, notably of protein, and a concomitant activation of some enzymes.

Changes in the amounts and activity of several enzymes have been described in plants infected by various viruses. The necrosis caused by some viruses has been attributed to increased polyphenoloxidase activity converting polyphenols into phytotoxic substances such as quinones, but the latter might result from, rather than cause, necrosis. This has been interpreted as a defence reaction of the infected tissue since tannins and quinones are known to inactivate viruses. Activation of other enzymes, including those involved in the pentose phosphate shunt, has been described in cells around virus lesions but the significance of these changes is uncertain. Increased oxidase activity is a general feature of many virus infections in plants.

The abnormal growth pattern of plants infected by some viruses suggests an interference with the growth regulating processes of the plant, and it is tempting to ascribe tissue hypertrophy, shortening of internodes, stimulation of axillary buds and other similar symptoms to such interference. Growth promoting substances are often reduced in virus infected plants and this could be due to their reduced synthesis or to their destruction by enzymes, for example IAA oxidase. Stunting of infected plants may also be associated with auxin changes; application of gibberellic acid reversed the stunting effect, but not the other symptoms, caused by several viruses (Maramorosch, 1957; Chessin, 1958). With other viruses subnormal growth is due to reduced photosynthesis and the generally abnormal condition of the infected plant.

There are many reports of increased respiration in virus infected plants. This frequently results from the enhanced synthetic activity which follows tissue injury, whether due to pathogen attack or wounding, and is in no way specific to viruses. There is little information as to whether viruses have a qualitative as well as a quantitative effect on the respiration of the infected plant. The general functioning of the plant is extensively disturbed by virus attack and it is to be expected that qualitative changes of this sort may well take place.

The combination of decreased photosynthesis and increased respiration should result in a fall in the carbohydrate content of virus infected leaves. This is so in some mosaics, but accumulation of carbohydrate, particularly starch, has been reported in virus diseases of the 'yellows' type. Such accumulation has been attributed to phloem necrosis or some other factor which reduces the movement of carbohydrate through and from the leaf, or to inactivation of the enzymes involved in carbohydrate conversions.

The nitrogen metabolism of virus infected plants is qualitatively and quantitatively disturbed although conflicting results have been reported with different viruses. Diener (1963) suggests that: (1) deficiency of non-protein nitrogen compounds occurs only when large amounts of virus are being synthesized, the latter taking place at the expense of the normal protein of the plant; this is likely to be aggravated when the plant is short of nitrogen; (2) in many viruses non-protein nitrogen compounds, particularly amides, accumulate in infected leaves; and (3) in diseases of the 'yellows' type the underground parts of infected plants contain more nitrogenous matter than those of healthy plants, whereas infected leaves may be deficient in total nitrogen and protein nitrogen but rich in soluble nitrogen.

It will be apparent from this very brief account that viruses exert a generalized disturbing effect on the metabolism of the infected plant, affecting such basic processes as respiration, photosynthesis, growth regulation, and nitrogen metabolism. Detailed information is lacking but the interference often appears to be indirect rather than direct.

Infection and movement of viruses within plants

Viruses either enter plants through damaged cells including leaf hairs (although the significance of the latter in relation to virus entry is uncertain), or are introduced into the plant by vectors as discussed later. Slight damage seems to be necessary for successful establishment of the virus within the cell and perhaps exposes receptor sites to which the virus particles 'bond', but gross mechanical damage may prevent infection.

The nature of these receptor sites is uncertain: they may be ectodes-mata, the fine canals or possibly strands which pass through the outer wall of leaf epidermal cells. This is suggested by the results of experiments reported by Brants (1964, 1965) who found that *Nicotiana* leaves sap inoculated with tobacco mosaic virus developed more lesions after treat-ment which increased the number of ectodesmata. Rubbing would pre-sumably expose the ectodesmata, thus admitting the virus which then enters the protoplast, possibly by pinocytosis or a similar process in which the virus is enclosed in small vesicles formed by invagination of the plasmalemma, as described by Cocking (1966). Receptor sites disappear at varying rates depending on the virus, the host, and other factors. Most of them appear to be relatively short lived, lasting only a matter of minutes, and they can be inactivated or blocked in various ways by heat and certain inhibitors. It is possible that different strains of a virus may compete for receptor sites, thus leading to cross-protection. The bonding of virus and receptor sites is thought to result in the formation of infective centres, some of which develop into lesions while others remain latent unless activated by heat or possibly in some other way. Such latent in-fection centres may be more widespread than is at present supposed and may occur in apparently resistant plants. Under natural conditions in the field it seems possible that virus particles deposited on the plant surface might pass through the cuticle and cell wall *via* small breaks and wounds caused by wind, animals and other agents which damage plants, thus reaching the plasmalemma of the cell.

After being taken into the plasmalemma of the cell in pinocytic vesicles the virus particles are liberated, presumably by some sort of dissolution of the vesicle membrane, possibly by lysosomal enzymes. Replication of the particles then occurs. This seems to involve removal of the protein-aceous coat of the particle, thus liberating the RNA within, and further virus particles are assembled within the plasmalemma from materials present in the infected cell. During this assembly period comparatively little movement of virus is likely to occur. After infection there is usually replication of the virus which seems to involve removal of the protein-aceous coat of the virus particle, thus releasing the nucleic acid within. There is some evidence that virus protein and nucleic acid are both formed within the nucleus, synthesis of the virus particles being initiated in the nucleolus and perhaps completed in the cytoplasm after extrusion from the nucleus (Schlegel and Smith, 1966). The details of these processes are uncertain and the subject is reviewed by Bald (1966) and Schlegel and Smith (1967). Aberrations in the replication mechanism may occur, as in the formation of incomplete viruses which are not infective. Some satellite viruses are probably incomplete viruses which cannot replicate without the help of a second virus (the 'activator'), but others appear to be complete and the reasons for their dependence on the activator are not understood. These aspects are discussed by Kassanis (1968).

Virus particles, or perhaps virus nucleic acid, move slowly from cell to cell, probably through plasmodesmata and possibly in other undiscovered ways since tobacco mosaic virus moved from cell to cell of tobacco callus tissue which is said to lack plasmodesmata (Kassanis, Tinsley and Quak, 1958). Virus particles in the cells of meristematic tissue are no doubt distributed during cell division. The virus may be restricted, as in local lesions, or it may become systemic, in which case there is a much more rapid translocation of the virus, probably through the phloem but possibly in the xylem (see Behnke, 1966). Several days may be necessary for the development of a lesion only a few millimetres in diameter whereas movement of virus in the vascular tissue may attain a speed of as much as 1–2 cm/minute although movement is generally slower than this (see Bennett, 1940).

Virus can move through the stems of plants and susceptible tissue without causing symptoms, and multiplication *en route* possibly occurs, thus facilitating successful transfer of the virus. Transportation of virus is more rapid in the direction of nutrient utilization or storage, but movement in the reverse direction can apparently occur, although virus movement from shoot to root is generally more rapid than from root to shoot. Only comparatively small amounts of virus may be transported in this way, subsequent multiplication of the virus occurring in the organ or tissue so infected. Some viruses fail to invade the apical meristem (possibly the latter reduces virus multiplication) whereas others are able to do so.

Movement of virus in other tissues, notably the xylem, has been postulated and merits further study. The entry of viruses into plants and their subsequent movement are discussed by Siegel and Zaitlin (1964), Siegel (1966), Schneider (1965), and Porter (1959: Biochemistry of infection).

Transmission of plant viruses

Many viruses are spread by vectors which feed on or parasitize plants. These vectors are chiefly insects but some mites, nematodes, fungi and parasitic flowering plants (dodder), are also involved. Other methods of transmission are by seed, vegetative propagation of infected plants, sap inoculation and grafting.

Insect transmission

A few viruses are transmitted by biting insects – beetles, grasshoppers, earwigs – in a largely mechanical fashion, the virus contaminating the mouthparts and being introduced into the plant by the insect while it is feeding. This would seem to be a rather non-specific process and likely to be of importance only with viruses which are easily sap transmitted, such as tobacco mosaic virus. The gross mechanical damage caused by some biting insects no doubt reduces their efficiency as virus vectors but there are some viruses in which the beetle vector remains infective for a day or so after feeding on the infected plant. This is perhaps a result of virus being retained in the insect's stomach and regurgitated during feeding.

With these few exceptions most viruses show varying degrees of specificity toward their vectors. Some are transmitted by several or many species of, for example, aphids whereas others are transmitted by only one vector, although other vectors possibly exist. Some vectors transmit only one virus or a few, others transmit many and the aphid *Myzus persicae* is notorious for its ability to transmit some fifty viruses. The vectors of viruses are not easy to find and the fact that a virus is known to have only one vector often means that only one has been demonstrated so far.

Viruses have been classified in various ways according to their vector transmission characteristics. They can be grouped as non-persistent or persistent, or as circulative or propagative. Non-persistent viruses remain transmissible by the vector for only a limited time, often less than an hour but sometimes for several hours. They are acquired after a very short feeding period, usually less than a minute, and become infective immediately after feeding on an infected plant although much of their infectivity is lost after transfer to a second susceptible plant (see Bradley, 1964). Many are easily sap transmissible, have aphid vectors, and are thought to be carried near the tip of the insect's stylet. Aphids and other members of the Hemiptera feed by means of these stylets which penetrate the plant, the feeding process involving injection of saliva into the plant and the removal of sap from it. It is possible that stylet borne viruses are acquired mainly from the epidermis rather than from the phloem, and their transmission is sometimes described as mechanical, although the situation is unlikely to be as simple as this. Some viruses remain infective within the vector for several hours and have been termed semipersistent.

The non-persistence of some viruses in their vectors has been attributed to virus inhibition by a substance or substances present in the salivary glands of the insect vector. Such inhibition has been suggested in the case of tobacco mosaic virus, which can be transmitted mechanically by needle puncture but not, apparently, through the stylets of aphids. Little is known about the inhibitory substance(s) involved except that it is heat stable and is thought to adhere to the virus particles without destroying them (Nishi, 1969).

With persistent viruses the vector remains infective for days or weeks, often for life, and may need to feed for several hours before becoming infective, although some become infective after feeding for as little as 10 or 15 minutes. Many of the viruses transmitted by leafhoppers (which are probably mycoplasmata rather than viruses, as discussed below), whitefly and thrips, and some of those transmitted by aphids fall into this category, and relatively few of them are easily sap transmissible – possibly because many infect only when introduced into the phloem of the plant. The latent period between acquisition of virus and the vector becoming infective ranges from an hour or so to several days in different persistent viruses.

Viruses can also be classified as circulative and propagative. These viruses seem to be more intimately associated with their vectors than are stylet borne viruses. Circulative viruses pass from the gut of the insect vector into its blood and thence into the salivary glands, and the insect does not become infective until this has happened. There is thus a delay – the latent period – between feeding and infectivity, and the vector tends to remain infective for a longer period. Many circulative viruses occur chiefly in the phloem and are rarely sap transmissible. Propagative viruses multiply within their vectors. There is evidence for such propagation in some aphid borne viruses, including potato leaf roll virus, but the situation with these viruses is obscure. Much of the work on propagative viruses has been done with those transmitted by leafhoppers and it now seems likely that most and possibly all of these diseases are due to *Mycoplasma*-like organisms rather than viruses; these are considered at the end of this chapter.

Viruses are known to be transmitted by aphids, whiteflies, thrips and mealybugs as well as by biting insects – beetles, grasshoppers, earwigs and possibly others – as described above. Aphids (Aphididae) are the most frequent vectors of plant viruses and some transmit a large number. They can transmit some viruses more or less immediately after acquiring them but with other viruses there may be a delay of hours or even days between acquisition and transmission. The feeding period for acquisition of virus may be seconds or hours and persistence is also varied, extending to several days with some aphid borne viruses. Some of the latter are stylet borne, some are circulative and some probably multiply within the aphid, as discussed above. The transmission characteristics of aphid transmitted viruses are varied, as might be expected when one considers the large number of viruses (about one hundred and sixty) which they transmit.

The reproductive capacity of aphids is enormous – it is said that a hectare of heavily infested beans may produce several million aphids daily. They would appear to be almost ideal vectors except that they probably transmit some viruses rather inefficiently. Swenson (1968) points out that many aphids fail to encounter a virus infected plant, that few of those which develop on infected plants are viruliferous when they leave, and that the virus content of heavily infested plants on which winged aphids are produced is likely to be fairly low. Many viruliferous aphids fail to infect the plants on which they feed, and the advantages of the quick acquisition and immediate infectivity of stylet borne viruses are no doubt offset by the very brief retention of these non-persistent viruses. The advantages of virus persistence in the vector are partly nullified by the short flight period and short life of migrating aphids, especially if there is a prolonged latent period during which the aphid is not infective. Semipersistent viruses which combine immediate transmission with some persistence are perhaps a useful compromise. Aphids are successful as virus transmitters and although only about 9% of the world total of aphid species have been investigated in this respect about two hundred species are known to be vectors (Swenson, 1968). A list of aphids which transmit viruses is given by Kennedy *et al.* (1962).

After aphids, leafhoppers (Jassidae) transmit the largest number of viruses (about sixty-five) but some of these are probably *Mycoplasma*-like organisms. About one hundred species of leafhoppers are reported to transmit these agents of disease in plants, and are discussed at the end of this chapter.

Whiteflies (Aleyrodidae) transmit several viruses, particularly in tropical and subtropical areas. They include those causing cassava mosaic and cotton leaf curl, and others no doubt await discovery. The few whitefly transmitted viruses which have been adequately studied require at least half an hour for acquisition by the insect, and duration of infectivity depends on the length of feeding. Several hours at least elapse between acquisition of virus and ability to transmit. These viruses are probably circulative but they have not been shown to multiply within the vector. A few are apparently transmitted with difficulty by sap inoculation although most whitefly transmitted viruses are not known to be transmitted in this way.

Thrips (Thysanoptera) are well known as the vectors of tomato spotted wilt virus (figure 4.8). Tobacco ring spot virus is also reported to be transmitted by nymphs but not by adults of *Thrips tabaci* from soyabean to soyabean, and behaves as a persistent or circulative virus in transmission (Messieha, 1969). It is also transmitted by the nematode *Xiphinema americanum*, and thus has two vectors in very different taxonomic groups. Sunflower mosaic virus has also been reported to be transmitted by thrips as well as by aphids and whiteflies (Traversi, 1949) but this needs confirmation. Transmission of tomato spotted wilt virus is exceptional in that the adult thrip cannot acquire the virus from an infected plant. The virus is transmissible by larvae and adult insects but the latter are viruliferous only through having acquired virus in the larval stage. Several days elapse between acquisition and ability to infect. The vectors apparently remain

c

Figure 4.8 Large local lesions, often composed of concentric zones of necrotic tissue, on leaves of *Nicotiana tabacum* infected by tomato spotted wilt virus.

infective indefinitely, suggesting that the virus multiplies within them. Tomato spotted wilt virus has a wide host range, is sap transmissible, unstable, and is said to be one of the few viruses which will pass from dicotyledons to monocotyledons (Smith, 1957). It is an interesting and unusual virus in many ways and is described in detail by Best (1968).

Several species of mealybugs (Pseudococcidae) transmit viruses of the swollen shoot disease of cacao complex. Mealybugs are rather sedentary although the nymphs crawl to a limited extent and the bugs themselves may be transported by ants. They thus tend to be rather inefficient vectors of viruses and are unlikely to travel far unless blown by wind or carried about in diseased plant material. They require several hours to acquire swollen shoot virus and quickly lose their infectivity except when subjected to fasting before feeding on the infected plant. Single insects rarely infect and the virus may be present in only small amounts in the diseased plants.

There are many aspects of insect transmission of plant viruses which are not understood. These include virus interactions in respect of transmission by vectors in one of which the vector becomes able to transmit virus A only if virus B, also transmissible by the vector, is present. This could be due to synergistic effects between the two viruses leading to an increased level of virus A, but these effects are difficult to explain.

Mite transmission

Eriophyid mites transmit several viruses, one of which is reversion disease of currant (*Ribes*) spread by the big-bud mite, *Phytoptus ribis*. In this disease the young buds of infected bushes are much more susceptible to mites than are those of uninfected bushes, probably because of the fewer hairs on the stems and leaves of virus infected plants (Thresh, 1967). Other viruses spread by mites include wheat streak mosaic virus, wheat spot mosaic, ryegrass mosaic and several others (Slykhuis, 1965). It is possible that some mite transmitted viruses are circulative but little is known about their transmission characteristics. It is of interest that the mite *Aceria tulipae* can simultaneously transmit the viruses causing wheat spot mosaic and wheat streak mosaic, and that the latter is acquired by nymphs but not by adults – a situation rather similar to that occurring in transmission of tomato spotted wilt virus by thrips. Mites cannot fly and presumably spread viruses by crawling from plant to plant or, more likely, by being dispersed by wind.

Nematode transmission

Nematodes of the genera *Xiphinema*, *Longidorus* and *Trichodorus* transmit a number of viruses as described by Harrison (1964) and Cadman (1964). These have been termed NEPO viruses (nematode transmitted polyhedral particles, for example arabis mosaic virus) and NETU viruses (nematode transmitted tubular particles, for example tobacco rattle virus). Nematode transmission was first reported by Hewitt, Raski and Goheen (1958) in fanleaf disease of grapevine spread by the nematode *Xiphinema index*, and several others have subsequently been notified as being nematode transmitted. It is not known whether there is any sort of biological relationship between nematode and virus. The limited information available suggests that viruliferous nematodes remain infective for much of their lives, perhaps indicating multiplication of virus within the nematode. Transmission through nematode eggs has not been demonstrated and little is known about the acquisition and transmission of viruses by these vectors. It is thought that nematodes feed on the epidermal cells near the root tip where, presumably, they acquire virus. The movement of nematodes through undisturbed soil is limited – possibly 30 cm or so per year – so that the viruses which they transmit are unlikely to spread rapidly unless some other method of transmission exists; many NEPO viruses are seed borne and pollen borne, and some are sap transmissible. Spread may, however, be expedited by dissemination of infested soil or infected planting material by wind, water or by man and his machines and animals. Some spread might also result from systemic root infection of plants with extensive root systems; the roots could thus be made available to nematodes feeding at some distance from the original site of infection.

NEPO viruses, although not very similar serologically, tend to have a wide natural host range, consist of polyhedral particles about 30 nm in diameter, have a thermal inactivation point (the temperature which when applied for 10 minutes completely inactivates the virus in crude plant sap) of between 55° and 70°C, and show a high degree of seed transmission, the virus coming from an ovule or pollen. NETU viruses include those causing tobacco rattle and pea early browning, both of which have wide host ranges and thermal inactivation points between 70° and 80°C. The tubular particles of both viruses are of two sizes – 210 and 105 nm (pea early browning virus) and 185 × 25 nm and 75 × 25 nm (tobacco rattle virus). Only the longer particles of tobacco rattle virus are infective.

Nematode transmitted viruses have been known for only some 14 years and there is little information about vector–virus relationships in these diseases, or about the ecology of the nematodes involved.

Fungus transmission

Several viruses, including those causing big-vein disease of lettuce and tobacco necrosis, are transmitted by certain species of Chytridiales, including *Olpidium* and *Synchytrium*, which infect plants. There is also some evidence that one or two species of Plasmodiophorales transmit certain viruses: *Polymyxa graminis* may be a vector of wheat mosaic virus, and *Spongospora subterranea* has recently been implicated in the spread of potato mop-top virus (Jones and Harrison, 1969). It may well be that other fungi which infect plants also transmit viruses, a possibility which merits investigation.* Bawden and Kassanis (1947), however, were unable to transmit tobacco necrosis virus by means of *Corticium* (*Rhizoctonia*) *solani* or *Thielaviopsis basicola*. There are viruses which attack fungi but their relationship, if any, with viruses which attack plants is a matter for speculation.

The virus is introduced into the roots by the zoospores of the fungus, but whether it is borne externally or internally, or both, is uncertain.

* C. E. Yarwood (*Pl. Dis. Reptr*, **55**, 342; 1971) has described experiments whose results suggest that tobacco mosaic virus might be spread by conidia of *Sphaerotheca lanestris* and *Erysiphe graminis*.

Rao and Brakke (1969) investigated the transmission of wheat mosaic virus by *Polymyxa graminis* and found that the zoospores remained infective after six washings in distilled water and that the resting spores were infective after treatment with 0·1N HCl or 0·1N NaOH which inactivated free virus. These results suggest that the virus is either carried within the zoospores or firmly enough adsorbed to resist separation or inactivation by the treatments used. Campbell (1962) performed similar inactivation experiments with lettuce big-vein virus and obtained results which indicated that the virus might be carried within the zoospores of *Olpidium*. Strains of *Olpidium* vary in their ability to transmit tobacco necrosis virus and some strains are apparently unable to do so. There is some reason to suppose that transmission of this virus in soil is not entirely dependent on *Olpidium*; the fungicide captan did not prevent infection by suspensions of the virus watered into sterilized soil whereas it did prevent infection of plants grown in naturally contaminated soil (Babos and Kassanis, 1963).

Fungus transmission of viruses has been recognized for only about 14 years and many aspects remain obscure, particularly those concerning virus–vector relationships. The few fungus transmitted viruses so far investigated have narrow host ranges (except for tobacco necrosis virus) and a fairly high thermal inactivation point (80–90°C). Except for tobacco necrosis virus they are difficult to transmit by sap inoculation, and are not known to be seed borne or to have insect or nematode vectors. Further information on these interesting viruses can be obtained from Smith (1968) and Grogan and Campbell (1966).

Viruses without known vectors

There are many diseases ascribed to viruses – more than half of those recorded (Gibbs, 1969) – for which no vectors are known. This does not necessarily mean that no vectors exist, and further investigation may well reveal that some are transmitted by insects, mites, nematodes, fungi or possibly other organisms. Neither have all these diseases been proved to be caused by viruses, although some undoubtedly are. Many are graft transmissible and some can be transmitted by sap inoculation but it is conceivable that other agents are responsible for some of these diseases. Only in recent years has it been realized that some so-called virus diseases are probably caused by mycoplasmata, and Yarwood *et al.* (1961) found that the disease of beet previously thought to be of virus origin (beet latent virus) is caused by a bacterium, probably *Pseudomonas aptata*.

Transmission by parasitic angiosperms

Some viruses can be transmitted from an infected plant to an uninfected one by means of dodder (*Cuscuta* spp.) which is allowed to parasitize both plants, thus establishing a bridge between them (see Hosford, 1967). This is a useful experimental technique which has enabled the host range of some viruses to be extended, but care must be taken to ensure that the dodder itself is not infected with virus. The importance of this method of transmission in nature and in agriculture is not known but is probably not great. It might, however, be of significance in heavily parasitized crops in which there is extensive spread of dodder from plant to plant.

Seed transmission

The number of viruses convincingly shown to be seed borne has increased markedly in recent years, but such viruses remain in a minority – probably about fifty to sixty of a total of perhaps six hundred. One might expect systemic viruses to enter the seed but this is not so, there seeming to be mechanisms which prevent or reduce this or which in-activate virus. There are no vascular connexions between the embryo and the parent plant so that seed transmission of viruses restricted to the vascular tract is unlikely, and it may be significant that most seed borne viruses are able to invade parenchymatous tissue. Viruses are generally thought to move from cell to cell through plasmodesmata and the lack of such protoplasmic connexions between the embryo and surrounding cells would seem to preclude entry of virus into the embryo.

The haploid tissue of the gametophyte is possibly more resistant to viruses than diploid sporophyte tissue but there is very little direct evidence for this. Haploid, diploid, triploid and tetraploid sugarbeet plants of comparable lines react similarly to several viruses, but it is conceivable that the physiological changes which accompany meiosis might make the plant a less favourable medium for virus development. There is some evidence that bean southern mosaic virus may be inacti-vated after it has entered the embryo, as indicated by the lower detect-able virus content of old seeds as compared with young ones, and it is of interest that extracts of mature or germinated seeds caused greater virus inactivation than extracts of immature seeds (Zaumeyer and Harter, 1943; Cheo, 1955).

As well as entering the young embryo from the parent plant viruses may be introduced with the pollen, and Fulton (1964) considers that most pollen transmitted viruses are also seed borne. The virus presumably enters the embryo sac from the pollen tube during fertilization. Whether the virus can move from the infected embryo sac into the parent plant is uncertain, but there is increasing evidence that this can occasionally occur. Pollen infected by some viruses shows varying degrees of sterility and this is true, but to a lesser extent, of infected ovules. Sterility is presumably due to interference with the normal meiotic processes in microspores and megaspores and is likely to reduce the number of infected seeds produced; such interference may be more frequent than is at present supposed.

Viruses which move through the phloem are likely to enter young developing seeds along with nutrients, and it is not surprising that virus has been detected in the seed coat and endosperm as well as, sometimes, in the embryo. Some of these seeds in which the virus is present in the extra-embryonic parts of the seed but not in the embryo itself can nevertheless germinate into infected seedlings, though the way in which this occurs is obscure. Many seed borne viruses are sap transmissible and it may be that the seedling becomes infected by contact with the virus during germination. Seedlings originating from seeds carrying extra-embryonic infection may be contaminated rather than infected but may become infected during transplantation or other handling which enables the virus to enter. This could be important with highly contagious viruses, such as that causing tobacco mosaic.

A few viruses are carried on the seed coat, and tobacco mosaic virus survived on tomato seed for a year or so in this way. Thereafter the virus declined sharply but could still be recovered after 3 years (Alexander, 1960). Whether this surface contamination gives rise to infected seedlings is uncertain, and experiments designed to investigate this have often given conflicting results, perhaps because some internal infection may also occur. Some investigators, however, have reported that surface contaminated tomato seeds can produce infected seedlings, especially if planted soon after extraction. Tobacco mosaic virus present on tomato seed extracted by fermentation or acid treatment may be inactivated during the extraction process. Here again it seems likely that the seedling becomes infected through contact with the virus during germination.

The percentage infection of seeds varies greatly with the virus and the species of host plant involved, and on the resistance of the plant to the virus, infected resistant plants tending to produce fewer infected seeds. Different strains of a virus may vary in their transmissibility through seed, and some strains are apparently not seed borne. Similarly, a virus may be seed borne in one genus of a susceptible plant but not in another, or there may be differences in this respect between different species of one genus or between different varieties of a species. When germinated, some of the seeds from a single pod borne by an infected plant produce infected seedlings, others do not. The stage at which the plant becomes infected is reported to affect seed transmission; for example, lettuce plants which are infected by mosaic early in life are likely to produce a greater percentage of infected seeds than later infected plants. The percentage of infected seedlings obtained on planting seed from infected plants varies greatly, being as low as 1–5% with some virus–host combinations and approaching 100% in others, as shown in the table given by Bennett (1969).

Virus infected seeds are sometimes lighter and smaller than uninfected ones, and virus persistence, as judged from the percentage of infected seedlings produced on planting the seed, declines during storage. The rate of decline is rapid in some virus–plant combinations, the seeds failing to produce infected seedlings after a few months. In others, however, there may be some activity after several years – as long as 14 years in seeds of *Chenopodium murale* infected with sowbane mosaic virus, according to Bennett (1969). It seems probable that some viruses may persist longer than the viability of the seed containing them.

On planting virus infected seeds, characteristic, but sometimes mild, symptoms of the disease appear on the plant, often on the young seedling, sometimes on the cotyledonary leaves or on the first true leaves. There is, however, considerable variation in the severity of symptoms, and symptom expression can be affected by environmental factors such as light and temperature. Seedlings of some plant species originating from seed infected with some viruses may be somewhat retarded in growth but in others the seedlings show only mild symptoms or none at all, the virus being detectable only by assay methods.

Seed transmission of virus can be important in two ways. First, although the percentage of infected seed may be small it may be large enough to produce infected seedlings evenly spread throughout the crop area and, if the virus is one which spreads rapidly, this can result in early and widespread infection of the fields, leading to heavy crop loss. Second, virus infected seeds are frequently normal in appearance and are thus unlikely to be detected by plant quarantine inspectors. Hence they constitute an efficient method for dissemination of seed borne viruses from one country or continent to another.

Transmission by grafting, budding and vegetative propagation

Transmission by grafting or budding is useful as a method of transmitting viruses when sap inoculation fails and a vector is unknown, but its use is restricted to systemic viruses and to plants which are sufficiently related for successful union to take place. Some degree of natural root grafting may occur between trees, but its significance as a method of virus transmission is not known. Grafting and budding can, however, be important in spreading systemic viruses of horticultural plants, particularly perennial fruit crops which are propagated in such ways, and the use of infected root stocks, scions or buds, and the subsequent distribution of the infected nursery stock can be a very effective way of spreading viruses. Such propagating material may carry a latent virus as in the classic example of tristeza disease of orange in which sour orange root stocks are killed by a virus present in the sweet orange scions which are grafted into them. This, of course, results in wilting and death of the grafted trees; the scions, although tolerant of the virus, are destroyed through being grafted into intolerant root stocks. Vegetative propagation of crop plants carrying systemic viruses – by tubers, bulbs, cuttings and so on – results in extensive spread of the viruses, which thus often become destructive in plants so propagated. Potatoes, dahlias and strawberries are examples of this.

Mechanical transmission

Some viruses, particularly circulative and propagative ones, seem to depend on specific vectors for successful infection and these viruses are often difficult or impossible to transmit by sap inoculation. Others are easily sap transmitted, particularly if a mild abrasive and a reducing agent which minimizes inactivation of the virus by oxidation are added to the inoculum. There are various other treatments which facilitate infection, as described by Smith (1968) and Bawden (1964). Contact transmission can also spread viruses in the field, for example, by virus-containing leaves or even roots of an infected plant rubbing against those of a healthy plant, by the use of virus contaminated implements (for example pruning knives), or by virus carried on the hands or clothing or introduced into, and spread through, the fields by ploughs, tractors and other agricultural machines. Mechanical transmission is described by Yarwood (1957), and by Fulton (1964, 1966).

Soil transmission

Susceptible plants sown in sterilized soil to which tobacco mosaic virus has been added can become infected but such transmission is unlikely to be of much significance under natural conditions. More often, so-called soil transmission is in fact transmission by nematodes, fungi or possibly other vectors in the soil. Infection from diseased plant material in the soil might, however, occur with viruses which are easily sap transmissible and which remain infective for a long time in dead plant tissue in the soil, especially under conditions which allow such tissue to remain intact and undecomposed.

Epidemiology of virus diseases

The sources of virus for newly planted fields are infected seeds, diseased crop plants which survive between successive crops, and infected alternative hosts, wild and/or cultivated, including symptomless carriers. The last named are, for obvious reasons, particularly dangerous. Their detection may involve examination for the presence of inclusion bodies and inoculation experiments between the suspected carriers and susceptible plants which show symptoms when infected. Infected perennial plants, especially those developing only inconspicuous symptoms which can easily be overlooked, are also likely to be troublesome. Wild plants growing in or near the cultivated area may contain viruses or they may contract them from infected cultivated plants introduced into the area. Infected wild plants are a more or less permanent and effective source of some viruses attacking crop plants, but in other cases they seem to be of little importance in this respect, presumably because the viruses are less easily acquired, or transmitted, from the infected wild host to the cultivated one. This may perhaps be associated with reduced virulence in the wild plant, reduced vector efficiency in the transmission of the virus, or to the cultivated plant being less attractive to the vector. Whatever the reason, it is clearly advisable to carry out cross-inoculation experiments to determine the extent to which wild plants can be effective sources of virus inoculum for crop plants.

Some wild plants contain one or more viruses, and further investigation along these lines may well reveal that some of the viruses which attack economic plants have as yet unsuspected hosts among wild plants. A recent example of this is described by Tomlinson *et al.* (1970) who attribute the severe outbreaks of cucumber mosaic virus in lettuce and other vegetables to infected weeds growing within and near the crops; some of these weeds, including chickweed (*Stellaria media*), groundsel (*Senecio vulgaris*) and nettle (*Urtica urens*), are symptomless carriers of the virus which was transmissible from them to lettuce. Cucumber mosaic virus is reported by Tomlinson and Carter (1970) to be transmitted by chickweed seed and to occur in chickweed pollen. Chickweed plants produce large quantities of seeds which remain in the soil, so that a small percentage of infected seeds might be able to produce sufficient infected plants to bring about severe outbreaks of cucumber mosaic, even if the aphid vectors were scarce. Thus Tomlinson and Carter (1970) have calculated that if there are 2 million chickweed seeds per hectare, of which 1% are infected, 10% emergence will result in one infected plant per square metre. This is no doubt a conservative estimate since in glasshouse experiments seed collected from symptomless infected chickweed plants in the field produced 4–29% infected symptomless plants when sown. Chickweed seeds recovered from field soil carried 4–5% infection and the virus persisted for at least 5 months in winter in infected seeds buried 12·5 cm deep in soil in the field. The results of these and other experiments indicated that symptomless infected chickweed plants originating from self-sown infected seeds may well play an important part in outbreaks of cucumber mosaic in lettuce and possibly other vegetable crops.

Another source of virus inoculum is the regrowth of diseased plants which have managed to survive the intercrop months after having been missed during harvesting. Such regrowth may also be infested with vectors of the virus and so provide a source of both virus and vector. This is most likely to happen with inherently perennial plants cultivated as annuals (for example cotton) rather than with obligate annuals such as barley. Self-sown seedlings growing from seeds scattered during harvesting may be infected if the virus is seed borne, and are also likely to harbour its vectors. Similar considerations apply to tubers and other organs of vegetative propagation remaining after harvesting. Viruses and vectors may also survive in plants, such as cabbages in south-west England, which grow throughout the year although the vectors are not necessarily active at all seasons. Spring and autumn sowings of some cereals might also facilitate virus persistence.

Some viruses are seed borne to varying extents and may persist from season to season in this way. Tubers and other vegetative overwintering organs produced by infected plants are likely to contain viruses and so to be of importance in their seasonal carry-over, particularly in vegetatively propagated crops such as potato. The distribution of infected planting material, including transplants which have become infected in the seed bed or propagation area, also leads to spread of viruses. Infected plants originating from infected seed are often more or less randomly distributed throughout the field but this pattern will become obscured as the virus spreads. By contrast, when the inoculum comes from an external source, there will be a tendency for infected plants to appear first in those parts of the crop area nearest the inoculum source. The persistence of these infection patterns in the crop area depends on how rapidly the virus spreads; with viruses which spread only slowly the original infection pattern may still be discernible at harvest time.

Many viruses are spread from plant to plant by insects and a smaller number by mites, nematodes, fungi and possibly by organisms which are as yet undetected. Their spread depends not only on the presence of suitable virus inoculum, effective vectors, and susceptible plants, but also on such characteristics of virus–vector behaviour as the ease and speed (acquisition time) with which the vector obtains the virus from the infected plant, the persistence and possible multiplication of the virus within the vector, and the efficiency of virus transmission. With a long acquisition period an insect vector may fly away or be blown off the plant before it has acquired sufficient virus to infect. A non-persistent virus may cease to be infective if there is a lengthy period between successive feedings by the insect, that is, if the period between acquisition and inoculation is unduly prolonged. Much also depends on the number and activity of the vectors and on their efficiency as transmitters: a single viruliferous insect may be able to transmit the virus but a higher percent-age of infection is likely with several or many such insects. Rapid spread of a virus occurs when the vectors are present in sufficient numbers, are efficient transmitters and are effectively disseminated by their own efforts or by wind: deficiency in any of these respects will reduce the overall effectiveness of the vector in spreading the virus. Climatic and other factors affect the number and activity of insects, and also their predators and parasites.

The time of year at which the vectors are active and the duration of their ability to fly determine in part the number of active vectors available for transmission of a virus. They thus greatly influence its spread, as do the amount and availability of virus inoculum and the susceptibility of the plants. Aphids or other insect vectors which quickly lose their ability to fly are likely to be less effective in spreading viruses than those which retain this ability. During their initial flight aphids tend to feed on a succession of plants before finally settling, and this type of behaviour expedites the spread of viruses, particularly those viruses which are rapidly acquired and transmitted.

Ecological aspects of virus transmission are discussed by Carter (1962) who distinguishes movement (changes of position within a localized area such as a field), dispersal (flights within the natural or permanent breed-ing area) and migration (flights out of the natural breeding area). Movement of insects within crops is greatly affected by temperature, humidity and wind. A temperature above about 21°C, a relative humidity below 80%, a wind velocity below 8 km.p.h., and a difference of more than about 7°C in maximum and minimum temperature for the day are necessary for the flight of aphids (Thomas and Vevai, 1940), and high light intensity is also said to favour their flight. Active flight occurs mostly in fairly still, dry air and is usually of short duration. Much of it is a few metres above the ground but air borne insects have been caught at heights of several thousand metres. Aphids have been recorded as travelling several hundred kilometres in a day under suitable atmospheric con-ditions. Only persistent viruses are likely to be transmissible after such long journeys which are likely to take a long time, although the low temperatures at high altitudes might enable non-persistent ones to be so transmitted.

The efficiency of virus transmission may vary considerably among different strains within one species of a vector, and such strains may feed on different species of plants. The ease with which virus is obtained from, or effectively inoculated into, plants depends partly on their susceptibility, and this often declines with age. Temperature and possibly other environmental conditions may affect the susceptibility of plants and the efficiency with which vectors transmit viruses. An interesting possibility is that plants infected by certain viruses may thereby become more susceptible to some insects, the latter breeding more rapidly and living longer. Cultural practices including fertilizer treatment and the spacing between plants can affect not only their susceptibility to viruses but also their attractiveness or palatability to insect vectors. The colour of plants is said to influence some insects and hence the incidence of the viruses which they spread. In considering vector transmission of viruses it should be remembered that the principal vector is not necessarily the most prevalent insect, mite, nematode or fungus attacking the plant. For these and other reasons it is sometimes difficult to ascertain the vector or vectors of a virus.

Many factors including the characteristics of the virus, vector, plant and environment affect the development and spread of viruses in crops. The interaction of these factors is frequently complex and difficult to disentangle. Epidemiological aspects of insect transmitted viruses are discussed by Swenson (1968: aphids) and Bennett (1967: leafhoppers). Compared with some of the fungi which attack plants – especially those with air disseminated spores – many viruses spread relatively slowly, and the spread of viruses which cause systemic infection of trees may be a leisurely process, particularly if the vector is a fairly inactive one, as in the case of swollen shoot virus of cacao transmitted by mealybugs. The longevity of tree crops, however, makes even slowly transmitted viruses a great potential hazard.

Control of virus diseases

Measures used to control virus diseases are generally similar to those used against other pathogens, except that as yet chemicals methods find little application in virus control although they may be used against vectors. The fact that many viruses are spread by vectors is an added complication in virus control.

Exclusion

Exclusion of the virus by destruction of all sources of inoculum (p. 66) can be effective in annual crops with a well defined interval between successive sowings, but needs to be very thorough if the virus is one which

spreads rapidly from a small amount of inoculum. Elimination of alternative host plants may be possible with viruses of narrow host range but
may well prove impossible if the host range is wide, although as mentioned
above, not all alternative hosts are necessarily an effective source of virus
for the crop plant which it is desired to protect. Removal ('roguing') of
diseased plants from seed beds and fields, thus reducing the likelihood that
they will infect others, may be worthwhile if the virus causes conspicuous
symptoms and spreads only slowly. Removal should obviously be done with
the minimum of delay and can be effective in reducing the spread of
viruses in perennial crops as described by Adam (1962) for banana mosaic
(cucumber mosaic virus) in Honduras.

Some viruses, notably tobacco mosaic virus, are contagious to varying
extents and special precautions are necessary to minimize their spread on
clothing, hands or implements of workers tending the plants. Tractors and
other machines which move through the crop are also likely to spread
contagious viruses. The precautions to be taken are largely a matter of
common sense – thorough washing of the hands with soap and running
water, wearing of clean overalls (especially plastic ones which can be
cleaned easily) and sterilization of implements by heat or, more conveniently, in a 3% solution of tri-sodium orthophosphate (tsop), a virus
inhibitor, as recommended by Broadbent (1964).

Use of virus-free planting material

It is of paramount importance that the planting material be virus-free.
The simplest way to ensure this is by selecting it from uninfected plants,
but this is not always possible. Planting material certified as virus-free
does not always live up to its name. There are, however, several excellent
schemes for producing and distributing healthy planting material, particularly plants such as potato and strawberry which are vegetatively
propagated. In many such schemes the plants destined to supply planting
material are grown under conditions unfavourable to viruses and/or their
vectors, with periodical removal of diseased plants. In tuber indexing the
individual potato tubers are tested for the presence of viruses by growing
excised pieces of tuber under conditions conducive to the development of
symptoms: infected tubers can thus be detected and rejected. All such
methods depend on human judgement so that occasional mistakes inevitably occur, but the production of virus-free planting material is very
valuable in the control of plant viruses.

If uninfected planting material is not available it may be possible to
obtain it by culture of excised stem tips or by heat treatment. Stem tips
can prove difficult to root and may be invaded by some viruses, so that a
combination of heat treatment and tip culture is often used; the parent

plants are kept for several weeks or months at temperatures often between 35° and 40°C depending on the plant, before the stem tips are taken. Heat treatment can be by hot water or hot air, although the latter is generally considered to be less damaging to the plant. The temperature and the exposure period vary and have to be determined by trial. Kunkel (1936) used water at 50°C for 10 minutes in treatment of dormant virus infected peach trees and air at 35°C for 2–4 weeks for trees in active growth. Sugarcane setts are immersed for 2–3 hours in water at 50°C to free them from ratoon stunting virus. It is probable that heat inhibits multiplication of some viruses, perhaps by bringing about some change in the plant inimical to the virus, but heat treatment is not effective with all viruses.

Chemotherapy has also been used in attempts to eliminate virus from infected plants, with varying results. Certain purine and pyrimidine derivatives including 2-thiouracil are promising, probably interfering with virus multiplication, and might prove useful as additives to the medium used for rooting stem tips. Malachite green (Thomson, 1956) and 2, 4-D (Quak, 1961) have also been used to free plant tissue from viruses. The methods used and the problems encountered in controlling virus disease by using virus-free planting material are discussed by Hollings (1965). Heat therapy is reviewed by Kassanis (1957) and Nyland and Goheen (1969).

Attempts have been made to eliminate viruses carried on or in seed, and there is some evidence that dry heat can reduce seed borne infection; for example, tobacco mosaic virus is reported to be almost eliminated by keeping infected tomato seeds at 70°C for 1 or 2 days, without damage to the seed. With the increasing number of viruses shown to be seed transmitted the importance of finding effective treatments to eliminate viruses from infected or contaminated seed is likely to increase.

Control by inhibitors and inactivators

As mentioned above the use of virus inhibitors and inactivators to control plant viruses has given conflicting and often unsatisfactory results but this work is in its early stages (see Matthews and Smith, 1955; Price, 1963). One of the difficulties is that some virus inhibitors, including the antibiotic cytovirin, are phytotoxic at the concentrations which are effective against viruses. Cows' milk apparently contains virus inhibitors (Fulton, 1943) and Hare and Lucas (1959) and others have reported reduced infection when plants were sprayed with milk before inoculation with virus. Some plants contain virus inhibitors and the possible use of the latter for control of virus diseases merits further investigation. Of interest in this respect is a recent report by Wheeler and Pirone (1969) that treatment of bean (*Phaseolus vulgaris*) plants with non-phytotoxic concentrations of victorin, the toxin produced by *Cochliobolus victoriae* (oat blight), greatly reduced the number of lesions which developed on subsequent mechanical inoculation with alfalfa mosaic virus and with tobacco mosaic virus. The toxin no doubt activated a defence mechanism effective against these two viruses.

Control by cultural practices

Agricultural and horticultural practices can sometimes be modified to reduce virus attack, sometimes through an effect on the vectors. For example, it may be possible to adjust the sowing date so as to involve minimal or late vector infestation in order that the attack will cause relatively little damage; also, the plants may become less susceptible when older. Close spacing reduces the damage caused by some viruses since more plants escape infection, and vectors may be discouraged. It is also likely to result in small plants which, because of their smaller surface area, are less liable to infection than larger ones. These effects will tend to be most marked with viruses which do not spread rapidly from plant to plant. The beneficial effects of close spacing – at least with respect to virus attack – have been demonstrated in several virus diseases but, as with all modifications of cultural practices, its effects on other pathogens and pests must be considered.

The newly sown fields should ideally be situated as far as possible from likely sources of inoculum and this should be borne in mind when planning crop rotation and layout. There may be little scope for this on small farms or market gardens where suitable land is limited or where one crop is intensively grown. No generally applicable 'safe' distance can be given since insect vectors differ greatly in the distance they fly or are transported by wind, and weather conditions also play a part. Distances ranging from as little as 90 m to 1·6 km or more have been recommended for different viruses. Such factors as how quickly the virus is acquired by, and for how long it remains transmissible in, the vector will affect the safe distance. Stylet borne viruses which disappear rather quickly from the vector are likely to have a smaller safe distance than viruses which persist for a longer time.

The spread of insect transmitted viruses is often slower in a mixed population of susceptible and non-susceptible plants than in susceptible ones alone, and some use can be made of this in virus control. Cultivation of susceptible plants beneath a cover of non-susceptible ones can reduce infection and barriers erected at intervals in the field may have the same effect. The barriers may be screens of cloth or some other suitable material, but are more often rows of plants which are neither susceptible to the virus nor colonized by the vectors. Plants used as barriers include sunflower, maize, oats and barley. Wide barriers are likely to be more effective than narrow ones, and spraying the barrier plants with an insecticide which kills the vector is an added refinement. Hedges may act as natural barriers to insects and it will be interesting to see whether the present tendency to remove hedges in Britain has any effect on the incidence of viruses spread by insects.

Control of vectors

Control of those insects or other vectors which spread many viruses takes several forms. Attempts can be made to reduce the vectors by destroying plants on which they overwinter and breed, and it should be remembered that such plants may also be sources of virus. Eradication by ploughing, herbicides, or a well timed insecticidal spray can be useful in reducing the number of vectors, and spraying the breeding areas of the vectors can be very effective if carried out when the vectors are most vulnerable.

Destruction of vectors within the crop has been useful in some cases, but there are practical difficulties in obtaining the rapid and high degree of kill required for effective control of viruses (the degree of kill is much higher than that required for control of direct plant injury by insects). This is a problem with those viruses which are acquired and transmitted rapidly, as is often the case with those which are stylet borne. The vector may have passed on the virus before being killed by the insecticide. Better results are likely to be obtained with vectors which take some time to acquire virus in effective amounts, and systemic insecticides – sometimes applied to the soil at planting time – may give adequate vector and virus control for weeks or months. No doubt similar considerations apply to control of viruses transmitted by nematodes or fungi but the high cost of effective fumigation or steam sterilization of soil is an additional problem here. The use of insecticides for control of vectors and the viruses they carry is discussed by Broadbent (1964) and Bawden (1964).

Control by resistant varieties

One of the most convenient methods of control is by growing virus resistant varieties of plants. Among the difficulties here – as discussed in chapter 28 – are finding adequate resistance genes, the difficulty of combining these with desirable agronomic or commercial qualities, and the fact that many viruses are variable and produce new strains which may be able to attack hitherto resistant varieties of plants. Nevertheless, resistant varieties have proved their value in control of several virus diseases including sugarcane mosaic.

Immune varieties are the most satisfactory but are comparatively rare.

Resistant varieties are less satisfactory in that the virus is still present so that there is a danger of new strains arising. Resistance may be associated with resistance to infection, reduced or inhibited virus multiplication or movement within the tissues after infection, or tissue hypersensitivity which results in localization of the virus or, in some cases, in death of the infected plant. The plant may be resistant or unattractive to the vectors of the virus. Holmes (1965) recommends that breeders aim at producing plant varieties which are hard to infect and from which, when infected, the virus is not easily transmitted. Such varieties should also show easily recognizable symptoms when infected, thus facilitating roguing.

Virus tolerant varieties in which the plants become infected but apparently suffer little serious damage are often grown. This is undesirable because a large population of the virus is thereby maintained which may be dangerous to plants that are not tolerant and which is likely to enhance the chances of new strains arising. Infected tolerant plants often show mild, inconspicuous symptoms so that they are easily overlooked. As Bawden (1964) says, 'It is well to appreciate that the growing of tolerant varieties may solve a disease problem in one crop only to raise one in another.' Another point is that any measure which reduces the virus population will thereby reduce the chances of new strains arising: hence control measures should be maintained even when virus resistant varieties of plants are grown. The genetical basis of resistance has not been studied in many cases. Resistance to some viruses seems to be determined by one or a few genes whereas many genes are apparently involved in others (Holmes 1954, 1965).

Other methods of control

Several other methods of controlling virus diseases have been used or suggested, for example cross-protection ('vaccination') in which infection of the plant with a mild strain of the virus protects it against subsequent attack by a more virulent strain, a possibility discussed by Posnette and Todd (1955) for control of swollen shoot disease of cacao in West Africa.

Legislation and international cooperation also have a part to play in minimizing the spread of viruses. Man has been responsible for the long distance dissemination of many viruses, often in the form of infected tubers and other planting material. Detection of viruses in dormant planting material is often impossible and may necessitate germinating the material before it can safely be released. More cooperation in effective and accurate certification of planting material is needed and would considerably ease the load of overworked plant quarantine inspectors. Internal legislation such as compulsory notification of certain diseases, destruction of infected plants, and a ban on the cultivation of alternative hosts of destructive viruses may be necessary. In general these methods are similar to those used for control of other pathogens.

Variation, classification and identification of viruses

Viruses are genetically variable and new strains differing in host range, virulence and other characteristics arise, these perhaps representing different arrangements of the four nucleotides in the nucleic acid molecule. Such aberrations no doubt occur during virus replication; many are probably harmful and disappear in a uniform environment but some survive and prosper under changed environmental conditions or in a different species or variety of plant, thus extending the host range of the virus. There are probably other mechanisms, perhaps including some form of genetical recombination, which bring about variation in viruses but little is known about them (see Hitchborn and Thomson, 1960; Bawden, 1964; Holmes, 1965). The problem is complicated by the difficulty of distinguishing between viruses and virus strains, and by the lack of any satisfactory system of nomenclature and classification.

Viruses have been named after the plants on which they were first found or on which they most frequently occur. They have also been classified according to the symptoms they produce, using a Latin binomial system. At present they are mostly grouped on a host-symptom basis, for example cucumber mosaic virus, and an annotated list of names and synonyms of plant viruses has recently been published (Martyn, 1968). Several other classifications based on the structure of the virus particle have been put forward in recent years (for example Pereira, 1966; Brandes and Bercks, 1965). Gibbs *et al.* (1966) suggest a classification based on Adansonian priciples, namely the grouping together of organisms which show the greatest overall similarity when all features are considered. In this the conventional name of the virus is followed by a cryptogram containing information on the chemical nature, molecular weight and morphology of the virus particle, on the kind of host organism, and on the kind of vector if any. The classification of plant-infecting viruses is reviewed by Gibbs (1969).

Several methods are used to identify plant viruses. (1) Viruses are inoculated into indicator plants which develop typical symptoms, often local lesions, when infected by specific viruses. It may be necessary to use several different species of indicator plant since most of the latter react to several viruses, but some are used to detect specific viruses and in virus assay (Steere, 1955). Indicator plants are discussed by Hollings (1966) and Ross (1964). (2) Serological tests are carried out using antisera of known viruses (Matthews, 1957, 1967; Ball, 1964; Wetter, 1965; Regenmortel,

1966). (3) Transmission aspects of the virus are considered – whether by sap inoculation, and the vectors, if any, involved; whether the virus is persistent or non-persistent in the vector; whether stylet borne, circulative or propagative, and other aspects of its transmission. (4) Such properties as the thermal inactivation point, the dilution end point, and survival outside the plant can be used to characterize viruses. (5) Interaction with other viruses is considered, notably cross-protection (Price, 1964). (6) Host range and symptoms are studied, as are (7) the morphology and chemical constitution of the virus particle (Brandes, 1966). Experienced virologists can often identify viruses on symptoms and host but sometimes, particularly with apparently new viruses, identification by the methods outlined above is necessary. Of these, serology and morphology are perhaps the most useful provided one has the facilities to carry them out satisfactorily. Much valuable information can, however, be obtained from a study of the host range of the virus, the symptoms it causes, and its effects on a series of indicator plants. Further information on the identification of viruses can be obtained from Ross (1964).

Mycoplasma-like organisms

During the past 5 years it has become apparent that some of the leaf-hopper transmitted diseases of the yellows and witch's broom type (and probably others) are caused by agents similar to Mycoplasmatales (pleuro-pneumonia-like organisms, PPLO) and not by viruses as was previously thought. The two groups are in many ways similar, especially in size and filterability, and *Mycoplasma* spp. from animals are said to be the smallest known microorganisms capable of extracellular growth in cell-free media. It is not surprising that viruses and mycoplasms have often been confused.

The cells of *Mycoplasma* spp. have a cell membrane but lack a cell wall and are thus pleomorphic and resistant to penicillin, although sensitive to tetracyclines. They appear to be a heterogenous group of saprophytes and parasites and are described by Eaton (1965), Browne and Officer (1968), and Razin (1969).

The *Mycoplasma*-like organisms found in certain leafhopper transmitted plant diseases are morphologically similar to animal mycoplasmata, but Ploaie and Maramorosch (1969) were unable to grow the leafhopper organisms in culture. The causal agent of aster yellows showed somewhat different antibiotic sensitivities and was different in other respects from known animal mycoplasmata, suggesting that the plant-infecting mycoplasmata are perhaps a new group of *Mycoplasma*-like organisms (Davis and Whitcomb, 1969).

More than a quarter of a century ago Black (1943) described fairly large infective particles in aster yellows disease but it was not until 1967 that Doi *et al.* (1967) in Japan observed *Mycoplasma*-like or *Bedsonia*-like (psittacosis–granuloma–trachoma agents, PLT) bodies in the phloem of plants infected with several leafhopper transmitted diseases. These bodies and the symptoms disappeared temporarily on treating infected plants with tetracycline or chlorotetracycline antibiotics which inhibit mycoplasmata and related organisms (Ishii *et al.*, 1967). Similar bodies have subsequently been described in several plant diseases hitherto ascribed to viruses, and Gibbs (1969) considers that most of the yellows or witch's broom diseases transmitted by leafhoppers may be of this type. Certain diseases transmitted by mites and whiteflies in which virus particles have not been observed might also be caused by mycoplasmata. Diseases in which *Mycoplasma*-like bodies have been reported include aster yellows, potato witch's broom, mulberry dwarf, maize stunt, rice yellow dwarf, several clover diseases (witch's broom, phyllody, dwarf, proliferation) and bunchy top of papaya (*Carica papaya*), and doubtless more will be reported in the near future.

Mycoplasma-like bodies have also been found in the salivary glands of the leafhopper vectors of aster yellows (Hirumi and Maramorosch, 1969) and in the phloem of dodder plants parasitizing plants infected with aster yellows (Dale and Kim, 1969). In electron microscope studies on periwinkle (*Vinca rosea*) plants experimentally inoculated with the causal agents of five yellows-type diseases, Ploaie and Maramorosch (1969) described various types of pleomorphic bodies resembling *Mycoplasma*, *Bedsonia* and L-forms of bacteria in the phloem of infected plants but not in uninfected ones.

Whether all the diseases in which the causal agent is transmitted by leafhoppers are caused by mycoplasmata or similar organisms has yet to be determined but this may well prove to be the case. In many respects mycoplasmata behave somewhat differently from viruses, and their transmission characteristics are varied. Many are not infective immediately after acquisition of the causal agent but having become so they tend to remain infective for a long time. There are exceptions to this and in some cases leafhoppers are able to transmit within a few hours of acquisition. Bawden (1964) points out that leafhopper transmitted agents fall into two main groups chiefly based on whether the vectors become infective within a few hours (beet curly top, maize streak) or not for several days (aster yellows) after acquisition. It may be that the former agents do not multiply within the vector (possibly they are viruses) whereas the latter do. Transmission of the agent through the eggs of the leafhopper vector can occur as first demonstrated by Fukushi in rice dwarf disease transmitted by *Nephotettix apicalis* and since reported for some others (see Maramorosch, 1963). This contrasts with the behaviour of viruses transmitted by other insect vectors, where the virus is confined to the larva or adult which has itself acquired it, and is not passed on transovarially to the progeny.

As well as propagating within their leafhopper vectors, some of these agents have an adverse effect on them. Thus the infected vectors may have a shorter life, produce fewer eggs, and sometimes show histopathological symptoms in ganglia and brain tissue (Maramorosch and Jensen, 1963). In these cases the vector as well as the plant can be regarded as diseased and the causal organism might originally have attacked the insect, subsequently developing the capacity to attack the plant on which the infected insect fed. The plant is usually more severely damaged than the insect and if one accepts that long association between pathogen and host leads to reduced virulence it would seem that the insect might indeed be the primary host (Bawden, 1957).

Some one hundred species of leafhoppers are known to transmit agents which cause disease in plants, and many of the vectors show a considerable degree of specificity. The diseases often involve disturbances in the vascular system, usually in the phloem but in the xylem in Pierce's disease of the grapevine (alfalfa dwarf virus). This is followed by such secondary symptoms as yellowing, stunting, leaf rolling, rosetting and witch's broom. Few of the causal agents involved are known to be sap transmissible or seed borne. These leafhopper transmitted agents are discussed by Sinha (1968) and Bennett (1967: epidemiology).

5 Plant diseases caused by parasites: the taxonomy of plant pathogens

The main parasitic agents which incite disease in plants are considered briefly in this and the following two chapters. Subsequent chapters on the principles of plant pathology are largely, but not entirely, concerned with fungi since much of the literature on plant pathology refers to diseases caused by these pathogens. For this reason, apart from the section on the taxonomy of plant pathogens (p. 81) little is written about fungi in the present chapter.

The main causes of disease in plants, excluding non-parasitic agents, are – in decreasing order of importance – fungi, viruses and *Mycoplasma*-like organisms, bacteria and parasitic flowering plants.

Fungi

The number of species of fungi which cause disease in plants is unknown but, according to Ainsworth (1963), there are about 4600 species of Uredinales (rusts), 700 of Ustilaginales (smuts), and 1000 of Erysiphales (powdery and 'dark' mildews), totalling 6300 species, which are obligate parasites of plants. In addition there are probably about 150 species of Peronosporales which attack plants, and substantial numbers of parasitic species in the Ascomycetes and Fungi Imperfecti – the genus *Cercospora*, for example, is said to comprise 1270 species of (mostly) plant pathogens, and *Ramularia* some 300 species. On this basis the species of fungi which attack plants are unlikely to number less than about 10,000 and may well amount to twice that number.

Fungi of one sort or another attack most groups of plants but they have been studied chiefly as pathogens of seed plants. Whereas more than fifty fungi attack apple, relatively few fungi have been recorded on other plant species. This may be due partly to inadequate investigation, the number of recorded diseases tending to be positively correlated with the economic importance of the plant and hence with the amount of attention it has received from plant pathologists. Many orders and families of fungi contain species which are parasitic on plants and some are known to comprise only parasitic species, for example Peronosporaceae, Albuginaceae, Erysiphales, Uredinales and Ustilaginales. Most or all of the known species of some fungal genera are plant pathogens, for example *Cercospora*, while others such as *Cladosporium* contain parasitic and saprophytic species. Important groups of fungal plant pathogens include the rusts, smuts, downy mildews and powdery mildews, but destructive diseases are caused by fungi in many other groups, notably the Sphaeriales, Hypocreales and Fungi Imperfecti.

On germination the spores of many fungi produce infection structures which grow into the plant, and in this respect fungi differ from bacteria and viruses, which lack the capacity to enter the plant by active growth. Fungi, or most of them, produce disseminatory spores and resistant over-wintering spores which serve for rapid spread and survival over unfavourable periods, respectively. Viruses and the plant infecting bacteria lack such spores and, generally speaking, appear to be less effective than fungi as plant parasites. Information on fungi can be obtained from Ainsworth and Sussman (1965, 1966, 1968), Burnett (1968), Alexopoulos (1962), Bessey (1950), Langeron and Vanbreuseghem (1952), Bisby (1953), Webster (1970) and Ainsworth (1963).

Viruses

Although perhaps not parasites in the usual sense of the term, these cause many diseases of plants. About 600 plant viruses have been recorded but there is evidence that some of these, particularly those transmitted by leafhoppers, are *Mycoplasma*-like organisms rather than viruses. More plant viruses undoubtedly await discovery and some of the 'diseases of unknown origin' may well be caused by viruses. There are some extremely destructive virus diseases of cultivated plants, notably of plants belonging to such families as the Solanaceae (potato, tobacco, tomato). The importance of viruses as agents of disease in plants has been increasingly realized during the past 35 years and much attention has been directed to them in recent times.

Bacteria

Only about 150–200 or perhaps some 10% of the known species of bacteria have been reported as pathogens of plants, but this figure is of doubtful significance since there is little agreement as to what constitutes a bacterial species. For reasons discussed elsewhere (p. 87), bacteria seem to be less effective than fungi as plant pathogens. There are, however, some exceedingly destructive bacterial diseases of plants, particularly in the warmer areas of the world, and it is possible that bacteria are more important as plant pathogens than is at present realized.

Parasitic flowering plants

These are also best developed in the tropics and subtropics. Although generally of little economic importance, some, including witchweed (*Striga*), dodder (*Cuscuta*) and the dwarf mistletoes which attack forest trees, can cause considerable crop loss.

Taxonomy of plant pathogens

Taxonomy, classification and nomenclature are interrelated and are of interest to the plant pathologist who is concerned that a pathogen should have a name which is universally used and that any proposed change in that name should be approved by competent taxonomists and thereafter universally adopted. These aspects are regulated by the International Code of Botanical Nomenclature (1966), any changes in which must be sanctioned by an International Botanical Congress. Changes in generic and specific names become inevitable as more is learned about the structure and interrelationships of organisms and, as pointed out by Shaw (1965), nomenclature aims at stability whereas taxonomy is an investigational science involving changes in concepts. Few pathologists engaged on full time investigation of plant diseases have the opportunity, or the inclination, to delve deeply into taxonomic problems and must perforce rely on the taxonomists for guidance. The latter should endeavour to base their taxa on reliable and consistent criteria which can be determined by pathologists working in the field but this, unfortunately, is not always possible.

Many criteria have been used in identifying plant pathogens: serological (especially with viruses and bacteria), chemical (bacteria), physiological, parasitic (chiefly host range), and morphological. Identification based on morphological characteristics is very convenient when such characteristics are sufficiently stable to give consistent results and where their range of natural variation is known. It is often difficult, however, to decide whether the morphological differences of two organisms justify their separation at a species or lower level. For example, Mason (1927) separated *Nigrospora oryzae* and *N. sphaerica* largely on conidial size whereas others (Simmonds, 1933; Standen, 1943) doubt whether this is justified. It is perhaps best to regard such fungi as varieties of one species showing minor but consistent morphological differences; a small spored form might, for example, be designated 'var. *microspora*'. The morphological characteristics – including those used in distinguishing species – of a very variable fungus often show a wide range of variation within which are groups of biotypes resembling each other more closely than they resemble those of other groups ('aggregate species') and these also present problems to the taxonomist.

Serological, physiological and chemical methods of classification, although widely used for viruses and bacteria, have so far found rather little application in fungi, but are being investigated. The host range of fungal and bacterial plant pathogens is sometimes used as a specific criterion, and morphologically similar pathogens which attack different species of plants have not infrequently been described as distinct species, as with *Xanthomonas pelargonii* and *X. geranii* on pelargoniums and geraniums respectively (Dowson, 1957). A somewhat different case is that of *Pseudomonas tabaci* (wildfire) and *P. angulata* (angular leaf spot), both of which attack tobacco and differ only in that the former produces a toxin whereas the latter does not; this is reflected in the presence of a chlorotic halo around *tabaci* lesions but not around *angulata* lesions.

The practice of basing species on host range is difficult to justify in opportunist pathogens of wide and apparently unselective host range although a case might be argued for those with a well defined and limited range of host plants. There is little justification for doing so unless the host range of the pathogens under consideration has been adequately studied, but this is not always the case. The parasitic capabilities of a pathogen are related to its physiology and as such should be taken into account by taxonomists; the present practice is to distinguish parasitically or physiologically different forms within a morphologically defined species as special forms (*formae speciales*) as, for example, those of *Fusarium oxysporum* which causes vascular wilt of a number of different host species. The term 'variety' is sometimes used as in *Puccinia graminis* var. *tritici* on wheat, var. *hordei* on barley and so on, and trinomials have been used. *Formae speciales* can be further subdivided into physiological (biological, parasitic) races according to their host range; this is a matter for consultation between pathologists working on the pathogens involved.

Numerical taxonomy in which the overall similarity of taxa is assessed by computer analysis of numerous characteristics (morphological and others) is now being applied to fungi and bacteria and is a promising approach; see Sneath and Sokal (1962), Sokal and Sneath (1963) and Kendrick and Proctor (1964: Fungi Imperfecti).

Physiological races

'Race' is an ambiguous term used to denote infraspecific categories defined by physiological, morphological or other criteria. It is normally applied to the pathogen, 'variety' being a somewhat similar term in respect of the host plant. Races of plant pathogens are conventionally described as physiological races, defined by Ainsworth (1963) as 'one of a group of forms like in morphology but unlike in certain cultural, physiological, biochemical, pathological or other characters'.

In an effort to reduce ambiguity Robinson (1969) has proposed a 'deme-type' terminology. He suggests a type system for designating infraspecific categories, for example, pathotype for a pathogen population in which all individuals have a particular character of pathogenicity in common, and similarly, serotype in respect of serology, and physiotype in respect of physiology (excluding pathogenicity). There is a corresponding deme system for the plant, a deme being a group of individuals of a specified taxon; for example, a pathodeme is a population of a host plant in which all the individuals have in common a particular character of resistance to a pathogen.

There is little uniformity among the systems used to designate races of different pathogens, many such systems having been developed by individual workers studying the pathogens. It is desirable, wherever possible, to relate the race names to the resistance genes of the host which they overcome, as was done by Black *et al.* (1953) for the races of *Phytophthora infestans* which attack potato. The four genes at that time known to confer leaf resistance were labelled *R1*, *R2*, *R3* and *R4* (about nine such genes are now known). The races able to overcome, for example, gene *R1* contain the number 1, that is races (1), (1, 2), (1, 3), (1, 4), (1, 2, 3), (1, 2, 4), and (1, 2, 3, 4). Races able to overcome genes *R1*, *R3*, and *R4* are labelled (1, 3, 4) and (1, 2, 3, 4), and so on.

The *P. infestans* system is a logical one which compares favourably with numerical systems, for example that used for *Puccinia graminis f. sp. tritici* in which the approximately 300 races are numbered from race 1 onwards with no reference to the host resistance genes which they overcome. Numerical systems of this sort are, however, inevitable until the genetical basis of resistance in the host plant has been elucidated, and this may take a long time. They are useful when the races can be satisfactorily defined and consistently distinguished in terms of differential host varieties, and provided the system is internationally accepted and used. This last proviso is important in that an internationally used system for distinguishing and labelling races of pathogens can obviate much of the confusion which inevitably arises when each individual worker has his own system for naming the races which he is studying.

The races of *Puccinia graminis f. sp. tritici* have been intensively studied. About 297 have been identified on the basis of their reaction to twelve standard differential varieties of *Triticum* spp. as described by Stakman *et al.* (1962), and additional races could no doubt be distinguished by using a wider range of differentials. Some races have been divided into 'subraces' by using supplementary differential varieties, and some of these subraces have been divided further. Thus race 15B has been separated from race 15 and four isolates of the former have been designated 15B-1, 15B-2, 15B-3 and 15B-4. These are all physiological races as defined by Stakman *et al.* (1962), a physiological race being 'a biotype or group of biotypes, within a species or lower taxon, which can be distinguished with reasonable facility and certainty from other biotypes or groups of biotypes by physiological characters, including pathogenicity'. They propose that the races identified solely by the standard differentials should be known as 'standard races' and should be numbered, whereas divisions of the standard races identified by using supplementary differentials should be termed subraces, designated as described for race 15 above. A universally accepted procedure for naming races and subraces, together with a Register of Races and Subraces and their characteristics, is highly desirable to ensure a uniform nomenclature throughout all areas where the races of the pathogen are being studied.

No other plant pathogen is known to comprise as many races as *P. graminis tritici* but this may be partly due to lack of investigation. When a pathogen comprises numerous races it becomes essential to devise a reliable system for identifying and naming those races and to ensure that the system is universally adopted.

Difficulties in defining species satisfactorily occur with most organisms, and fungal taxonomists face other problems. One of these concerns the extent to which parasitic characteristics should be considered, as discussed above. Another is how to classify Fungi Imperfecti – those fungi in which a perfect (sexual) state is not known. Classification of such fungi into orders and families is at present based largely on the structure of the conidial fructification, or lack of it, while generic distinction rests chiefly on the morphology of the conidia and conidiophores. Although this system is unsatisfactory in many ways it is the only one which can be applied to all Fungi Imperfecti producing conidia. Attempts are being made to devise other methods of classification based, for example, on the way in which the conidia develop on the conidiophores, but it will be many years before these can be applied throughout this very large form-class. The perfect, usually Ascomycete, states of some imperfect fungi have been and are being discovered but the number of new species of Fungi Imperfecti described annually far exceeds the number for which perfect states are found.

When an Ascomycete or Basidiomycete is satisfactorily shown to be the perfect state of a hitherto imperfect fungus the name of the former should thereafter be used although, where convenient, it is permissible to use both. The name of the perfect state has often been more or less universally adopted. Thus, *Diplocarpon rosae* rather than *Actinonema rosae* is almost invariably used to denote the cause of black spot disease of rose, but there is a tendency for the conidial names of some fungi to persist through established usage, as with *Septoria nodorum* (*Leptosphaeria nodorum*). It is sometimes argued that the conidial name should be used unless the perfect state occurs in the area concerned, and this practice can cause considerable confusion which could be avoided. Another difficulty arises with very variable species of Fungi Imperfecti; thus the Ascomycete *Sclerotinia fuckeliana* has a conidial state referable to *Botrytis cinerea*, but the question arises as to whether all the numerous forms of the latter fungus should be included in *S. fuckeliana*. Some Ascomycete genera have conidial states which fall into different genera of Fungi Imperfecti; for example, different species of *Mycosphaerella* produce conidia referable to *Cercospora*, *Ramularia*, *Phyllosticta*, *Septoria* and *Ascochyta*. Conversely, different species of one genus of Fungi Imperfecti may have different Ascomycete states – *Septoria* spp., for example, have been referred to the Ascomycete genera *Mycosphaerella* and *Leptosphaeria*. In other Fungi Imperfecti only one Ascomycete genus appears to be involved, as with *Cercospora* in which all species with known Ascomycete states are apparently referable to *Mycosphaerella*.

These aspects are of some importance to pathologists working on diseases caused by Fungi Imperfecti, Ascomycetes and, to a lesser extent, Basidiomycetes. The perfect state may be a means of overwintering and a source of new races resulting from hybridization, and any indication as to the form the perfect state of an apparently exclusively conidial fungus is likely to take will help the pathologist to make a more intelligent search for it. Some guidance can be obtained from a consideration of the known perfect states of other species of the genus to which the fungus under study belongs. Many Ascomycete plant pathogens spread by conidia and an indication of what form these are likely to take will help in searching for them in an Ascomycete apparently lacking conidia. One should, however, be prepared to find that the perfect or the conidial state may be different from that expected from the information available.

In their discussion of the taxonomy of *Fusarium*, Snyder and Toussoun (1965) suggest that species and higher taxa should be delimited purely on morphological characteristics, that species should be based on similarities rather than differences between isolates, and that a satisfactory taxonomic system should be readily usable by any biologist. If such techniques as serology, pathogenicity tests, protein analysis and electrophoresis have to be used in delimiting species there is, they conclude, something wrong with the system, although these criteria may be useful at the infraspecific level; many plant pathologists would agree with these sentiments.

The taxonomy of microorganisms is discussed by Shaw *et al.* (1965: pathogenic fungi), Bisby (1953: fungi), Ainsworth and Sneath (1962: microbial classification), Ainsworth and Sussman (1968), Ainsworth and Cowan (1954: rules of nomenclature), Barnett *et al.* (1966: chemical, serological and other techniques for identifying fungi), Martin (1958: taxonomy and microbiology) and Luttrell (1958: taxonomy and mycology). Bacteria and viruses present special problems to the taxonomist, as discussed in the chapters on these groups. A taxonomic review of the fungi is in preparation: *The Fungi: An Advanced Treatise*. Vols **4**A and B. *A Taxonomic Review with Keys*, edit. by Ainsworth, G. C. and Sussman, A. S. (Academic Press, London and New York).

6 Bacteria as plant pathogens

Bacteria are less important than fungi or viruses as agents of disease in plants, but as mentioned previously there are some very destructive bacterial diseases (bacterioses), particularly so in the warmer, wetter parts of the world. They are, however, more important than fungi as pathogens of warm-blooded animals, including man. Several reasons for the comparatively minor importance of bacteria as plant pathogens have been suggested. On the whole bacteria tend to be thermophilic and perhaps find warm-blooded animals a more congenial habitat than relatively cool plants. The greater incidence of bacterial diseases among plants in warmer areas perhaps supports this, and bacteria may have difficulty in surviving the cold winter months in temperate regions. The significance of this is doubtful since many bacteria can withstand cold conditions and many occur in cold soils. Many bacteria seem to grow best in a slightly alkaline medium whereas the cell sap of most plants is generally somewhat acidic (pH 5–6): many fungi, however, grow best at neutral or slight acidity. This is a generalization to which there are many exceptions and it is unlikely that pH is a critical factor in the infection of most plants by bacteria, although it may be so in a few cases. Bacteria commonly enter animals during breathing or through wounds and thereafter many circulate in the bloodstream. The shoots of plants are to some extent protected by a cuticle except for natural openings (stomata, hydathodes and others) and accidental breaks, and there are no reports of bacteria being able to penetrate the unbroken cuticle by physical or chemical means. Fungi can often penetrate the cuticle but the latter is probably an effective barrier against bacteria.

After entry into the plant most fungi grow through the tissues to varying extents; this method of colonizing plant tissue is not possible for bacteria, although they may to some extent move or be moved in the moisture film between cells. Mucilaginous tendrils of aggregated bacteria may 'grow' through plant tissue in some cases but many bacterial pathogens colonize tissue by means of their toxins and/or enzymes acting in advance. There are, however, some which cause proliferation rather than necrosis, as in crown gall (*Agrobacterium tumefaciens*), and some are transported in the vascular tissue. Those bacteria which attack plants lack specialized disseminatory propagules such as are produced by many fungi. Spread is by bacterial cells, sometimes in fragments of diseased plant tissue dispersed by wind. Bacteria lie in and on the dead tissue, probably partially adhering to it, and have no means of elevating themselves above the boundary layer of still air which normally encases much of the aerial parts of the plant; hence they have difficulty in leaving plant tissue as well as in entering it, and insects, rain splash and tissue dispersal are all methods by which this is achieved. The lack of resistant overwintering propagules in plant pathogenic bacteria raises problems of survival between successive crops, especially in regions with climatically severe intercrop periods. This is to some extent counteracted by the bacteria being encased in slime which dries to form a protective coat, or by immersion in the diseased plant tissue, but these are unlikely to be as effective as overwintering fungal propagules, many of which have a built-in dormancy mechanism which reduces the risk of premature germination.

These difficulties in entering and colonizing the plant, in dissemination of propagules, and in overwintering are the major factors which tend to make many bacteria somewhat inefficient plant pathogens as compared with fungi.

Some of the bacteria which attack plants resemble those occurring naturally on the shoots as saprophytes, and there is evidence that some undergo a saprophytic phase on the plant surface as well as having a parasitic phase. Apparently non-parasitic bacteria are said to occur within plants in limited numbers. These considerations suggest that some plant-pathogenic bacteria may have originated from those associated with plants as saprophytes. There are also resemblances between some bacteria in the soil and some which attack plants, for example *Pseudomonas*, and there may be a connexion here. Some normally saprophytic soil bacteria become parasitic on plant roots under some conditions, and these aspects are discussed by Gorlenko (1965). The bacteria which attack animals do not appear to attack plants, although Stapp (1961) reports that *Pseudomonas aeruginosa* isolated from a human abscess caused soft rot of potato tubers. Such typical bacterial pathogens of animals, such as streptococci, staphylococci and spirochaetes, are not known to attack plants.

Symptoms of bacterial diseases

Many bacterial pathogens kill plant tissue but some cause hypertrophy. Young tissue of high water and nutrient content is often more susceptible than older tissue. Symptoms of bacterial diseases generally resemble those caused by fungi and, to a lesser extent, viruses, and are conventionally grouped into four main types although these are not completely distinct— parenchymatous, vascular, generalized and hyperplastic diseases.

Parenchymatous diseases

Necrosis of parenchymatous tissue is involved in many bacterial blights of the shoots and in soft rot diseases of storage organs. Bacterial spotting and blighting can affect almost all the aerial parts of plants – leaves, petals, buds, fruits and stems. The first symptoms are often small, translucent ('water soaked') spots of a dark green colour which increase in size and become brownish or black as the tissue dies: this discolouration may be due to the activity of the enzyme tyrosinase produced by the bacteria. There is evidence that the bacteria multiply within the infected tissue until sufficient toxins and/or enzymes accumulate to kill the adjacent plant cells. Lesions may have a chlorotic margin and are often somewhat angular ('angular leaf spot') in outline due to limitation by the veinlets of the leaf. Under favourable conditions, especially prolonged wet weather, they tend to spread alongside the veins causing necrotic streaks. Neighbouring lesions often coalesce and bring about extensive necrosis and abscission of the infected organ. Severe infection leads to a generalized blighting of the plant and, in some cases, to its death. There may be secondary invasion of the necrotic tissue by other microorganisms.

Bacterial lesions may girdle the stem causing weak points which subsequently break if exposed to strain, such as occurs when fruits are produced further up the plant (figure 6.1). Buds and growing points are often destroyed, and lesions on young fruits may lead to seed infection or contamination. Bacterial blighting of this sort can be extremely destructive when climatic conditions favour its development, especially in highly susceptible plants. If conditions are unfavourable the disease is likely to dry up and cause only minor damage, although the lesions may still contain bacteria capable of becoming active if favourable conditions return; hence further outbreaks can occur. In wet weather the bacteria often ooze from the lesions, subsequently drying to form thin scales which can be a useful diagnostic feature. Bacterial blights are often caused by species of *Pseudomonas* and *Xanthomonas*, for example *P. tabaci* (tobacco wildfire) and *X. citri* (citrus canker).

Bacterial soft rot, such as caused by *Erwinia carotovora*, often affects parts of the plant rich in stored nutrients and water, for example tubers. Many of the bacteria involved secrete pectolytic enzymes which disorganize the middle lamella between cells, thus partially or completely transforming the affected organ into a soft, pulpy mass of cells which is subsequently

D

Figure 6.1   A severe attack of bacterial blight (*Xanthomonas malvacearum*) on cotton. The leaves of infected plants are withered, the stems of many of the plants have broken at the stem lesions ('blackarm'), and diseased plants produce virtually no crop.

discoloured and rotted by secondary invaders. Many aspects of soft rot diseases remain obscure and it is possible that toxins as well as enzymes are involved. They appear to be favoured by high water content of the tissues and by wet soil. The causal bacteria enter through small wounds, perhaps caused by insects, and natural openings. If conditions are un-favourable the rotted area may be sealed off by a corky barrier.

Vascular diseases

In these, the bacteria invade and multiply within the xylem vessels and also in the adjacent parenchyma. Initial entry of the root or stem is through wounds or by insects. The affected plant wilts and may die. On cutting across the stem the vessels are often seen to be discoloured and full of bacteria which exude as a viscous slime. The precise cause of wilting is not clear and it has variously been attributed to toxins which damage the leaves or increase their permeability, slowing up of the transpiration stream due to the physical presence of large quantities of bacteria and bacterial slime in the vessels, gelatinous pectic substances which enter the vessels from adjacent disorganized parenchymatous cells, and other causes. It seems likely that the bacteria can be distributed in the transpiration stream to various parts of the plant including the seeds, and seed infection might originate in this way. Some bacterial pathogens which normally attack parenchymatous tissue can probably invade xylem vessels, as described by Wickens (1956) in bacterial blight of cotton caused by *Xanthomonas malvacearum*. Vascular diseases include maize wilt (*X. stewarti*), gumming disease of sugarcane (*X. vasculorum*), cucumber wilt (*Erwinia tracheiphila*) and watermark disease of willow (*E. salicis*). The last named pathogen is of interest in that it is said to attack only the wood of the tree. The histopathology of plants infected by vascular bacterial wilts is described by Nelson and Dickey (1970).

Generalized or systemic diseases

Parenchymatous and vascular tissue are attacked, resulting in a generalized infection over much of the plant. Thus in halo blight of dwarf beans caused by *Pseudomonas phaseolicola* all tissues and organs except the roots are liable to become infected. Lesions develop on the cotyledons, leaves, stems, petioles, pods and seeds. *P. solanacearum* (brown rot of Solanaceae and other plants) causes a general wilting and collapse of the plant, the bacteria developing in the vascular tract and subsequently rotting the pith and cortex. These systemic diseases can be very destructive when conditions favour their development and spread.

Hyperplastic diseases

In these, the bacteria have a stimulatory effect on the plant, the affected tissues undergoing irregular and accelerated cell division which results in proliferations of various kinds – galls, tumours, tubercles, fasciation, witch's brooms and others. These overgrowths are thought to be associated with disruption of the growth-regulating processes of the plant, but their origin is not well understood even in crown gall (*Agrobacterium tumefaciens*) which has been intensively investigated. In this disease, the galls may develop on stems or roots and their size and structure depends partly on the species of plant involved; they are soft in herbaceous plants, woody in woody ones, and range from the size of a pea to that of a cricket ball or larger. Secondary galls may develop on other parts of the plant and some of these are apparently sterile, presumably deriving from substances produced

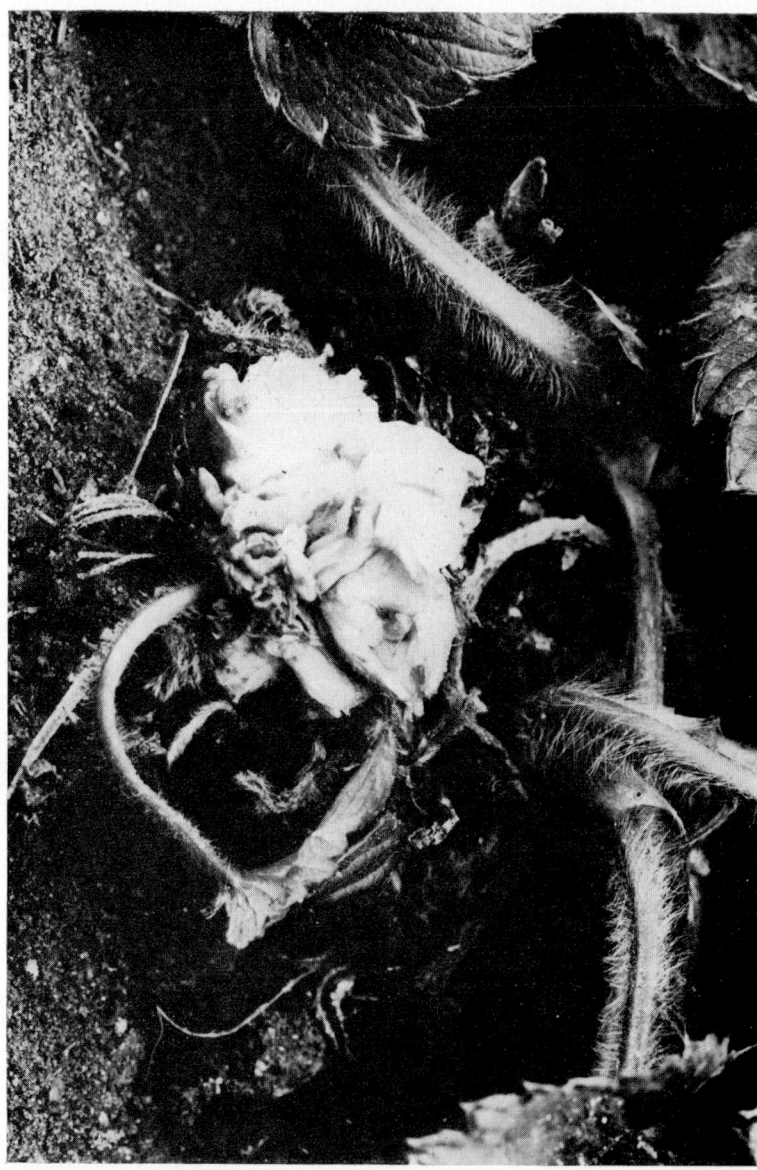

Figure 6.2 'Cauliflower' disease of strawberry caused by *Corynebacterium fascians* in association with the eelworm *Aphelenchoides ritzema-bosi*. The bacterium causes proliferation of axillary buds, reducing the plant to a masss of fleshy gall tissue.

by the pathogen. Young galls show little or no necrosis but older ones eventually decay from the outside inwards, due mainly to secondary invaders. New shoots sometimes arise from galls in the soil but they rarely develop to any great extent, probably because the vascular elements of the galls are irregularly arranged and not properly connected with those of the plant.

Olive knot or tubercle disease, caused by *Pseudomonas savastanoi*, occurs in most countries where olive trees are grown. The bacteria enter the twigs through wounds, including those caused by olive flies which harbour the bacteria, and lay contaminated eggs. The internal tissue of the tubercles tends to decay and infected twigs are stunted and may be killed. Apparently similar diseases occur on ash (*Fraxinus*) and oleander (*Nerium*) and are probably caused by different strains of *P. savastanoi*. Other hyperplastic diseases include hairy root of apple caused by *Agrobacterium rhizogenes*, and the striking malformations due to *Corynebacterium fascians* and variously described as leafy gall of chrysanthemum, dahlia and other ornamental plants, fasciation of sweet pea, and cauliflower disease of strawberry (figure 6.2). The root nodules of Leguminosae caused by *Rhizobium* spp. perhaps originated as hyperplastic diseases.

Pathogenesis

Bacterial pathogens enter plants through natural openings such as stomata, hydathodes and nectaries, and through wounds caused by adverse weather (for example hail), insects or by man (pruning, grafting, etc.). Gorlenko (1965) considers that those which penetrate through natural openings are more highly specialized than wound parasites, many of which are relatively unselective in their host range. The bacteria are probably drawn into the substomatal cavity during wet weather and there multiply and form mucilaginous masses in the intercellular spaces, pushing aside and killing the plant cells by enzymes and toxins and in some cases entering the vascular tissue. Entry is facilitated by abundant moisture and factors which keep the stomata open. There are reports of bacteria multiplying in tissue of non-host plants without causing symptoms, and apparently non-pathogenic bacteria sometimes occur in lesions caused by pathogenic ones; possibly some of them are avirulent strains. Other natural openings may be utilized. *Erwinia amylovora* (fireblight of pears and other Rosaceae), in part spread by bees and flies, can also apparently invade through nectaries, anthers and stigmas (figure 6.3). *E. carotovora* (soft rot) can enter potato tubers through lenticels as well as wounds, and *Corynebacterium michiganense* (bacterial canker of tomato) invades leaves through trichomes, especially damaged ones; the greater resistance of older leaves has been

Figure 6.3   Fireblight of pear caused by *Erwinia amylovora*. The infection originated through the diseased blossom at the end of the shoot on the right.

attributed partly to their having fewer trichomes (Kontaxis, 1962; Layne, 1967).

Wound parasites enter through breaks in the outer tissue which inevitably occur during transplanting, division of propagating material, pruning, mowing and other cultural operations, or through damage caused by frost, hail, wind, insects or nematodes. Some bacteria progress further by colonizing the plant tissue after killing it by toxins (for example tabtoxinin produced by *Pseudomonas tabaci*, tobacco wildfire) or by pectolytic, cellulolytic or other enzymes which attack the cell walls. Others enter the xylem vessels and are distributed within the plant in this way. *Corynebacterium fascians* is carried to the meristematic regions of strawberry plants by leaf and bud nematodes of the genus *Aphelenchoides* (Pitcher and Crosse, 1958). Some bacteria which enter living cells may be distributed during cell division.

The defence mechanisms of plants against bacteria have not been intensively studied but, among others, the following have been suggested. (1) Resistant plants lack a specific nutrient or nutrients required by the pathogen; for example, mutant strains of *Erwinia aroideae* lacking histidine did not attack turnip, in some cases perhaps due to low histidine content of the plants (Garber and Schaeffer, 1957), and somewhat similar results were obtained with *Pseudomonas tabaci* (tobacco wildfire: Garber and Heggestad, 1958). (2) Multiplication of the bacteria is limited and insufficient toxin for successful invasion of the plant is produced. (3) Bacteristatic substances are present in, or develop in, resistant tissue: there is evidence that such substances, including phytoalexins, develop in some bacterial infections and this merits further investigation. A combination of adequate nutrition and absence of bacteristatic substances is presumably needed for successful colonization of the plant by the bacteria, somewhat on the lines of the hypothesis put forward by Lewis (1953). (4) Some resistant plants show a hypersensitivity reaction when infected, numerous small necrotic spots developing. These represent infection sites and in them the bacteria appear to be inactivated and do not develop further, as in varieties of cotton resistant to *Xanthomonas malvacearum* (bacterial blight). Hypersensitivity in relation to bacterial plant pathogens is discussed by Klement and Goodman (1967). (5) Other resistance mechanisms which have been suggested include unsuitable *p*H (usually acidity) of the cell sap, and development of corky barriers which prevent spread of the bacteria.

Epidemiology

Bacteria spread from infected to healthy plants in various ways. Diseased leaves may be shed and disseminated by wind and irrigation water, or small droplets containing bacteria are splashed up by raindrops falling on diseased tissue, these droplets then being disseminated by wind. Insects carry some bacterial pathogens from plant to plant, often acting as inoculators as well as disseminators, and this is true of some root infecting as well as some shoot infecting bacteria. Man spreads some bacterial pathogens during such operations as mowing (for example *Corynebacterium insidiosum*: lucerne wilt) and propagation of plants. It is probable that long distance dissemination is chiefly on or in seeds or other planting material transported by man. Direct aerial dissemination of bacterial cells, as distinct from those cells in droplets or plant tissue, is probably not of great importance as such cells would probably not survive for any length of time the accompanying desiccation and exposure to radiation. Dispersal is discussed by Crosse (1957).

As mentioned previously, overwintering can be a problem for bacteria which attack plants. Those which infect woody plants can remain alive but dormant in cankers, lesions, galls, bud scales, crevices in the bark or other sheltered places, and may be further protected by being encased in mucilage (figure 6.4). Similar carry-over in diseased plant residues can occur especially if they are woody but the extent of this will be related to the survival of the plant material which is in turn dependent on climatic conditions. Thus through its effects on the activity of soil microorganisms, the weather during the intercrop period can greatly influence the survival of pathogens in plant residues; dry weather will tend to preserve such residues whereas warm, wet weather will favour their decay. The activity of animals which destroy plant material, for example termites, has also to be taken into account.

Bacteria may survive from season to season in infected plants missed during harvesting ('ground keepers') if the plant is not a strict annual, in self-sown seedlings originating from seeds scattered over the soil, or in infected weeds, especially perennial ones, if the bacterium has a wide host range. All these will be affected by the weather conditions during the intercrop months. Contaminated or infected seeds and other planting material are also important in carry-over of bacterial pathogens as well as in their dissemination, and such material may remain infective for several years. When planted under suitable conditions it will produce diseased plants which act as foci of infection for adjacent plants.

Some of the bacteria which attack roots, including *Agrobacterium tumefaciens*, can probably survive saprophytically in soil although the significance of this is uncertain. Gorlenko (1965) suggests three groups: (1) those which survive but do not multiply in soil – *Pseudomonas solanacearum* perhaps belongs here, (2) those which survive but may lose their pathogenicity in soil, for example *A. tumefaciens in* acid soils, and (3) those which survive and multiply in soil; many of these are probably saprophytes

Figure 6.4 *Pseudomonas mors-prunorum* (bacterial canker of stone fruits), causing stem canker of a young plum tree; the bacteria probably overwinter in such stem cankers.

able to attack plants under certain conditions, but there are conflicting views on this. Most of the bacteria which attack the aerial parts of plants do not survive for long in natural soil, probably due to antagonistic effects and inability to compete with saprobes for the limited food available, but may do so for longer periods in sterile soil. Survival in soil is no doubt related to weather conditions as they affect the activity of the other microorganisms present.

A few bacteria overwinter in their insect vectors, as with *Erwinia tracheiphila* in cucumber beetles, but this method of survival is apparently rare. It is not known whether the bacteria multiply within the vector, whether the latter is adversely affected by the bacteria within it, or whether there is any sort of biological relationship between the two organisms.

Parasitic specialization

Plant pathogenic bacteria can be grown with varying degrees of ease on fairly simple culture media such as nutrient agar. Many appear to be rather unspecialized parasites, some seem to have a rather wide host range, whereas others, often considered as parasitically more highly specialized, may attack only a few closely related species of plants. For example, *Xanthomonas malvacearum* is restricted to *Gossypium* and possibly one or two other Malvaceous plants. Bacteria with a wide host range probably comprise a number of strains each specialized to a limited range of plants. The problem is complicated by the difficulty of defining a bacterial species satisfactorily. In the past, some so-called species have been based on the host plant attacked; for example, *X. pelargonii* on pelargoniums and *X. geranii* on geraniums appear to be identical. Some bacteria at present described as distinct species are perhaps better regarded as *formae speciales* of a larger species comprising a number of parasitically specialized strains. The application of computer techniques which assess the overall similarity of organisms as based on numerous characteristics may shed light on this problem.

There are a few bacteria which attack fungi. These include *Pseudomonas tolaasii*, *Erwinia carotovora* and *Bacillus polymyxa* on mushrooms (*Agaricus*), and *Xanthomonas uredovorus* on urediospores of cereal rusts in the U.S.A. (Pon *et al.*, 1955; Hayward and Hodgkiss, 1961). The significance of the bacteria sometimes found in open smut sori is uncertain but some are probably antagonistic. There are many reports of parasitic specialization in plant pathogenic bacteria. Thus Brinkherhoff (1963) in Oklahoma reported ten new races of *Xanthomonas malvacearum* in addition to the two already known.

Bacteria, including those which attack plants, are very variable organisms, new biotypes arising through mutation, recombination and in other ways. Acquisition and loss of pathogenicity are not uncommon. Some bacterial plant pathogens tend to become non-pathogenic in culture but can often be rejuvenated by passage through their host plants. Pathogenicity can often be increased by repeated passage through resistant plants and decreased by passage through very susceptible ones, presumably due partly to selective survival of races best adapted to the plant used. There is also evidence that some bacteria can be 'trained' to attack new hosts; for example, cultures of several species of *Xanthomonas*, including *X. juglandis* (from walnut), *X. malvacearum* (cotton) and *X. begoniae* (begonia) became pathogenic to bean plants after four successive passages through beans (Dye, 1958). The extent to which this occurs in the field, if at all, is problematical. According to Starr (1959) the saprobe *Aerobacter cloacae* becomes the parasite *Erwinia tracheiphila* (cucumber wilt) on exposure to extracts of cucumber tissue or DNA, and pathogenic strains of *Agrobacterium tumefaciens* can apparently be changed into non-pathogenic *A. radiobacter* by exposure to various substances including extracts of crown gall tissue, a heat-killed suspension of *A. tumefaciens* or crude nucleic acid from the latter bacterium. The pathogenicity of bacteria tends to be rather unstable and is perhaps affected by the plant with which the bacterium is associated: possibly the plant donates genetical material to the bacterium, thereby modifying its pathogenicity.

Control

Some bacterial pathogens are seed borne and only clean planting material should be used. If this is not possible some form of seed treatment with a bactericide, very often containing organo-mercurial compounds, will be necessary. If the bacteria are within the seed a carefully controlled heat treatment is sometimes possible, or soaking in suitable antibiotics although these are likely to be phytotoxic. Disinfection of seeds by bacteriophage preparations has been suggested.

Soil treatment may be possible on a small scale for the few bacterial pathogens which survive in soil but such treatment is likely to be expensive. Destruction of infected crop residues, plants surviving between seasons, and self-sown seedlings and infected weeds should be carried out wherever possible although this has to be very thorough for successful control of bacteria which spread rapidly. Burning is the most effective method but ploughing which buries the crop residues can be effective as it encourages their microbial breakdown and also reduces their dissemination by wind. Such cultural practices as crop rotation, sowing date, and fertilizer treatment can sometimes be modified to reduce infection; also the destruction of insects or nematodes which spread the pathogen or enable it to enter the plant.

Spraying or dusting of foliage with bactericides is not widely used as a control measure although its scope is likely to increase as more effective bactericides become available. Antibiotics show some promise in this direction, for example Agrimycin 100 (a mixture of streptomycin and Terramycin), but it is difficult to find effective bactericides which do not damage the foliage. Bactericidal pastes, often containing antibiotics, can be used to treat bacterial cankers of trees. There is some evidence, however, that antibiotic resistant strains of the bacterium tend to arise if spraying is carried out over a number of years. This is particularly true with streptomycin, the antibiotic at present most widely used against bacterial pathogens of plants.

There are several other common-sense precautions; if, for example, the bacteria are spread by cutting knives the latter should be sterilized between use on successive plants.

Wherever possible the cultivation of immune varieties of crop plants is undoubtedly the best method of controlling bacterial, and other diseases. Resistant or tolerant varieties are less satisfactory in that the pathogen is still present so there is always the possibility of new strains arising; this is in fact one of the main difficulties in breeding crop varieties resistant to bacterial pathogens. Nevertheless, considerable success has been achieved in producing sugarcane varieties resistant to gumming disease (*Xanthomonas vasculorum*) and leaf scald (*X. albilineans*), and varieties of crop plants resistant to several other bacterial diseases. The genetic basis of resistance to bacterial pathogens has been investigated in only a few cases and in these seems often to be determined by a small number of major genes with supplementary modifiers of various sorts. Resistance is often dominant but is not always a stable quality; it may be overborne if conditions are very favourable to the pathogen and it often varies with the age of the plant and in different parts of the plant. Pathogenically different races of bacterial pathogens have been reported, for example by Brinkherhoff (1963) for *X. malvacearum*, although Arnold and Brown (1968) have recently concluded that this pathogen shows continuous variation in virulence and cannot satisfactorily be grouped into races.

It may be possible to eradicate a bacterial disease if the host range is narrow and does not include weeds, and citrus canker (*Xanthomonas citri*) was eradicated from Florida in 1914–27 by burning the standing trees with an oil spray. This is said to have involved the destruction of about twenty million trees (Dopson, 1964).

Classification

The genera of plant pathogenic bacteria are distinguished largely on morphological and biochemical characteristics, including the presence, number and position of flagella, production of pigment, and others as described by Dowson (1957). Serological tests and bacteriophage typing are now being used in classification, and so is numerical taxonomy. In the past, species have sometimes been delimited according to the plant attacked, often with no real attempt to determine the host range, with the result that two so-called species may be identical in all respects except their host plants; it would seem more logical to regard these as *formae speciales* as is customarily done with fungal pathogens. Although there is considerable confusion as to species, especially with the numerous ones of *Xanthomonas* and *Pseudomonas*, there is fair agreement on generic classification, some five genera being recognized. These are:

Pseudomonas : Gram-negative, non-sporing, with one to several polar flagella or occasionally aflagellate, and characteristically but not always producing a yellowish-green fluorescent pigment (fluorescin) which diffuses into the medium. Many pseudomonads are saprophytes in soil or on plant material and the parasitic forms may have been derived from these. Most species cause parenchymatous diseases of the aerial parts of plants, but some become systemic (*P. solanacearum*) and *P. savastanoi* causes hypertrophy.

Xanthomonas : Gram-negative, non-sporing, usually monotrichous, and the colonies often produce a yellow pigment which is insoluble in water. Xanthomonads frequently occur as epiphytes on plant surfaces but rarely in soil, and plant pathogenic ones may have evolved from these epiphytic forms. Most species cause tissue necrosis in the form of parenchyma, vascular or systemic diseases, but there appear to be no reports of hyperplastic diseases caused by xanthomonads.

Erwinia : Gram-negative, non-sporing, with a few peritrichous flagella or occasionally aflagellate. This genus in many ways resembles coliform bacteria and may have been derived from them. Some species cause vascular or parenchyma diseases, but others cause soft rots of various types. The soft rot forms have been separated off as *Pectobacterium* by Waldee (1945) on their ability to produce pectolytic enzymes, but this seems illogical in that some pseudomonads and xanthomonads are also strongly pectolytic but are not on that account placed in separate genera.

Agrobacterium : Gram-negative, non-sporing, short bacteria with one–four peritrichous flagella. They often occur in soil, plant roots or stems and cause hypertrophy of the infected tissue, being similar to *Rhizobium* in many ways.

Corynebacterium: Gram-positive, non-sporing rods often flagellate in plant pathogenic forms but technically lacking flagella. The cells often show club shaped swellings and contain irregularly staining segments or granules. Some species are pathogens of man (for example *C. diphtheriae* causing diphtheria), others are saprophytic on plant residues and may have given rise to the plant pathogenic forms (Gorlenko, 1965).

Phytomonas and *Bacterium*, although occasionally used, are invalid names, and *Bacillus* can be used only for certain spore-forming bacteria. *Aplanobacter* has been used for non-sporing, non-motile, rod-like plant pathogens. Many of the bacteria which attack plants have undergone several changes of name in their time, for example, *Erwinia carotovora* = *Bacterium carotovorum* = *Bacillus carotovorus* = *Pectobacterium carotovorum*, and this must be borne in mind when consulting the literature.

Dead or rotting plant tissues often harbour other bacteria whose significance is sometimes hard to assess. Among these are *Bacillus polymyxa* associated with rotting potatoes and *B. mesentericus* (rotting of flowers and fruits). It is possible that these and other similar bacteria contain strains which are able to attack plants under certain conditions. Several apparently saprophytic bacteria are commonly associated with plants, including *Erwinia lathyri* (a common yellow saprophyte) and *Aerobacter aerogenes* which is said to occur within the dead tissue of living plants. These are discussed by Gorlenko (1965) and Dowson (1957).

Several Actinomycetes cause disease in plants, the best known being *Streptomyces scabies*, the cause of scab on potato tubers.

For further information on bacteria as plant pathogens the following sources can be consulted: Gorlenko (1965); Burkholder (1948); Starr (1959); Dowson (1957); Stapp (1961); Crosse (1966: pseudomonads attacking deciduous fruit trees); Stolp *et al.* (1965: pseudomonads and xanthomonads); Graham (1964: soft rot coliform bacteria); Buddenhagen and Kelman (1964: *Pseudomonas solanacearum*); and Okabe and Goto (1963: bacteriophages of bacterial plant pathogens). Many of the bacteria which attack plants are described by Elliott (1951) who also gives an extensive bibliography. Nutritional and genetic aspects are discussed in Bailey (1961), and the three volumes by Erwin F. Smith (1905, 1911, 1914) are still a useful source of information.

7 Angiosperms, algae and Protozoa as plant pathogens

Angiosperms

Parasitic species occur in some families of angiosperms but rather few are important causes of disease in economic plants. Some families such as the Rafflesiaceae are thought to comprise only parasites but most of the families involved contain non-parasitic and parasitic species which are evidently related, the parasitic forms presumably being derived from the non-parasitic ones. Among the more important families containing parasites are the Loranthaceae, Convolvulaceae, Scrophulariaceae, Orobanchaceae, Lauraceae, Santalaceae and Balanophoraceae.

Parasitic flowering plants tend to be more prominent in the tropics and subtropics where they take very varied forms. *Rafflesia arnoldi* is parasitic on *Vitis* roots and produces flowers up to 0·9 m in diameter, said to be the largest in the world whereas in *Apodanthes caseariae*, a more or less systemic parasite, all that is seen are the small flowers and stalks, often less than 0·6 cm high (Wellman, 1964).

Those parasitic angiosperms which have been investigated so far appear to be dicotyledons and frequently attack dicotyledons although some attack grasses and gymnosperms. Some have a narrow host range whereas others, such as *Cuscuta* and *Orobanche*, are said to attack numerous species of plants but the degree of host specialization has not often been established. 'Self-parasitism' has been reported in some species of *Cuscuta*, the parasite invading its own stem, and *C. americana* is parasitized by other species of the genus (Lackey, 1946). As well as the direct damage which these parasites can cause to their host plants they may also enable viruses to spread from virus infected to healthy plants through the parasite which is attacking both; for example, *Cuscuta* is often used to transmit viruses from plant to plant as described by Hosford (1967).

Several types of parasitism have been described. (1) The parasite is rooted in the soil and is attached to the roots of the host plant by haustorial discs through which the vascular tissues of host and parasite become

(a)

Figure 7.1   Mistletoe (*Viscum album*) on the trunk of a crab-apple tree: (*a*) general view; (*b*) close-up showing the attachment of the parasite to the trunk. This is a semiparasitic evergreen flowering plant.

joined, for example, witchweed (*Striga*). Green aerial shoots and flowers are produced and in some cases the host plant seems to suffer little damage. (2) The parasite has perennial underground stems which are attached to the host roots and which produce aerial flowering shoots each year, for example, toothwort, *Lathraea squamosa*. The leaves are without chlorophyll. (3) The tissues of the parasite merge with those of the host root to form a swelling from which aerial flowering shoots arise. These may bear rudimentary or scale-like leaves to varying extents, or may be leafless, for example, broomrape, *Orobanche*. (4) The parasite invades the branches of the host, often a tree, and develops as a bushy perennial plant with green leaves but does not root in the soil, for example, mistletoe, *Viscum* (figure 7.1). (5) The seeds of the parasite germinate in the soil and produce a hair-like shoot which describes circular movements until a suitable host plant is found, after which it twines around the host stem, obtaining nutrients through haustoria. The stem of the parasite dies away at its lower end so that connexion with the soil is lost. Chlorophyll is absent although there may be small, rudimentary scale leaves. The best known of this

(b)

group are the dodders, *Cuscuta* spp. (figure 7.2). (6) There may be a more complete integration of parasite and host, the former developing as a kind of hollow cylinder between the wood and cortex of the host root or shoot. The flowers eventually burst through the cortex to the exterior. This situation is found in the Rafflesiaceae, for example, *Rafflesia arnoldi* where

Figure 7.2 Dodder (*Cuscuta*) on gorse. Note the slender stems of this totally parasitic flowering plant; these stems attach themselves to other branches and eventually smother the host plant.

the vegetative organs of the parasite are reduced to a network ramifying in the tissues of the host, somewhat suggestive of a mycelium.

An interesting range in parasitism is described by Wellman (1964) among certain Loranthaceae. In some the plant, although parasitic in early life, may subsequently become independent, and in others there may be apparently functional roots in the soil as well as absorbing ones in the host plant. Yet others lack independent roots and show varying degrees of adaptation to their host plants, in extreme cases being almost entirely within the latter except for short branches bearing small leaves, flowers and fruits.

The parasite is dependent on its host to varying degrees. Those with green aerial shoots can presumably photosynthesize but are dependent on the host for water and dissolved mineral substances and are often referred to as hemi- or semiparasites or water parasites. Those which lack chlorophyll are dependent on the host for elaborated nutrients. All these are obligate parasites in the sense that they cannot grow apart from the host although, as noted above, some have functional roots and a few are reported to be parasitic only in the early stages.

Invasion of the host is frequently by appressorium-like bodies from which arise pointed infection structures – modified roots or outgrowths from the stem. The way in which penetration occurs is uncertain. It often appears to be largely by mechanical pressure due to growth but enzymic softening of the host is said to occur in some cases. After entry, the infection structure produces haustoria which grow through the host tissue and establish contact with the vascular elements, their progress perhaps being facilitated by pectolytic and cellulolytic enzymes which soften the host tissue. The infected plant is affected to varying degrees ranging from slight to severe stunting and chlorosis and, in severe attacks, death; corresponding losses in yield occur.

Semiparasites generally cause less damage to their hosts than do total parasites, although some semiparasites which attack the roots may not emerge above the soil for several weeks or months after infection has occurred. During this period they are totally parasitic and impose a considerable strain on the host plant, itself in the early stages of growth. Some investigators have suggested that *Striga asiatica* (witchweed) produces phytotoxic substances, largely on the grounds that host injury seemed to be too severe to be accounted for by the few haustorial attachments present, but this needs further investigation. The haustoria of parasitic flowering plants apparently have a higher osmotic pressure than that of the host tissue, presumably facilitating absorption of nutrients by the parasite, but many aspects of their parasitism remain to be investigated.

Some parasitic angiosperms, especially stem parasites such as *Viscum*, produce fleshy mucilaginous berries containing a viscous substance (viscin). These berries are eaten by birds and the seeds are distributed in the droppings, often on other branches where they adhere and eventually germinate and invade. It may be that seeds are also distributed on the feet and bills of birds, although Wellman (1964) was unable to observe this. The sticky seeds of the dwarf mistletoe (*Arceuthobium = Razoumofskya*) are forcibly discharged up to a distance of about 9·9 m. In others, large quantities of small seeds are produced, sometimes so small as to be dust-like and transportable by wind. They are often roughened and tend to cling to the seed of the host plant, thus being disseminated. This is particularly true of plants cultivated by man, and dodder seeds, for example, may contaminate the seed of legumes and other crops. Legislation forbidding the sale of such contaminated seed is in force in many countries, and methods of removing the dodder seeds have been devised.

The tiny seeds of some parasitic angiosperms contain little food material and may show progressive maturation over a number of years. Under normal conditions such seed may remain dormant in the soil for many years and its germination appears to be brought about by exudates from the roots of certain plants which may or may not be hosts. These germination stimulants have been studied in *Striga* and *Orobanche* and have been compared with eelworm hatching factors; they are discussed by Tarr (1962), and Brown (1946) has reviewed the subject of biological stimulation of germination. Progressive maturation and stimulation of germination by plant roots are clearly advantageous to the parasite as they increase its chances of successful infection. Another useful adaptation is that the seed of the parasite often germinates a little later than that of its host plant, and frequently ripens even if the host is destroyed prematurely before the flowers of the parasite have matured.

Various other methods of spread have been described. Dodder plants, for example, spread from infected to adjacent healthy plants by means of long, thin aerial shoots which wave about in the air and 'search' for new hosts. Pieces of broken stem may act as organs of vegetative propagation, attaching themselves to plants with which they come into contact. Seeds may be disseminated by flowing water, in soil, on implements and boots, and in manure.

Some parasitic angiosperms have a wide and apparently unselective host range but in others there seems to be some degree of host specialization. Thus Jones (1955) concluded that there were at least two strains of *Striga hermonthica* (witchweed) in the Sudan, one adapted to sorghum and a second adapted to pearl millet (*Pennisetum typhoides*). Similarly, there may be different strains of the European mistletoe (*Viscum*), but little critical work has been done, and the degree of host specialization in parasitic angiosperms remains uncertain.

Control of parasitic angiosperms includes the following practices, not all of which are applicable in all cases: (1) Only seed or planting material known to be free from contamination should be sown. (2) Wherever possible, the parasite should be cut out from the infected plants, particularly so in trees. (3) Severely infected trees should be destroyed. (4) Suitable crop rotations should be used to avoid build-up of the seeds of the parasite in the soil. (5) In some cases trap crops can be grown; these induce germination of the seeds in the soil and the trap crop is then destroyed, generally by ploughing-in, before the parasite has a chance to flower. A refinement of this is to sow an eradication crop which induces germination of the seed of the parasite but is itself sufficiently resistant to prevent the parasite from establishing itself and flowering. Trap cropping may have to be carried out several times to bring about a worthwhile reduction in the concentration of the parasite in the soil. A preferable method would be to apply substances to the soil which bring about premature germination of the seeds in the absence of susceptible plants, but suitable substances for this purpose have yet to be found. (6) Application of selective herbicides which kill the parasite but not the host plant: promising results in control of witchweed were obtained in the Sudan by spraying contaminated soil with hormone weed killers (2,4-dichlorophenoxyacetic acid at about $1 \cdot 1$ kg/ha) 2–3 weeks after sorghum seed had been sown (Jones, 1953; Tarr, 1957a). In this way the parasite is attacked at its most vulnerable stage – after its seed has germinated but before it becomes firmly established in the host roots. Such treatment gave reduced witchweed incidence and increased yields but did not eradicate the parasite from the soil, although it might do so if repeated over several years. Similar methods might be applicable to other parasitic angiosperms and merit further investigation. (7) Application of suitable fertilizers may enable the parasitized plants to produce a worthwhile yield, although this is in no sense control of the parasite – only an alleviation of the damage it causes. (8) Resistant or tolerant varieties of plants can be cultivated if available: little work has been done along these lines although varieties of plants are known to differ in their susceptibility to some parasitic angiosperms and these could presumably be utilized in breeding resistant varieties. At present, information on the biochemical, physiological and genetical basis of resistance to parasitic angiosperms is meagre.

Parasitic angiosperms which are of economic importance include the following:

Dodders : *Cuscuta* spp. (Convolvulaceae) can cause severe damage to such legumes as clover and alfalfa and also to flax: see Chester (1947), Gill (1953).

Broomrapes : *Orobanche* (Orobanchaceae) is sometimes damaging to hemp and clover in Europe and can also attack tobacco, but is not generally severe : see Gill (1953).

Mistletoes: *Viscum* (Loranthaceae), the European mistletoe, is a semiparasite on some trees including apple and can adversely affect growth and yield as well as bringing about premature death of severely infected trees. The American mistletoe, *Phoradendron* (Loranthaceae), is chiefly a parasite of broad leaved trees in the U.S.A. but is less serious than the dwarf mistletoe, *Arceuthobium* (Loranthaceae) which can cause extensive damage to coniferous forest trees in parts of the U.S.A. Dwarf mistletoes reduce the growth rate of the infected tree, thus resulting in a diminished yield of timber in terms of quantity and quality. The greatest damage is usually to saplings but older trees can also be deformed and killed. The quality and quantity of seed produced are also reduced and heavy infection is said to predispose trees to attack by bark beetles. American mistletoes are discussed by Boyce (1938), Hawksworth (1961), Shea (1961), Greenham and Hawksworth (1964), Hawksworth and Wiens (1970) and Kuijt (1955).

Witchweeds: *Striga* spp. (Scrophulariaceae), are semiparasites on the roots of cereals, grasses and some other plants, mainly in tropical and subtropical areas. They are serious parasites of maize and sorghum, and other cereals (rice, pearl millet) may be attacked. The severe outbreaks which are likely to occur on maize and sorghum under continuous cultivation in the same field often render cultivation of these crops uneconomic. *S. euphrasioides* attacks sugarcane in India, *S. hermonthica* causes severe losses to sorghum in northern and central Africa, and *S. asiatica* (*S. lutea*) is a destructive parasite of maize and sorghum in central and southern Africa and throughout Asia. It was reported on maize in the U.S.A. in 1956 by Garriss and Wells (1956) and a comprehensive annotated bibliography has been published (McGrath *et al.*, 1957). Details of the witchweeds on sorghum are given by Tarr (1962). *S. gesnerioides* attacks tobacco in central and southern Africa, and the angiospermic parasites of this crop are described by Hopkins (1956) and Lucas (1965). The biology of parasitic flowering plants is discussed by Kuijt (1969).

Algae and Protozoa

A few algae are reported to be parasitic on plants, the best known being *Cephaleuros mycoidea* which attacks tea, citrus and other plants, usually perennials, in the tropics and subtropics, causing 'red rust' on the shoots. According to Butler (1918) this alga is sometimes epiphytic and sometimes parasitic on the leaves of the tea plant in India, but is usually parasitic on the stems. It appears to have a wide host range and in the Sudan has been found on cashew, coffee, mahogany (*Khaya*), citrus, and guava (Tarr, 1955, 1963); doubtless it occurs on other plants. *Cephaleuros* causes leaf spotting and shedding and the photosynthetic activity of the foliage is reduced. Branches and twigs may be girdled and die back in severe infections. Little is known about this disease but it is said to spread by air borne sporangia which produce zoospores which invade the leaf or stem through stomata, thereafter growing through the host tissues as a chain of algal cells (Chester, 1947). Further details are given by Butler (1918).

Flagellate Protozoa are said to occur in plants, particularly in laticiferous ones (Euphorbiaceae), but their pathogenicity is uncertain. A flagellate named *Phytomonas leptovasorum* has been implicated as the cause of phloem necrosis of coffee in Surinam as described by Leach (1940), who also discusses Protozoa as plant parasites. As agents of disease in plants Protozoa, although of interest, are of no importance.

8 Root diseases

Underground parts of plants live in a much more complex biological medium than shoots in that soil normally contains large and fluctuating numbers of fungi, bacteria, actinomycetes, Protozoa, nematodes, insects and other organisms which interact and are affected by its chemical and physical conditions. Natural soil in which plants grow is in a dynamic state, and such agricultural operations as ploughing, addition of fertilizers and manure, application of crop protection chemicals, burning of crop residues, irrigation and indeed any procedure which alters its chemical composition, structure, moisture content or pH are likely to disturb to varying extents its microbiological equilibrium. As Park (1963) points out, the fairly simple host–pathogen (H–P) interaction which commonly obtains with air borne pathogens is rarely encountered in root diseases – a triple interaction between host, pathogen and soil microbial population (S) being the rule. Each of these three components is affected by such environmental factors as temperature and moisture. Although a straight H–P interaction is probably an over-simplification for air borne pathogens, in that the activity of pathogens on shoot surfaces is influenced by nearby epiphytic microorganisms, this effect is much greater in the case of root pathogens surrounded as they are by the numerous other inhabitants of the soil and root surface. A knowledge of the complex microbial interactions occurring in soil and of the ecology of soil microorganisms, saprophytic and parasitic, is essential for a proper understanding of root diseases and for a rational approach to their control. For these and other reasons the study of root diseases is a rather distinct branch of plant pathology which impinges on soil microbiology (Garrett, 1959), and merits a brief chapter to itself. Further information can be obtained from Garrett (1956; 1970), Park (1963), and Baker and Snyder (1965).

Soil-inhabiting fungi are classified by Garrett (1956) as obligate saprophytes (including many species of Mucorales, *Agaricus campestris* and other saprophytic agarics) and unspecialized parasites which can live as saprophytes on plant material in soil and can also infect roots under the right conditions, for example *Corticium solani, Macrophomina phaseoli* and *Fusarium culmorum*. Root-infecting fungi also include more highly specialized parasites with little or no ability to survive as free-living saprophytes in soil although often surviving in the form of resistant propagules of various sorts. A few of these are obligate parasites and some appear to have attained a state of near-mutualism with their host roots, as perhaps in some forms of mycorrhiza. These groups are conveniently summarized in the following diagram taken from Garrett (1956).

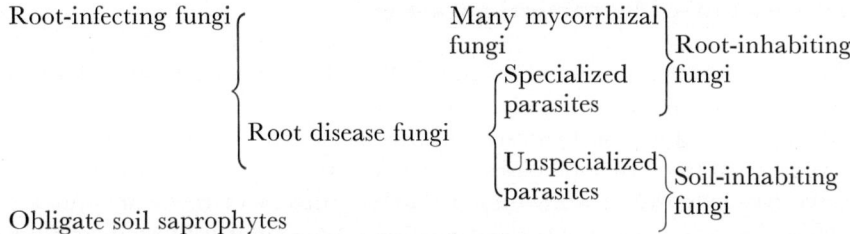

The more highly specialized root disease fungi are often more sensitive to antibiotics than soil saprophytes (many of which produce antibiotics), do not grow through natural soil in the absence of host tissue (although mycelial strands and rhizomorphs attached to a food base may do so), and invade living rather than dead root tissue. Hence their distribution in soil tends to be localized and related to that of susceptible plants. The fungi attacking the underground parts of plants show varying degrees of parasitic specialization ranging from those apparently able to attack only juvenile tissue, through those causing extensive necrosis of older root tissue, to those in which destruction of host tissue is reduced and delayed and in which tissue stimulation may occur. Among the types of disease affecting the underground parts of plants – roots and seedlings before emergence – are the following:

Pre-emergence killing, damping-off, and seedling blight

In these the soft, immature parenchymatous tissue of the seedling is destroyed, toxins and/or enzymes (especially pectic enzymes) often being involved. Considerable tissue destruction occurs and the infected seedlings are usually killed or so severely disabled as to be unable to compete with healthy ones. The fungi responsible include species of *Pythium, Phytophthora, Fusarium* and *Corticium,* and they are generally considered as rather unspecialized parasites able to infect only juvenile tissue and young rootlets; older tissues appear to be resistant except perhaps when weakened by adverse environmental conditions. They are characterized by the ability to survive more or less indefinitely as soil saprophytes and by rapid growth and colonization of the host. Many are thought to utilize simple carbohydrates as food ('sugar fungi'). Some types of foot rot and crown rot probably fall into this group and, generally speaking, the fungi involved appear to be basically soil inhabitants with the ability to invade immature plant tissue when conditions favour them.

Root rots caused by cortical parasites

In this type of root rot it is mainly the extravascular tissue which is invaded. Localized necrotic lesions are formed and if conditions favour the pathogen there may be extensive rotting of lateral rootlets and even of the young tap root. In such cases the plant is likely to be killed but it may survive less extensive rotting, particularly if the dead roots are quickly replaced by new ones. Toxins and enzymes, particularly those degrading cell walls, are doubtless involved although there is comparatively little information on these aspects. Host damage results from impairment of its water absorbing capacity and possibly from toxaemia. The mycelium of the fungus develops as an ectotrophic growth on the root, which may be penetrated at many places. Such multiple infections are facilitated by the formation of mycelial sheets, runner hyphae or rhizomorphs, some of which may grow through the soil and infect the roots of adjacent plants. Ectotrophic growth is sometimes restricted by host resistance or unfavourable conditions, but extensive colonization of much of the root system can be achieved in this way, as discussed by Garrett (1956). It is possible that tropic responses, especially chemotropic ones, may sometimes enable the fungus to 'find' susceptible roots. Extravascular rotting sometimes spreads upward to cause foot rot, crown rot or stem rot. Diseased fine roots die and if there is sufficient root incapacitation the plant wilts and dies, the damage often being accentuated by the activity of secondary invaders. On removing severely infected plants from the soil the disorganized cortical tissues are often left behind so that only the vascular core of the root remains.

According to Wilhelm (1959) the extravascular tissues of seemingly healthy roots are often invaded by fungi which are considered to be injurious. Using a sand culture technique Wilhelm (1956) isolated several pathogenic fungi including *Verticillium albo-atrum*, *Colletotrichum atramentarium*, *Pyrenochaeta terrestris* and *Macrophomina phaseoli* from surface-sterilized, white, apparently healthy roots of *Solanum sarachoides* in California. Such symptomless carrier plants could presumably act as an inoculum source.

Extravascular root rots can be destructive when environmental conditions favour their incidence but the plant may be able to restrict the infection and replace the rotted roots.

Vascular wilt diseases

The pathogen enters the apical region of young roots or through wounds caused mechanically or by nematodes or insects. It thereafter grows in the xylem vessels and ultimately colonizes the surrounding parenchymatous tissue when the plant dies. These destructive wilts include such economically important diseases as Panama disease of banana (*Fusarium oxysporum f.sp. cubense*) and cotton wilt (*F.o. f.sp. vasinfectum*). Some have been intensively investigated but there is still considerable controversy about them. They appear to be fairly specialized parasites probably surviving as resistant propagules (chlamydospores) in soil. Vascular wilt pathogens may be confined to the xylem by the active resistance of the living tissue of the root, and seem to be able to enter and grow in the xylem vessels. They cause a complex of symptoms including vein-clearing, epinasty, browning of the vascular elements, occasional development of adventitious roots on the stem, and in severe cases wilting, necrosis and death. Not all of these symptoms are present in all cases and the pathogenesis of vascular wilt diseases remains obscure.

Wilting has been attributed to several causes. (1) Toxic metabolites produced by the pathogen are carried upward in the transpiration stream. These have been studied chiefly in *Fusarium oxysporum* but their role is uncertain. They include fusaric acid, lycomarasmin, vasinfuscarin, phytonivein and others (p. 236). Certain substances of high molecular weight, including glucosans and other polysaccharides, can impede the upward movement of water through the xylem vessels and so bring about wilting, as discussed elsewhere (p. 238). (2) Xylem vessels are blocked by the pathogen itself or, more probably, by viscous substances (perhaps pectinaceous) resulting from degradation of the cell walls of the vascular tissue by pectic enzymes – and possibly by cellulases and hemicellulases – produced by the pathogen. The brownish discolouration of the vascular tissue, a characteristic of many vascular wilts, has been attributed to changes in phenol metabolism. (3) The transpiration stream is reduced due to the formation of tyloses within the xylem vessels. In some vascular wilts tyloses are more abundant in infected than in healthy plants, presumably associated with changes in concentration of growth regulating substances although the significance of the latter is far from clear. New conducting elements may be formed in infected plants and partly compensate for the reduced efficiency of the blocked vessels, so that the extent to which tyloses cause wilting is uncertain. Beckman (1964) and others suggest that tylosis and gel formation are basically a defensive reaction of the infected plant and that in susceptible plants tylosis is inhibited or delayed. This inhibition is perhaps due to pathogen metabolites which, when present in sufficient quantities, reduce the plant's capacity to produce the growth regulating substances which bring about tylosis. In lower concentrations they may promote tylosis and it may be that growth regulating substances produced by the pathogen are involved. It is thought that the pathogen moves through the xylem vessels by transported propagules and that rapid tylosis reduces such transport and so more or less immobilizes it. Rapid tylosis thus confers resistance, slow tylosis susceptibility. This interpretation of tylosis as a resistance mechanism is questioned by Dixon and Pegg (1969) on the grounds that tyloses in tomato plants attacked by *Verticillium albo-atrum* always appeared after colonization of root, stem and petiolar xylem by the fungus. Tyloses never appeared earlier than 3 weeks after inoculation whereas the fungus had spread to the apical internode within a week of inoculation.

The tylosis hypothesis outlined above is of doubtful validity and other defence mechanisms have been suggested. Talboys (1964), although not excluding 'secondary' defence mechanisms operating in the vessels and possibly in the extravascular tissue of stem and leaves, suggests that the factors determining the frequency and intensity of wilt operate primarily in the prevascular stage of infection. They include the inherent resistance of the extravascular tissues (for example, preinfectional and postinfectional chemical and histological barriers), the aggressiveness of the pathogen (including ability to produce toxins and enzymes which degrade cell walls), the concentration of the pathogen in the soil, and environmental conditions. These aspects are discussed by Beckman (1964) and Wood (1967), and the vascular wilt syndrome is reviewed by Dimond (1970).

Vascular wilts are caused chiefly by various host-specialized forms of *Fusarium oxysporum*, by *Verticillium albo-atrum* and *V. dahliae*, and by a number of bacteria including *Erwinia tracheiphila* (cucumber wilt), *Xanthomonas stewarti* (maize wilt), and *Pseudomonas solanacearum* (brown rot of tobacco and other plants). *Phytophthora fragariae* (red core of strawberry) and *Cephalosporium gramineum* (wheat stripe) cause diseases which in some ways resemble vascular wilts, and there are also the vascular wilts of trees, for example, oak wilt (*Ceratocystis fagacearum*) and Dutch elm disease (*Ceratostomella ulmi*), in which the pathogen enters the shoots through wounds often made by their insect vectors.

Hypertrophy diseases

The tissue of the infected root is stimulated to excessive cell division and/or enlargement, thereby producing galls or overgrowths of various types and sizes. In the early stages of infection, there is little if any necrosis and this may be so throughout, although secondary invaders usually bring about decay of old, infected roots. Some approach a state of mutualism with the host root. Examples, although not numerous, include *Plasmodiophora brassicae* (club root of crucifers), *Spongospora subterranea* (potato powdery scab), and *Synchytrium endobioticum* (potato wart disease). These are obligate parasites in that they have not yet been grown in axenic culture and are unable to live in soil as saprophytes or to colonize dead host tissue. They survive between crops on alternative hosts or as resistant propagules which may be stimulated to germinate by host and other roots and which may undergo progressive maturation. Not all pathogens which induce root hypertrophy are obligate parasites; *Agrobacterium tumefaciens* (crown gall), for example, can be grown in axenic culture and is said to occur in soil. *Rhizobium leguminosarum* (root nodules of Leguminosae) may also belong here.

Non-parasitic root pathogens

There are cases in which plants are adversely affected by metabolites produced by microorganisms living in the soil in close proximity to, but not invading, the roots. Frenching of tobacco is thought to be caused by metabolites of certain soil bacteria, possibly *Bacillus cereus*, which occur in large numbers near the root. These metabolites are presumably taken up by the plant (Steinberg, 1947, 1951, 1952) and in some way cause the frenching symptoms which are perhaps associated with auxin deficiency (Kefford, 1959). The symptoms of Milo disease of sorghum are apparently due to periconin, a toxin produced by *Periconia circinata*, and it seems that the disease can occur apart from infection although it is uncertain whether the fungus invades the living root (Wilhelm, 1959). Also uncertain is the extent to which the 'natural' root-browning often seen on the roots of apparently healthy plants might be due to phytotoxic metabolites of soil fungi. This type of root injury is possibly more widespread than is at present realized and merits further investigation.

The growth of a plant depends largely on the effectiveness of its roots which, in turn, are greatly influenced by the efficiency of the aerial photosynthesizing organs on which they depend for elaborated food materials. Young, active roots would at first glance appear to be very liable to attack by the numerous microorganisms present in soil. They are fairly succulent, lack a cuticle of the protective kind found over the aerial parts of the plant, and are exposed to injury by nematodes and insects which may be carrying microorganisms able to invade roots. Root exudates, discarded root hairs and the feeder rootlets themselves after death would seem to provide nutrients conducive to development of fungi and bacteria. Most temperate soils in which plants grow are favourable to microbial growth, being moderately moist, adequately aerated, and of a more even temperature than the air surrounding the shoots. The amount of organic matter present varies but is normally sufficient for growth of numerous microorganisms, although there is intense competition for the limited available nutrients, competition which root-inhabiting fungi largely avoid. These factors would seem to favour root infection and yet roots in general are not extensively invaded by soil microorganisms or, if they are, they are not usually severely damaged. There are exceptions to this, particularly in cultivated crops, but it seems likely that under natural conditions plants which are very susceptible to root pathogens would rarely survive long enough to produce seed, so that the population as a whole would tend to become resistant or tolerant.

Effective defensive reactions such as detoxification mechanisms and the formation of histological and chemical barriers (for example phytoalexins) doubtless operate in resistant roots but comparatively little is known about these aspects. A protective effect is perhaps exercised by certain rhizosphere microorganisms which produce antibiotics, and fungistasis may also be involved. The more highly specialized root pathogens have a low competitive saprophytic ability as compared with soil saprophytes and this reduces their ability to grow through soil and to survive in the absence of the host. Fungistasis probably enables some pathogens to remain alive but inactive in soil until a suitable host or favourable climatic conditions occur (compare dormancy, p. 147) and may to some extent reduce premature germination of propagules before dispersal (compare self-inhibition, p. 139). The position is further complicated by the effects of root exudates on pathogens in the soil, these effects including inhibition and stimulation of vegetative growth and of germination of spores and other propagules, stimulation of pathogenicity, and tactic and tropic responses, as discuessd by Rovira (1965).

A further problem facing many root pathogens is that of effective dissemination of their propagules. These are usually liberated into the soil and tend to remain localized except for passive transport by such agents as wind, irrigation water, run-off of rain, soil-inhabiting animals, and transfer by man and his machines. Of these dissemination by man and in wind transported soil or dust, which can be carried considerable distances, are probably the most important. Dispersal of root pathogens which do not produce aerial fructifications is likely to be slow compared with that of air borne pathogens. Seed transmission of some root pathogens, for example *Fusarium oxysporum*, occurs as internal infection, superficial contamination or as fragments of diseased plant tissue mixed with the seed or other planting material. Some fungi which attack roots, particularly those of trees or shrubs, produce fruiting bodies on the above ground parts or on exposed roots of the host and so can disseminate their spores aerially, for example some species of *Fomes* and *Armillaria mellea*. There are several other ways by which root pathogens spread, for example by root contact; see Hirst (1965).

Some root infecting fungi produce mycelial strands or rhizomorphs which may facilitate their spread from plant to plant. Garrett (1956) lists four types of spread: (1) by individual hyphae as in *Ophiobolus graminis* (take-all of cereals), (2) by simple mycelial strands, as in *Helicobasidium purpureum* (violet root rot of numerous plants), (3) by differentiated mycelial strands as in *Phymatotrichum omnivorum* (root rot of cotton and other plants), and (4) by rhizomorphs as in *Armillaria mellea* (root disease of trees and shrubs). The morphology of some of these structures is described by Townsend (1954). Highly organized rhizomorphs are usually produced by fungi attacking trees or shrubs, whereas fungi attacking herbs usually produce mycelial strands or runner hyphae.

Although rhizomorphs have been recorded as growing through soil from a food base (for example diseased roots) for considerable distances – 9·1 metres for *Armillaria mellea* (Findlay, 1951) – their chances of successfully invading roots tend to decrease as the rhizomorph lengthens. A long rhizomorph probably has increasing difficulty in transporting sufficient nutrients to its growing apex to enable infection to occur, and the nutrient reserves of the food base are steadily depleted as the rhizomorph grows; spread of the disease will thus tend to be considerably less than spread of the rhizomorphs (Garrett, 1956).

Another factor which may reduce the incidence of some root diseases is the distribution of the pathogen in the soil as related to that of susceptible roots. Irregular and sparse distribution of the pathogen may result in susceptible roots escaping infection simply because root and pathogen fail to meet or because, by the time they do meet, the root has passed its susceptible phase. The chances of such escape will decrease as the pathogen content of the soil increases, a point which stresses the importance of crop rotation in control of root diseases.

The depth at which soil borne pathogens occur is discussed by Kreutzer (1960) who considers that at least 60% of soil borne diseases, chiefly seed and seedling rots and basal stem rots caused by *Pythium*, *Rhizoctonia*, *Phytophthora*, *Fusarium*, *Sclerotinia*, *Sclerotium* and *Helminthosporium*, are initiated in the top 7·6 cm of soil. Root disease fungi, comprising perhaps 30% of the total, occur at 7·6–30·5 cm and include *Fusarium solani*, *F.*

oxysporum and *Verticillium albo-atrum* as well as some of the root attacking nematodes. The remaining 10% occur below 30·5 cm and include root pathogens such as *Phymatotrichum, Armillaria, Fomes* and others. These are, of course, generalizations and no doubt there are many exceptions according to type of soil and environmental conditions. The roots of annual plants grow chiefly in the top-soil where organic matter tends to accumulate; those of biennials and perennials may penetrate into the sub-soil, and tree roots into the underlying rocky material from which soil is formed.

Predisposing factors

Soil conditions including moisture content, temperature, pH, physical and chemical structure, and content of organic matter and nutrients play an important role in the development of root diseases, affecting pathogen, plant, plant–pathogen interaction, and also the activity of other soil micro-organisms, some of which may be involved in invasion of the root, for example vectors of pathogens. Many examples of these predisposing factors could be given.

Root pathogens which produce zoospores – *Plasmodiophora, Spongospora, Synchytrium, Aphanomyces, Pythium, Phytophthora* – are often favoured by wet soil whereas the reverse is true of *Streptomyces scabies* and many cereal smuts. The wilt diseases of cabbage and tomato caused by forms of *Fusarium oxysporum* are most severe at high temperature whereas low temperatures are reported to favour stem canker of potato (*Corticium solani*) and tobacco root rot (*Thielaviopsis basicola*), among others. Fusarial wilt of tomato (*F. oxysporum f.sp. lycopersici*) has an optimum temperature of about 28°C, whereas that of *Verticillium* wilt (*V. albo-atrum*) is about 20°C. Many fungal root diseases seem to be encouraged by soils of light texture, possibly an aeration effect, and by high nitrogen and low potassium content. Club root and many of the wilts caused by *Fusarium oxysporum* are most severe on acid soils whereas alkaline soils appear to favour cotton root rot caused by *Phymatotrichum omnivorum*, take-all of cereals (*Ophiobolus graminis*), potato scab (*Streptomyces scabies*) and root rot of pines (*Fomes annosus*). Other examples are given by Garrett (1944, 1956). These soil factors are to some extent interdependent; for example, heavy clay soils tend to be wet, and this must be taken into account when considering their significance. Furthermore, the unfavourable effects of a particular factor may be overridden if other conditions are very favourable to the pathogen, as shown by Colhoun (1953) who found that club root could be severe on alkaline soil if abundant inoculum of the pathogen was present.

Nevertheless, predisposing factors greatly influence the incidence and severity of many root diseases, and some soils and climates do exercise a restrictive influence on their geographical distribution and severity. Worthwhile control of some root diseases may be possible by appropriate manipulation of such soil conditions as pH, fertilizer treatment, and content of organic matter. Soil moisture can be regulated to some extent in irrigated crops as can temperature with crops under glass.

Although some pathogens can invade young roots under the right conditions it is probable that invasion is often facilitated when the root is damaged or weakened. Nematodes and insects may nibble roots, and mechanical injury is likely to occur when lateral rootlets emerge. Agricultural implements may also cause root damage and so encourage disease. Entry is very often by means of appressoria or infection cushions but detailed studies on root penetration are few. In the later stages of root diseases the open lesions caused by cortical parasites are often colonized by secondary saprophytes, which are unable to invade the roots on their own ('ineffective secondary invaders' of Flentje, 1965). In other cases, however, there appears to be a synergistic effect. Kerr (1963) found that pea wilt was much more severe in soil inoculated with a mixture of *Fusarium oxysporum f.sp. pisi* and *Pythium ultimum* than when either fungus was inoculated separately. Some root pathogens are thought to be partially dependent on nematodes for entry into the root and there may be a symbiotic relationship in such cases. Pathogenesis by soil fungi is discussed by Flentje (1965).

Control of root diseases

The incidence of diseases caused by soil borne pathogens is greatly influenced by soil conditions as they affect the pathogen, the underground parts of the plant and the complex of microorganisms living in the soil. Conditions which favour the plant and/or discourage the pathogen either directly or indirectly through their action on other soil microorganisms will tend to lead to disease outbreaks and *vice versa*. Hence control of many root diseases is closely bound up with agricultural practices which keep the soil in good condition and so encourage vigorous growth of the crop; crop rotation, judicious application of fertilizers, soil preparation, and crop sanitation are important in this respect. Much depends on the diligence and skill of the farmer and, as Garrett (1956) points out, control of root diseases is in some respects more of an art than a science. Some of the methods used are briefly considered below.

E

Crop rotation

Cultivation of a disease susceptible crop in the same field every year leads to a build up of the causal pathogen in the soil and so is to be avoided wherever possible. Special methods of control will probably become necessary if such continuous cultivation cannot be avoided. To be effective the rotation must involve the alternation of botanically un-related crops which are likely to be resistant to one another's pathogens and pests. Rotation is thus most useful with pathogens of narrow host range rather than with unspecialized parasites which attack a wide range of plants and which may survive as saprophytes in the soil. The problem is aggravated if the pathogen can survive in weeds or if it produces resistant propagules which survive in the soil for long periods. In such cases the rotation must be geared to the effective survival period, which may differ in different soils; for example, wider rotation is necessary for control of *Plasmodiophora brassicae* in acid soils, which favour this pathogen, than in alkaline ones. Crop rotation rarely, if ever, completely eradicates a pathogen from the soil but it can reduce it to a 'safe' level at which the damage is minimal and acceptable. Generally speaking, many of the resistant propagules produced by fungi can survive for several years in the soil (Stover, 1959), so that a 3–4 year rotation is often effective. Others, including *Plasmodiophora* and *Synchytrium* produce resistant pro-pagules which survive in soil for considerably longer periods and an impracticably wide rotation would be necessary to render contaminated soil safe.

Crop rotation should be practised from the very beginning so that build up of pathogens and pests in soil is not allowed to occur, and it may be advisable to combine it with other control measures such as crop sanita-tion. The safe interval between plantings will depend on the nature of the pathogen and the longevity of its survival propagules in the particular soil being cultivated; this may have to be determined by experiment or experience.

Crop sanitation

This includes the elimination of sources of infection for the newly sown crop. Burning the aerial parts of the crop after harvesting may be useful if the pathogen sporulates thereon, but the destruction of pathogens in roots remaining in the soil is a difficult problem. It may be possible to reduce the pathogen by soil amendments which encourage competitive and possibly antagonistic saprophytes, or to bring about premature germination of survival propagules in the absence of susceptible plants, for example by decoy crops or by manuring. Some pathogens which attack seedlings and roots are seed borne and in such cases the sowing seed should be taken from disease-free fields or given an effective treatment. Weed hosts of the pathogen should be destroyed and a knowledge of the host range of root pathogens is important in this respect. Nematodes or insects which are known to facilitate entry of a pathogen into roots should be controlled if possible, but this may be impracticable.

Palliative measures

Predisposing environmental factors play an important part in the development of most root diseases and can sometimes be manipulated to give some degree of control, particularly with irrigated and glasshouse crops where such conditions as moisture and temperature can be adjusted. Other factors which can be used in this way include planting date and depth (seedling diseases), application of manure and fertilizers, adjustment of soil pH by lime and more rarely by sulphur, control of soil tilth and aeration by ploughing and other means, the use of sound mature sowing material, the spacing between plants and the numbers of plants per hectare.

Soil treatment

Sterilization and, more often, partial sterilization of soil containing harmful pathogens or pests can be achieved by physical or chemical agents. Both are expensive and so are feasible only for intensively cultivated crops in glasshouses and market gardens or for valuable field crops.

Methods of sterilization include steaming, injection of volatile chemicals (fumigants) by machines or hand-operated 'guns', and application of chemicals as drenches or, more recently, as powders to the soil (see p. 504). Treatment is generally most effective with warm, moist, light soils, and with fumigants it is advisable to cover the treated soil with plastic or water to minimize escape of the fumes. Many of the substances used in soil treatment are fungicidal, nematicidal and insecticidal to varying extents. Most of them are unpleasant and dangerous to handle, tending to be volatile, corrosive and sometimes inflammable. Depending on soil, weather and fumigant a week or several weeks must be allowed between treatment and sowing, to avoid phytotoxicity.

Soil fumigation sometimes results in improved growth and yield of plants in the apparent absence of harmful pathogens and pests. This has been attributed to beneficial microbiological changes in the soil, but fumigation may in fact be eliminating pathogens which normally attack roots but not sufficiently severely to cause above ground symptoms. Soil treatment may have other indirect effects. *Trichoderma viride*, for example, is said to be more tolerant of formalin than most soil fungi and so tends to increase in soils disinfected with this chemical. Fumigation is likely to destroy vegetative mycelium of soil fungi but resistant propagules may be less affected, so that fungi producing, for example, sclerotia may temporarily increase after fumigation. This may lead to root attack by sclerotial pathogens; thus stem canker of cotton seedlings, caused by *Macrophomina phaseoli*, was more severe in soil which had been fumigated with chloropicrin (Tarr, 1956). The sclerotia of this pathogen perhaps withstood chloropicrin treatment better than mycelial fungi, resulting in its temporary dominance and increased incidence of stem canker. There are other possible explanations but this example illustrates the unexpected – and sometimes unwelcome – indirect effects which sometimes result from soil sterilization.

Biological control

This generally involves the control of soil borne pathogens through the agency of other microorganisms, whose activity is encouraged by appropriate manipulation of environmental conditions. It also includes the introduction of controlling organisms not hitherto present, although the scope of this method is limited since the soil microflora is not widely different in different parts of the world. The introduction of more effective strains of a controlling microorganism might be a more promising approach.

Death of a pathogen in soil may be due to starvation because of its inability to compete with soil saprophytes for a limited supply of nutrients, to antibiotics produced by other soil inhabitants, or – probably less often – to attack by hyperparasites. Measures which enhance these effects may reduce the incidence of the pathogen and so give some degree of disease control. Many such measures involve altering soil conditions by the addition of organic matter in various forms (crop residues, green manures). For example, potato scab (*Streptomyces scabies*), root rot of cotton (*Phymatotrichum omnivorum*) and various other diseases can be controlled by ploughing in suitable fresh organic matter. As might be expected these methods are often most effective against specialized parasites in the soil, but some success has been reported in control of such relatively primitive soil inhabiting parasites as *Corticium solani*. The microbiological effects of such soil amendments are likely to be complex and the mechanisms involved in control are often obscure. Selective encouragement of antagonisst such as *Trichoderma*, premature germination of survival propagules in the absence of host roots, increased carbon dioxide and reduced available nitrogen in the soil, and other possibilities have been suggested, of which the first named is perhaps best known. Similar considerations apply to the changes occurring in fumigated soil. *Trichoderma viride*, a prominent soil inhabiting antagonist, can rapidly recolonize fumigated soil under conditions suitable for its growth (a fairly warm, acid, well aerated soil) and this, combined with moderate resistance to some fumigants, enables it to become temporarily dominant. It may be uncertain whether disease control by a fumigation treatment results from direct destruction of the pathogen or from its destruction by *Trichoderma* and possibly other antagonists which have become dominant as a result of fumigation.

Many problems await solution but biological control of soil borne pathogens offers interesting and promising prospects: the subject is discussed by Garrett (1965) and Baker (1968).

Control by resistant varieties and other means

Varieties of cabbage, tomato, and peas resistant to the several forms of *Fusarium oxysporum* (vascular wilt) have been produced and successfully grown for several years. In some cases resistance is determined by a few major genes, in others it appears to be polygenic. Some success has also attended the breeding of plants resistant to *Verticillium albo-atrum* and *V. dahliae* but less with such relatively unspecialized root rotting fungi as *Fusarium solani*, *Corticium solani* and *Pythium* spp. in which resistance appears to be chiefly polygenic. These aspects are discussed by Walker (1965). There are also several special control methods which can be applied to some fungal root diseases of trees, as described by Garrett (1956). Diseased roots left in the soil after clearing the jungle or old plantations before replanting are an important source of inoculum. Spread from such sources may be by air borne infection of the cut stumps of the felled trees or by growth of the fungus along the moribund roots of felled trees. Air borne infection can be reduced by painting the cut surface of the stump with a suitable fungicide immediately after felling as shown by Rishbeth (1959) for *Fomes annosus* on pines. A similar result can apparently be obtained by inoculating the cut stumps with *Peniophora gigantea* which successfully competes with *F. annosus* (Rishbeth, 1963). Growth of the fungus along the moribund roots of the tree stump can be reduced by ring-barking, while in full leaf, those trees destined for felling, so that the roots are dead and colonized by saprophytes when felling is carried out a year or more later (Leach, 1937, 1939, with *Armillaria mellea*). Tree or stump poisoning with chemicals can also be used for the same purpose.

9 Plant injury due to insects, mites, nematodes and other pests

Many insects, mites and nematodes feed on plants, thereby causing injury and symptoms which can resemble those caused by pathogens. The damaged tissue may subsequently be colonized by fungi and bacteria, so that it is sometimes difficult to ascertain the primary cause of the symptoms unless there is evidence of pests in the form of excreta, eggs or other products. Pests are also involved in the dissemination, inoculation and occasionally in the overwintering of plant pathogens, and many wound parasites enter through lesions caused by pests. There are symbiotic relationships between insects and pathogens, in some cases apparently obligate for the latter. The plant pathologist investigating diseases in the field will almost certainly be confronted with these aspects at one time or another in his career, and a working knowledge of plant pests is likely to be useful to him. The reactions of plants to pathogens, pests and mechanical and chemical injury show many parallels which are of interest to all concerned with plant injury, and which lead to a fuller understanding of the problems involved.

In the following account an attempt is made to point out some of the more important aspects of insects, mites and nematodes as they affect plants. This is necessarily brief and selective; further information can be obtained from the references given.

Insects

Insects damage plants by chewing, rasping, sucking, by injecting phytotoxic saliva and in other ways, quite apart from acting as vectors and inoculators of pathogens, especially of viruses (p. 54). The more important orders of insects which cause plant injury are:

Collembola: springtails. Some species of these small wingless insects feed on plants, causing small holes in leaves, cotyledons and stems, but they are not usually destructive.

Orthoptera: grasshoppers, locusts, crickets and cockroaches. These are often relatively large insects with biting mouth parts. The devastation caused by swarms of locusts in many parts of the world is well known but apart from locusts, few of this order are serious pests of plants. Some grasshoppers transmit certain viruses (for example turnip yellow mosaic), probably acting chiefly as mechanical carriers.

Dermaptera: earwigs. Leaves and flowers are sometimes damaged by earwigs but serious damage to field crops is rare.

Isoptera: termites (white ants). Apart from the serious damage which they cause to wood, these insects can be destructive plant pests in the warmer parts of the world. Roots and stems, often at ground level, are attacked, the plant thereafter wilting and often dying. Young seedlings are likely to be killed but older plants may survive although crippled to varying extents.

Thysanoptera: thrips. These insects can cause damage to some crops in dry years and in glasshouses. The infested tissue often takes on a silvery sheen due to air filling the punctured epidermal cells. Leaves, flowers and pods may be attacked with resulting malformation and sometimes sterility. Rain discourages thrips infestation and these insects are only occasionally serious. Messieha (1969) has recently described thrips transmission of tobacco ring spot virus, but prior to this the only virus known to be transmitted by thrips was that causing tomato spotted wilt.

Hemiptera: plant bugs. These are important plant pests which cause direct damage by piercing and sucking and also by injecting toxic saliva which causes necrotic or discoloured spots, leaf distortion, or hypertrophy. Some are important vectors of viruses. Included here are the following families:

Capsid bugs (Miridae, Capsidae). When feeding, these secrete toxic saliva which causes necrotic spots in the plant tissue, the latter thus becoming distorted and torn during growth. Yellowing of leaves, scabbing of fruit, and seedling damage may also occur, and the symptoms can resemble those caused by viruses.

Aphids: plant lice (Aphididae). Such aphids as *Myzus persicae* are well known vectors of viruses, and many are destructive pests of crops, for example, *Aphis fabae*, the bean aphid ('black army'). Severe infestation results in distortion and withering of the aerial parts of the plant and generally reduced growth. Aphids can multiply rapidly and under favourable conditions are very damaging. They can be dispersed, sometimes over quite long distances, by wind.

White flies (Aleyrodidae). Besides being frequent vectors of viruses in warm regions these insects can also cause severe direct damage in feeding. They are typically covered by a whitish powdery or waxy material. Severe infestations cause withering of the affected organs and the whole plant may show symptoms of wilt.

Scale insects (*Coccidae*). These are of importance as pests of trees and shrubs rather than herbs, especially so in tropical and subtropical areas. They are rather immobile, relying on man and other agents, notably ants, for distribution. Many are very prolific and produce copious honeydew which is attractive to ants. Scale insects can be destructive in warm areas and in glasshouses but are rarely so in field crops in temperate regions. Heavy attacks can cause considerable weakening of the plant with accompanying development of honeydew in which fungi and bacteria often grow ('sooty moulds').

Mealybugs (*Pseudococcidae*). Although relatively immobile these insects can be serious pests in warm areas and glasshouses. *Pseudococcus* spp. are vectors of the virus causing swollen shoot disease of cacao, but neither mealybugs nor scale insects are generally virus vectors.

Leafhoppers (*Jassidae*). Important pests in this family include *Empoasca* spp. causing 'hopperburn' of potato and cotton, and *Nephotettix* on rice. Plant damage is apparently chiefly due to toxic saliva. Hoppers are important vectors of viruses (or *Mycoplasma*-like organisms), more than 100 species of hopper vectors having been reported. Delphacids (Delphacidae) and frog hoppers (Cercopidae) are similar to jassids but are of little economic importance although *Delphacodes* spp. transmit wheat striate mosaic virus.

Lepidoptera : butterflies and moths. The larvae of these insects are voracious eaters, causing severe damage to almost all parts of plants. Leaves may be consumed and skeletonized (for example the cabbage white butterfly), or seeds (cotton boll worms) or tubers (potato tuber moth) may be attacked. The larvae may bore into fruits and facilitate the entry of fruit rotting fungi such as *Sclerotinia* (brown rot). Cutworms feed on plants near the soil surface and can cause extensive seedling mortality leading to poor stands. Cotyledons and growing points may be destroyed, resulting in unthrifty deformed plants. Army worms can be very damaging to grasses, cereals and some other plants, crawling in large numbers from consumed plants to fresh ones.

Coleoptera : beetles. In this very large order the adult beetles, the larvae, or both may attack plants or stored plant products. Wireworms, the larvae of the Elateridae (click beetles), feed on grasses, cereals and other plants and can cause heavy crop loss. The plant is often attacked near soil level and although comparatively little tissue is destroyed it usually wilts and dies. Mealworms are the larvae of tenebrionid beetles and attack meal, flour and stored goods. The Chrysomelidae comprise numerous species of leaf-eating beetles and flea-beetles including the well known Colorado beetle (*Leptinotarsa*), a serious pest of potato. Plant damage results from the adult beetles and larvae feeding on leaves, and from larvae burrowing into stems and leaves and attacking the roots. The larvae of bruchid beetles attack pods and seeds, especially those of Leguminosae. Weevils (Circulionidae) attack seeds, roots, leaves, stems and flowers. Other important plant pests are the cockchafer (chafer) or white grubs (Melolonthinae); the adults, variously known as 'May bugs' or 'June bugs', feed on foliage, flowers and fruits, while the larvae feed on the roots. The latter may be completely bitten through and even large tap roots in the soil may be severely damaged, so that plant mortality can be high. Old grassland is particularly prone to attack.

Hymenoptera : sawflies, bees, wasps and ants. Relatively few of these are serious pests of crops although the larvae of some sawflies (Symphyta) attack stems and leaves and can cause appreciable reduction in yield of some cereals. Sawflies often have serrated ovipositors which enable them to lay their eggs in stems, the larvae thereafter burrowing through the latter and so weakening them that they tend to break. Other Hymenoptera are involved in the formation of galls on plants. Ants may transport aphids and coccids, and can damage plants by feeding on leaves, seeds and fruits.

Diptera : two winged flies. The larvae of Diptera sometimes damage crops; those of Cecidomyidae (gall midges) cause a complex of symptoms on most parts of the plant – distortion, leaf curl, galls, and sterility. Some species attack the flowers and seeds of grasses and cereals, and the Hessian fly attacks the stems. Others attack the roots or leaves of Leguminosae, including clover, and can be destructive. Leatherjackets, the larvae of craneflies ('daddy long legs'), feed chiefly on grass roots but those of other plants – sugarbeet, flax – may be attacked. Other important dipterous pests are frit fly on cereals, carrot fly, wheat bulb fly and cabbage root fly. These affect the plant in various ways – by killing growing points and by boring into stems, leaves, roots and bulbs.

Plant injury caused by insects

Apart from causing direct mechanical injury some insects, particularly sucking ones, inject toxic salivary secretions into the plant tissue on which they are feeding. These secretions may diffuse into the tissues beyond the actual point of feeding and cause symptoms similar to those caused by fungi, bacteria and viruses, presumably interfering with the plant's metabolism in some way. Such insects have been described by Carter (1936) as toxicogenic. Little is known about the nature of insect toxins although various substances with biological activity have been identified in the salivary glands and secretions of different insects. These include proteolytic, cellulolytic and pectolytic enzymes, enzymes which break down carbohydrates, and growth regulating substances. Carter (1962) describes four categories of these 'phytotoxemias', but emphasizes that they are not completely distinct. They include:

(1) Local lesions which develop at the feeding site and which take the form of leaf spotting and stippling. The lesions may be: (*a*) of a darker green colour, caused by increase in chlorophyll content, and possibly comparable with the 'green islands' found in some fungal diseases; (*b*) chlorotic (yellow) spots, presumably caused by failure of chlorophyll to develop; (*c*) whitish spots which may take the form of flecks or stippling, perhaps caused by the affected cells losing their contents and filling with air; (*d*) necrotic lesions caused by toxic substances produced by the insect or by the plant tissue as a response to the insect – there may be development of cork or pigment in some cases. Various combinations of these symptoms have been described.

(2) Local lesions with subsequent development of secondary symptoms, leading to cankers, cork formation, gummosis, scabbing, abortion of pods, and premature abscission of leaves and fruits. These reactions of the plant often involve tissue hypertrophy, and it may be that some change in the growth regulating processes of the plant is brought about by substances in the insect saliva. Premature abscission of leaves and fruits might, for example, be related to auxin inactivation by inhibitory substances such as IAA-oxidase, as is suspected to occur with fungi which cause premature abscission. Secondary invasion of damaged tissue by fungi and bacteria may follow. This type of damage is often caused by capsids.

(3) Tissue hypertrophy and malformation. This results in misshapen fruit, leaf curling, witch's brooms, galls, phyllody, shortening of the internodes and petioles, rosetting, stunting, and other symptoms which can be similar to those caused by viruses, and only a few insects may cause considerable damage to the plant. Little is known about the substances presumed to be involved in these symptoms, but many insects – aphids, mealybugs, capsids, leafhoppers and flies (Diptera) – can bring about this type of damage.

(4) Systemic phytotoxemias. In these the symptoms appear some distance from the feeding site, suggesting translocation of the toxin. Such translocation may be relatively limited and cause such symptoms as chlorosis, leaf stripe, vein-clearing or slight wilting, or there may be a systemic effect involving reduced growth, root injury, wilting, chlorosis (as in 'aphid yellows' of celery), phyllody and colour breaking of flowers, reduction of flower buds, leaf blistering and other malformations, and necrosis. The symptoms of systemic phytotoxemias frequently resemble those caused by viruses and it is sometimes difficult to determine the causal agent. Insect toxins are reviewed by Carter (1939, 1952).

From this brief outline it is apparent that plant injury caused by insects often resembles that caused by fungi, bacteria and viruses. The limited information available suggests that similar mechanisms of pathogenicity may be involved – toxins which bring about tissue necrosis and are produced either by the pathogen/pest or by the plant tissue as a result of attack, enzymes which destroy cell walls or cell contents, and substances which interfere with the growth regulating processes of the plant thereby causing hypertrophy, stunting, premature abscission or other abnormal growth. The extensive destruction of plant tissue occasioned by relatively unspecialized pathogens might perhaps be compared with the gross mechanical damage caused by insects which consume large amounts of plant tissue. To what extent the defence mechanisms of plants against insects are comparable with those against pathogens is uncertain and merits study. The resistance of plants to some pathogens is thought to be partly due to nutritional inadequacy or, probably more often, to toxicity of the tissues to the pathogen, and a similar situation perhaps obtains with insects, mites and nematodes. Some pests, such as locusts, consume almost any vegetation, but most show some selectivity as to the species of plants upon which they feed.

Associations between insects and plant pathogens

Insects and plant pathogens are associated in various ways. First, the insect acts as a disseminator and frequently as an inoculator of the pathogen, thus enabling the latter to spread from plant to plant; many viruses are so transmitted as are some of the bacteria and fungi which cause disease in plants, as discussed elsewhere (p. 369). Second, pathogens enter through wounds made by insects although the latter are not necessarily vectors; the saprophytic fungi which rot fruit, vegetables and grain often enter through injuries, some of which are made by insects. Third, heavy insect infestation of plants frequently leads to production of a sticky sugary honeydew which is often rapidly colonized by saprophytic fungi and, to a lesser extent, by bacteria and other microorganisms. Although such 'sooty mould' fungi are not parasitic on the plant their presence reduces the photosynthetic efficiency of the affected leaves and so adversely affects the plant. It is possible that phytotoxic substances are produced by these epiphytic microorganisms but little is known about this. Fourth, insects function as diploidizing agents for some fungi, transferring spermatia or other fertilizing spores and so enabling the perfect stage to develop. This is exemplified by the fertilization of the receptive hyphae of some rusts by insect borne spermatia, and other cases occur in Ascomycetes and Basidiomycetes. This can have important consequences in that the perfect state is often an overwintering structure and genetical variation through hybridization is also likely to occur. Fifth, a few plant pathogens overwinter in their insect vectors but this is relatively rare.

Sources of information on insects

There are numerous books and an extensive literature on insects as pests of plants; the following are a selection:
Destructive and Useful Insects, Metcalf, C. L. and Flint, W. P., New York: McGraw-Hill, 1939. *Pests of Fruit and Hops*, Massee, A. M., London: Crosby Lockwood, 1954. *Insect Pests of Glasshouse Crops*, Miles, W. M. and Miles, M., London: Crosby Lockwood, 2nd ed., 1948. *The Principles of Agricultural Entomology*, Edwards, C. A. and Heath, G. W., London: Chapman and Hall, 1964. *Pests of Farm Crops*, Stapley, J. H., London: Spon, 1949. *Horticultural Pests: Detection and Control*, Wilson, G. F. (revised Becker, P.), London: Crosby Lockwood, 3rd ed., 1960. *The Principles of Insect Physiology*, Wigglesworth, V. B., London: Methuen, 5th ed., 1953. *Chemical Control of Insects*, West, T. F. and Hardy, J. E., London: Chapman and Hall, 1961. *Outlines of Entomology*, Imms, A. D. (revised Richards, O. W. and Davies, R. G.), London: Methuen, 1961. *Pests of Field Crops*, Jones, F. G. W. and Jones, M. G., London: Arnold, 1964.

See also Leach (1940) and Carter (1962) for insects in relation to plant pathogens. Entomological journals include the *Bulletin of Entomological Research* and the *Annual Review of Entomology*. Papers on pests are also published in the *Annals of Applied Biology, Plant Pathology, F.A.O. Plant Protection Bulletin* and other journals. The *Review of Applied Entomology* is a useful abstracting journal.

Mites, spiders and other arthropods

Although many mites are thought to be scavengers rather than pests some cause serious damage to plants. Red spider mites (Tetranychidae) can cause severe defoliation of fruit trees and also chlorotic mottling rather reminiscent of virus symptoms. Others bring about distortion and hypertrophy, as in 'big bud' of blackcurrant caused by the gall mite *Phytoptus ribis* which also transmits blackcurrant reversion virus – one of the few recorded cases of mites as vectors of viruses. Mites are frequently present on diseased plant tissue and it is sometimes difficult to assess their significance.

Insects have three body regions, three pairs of walking legs, and one or two pairs of wings except in wingless species. Mites have a sac-like body which may be divided by a furrow into anterior and posterior regions, four pairs of legs when adult (three pairs in larvae) and no wings. Spiders have two body regions, four pairs of seven-segmented legs, and are wingless.

Other arthropods including woodlice, millipedes, symphylids and possibly centipedes can cause injury to plants, though they are more often secondary feeders and are seldom destructive.

Nematodes (eelworms)

Those nematodes which attack plants are relatively small, averaging about 1 mm in length with considerably smaller juvenile stages. They are responsible for many serious diseases of crops as, for example, the potato cyst nematode (golden nematode) *Heterodera rostochiensis*.

Many nematodes live for part of their life in the soil where their survival and incidence are greatly influenced by the prevailing microbiological, chemical and climatic conditions. There are numerous saprozoic forms which live on decaying organic matter in soil and elsewhere. Most of those which parasitize plants attack roots or other plant organs in the soil and are affected by plant exudates which repel or 'guide' them to suitable host plants. Others migrate up the plant in a film of moisture, or attack the seedling and are carried up above the surface of the soil during subsequent growth of the plant. Most species show some restriction in host range although some have been recorded on numerous host species. Relatively few of the soil inhabiting nematodes are known to attack plants – about 100 of some 5000 species recorded from soil (Peacock, 1957).

Nematode attack sometimes kills plants but it more often results in weakening, reduced growth and diminished yield, and it may also enable other more destructive pathogens to enter the plant. When feeding on roots, nematodes can cause several types of injury. (1) Necrotic lesions, probably caused by toxic salivary secretions injected during feeding, are caused by some nematodes, for example *Radopholus*. (2) Feeding may induce the formation of 'giant cells' in the host tissue and cell division may be stimulated and lead to the formation of galls of various sorts, as with the well known root knot nematodes *Meloidogyne* spp. (3) Nematodes feeding ectoparasitically at the root tips suppress cell division in the apical meristem and so bring about short roots, as in *Trichodorus* the stubby root nematode.

Root-infecting nematodes can be classified on an ecological basis as ectoparasites, endoparasites or semiendoparasites. Ectoparasites feed by thrusting their hollow stylet ('spear') into the plant cell, the body of the eelworm remaining outside; saliva is then injected through the stylet and the juices are sucked back. Some nematodes may remain sedentary in this position for long periods, others are migratory. Endoparasites live within the root tissues and semiendoparasites normally feed with the front end of the body embedded to varying extents in the root. In some species the female nematodes are sedentary and become swollen so that at maturity they are little more than egg containers, whereas males usually remain active.

Nematodes which attack the aerial parts of plants may cause discolouration, necrosis, blotches, spots, distortion, and galls on leaf, stem and seed. Buds, growing points or flower primordia are attacked by some nematodes, resulting in abnormal growth of the affected plant. These symptoms are thought to result from substances secreted by the eelworm or perhaps by the invaded plant tissue. The nature of plant reaction to infection by nematodes is reviewed by Krusberg (1963).

Nematodes may cause tissue hypertrophy by secreting growth promoting substances or by stimulating the invaded tissue to do so. Necrosis could result from the activity of enzymes or toxins produced by the nematodes, and there are reports of the latter secreting pectolytic, cellulolytic, proteolytic, and carbohydrate splitting enzymes. Pectolytic and cellulolytic enzymes no doubt facilitate penetration of the cell wall, and other enzymes in the injected saliva might partially hydrolyse the cell contents and so render them available to the parasite. The mechanisms of nematode injury to plants are discussed by Christie and Perry (1959).

Accumulation of phenolic substances has been reported in discoloured plant tissue killed by nematodes, but the significance of this is doubtful since such substances frequently form in damaged plant tissue. Of interest are the reports that resistance to nematodes is sometimes associated with a hypersensitive reaction of the invaded tissue, and that infected resistant plants produced phenolic compounds much more rapidly than infected susceptible ones; this has parallels with the hypersensitivity of plant tissues to pathogens.

Peacock (1957) points out that resistance may be associated with failure of the nematodes to enter the root, perhaps because it lacks the appropriate attractant or because it produces a repellent or masking substance. Some nematodes enter the roots in varying numbers but few or none develop further, eventually dying. This could be due to lack of specific nutrients required by the eelworms or to the presence or development of nematicidal substances in the invaded tissue. Another possibility is that resistant plants produce antitoxins which neutralize the toxic action of the salivary secretion produced by the nematodes.

The preadult stages of some nematodes can become dormant and so withstand unfavourable conditions for a considerable time, but survival is normally by means of resistant eggs which may require a hatching factor for larval emergence, the latter being stimulated by the roots of some plants. Crop rotation and sanitation, chemical or steam treatment of infested soil in seed beds, glasshouses and market gardens, hot water treatment of infected planting material, and the breeding of resistant varieties of plants are all used in the control of plant-parasitic eelworms (see Anon, 1968). The application of fertilizers to encourage vigorous growth may enable a worthwhile yield to be obtained even when the plants are attacked. Biological control by fungi which parasitize eelworms has been attempted and merits further investigation, as does the search for suitable chemicals which would induce premature hatching of nematode eggs in the absence of susceptible plants. One of the difficulties here is that of obtaining a high percentage hatching and another is that some nematodes have a wide host range and may survive in weeds.

Most of the nematodes known to feed on plants belong to the orders Dorylaimida and Tylenchida. Included in the former are *Xiphinema* (dagger nematodes), *Longidorus* (needle nematodes) and *Trichodorus* (stubby root nematodes), best known as vectors of some viruses (arabis mosaic, tobacco rattle and others). The order Tylenchida contains most of the eelworms known to attack plants. Some of the more important ones are *Pratylenchus*, causing lesions on roots and other underground organs, sometimes thereby enabling fungi to enter; *Ditylenchus*, attacking most parts of the plant but often stems, leaves and bulbs; *Aphelenchoides*, bud and leaf nematodes; *Anguina*, causing galls on leaves, flowers and seeds of grasses, cereals and other plants; *Heterodera*, cyst nematodes which attack roots; *Meloidogyne*, root knot nematodes; *Radopholus*, on roots especially in warm areas of the world and *Tylenchulus*, on roots (*T. semipenetrans*, quick decline of citrus).

Associations between nematodes and plant pathogens

The role of certain nematodes as vectors of plant viruses has been studied in recent years and there is an increasing awareness that they may also be involved in the transport and inoculation of other pathogens, notably bacteria and fungi attacking roots or other plant organs in the soil as discussed elsewhere (p. 374). Eelworms probably do not move very far or quickly in soil, and the spread of nematode-transmitted pathogens will tend to be slow unless there are other means of dissemination. Several types of nematode–pathogen interaction are suggested by Pitcher (1965) of which the following are examples. (1) The nematodes transport the pathogen from soil to plant or from one part of the plant to another, and the pathogen may fail to develop fully in the absence of the eelworm, as in twist of grasses and cereals caused by the fungus *Dilophospora alopecuri* in association with *Anguina tritici* (p. 374). (2) The nematodes are vectors of viruses which are thus inoculated into the roots, possibly with some sort of biological relationship between virus and vector. (3) Pathogens enter through wounds made by nematodes. It is possible that the latter modify the plant tissue which they attack in such a way as to make it a more favourable medium for growth of pathogens, as may be the case in vascular wilt of cotton caused by *Fusarium oxysporum f.sp. vasinfectum* (Powell and Nusbaum, 1960; Powell, 1963). No doubt there are other nematode–pathogen interactions yet to be discovered.

Many aspects of plant parasitic nematodes have perforce been omitted or treated cursorily in this brief outline. There are, however, several recent accounts of which the following are a selection: *Plant Nematology* (ed. Southey, J. F.), *Tech. Bull. Min. Agric., Fish. Fd*, **7,** 1965. *Plant Nematology*, Jenkins, W. R. and Taylor, D. P., New York, Amsterdam and London: Rheinhold, 1967. *Plant Nematodes. Their Bionomics and Control*, Christie, J. R., Gainsville, Florida: Univ. Florida agric. Exp. Stn, 1959. *Soil and Fresh Water Nematodes*, Goodey, T. (revised Goodey, J. B.), London: Methuen, 1963. *The Nematode Parasites of Plants catalogued under their Hosts*, 3rd ed. Commonwealth Agricultural Bureaux, 1965. *Principles of Nematology*, Thorne, G., New York: McGraw-Hill, 1961. *Pests of Field Crops*, Jones, F. G. W. and Jones, M. G., London: Arnold, 1964. *The Biology of Plant Parasitic Nematodes*, Wallace, H. R., London: Arnold, 1963.

Among useful papers are those of Pitcher (1965) and Slack *et al.* (1963) – both on nematode–pathogen relationships; Krusberg (1963: host response to nematode infection); and Peachey and Chapman (1966) on chemical control. Journals include *Helminthological Abstracts*, *Journal of Helminthology*, and *Nematologica*. Papers on nematode diseases of plants are also published in the *Annals of Applied Biology*, *Plant Pathology*, *Plant Disease Reporter*, *Annual Review of Phytopathology*, and other journals.

Other pests

Some molluscs cause damage to plants, especially in gardens and glasshouses, and the ravages caused by slugs and snails are too well known to require further comment. Snails are also said to disseminate the spores of fungi and probably other pathogens. Birds can be responsible for considerable yield losses by consuming grain, fruit, and other produce on the standing crop, by consuming sown seed, by pulling out seedlings and in other ways. They also disseminate fungal spores and possibly viruses. Woodpigeons, starlings and sparrows in temperate areas, and weaver birds in warmer areas, can be very destructive, as can rats, mice, voles, rabbits, squirrels and other mammals. Standing plants or their roots may be attacked, grain in the ear or in store may be eaten, and plants are damaged by these animals in other ways. These aspects are described by Jones and Jones (1964) who give a comprehensive and useful account of the pests which attack plants.

10 The entry of pathogens into plants

When a pathogen comes into contact with a potential host plant a complex of interacting factors including temperature, moisture, susceptibility of the plant tissue, effects of other microorganisms present, aggressiveness of the pathogen, and others determines whether infection occurs. Although some pathogens can attack almost all parts of the plant, most show some degree of specialization as to the tissues and organs invaded, as discussed later (p. 182). Broken or damaged tissue, unless it is toxic to the pathogen, is generally more liable to invasion by rather unspecialized parasites (necrotrophs), and wound parasites may enter the plant in this way only. More specialized parasites (biotrophs, obligate parasites) are likely to have difficulty in colonizing grossly damaged tissue as they require living host cells for their development, although they may be able to invade slightly damaged tissues. The processes of infection are conventionally grouped into prepenetration, penetration (p. 149) and postpenetration, although these stages are not completely distinct. The first two stages are described below, and the third, the further colonization of the infected plant, is discussed in the next chapter.

Prepenetration

In fungi this includes spore germination and growth of the resulting germ tube on the surface of the plant. The entry of bacteria, viruses and parasitic angiosperms into plants is achieved in various ways as described on pp. 52, 93, 107. Fungal invasion is chiefly by germ tubes or structures derived from them, by hyphae which may be single or aggregated to form mycelial strands or rather elaborate rhizomorphs (mainly soil fungi), or by spores or hyphae injected into the tissue by external agents such as insects (p. 371).

Spore germination

Only a brief account of this complex process can be given here, and the papers by Gottlieb (1950, 1964, 1966), Cochrane (1960) and Allen (1965) should be consulted for further details. General accounts are given in most books on physiology of the fungi, for example Hawker (1950), Cochrane (1958), Lilly and Barnett (1951), and Wolf and Wolf (1947).

Germination of fungal spores occurs in various ways according to the nature of the spore and, to some extent, environmental conditions. Sporangia and oospores of some Phycomycetes produce zoospores in wet conditions and germ tubes in dry conditions, whilst those of other Phycomycetes appear always to germinate by zoospores (for example *Plasmopara viticola*) or always by germ tube (*Peronospora* spp.). Teliospores of Uredinales and Ustilaginales normally germinate by producing a promycelium (basidium) on which basidiospores, often termed sporidia, are borne. Budding and fission, sometimes regarded as forms of germination, are more logically reproduction and are characteristic of some yeasts and bacteria, although conidia, ascospores (for example *Taphrina*), and basidiospores (Ustilaginales) may bud under certain conditions; budding is in fact quite widespread among fungi. The promycelia of Ustilaginales may produce sporidia or hyphal branches depending on biotype and environment, and conditions conducive to budding are often unfavourable for development of infection hyphae. Many fungi produce several types of spore which may germinate similarly or differently, and germination can be influenced by the genetical constitution of different biotypes and by environmental conditions.

Resting spores

Some spores germinate immediately on release, sometimes before release, while resting spores have a dormancy period during which they do not normally germinate. Others undergo a progressive maturation. Resting spores may be produced asexually (chlamydospores and other thick walled conidia) or sexually as teliospores, oospores, zygospores and some ascospores. Many spores will not germinate until they are mature and liberated naturally from the sporophore, but this is to be distinguished from dormancy in which the spore must have a resting period of several months before it can germinate. This period is an essential stage in the life cycle of some pathogens, enabling them to survive the months when the host plant is absent, leafless, or when conditions are unfavourable for infection. The physiology of dormancy and methods of overcoming it are thus of potential importance in control of some plant diseases as, for example, by inducing premature germination of overwintering spores in the absence of susceptible plants. Some spores ripen slowly during the resting period, as ascospores in the perithecia of *Venturia inaequalis* and the cleistothecia of Erysiphaceae, and some require full outside exposure ('weathering') before they will germinate. Thus teliospores of *Phragmidium violaceum* (blackberry rust) germinated well in spring after overwintering out of doors but poorly when kept indoors at various temperatures or when kept outside but protected from rain: exposure to rain and fluctuating winter temperatures was apparently necessary.

Some degree of softening of the resting spore wall, leading perhaps to increased permeability to water or to leaching out of germination inhibitors, may have to precede germination, or a number of processes in addition to ripening and weathering may be involved. Various experimental treatments reduce the dormancy period of resting spores, for example alternate wetting and drying and freezing and thawing (teliospores of *Puccinia graminis*: Johnson, 1947), storage under moist conditions at 35°C (teliospores of *Ustilago striiformis*: Kreitlow, 1945), soaking in tap water at 4°C for 3 months (teliospores of *Tilletia* on wheat: Holton, 1943) and others. Treatment with certain organic substances such as citric acid, chloroform, aldehydes and auxins breaks the dormancy of some resting spores but not of others and there seems to be little consistency in this. Treatment with enzymes, such as chitinase, which are likely to change the structure or permeability of the spore wall might be a promising approach. It is possible that soil or plant tissues may have a similar effect but little is known about this.

Resting spores generally have thick walls, sometimes ornamented in various ways, are frequently yellow or dark, contain stored nutrients (often fats) and are often relatively large. Those of phytopathogenic fungi tend to develop at the end of the season in dying or dead host tissue, and overwinter there or in the soil until the following spring. They may, however, remain dormant but viable for a number of years, and some probably require the presence of host tissue before they germinate. On germination the thick wall of the resting spore cracks open, or the germ tube may emerge through germ pores in the wall. Germination is by germ tube (chlamydospores, some oospores, ascospores, basidiospores), by zoospores (some oospores) or promycelia (teliospores).

Propagative spores

In contrast to resting spores, propagative spores tend to be thin walled, fairly short lived, and to contain less nutrients. They are extremely varied in morphology, colour and size, as are the fruiting bodies in or on which they are produced, and include many conidia, pycnospores, zoospores, ascospores, basidiospores, uredospores and others. They are produced in immense numbers during the growing season and serve for rapid spread of pathogens rather than for overwintering, although some may be able to survive between crops in areas with mild winters. Provided that environmental conditions are favourable they can usually germinate immediately they are mature and liberated from the sporophore. Germination is by one or several germ tubes, or by zoospores in the case of sporangia of some

Phycomycetes. The multicellular spores of some fungi, including *Alternaria* (Joly, 1964), may show 'second germination', that is, if the first germ tube dies a second one is produced, usually by another cell of the spore. This is useful in that if the first germ tubes are killed by desiccation before they have invaded the plant, the second ones may encounter more favourable conditions and succeed in penetrating. Similarly the capacity of the germ tube to bear secondary conidia (proliferation) under unfavourable conditions is likely to be advantageous to plant pathogens.

Biological stimulation and inhibition of germination

The physiology of spore germination will not be discussed in detail here. Germination is essentially the transition from a low to a high metabolic rate, from near-dormancy to intense activity, and an energy source (usually fat or carbohydrate) is needed. Some spores contain all the nutrients needed for germination and will germinate in pure water, using energy derived principally from oxidation of fats within the spore. This is true of spores of many air borne pathogens and particularly those of Erysiphaceae and Uredinales, but germination is sometimes improved by supplying extra nutrients. Certain vitamins and amino acids stimulate germination of some spores although this does not seem to be generally so. The improved germination resulting from extra nutrients may enhance the ability of the spore to invade the plant, and a spore suspension in, say, 1% glucose may be more effective in this respect than a suspension in pure water. Exudates from plant tissues may stimulate spore germination and in extreme cases the spores germinate only when these are present. This could be an ecological advantage for specialized parasites as it would ensure that germination occurred only on susceptible plant tissue. An interesting case of increased pathogenicity ascribed to leaf exudates has recently been described by Milholland (1970) in blueberry (*Vaccinium corymbosum*) leaf spot caused by *Gloeosporium minus*. The lesions due to this fungus, which infects through wounds or hydathodes, were larger near the hydathodes where high concentrations of carbohydrate were exuded. Whereas inoculation with conidial suspensions in distilled water resulted only in small flecks, leaf spot severity was increased by suspending the conidia in leaf exudate or in simulated exudate containing the major components of leaf sap.

Infusions of such natural organic substrates as manure and soil, pieces of plant tissue (especially of susceptible plants), pollen and expressed plant juices may stimulate germination not only of propagative spores but also occasionally of resting spores; for example, oospores of *Pythium mamillatum* germinated in soil only when near young turnip roots or in water in which turnip seeds had germinated (Barton, 1957). Linderman and Gilbert (1969) have shown that volatile compounds, (including methanol, acetaldehyde, isobutyraldehyde and isovaleraldehyde) produced by alfalfa hay stimulate the germination of the sclerotia of *Sclerotium* (*Corticium*) *rolfsii* in or on soil. Survival of sclerotia in soil was reduced by exposing them to the vapour of a distillate prepared from alfalfa hay; this reduction of viability was attributed to depletion of the food material of the germinating sclerotia and to lysis of the sclerotia and mycelium by antagonistic microorganisms which were also stimulated by the vapour. Roots of non-host as well as of host plants stimulated germination of spores of *Plasmodiophora brassicae* (Macfarlane, 1952), *Urocystis tritici* (Noble, 1924), *Fusarium* spp. (Jackson, 1957) and others.

Pollen stimulates spore germination in *Alternaria brassicicola* (Channon, 1970: cabbage pollen) and in *Botrytis cinerea* (Chou and Preece, 1968). The latter authors found that aqueous diffusates of strawberry pollen, as well as the pollen grains, were stimulatory. The stimulatory principle is water soluble, dialysable, heat stable and contains glucose and fructose, although neither of these sugars, alone or mixed, was as active as pollen. Pollen diffusates also enabled apparently moribund *Botrytis* spores to germinate and infect. The practical effects of this stimulation are not only that the presence of pollen increases infection but also that it enables infection to be brought about by smaller numbers of *Botrytis* spores.

Stimulation of germination also occurs in other organisms. Seed of the phanerogamic parasite *Striga* (witchweed) is stimulated to germinate by root secretions of various plants, some susceptible some not, and this applies also to other parasitic phanerogams (for example *Orobanche*) and to nematode eggs (the 'hatching factor'). In *Striga* the germination stimulant appears to be a complex of organic substances, and *D*-xyloketose was quite effective (further details are given by Tarr, 1962).

Propagules which need stimulation may have lost the ability to produce some substances necessary for germination which are present in the stimulant (Brown, 1946) but the nature of these hypothetical compounds is unknown. Among the many organic compounds reported to stimulate spore germination in different fungi are certain aldehydes (for example, benzaldehyde, pelargonaldehyde = *n*-nonalal), organic acids, esters, oils, acetone and chloroform. Their mode of action is unknown although Stakman and Harrar (1957) point out that many of them reduce surface tension and thus permit greater hydration of the spore.

Soil may contain a widespread fungistatic factor which inhibits spore germination and which may be annulled by complex organic substances including plant exudates (Dobbs and Hinson, 1953; Lockwood, 1964): antibiotics may be involved and the phenomenon is complex and not well understood. It is reported to operate largely in the upper layers of soil and to be destroyed by autoclaving. This may be another way in which spore germination in the absence of suitable nutrients or hosts is discouraged.

For example germination of the sclerotia of *Sclerotium cepivorum* (onion white rot), normally subject to soil mycostasis, was stimulated by a volatile principle produced by onion and leek seedlings (King and Coley-Smith, 1968; Coley-Smith *et al.*, 1967).

Although some plant materials stimulate spore germination, others have the opposite effect. Orange peel, potato, and onion may reduce germination, and substances in the waxy leaf surfaces of apple and other plants inhibited germination in *Podosphaera leucotricha* and *Botrytis fabae* (Martin, Batt and Burchill, 1957). Germination in *B. cinerea*, *Ascochyta pisi* and *Puccinia triticina* is stimulated or depressed by plant secretions (Topps and Wain, 1957; Kovacs and Szeoke, 1956), resistance of certain varieties of gram (*Cicer*) to *Mycosphaerella rabiei* is associated with secretion of malic acid which reduces spore germination and hyphal growth (Hafiz, 1952), and protocatechuic acid in the scales of some varieties of onion prevents germination of the spores of *Colletotrichum circinans* (Walker, Link and Angell, 1929). Metabolites secreted by other microorganisms on or near the plant surface may also affect germination of fungal spores, notably antibiotic substances produced by *Trichoderma* and other rhizosphere inhabitants. Such effects are well known in roots but probably also occur on shoots.

These stimulatory and inhibitory effects also influence growth of germ tubes and formation of appressoria. They are probably more pronounced in the rhizosphere than in the phyllosphere because the cuticle of shoots reduces exudation; rain removes shoot exudates and microbial growth is encouraged by superficial tissue sloughed off as roots grow through the soil. Root exudates may directly inhibit spore germination and hyphal growth or may selectively favour growth of soil saprophytes antagonistic to fungi which attack roots, as has been reported for *Fusarium oxysporum f.sp. lini* on flax (Timonin, 1940), *F. oxysporum f.sp. pisi* on peas (Buxton, 1957), and *Thielaviopsis basicola* on tobacco (Lockhead, Timonin and West, 1940).

Requirements for spore germination

These are briefly considered below. They affect not only the percentage of germination but also the speed and sometimes the method of germination. The spores of some fungi germinate over a fairly wide range of environment, but others are less tolerant in this respect and the diseases they cause can develop only under certain well defined conditions.

Moisture

Many spores require water for germination and some germinate best when completely immersed rather than floating, although poor aeration sometimes reduces germination in, for example, waterlogged soil. A film of moisture as provided by dew or light rain is probably best as it permits adequate aeration. The sporangia of Peronosporales and many uredo-spores, basidiospores, ascospores, and conidia of Fungi Imperfecti and Ascomycetes mostly require free water for germination. Some spores, however, germinate at 100% relative humidity. These include the uredo-spores of *Puccinia coronata* and *P. graminis* (Clayton, 1942), but unless the temperature is precisely controlled (and this does not happen in nature) a film of moisture is likely to condense on the spore; hence experiments carried out at 100% humidity require accurate temperature control.

With decreasing humidity the number of fungi whose spores germinate falls off. Spores of some *Ustilago* spp., *Botrytis cinerea*, *Verticillium albo-atrum*, *Venturia inaequalis* and others germinate at 90–100% relative humidity, and those of *Cladosporium herbarum* and some species of *Penicillium* and *Aspergillus* at humidities as low as 75%, the latter being the lower limit for fungi in general. There are exceptions, notably in the Erysiphaceae where the conidia of some species, for example *Erysiphe polygoni* can germinate at zero humidity, whereas the conidia of other species require high humidity. Schnathorst (1965) in his review of environmental relationships in this group suggests three categories: (*a*) species with conidia which germinate best at high humidity, near saturation, for example *Sphaerotheca pannosa*; (*b*) those in which germination occurs at 75–100% relative humidity, often with the optimum near saturation and with some germination at low humidity, for example *Erysiphe cichoracearum*, *Leveillula taurica*; and (*c*) those in which germination occurs over a wide range of humidity, from near-zero to near-saturation, depending on temperature, for example *Erysiphe polygoni*, *Uncinula necator*. Free water inhibits spore germination in some Erysiphaceae, especially if the spores are completely immersed. Different races of a species may have a different requirement for ger-mination, and even the time of collection may have an effect, as reported by Yarwood (1936) in *E. polygoni*. These aspects have important practical implications in that some powdery mildew diseases can be prevalent and destructive under quite arid conditions, and similar considerations may well apply to other leaf pathogens attacking plants in arid areas, notably certain rusts and leaf spotting fungi.

Fungal spores on substrates which absorb atmospheric moisture (agar, textiles, grain) seem able to germinate at lower humidity than on non-absorptive substrates like glass, presumably by obtaining moisture from the substrate in some as yet unexplained way (Block, 1953; Groom and Panisset, 1933), and spores able to germinate at low humidity can also do so in substrates of high osmotic pressure (Armolik and Dickson, 1956). Such spores may have a higher moisture content – about 70% in *E. polygoni* (Yarwood, 1950, 1952) – than others, this water being only slowly lost in dry air. Possibly, spores of lower moisture content absorb water to about 70% before germination occurs, and the frequent swelling of spores in water may be due to this. Thus, the conidia of some Erysiphaceae may have a 'built-in' water supply which renders them more or less independent of external sources and enables them to flourish in dry areas; even in the latter, however, there may be sufficient dew for germination of some fungal spores. Moisture and temperature are closely associated and the optimum humidity for spore germination tends to increase with rising temperature.

Temperature

Many fungal spores germinate over a rather wide temperature range, often from just above freezing point to 30°C or so (more in thermophilic species) with an optimum of about 15–25°C. Arbitrarily, they can be grouped as cryophilic (optimum below 15°C), mesophilic (15–25°C), semithermophilic (25–35°C) and thermophilic (above 35°C). Temperature requirements of individual fungi are given by Togashi (1949), Hawker (1950), Wolf and Wolf (1947) and others.

Different races of a fungus may have different temperature requirements. Some species have a sharply defined optimum temperature for germination but more show a fairly broad optimum extending over 5°C or more, this range being narrower when other factors such as pH, moisture and nutrient supply are suboptimal. The optimum for germination may not be the optimum for growth of the germ tube or for general vegetative growth, although the last two are often somewhat similar. Spores of *Urocystis occulta*, for example, germinate best at about 15°C whereas the germ tubes grow best at about 24°C (Stakman and Harrar, 1957). A limited preliminary exposure to higher temperature sometimes stimulates germination, as in *Phytophthora infestans* where a short exposure to 40°C greatly increased germination of sporangia thereafter incubated at 20°C (Taylor *et al.*, 1955), suggesting that the metabolic processes of early germination have a different optimum from the later ones. An unfavourable temperature delays germination, but once the latter starts it may proceed at the optimal rate (Cochrane, 1960), and the final percentage germination may be nearly as high as under optimal conditions. The speed of germination is, however, less and this may be of critical importance in diseases in which the plant is susceptible for only a fairly short period of time, as in some species of Ustilaginales which can infect only the young seedling. Temperature is not constant for any length of time in the field although it is less variable in soil than above soil level. It normally follows a seasonal rhythm and also a diurnal one of lower temperature at night, and it is this overall pattern of temperature and other factors, which is significant in the development and spread of plant pathogens. Temperature can also influence the method of germination as in *Phytophthora infestans* where the sporangia liberate zoospores at the optimum temperature (12–13°C) but tend to produce germ tubes at higher temperatures.

Light

Natural visible light of about 4000–8000 Å appears to have little effect on spore germination although intense light may cause heating and so inhibit it. Ultraviolet rays are injurious and mutagenic, and the pigments (especially carotenoids) of some spores may protect against harmful radiation in prolonged bright sunlight. Thus many of the fungi living epiphytically or parasitically on the surface of leaves in the tropics tend to be pigmented – *Cladosporium*, *Alternaria* and others in insect honeydew (p. 322), parasitic sooty moulds such as Meliolaceae and some Hemisphaeriales, and even Erysiphaceae may take on a greyish tinge. Near ultraviolet light of about 3100–4100 Å, peaking at 3650 Å, induces sporulation of many fungi as described by Leach (1962). Light near the red end of the spectrum can inhibit germination (Cochrane, 1945), particularly in moist and partly germinated spores, whereas shorter wavelength light can accelerate it, and Hebert and Kelman (1958) report that germination of the resting sporangia of *Physoderma maydis* increases at higher light intensity. Light also affects production and longevity of spores, and the germ tubes of some fungi, especially Uredinales (Forbes, 1939), are negatively phototrophic, particularly to the blue-violet rays.

*p*H

Although the spores of many fungi germinate best under slightly acid conditions (about *p*H 5–6·5 with a range of about *p*H 3–8), those of other fungi have an alkaline optimum no doubt related to the substrates they colonize. Spores of *Botrytis cinerea* are tolerant of a wide range of *p*H – 1·6–6·9 (optimum *p*H 3–4). The overall effect of *p*H on germination is probably complex, involving availability of nutrients and other factors which cannot be discussed here. *p*H is not generally considered to be an important factor limiting spore germination but it is possible that plant secretions might render the *p*H of the infection droplet unsuitable for germination and subsequent growth of the germ tube. Similar effects perhaps occur in the rhizosphere.

Oxygen and carbon dioxide

The spores of many fungi are reported to germinate over a fairly wide range of oxygen concentration, up to about 50% in the few species investigated. Germination rarely occurs under completely anaerobic conditions and it may well be that it is sometimes reduced in waterlogged soils. Little is known about the optimum oxygen pressure for germination, but 30–38 mm seems to be sufficient for *Puccinia graminis tritici* (Allen,

1955), *Botrytis cinerea* (Brown, 1922) and *Ustilago zeae* (Platz, 1928). Carbon dioxide concentration probably has little effect on spore germination, although an increase may stimulate it and some spores are reported to germinate in concentrations of 60–70% (Stakman and Harrar, 1957). Inhibition of germination by carbon dioxide is also reported by Gottleib (1950) and this might occur in waterlogged soils under conditions favourable to accumulation of the gas.

Biological factors

Among these can be mentioned the mucilage which envelopes some spores (for example Gloiosporae: Wakefield and Bisby, 1941) and protects against desiccation and (possibly) harmful radiation, and the sugary honeydew surrounding such spores as the conidia of *Claviceps* and the spermatia of the Uredinales which is said to promote germination when suitably diluted (Garay, 1956).

Spores of some fungi show self-inhibition in that they do not germinate if too densely crowded. This is probably due to toxic, volatile, thermostable substances, including trimethylethylene, produced by the spores and probably removable by washing. Self-inhibition has been investigated in several rust fungi by Allen (1955), Yarwood (1956), Forsyth (1955), and others, and probably occurs in other fungi. Its biological significance may lie in preventing germination of spores still crowded within the fruiting body before dispersal. Fungi probably produce volatile compounds, particularly aldehydes, which inhibit germination of their own and other spores (sporostasis) as is frequently observed in culture (Robinson and Park, 1966; Robinson, Park and Garrett, 1968).

The reverse has also been reported, germination failing to take place at very low concentrations of spores, suggesting the presence of stimulatory substances (Gottlieb, 1964). The natural significance of this is obscure but possibly it prevents germination in infection droplets containing too few spores for successful infection to occur (p. 315). Allen (1956) has shown that germinating uredospores of *Puccinia graminis* release volatile substances which inhibit elongation of germ tubes and induce formation of appressoria in other spores.

Growth of germ tubes

The behaviour of germ tubes growing on the plant surface depends on many factors. If environmental conditions are suitable and the plant susceptible they may enter the tissue through wounds, through natural openings, or by direct penetration, often forming appressoria in so doing. If conditions are unfavourable or the plant is resistant or immune the germ tubes may perish before or after entering the plant. There has been considerable discussion (for example, Stakman and Harrar, 1957) as to which factors bring about the entry of germ tubes and hyphae into plants, and various suggestions have been put forward.

Some germ tubes are negatively phototropic and this might partly explain their entry except that it can occur in darkness. The possibility that germinating spores can produce substances which induce formation of appressoria in other germ tubes, as noted above, is interesting. Although Brown (1936), Dickinson (1949) and others have concluded that appressorial development is largely a thigmotropic response, there is evidence that substances of host origin are also involved, and that these also affect the behaviour of germ tubes. Thus, germ tubes which enter through stomata may grow towards the latter, presumably a tropic response to water soluble or volatile secretions or to water itself (Bald, 1952; Brown, 1936; Dickinson, 1949). Some zoospores move towards stomata, probably following a concentration gradient of some host secretion as described for zoospores of *Plasmopara viticola* by Arens (1929).

These directional effects also occur near roots and germinating seeds; for example, seeds of pea varieties liable to damping-off (*Pythium*) released considerable sucrose during the early stages of germination and the fungus followed the resulting concentration gradient to the seed. The varieties which escaped attack, although susceptible, released insufficient sucrose to stimulate growth of the fungus (Flentje, 1959). Exudates of pea seeds influenced germination and subsequent hyphal growth of chlamydospores of *Fusarium solani f.sp. pisi* (Cook and Flentje, 1967). Root exudate preparations from sugarbeet seedlings attracted zoospores of *Aphanomyces cochlioides* and stimulated their germination and subsequent growth of germ tubes. Chromatographic analysis indicated that the amino acid fraction of the exudate stimulated germination and growth, whereas the organic acid and neutral fractions were chemotactic, as were gluconic acid, glucose and maltose. Raffinose and ribose tended to repel zoospores (Rai and Strobel, 1966). Zoospores of *Phytophthora cinnamomi* are attracted to susceptible avocado (*Persea*) roots and those of *P. citrophthora* to susceptible citrus roots (Zentmyer, 1961), and the factors influencing the behaviour of zoospores of *Pythium aphanidermatum* near roots are reported by Royle and Hickman (1964). Similar tactic and tropic responses are probably more frequent than is at present realized and merit further investigation, as does the possible occurrence of negative chemotropism, for example, host secretions which repel germ tubes. The behaviour of zoospores of plant infecting fungi is reviewed by Hickman and Ho (1966).

It is clear that the events proceeding on the plant surface – principally spore germination, growth of germ tubes and often formation of appressoria – are complex and influenced not only by environmental factors but also by the nature of the plant surface, by substances secreted by it, and by the other microorganisms present on it. The latter two factors have particular application in root diseases. The events occurring after penetration are affected less by environmental factors, and more by the reaction of the invaded plant tissue; it is here that the metabolic systems of parasite and host come into intimate contact and the defensive reactions of the latter begin. Hence it is not surprising that some microorganisms are able to enter plants which they do not parasitize.

Although the foregoing is concerned largely with spore germination and growth of germ tubes it is likely that other fungal structures such as hyphae, mycelial strands and rhizomorphs show similar responses to plant exudates.

Penetration

Pathogens invade plants through wounds, natural openings (p. 152), or by direct penetration (p. 157). Some enter in one way only, others in more than one. In the Uredinales the basidiospores penetrate directly whilst uredospores generally but not invariably invade through stomata. *Botrytis cinerea* may invade directly or through wounds, and some fungi which normally grow through stomata may penetrate directly under some conditions. Direct penetration seems to be the method most frequently encountered. The infection of plants by fungi is reviewed by Eide (1955) and Wood (1967).

Entry through wounds

Much of the plant is covered by the epidermis (piliferous layer in roots) and in shoots the outermost part of the epidermis consists of a non-cellular waxy membrane, the cuticle (p. 158). Secondary thickening results in development of bark (periderm) which is an effective obstacle against many pathogens. Pathogens which are apparently unable to penetrate these protective structures or to enter through natural openings frequently invade through wounds of various sorts and are known as wound parasites. These include many wood rotting and canker fungi, some of those causing decay of fruit and vegetables, and many soft rot bacteria and fungi. In stigmatomycoses the fungus is injected into the plant tissue by an insect, often by means of its proboscis, and the fungus may be dependent on the insect for its spread and inoculation, as described by Leach (1940) and Carter (1962).

The agents of plant injury are numerous and diverse, the most important being:

Climatic factors

These include wind, especially when it is carrying soil or sand particles which lacerate plants or, if of sufficient force, breaks off branches of trees or buffets plants violently against each other; hail and sleet; snow, which may accumulate on branches and break them down; lightning; extreme or prolonged cold (frost) or heat (scorching); and heavy rain which may beat down herbaceous plants. Fire is a very important cause of damage in forests and many of the wound parasites attacking trees enter in this way. Damaged plant tissue is liable to be colonized by such omnivorous fungi as *Botrytis cinerea* which aggravate the original damage.

Insects, nematodes and other animals

Insects, particularly the biting and sucking ones which feed on plants, may disseminate and inoculate pathogens into plants as well as causing injury through which unassociated fungi and bacteria enter. Fungi may also colonize tissue killed by insect toxins. There may be a near-obligate relationship between pathogen and insect in some viruses, some bacteria (for example, cucumber wilt, *Erwinia tracheiphila* and cucumber beetles) and some fungi (for example Dutch elm disease, *Ceratostomella ulmi* and bark beetles). Nematodes also come into this category, particularly in root disease fungi, in which some degree of obligatory association seems likely, the fungus invading the root through small feeding lesions made by the nematode. Grubs, wireworms, termites and other soil insects may play a similar role, also mites. Larger animals such as slugs, rodents, rabbits and herbivores grazing vegetation may facilitate the entry of fungi into plants, as may the damage to tree branches caused by the antlers of deer, the beaks of woodpeckers, and the passage of elephants and other large animals.

Man

Man is a frequent source of plant injury caused by garden implements, agricultural machines, mechanical grading of fruit and other produce, chemical injury from heavy application of fertilizers, herbicides and pesticides, damage occurring during sowing, harvesting, pruning, grafting, transplanting, threshing, seed treatment and many other operations. Falling trees may damage adjacent ones, and heavy atmospheric pollution can injure plants and thus encourage invasion by pathogens.

Self-inflicted injury

Ripping of foliage by thorns, whipping of branches in strong wind, and natural splitting of seeds and bark can also facilitate the entry of wound parasites. Spores may be drawn into the exposed tracheids for an hour or more after leaf-fall (for example *Nectria galligena*: Crowdy, 1952) and leaf scars may remain liable to infection for several days. Root scars and the exit points of secondary roots may also provide entry points.

Lesions

Some pathogens enter plants through lesions caused by other pathogens and there may be a fairly regular sequence in this, the second invader sometimes causing more damage than the primary one. Fusaria attacking potato tubers may invade through lesions caused by *Phytophthora infestans* or *Spongospora subterranea*, and *Nectria galligena* (apple canker) often invades old scab (*Venturia inaequalis*) infections.

There is a better chance of successful invasion when the wounding agent also introduces the pathogen, and deep or extensive lesions are more likely to be colonized by secondary invaders than are superficial scratches. The plant may seal off wounds by producing cork, callus, resin or gum and, if sufficiently rapid, this may prevent wound parasites from establishing themselves. Entry through wounds will thus be minimized by factors which promote rapid healing of the injured tissue and which discourage growth of the parasite.

In nature almost every part of the plant is likely to show wounds to varying extents, many so small as to be virtually invisible, but even minor lesions caused by feeding nematodes or by other agents may be sufficient for entry of some pathogens if conditions are favourable for infection. Slight wounding may thus be regarded as a normal condition for most plants in nature, and many pathogens take advantage of this.

Rather little is known about the precise mechanism of entry through wounds. Presumably the pathogen grows on the disorganized dead plant cells and thereafter either invades adjacent cells or destroys them by means of its toxins and enzymes. Appressoria and enzymes may be formed (Brown, 1915, 1936), and according to Kerr and Flentje (1957) *Corticium solani* (*Pellicularia filamentosa*) does not form appressoria on the external cell wall if the cuticle is removed, although it does so in the internal tissues. Possibly the capacity successfully to colonize wounds is dependent on the ability to produce appressoria in the absence of cuticle. Alternatively, wound parasites, although unable to breach the undamaged cuticle, may produce enzymes able to degrade the inner cell walls. The physiology and mechanisms of wound penetration merit investigation.

Wound parasites show many interesting features and some can apparently survive as saprophytes on the plant surface. *Cercosporella primulae*, although able to enter *Primula* leaves through stomata, often does so through wounds, and its conidia frequently germinate to produce a presumably saprophytic mycelium on the leaf surface. This mycelium can be quite extensive, may bear spores, and produces appressoria. An appressorium may produce several hyphae, one of which enters a stoma while the others grow over the leaf surface and subsequently produce appressoria. Multiple penetration thus occurs, resulting in the formation of numerous small flecks or lesions over a small area of leaf surface (Adebayo, 1969). This capacity to survive on the plant surface and to infect at a number of different places more or less simultaneously, or over a period of time, is likely to be advantageous to a plant pathogen.

Entry through natural openings

Although less frequent than direct penetration and, probably, wound penetration, there are many fungi and bacteria which enter plants through stomata and, less often, hydathodes and lenticels.

Stomata

Stomata occur in large numbers, ranging from several hundred to several thousand per square millimetre, on the lower side of leaves, but except for grasses and a few others, for example alfalfa and red clover, are much fewer on the upper side. The stomatal pore varies considerably in size, ranging from about 5 to 40 μm (mostly 10–20 μm) in length and 1–15 μm (5–8 μm) in width. Size will also depend on movements of the guard cells and other factors. Numerous small stomata measuring 5×1 μm occur in *Quercus triloba* whilst those of *Tradescantia zebrina* are much fewer but larger (8×38 μm); data are given by Curtis and Clark (1950). Fungal germ tubes also vary considerably in size depending on species and environment, and many are a few micrometres in width although those from large spores may be wider. Thus, it should be physically possible for some germ tubes to pass freely through some open stomata as sometimes happens in *Cochliobolus victoriae* on oats (Paddock, 1953) and *Cladosporium fulvum* on tomato (Butler and Jones, 1949), but most fungi form appressoria.

Details of appressorial formation vary in different fungi and the process has been studied in rust uredospores, especially those of *Puccinia graminis*. The germ tube grows more slowly, perhaps due to inhibiting substances secreted by the spores (Allen, 1956). Its tip appears to adhere to the surface of the guard cells by sticky mucilage in some cases and develops into a characteristic swollen, often lobed or irregular appressorium which may fit closely over the stoma. Some fungi (for example *Puccinia striiformis*: Pole-Evans, 1907) produce small inconspicuous appressoria and some (for example *Corticium solani*: Kerr and Flentje, 1957) produce multiple ones. Much of the protoplasm of the germ tube moves into the appressorium and a cross septum often develops between the two structures. Nuclear division has been reported to occur at this stage but this needs investigation. A small finger-like penetration hypha grows from the underside of the appressorium through the stoma, sometimes forcing the guard cells apart.

Stomata are rarely if ever completely closed and many fungi can thus invade at night. Several penetration hyphae may develop from one appressorium but normally only one appears to be functional. In the substomatal cavity the penetration hypha enlarges into a vesicle of different shape and size in different fungi – irregular in *Phytophthora infestans* (Pristou and Gallegly, 1954), cylindrical in *Puccinia graminis* (Pole-Evans, 1907) – and septa may develop, especially if several infection hyphae

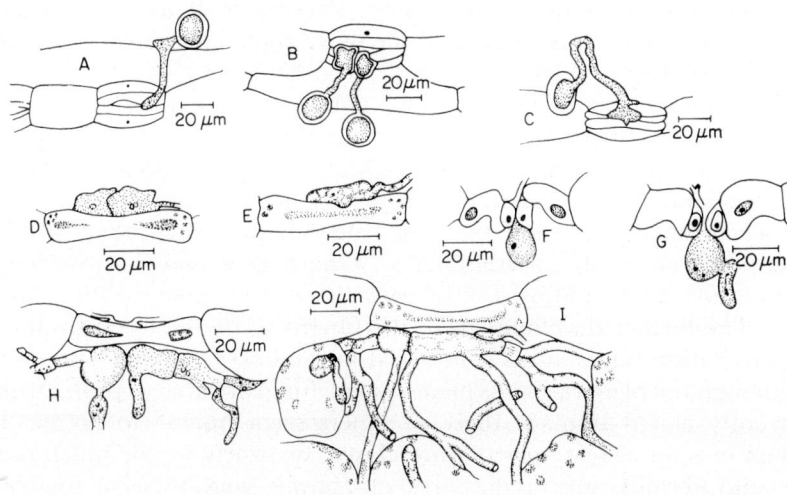

Figure **10.1**   Stomatal penetration. A–I, germination of uredospores of *Puccinia hordei* on barley. A, the spore showing a germ-tube, at end of which is a young appressorium (swelling), the latter producing a fine penetration peg, as if to enter a guard cell of a stoma. B, appressoria from two spores close to a stomatal aperture. C, an appressorium with a penetration peg formed over a closed stoma. D, section of a stoma showing two appressoria resting on a guard cell. E, an appressorium putting forth its first infection hypha. F, G, substomatal vesicles. H, a 2-day-old infection from two vesicles in the same substomatal cavity; note haustorium sent into epidermal cell on left. I, a 3-day-old infection; note two haustoria, the one on left in contact with host nucleus.

subsequently form. The protoplasm of appressorium and vesicle is often granular, sometimes pigmented (especially in Uredinales), and nuclear division has been reported in both. Stomatal penetration by uredospores of *Puccinia hordei* is shown in figure 10·1.

The speed of stomatal penetration depends on fungus and environment. In optimal conditions, germination and penetration may be completed in a few hours whilst some fungi may require about 12 hours. (*Puccinia coronata*: Rothman, 1960) or longer. Speed of penetration can be critical in that once the pathogen is inside the plant tissue it is largely protected from desiccation, bright light and other harmful agents.

One or several small infection hyphae then grow out from the substomatal vesicle and these are the structures which actually invade the cells of the host plant. Their further development depends on the reaction of the plant, the nature of the pathogen, and environmental factors. In resistant tissue the infection hyphae may fail to develop further, form a small mycelium which has no apparent effect on adjacent host cells, or form haustoria which penetrate the latter but do not appear to absorb nutrients. In all these cases the pathogen is checked although it may meantime have killed plant cells in its immediate vicinity, causing small necrotic spots, and many of the defence mechanisms of the plant come into play at this stage, as described later (p. 258).

If invasion is successful the infection hyphae penetrate the adjacent plant cells either directly or by means of specialized branches (haustoria, p. 178) which often absorb nutrients with apparently minimal damage to the cells and are characteristic of many biotrophs. Other pathogens secrete toxins and/or enzymes which kill the host cells and so render their contents available (necrotrophs, perthophytes). Guard cells may be invaded by some pathogens, including *Lophodermium pinastri* on pine needles (Jones, 1935). The further development of the fungus in the host constitutes the postpenetration stage and is considered in the next chapter.

Although the penetration hyphae of some fungi are able to push through apparently closed stomata those of others seem unable to do so. The stomata of some wheat varieties are closed, or nearly so, for much of the time, and germinating uredospores of *Puccinia graminis* seem unable to enter them (Hart, 1929); the germ tubes of some races of this fungus cause the stomata of some wheat varieties to close (Allen, 1926), possibly a defence reaction. More recently Burrage (1970) reported that stomatal closure reduced the number of infections of wheat leaves by *Puccinia graminis* var. *tritici* and pointed out that the factors which influence stomatal movement should be borne in mind when considering infection by this rust. The stomata of some flax varieties moderately resistant to rust (*Melampsora lini*) tended to open later in the morning, after dew had disappeared, than those of susceptible varieties in which stomata were open at sunrise (Sharvelle, 1936). The distinction is doubtful and stomatal closure has been reported as having no appreciable effect on entry by such rusts as *Puccinia triticina* and *Uromyces fallens* (Caldwell and Stone, 1932). Stomatal closure may prevent entry of some fungi but this does not seem to be generally true. Conidia of *Cercospora beticola* produce germ tubes which enter only open stomata of beet leaves and the disease is encouraged by factors which encourage stomatal opening (Pool and Mackay, 1916). There may be some connexion between the greater numbers and activity of stomata on older leaves and the fact that the disease is largely confined to the latter, but other factors may well be involved. The relationships between stomata and germ tubes entering them are complex and little understood.

The reasons why some fungi enter plants directly and others through natural openings are obscure. The method of entry is no doubt genetically determined but environmental and host factors are also involved. Apparently obligate or near-obligate stomatal invaders include uredospores and aeciospores of Uredinales, certain Peronosporales (for example *Plasmopara viticola*, *Peronospora destructor*), *Cladosporium fulvum* and *Lophodermium pinastri* (Gaumann, 1950, suggests that the thick cuticle of pine needles prevents direct penetration by this fungus). Others, including the basidiospores of Uredinales, the spores of Ustilaginales, sporangia and zoospores of some Peronosporales, and the conidia of many Fungi Imperfecti and Ascomycetes frequently penetrate directly. Some appear unable to enter stomata, and the germ tubes of some Erysiphaceae grow over stomata without reacting appreciably.

At first sight stomatal penetration would seem to be easier for the fungal germ tube than direct penetration, but in the former the germ tube has to find a suitable stoma and overcome its defensive reactions, if any develop. Furthermore, after entering the stomatal cavity the germ tube still has to invade the adjacent plant cells which, however, may be less of an obstacle than the cuticularized epidermal cells. It can be argued that a fungus has entered a plant once it has passed through the stoma, but physiological interaction of the two organisms is usually considered to begin in the early stages of invasion. Comparatively little attention has been paid to possible host responses during the interval between entry and invasion, for example at the stage when the substomatal vesicle is forming, and they merit further study.

Precise figures are lacking, but fungi with direct penetration probably outnumber stomatal invaders. Some fungi enter plants by either method according to circumstances, as do *Botrytis gladiolorum* (usually direct, particularly under wet conditions: Bald, 1952) and *B. cinerea* which infects healthy bean (*Vicia faba*) leaves directly but invades through stomata if the leaves are already diseased (Gaumann, 1950). *Phytophthora infestans* is versatile in this respect, germ tubes from zoospores entering through cuticle and stomata and also through wounds and lenticels in potato tubers. Indeed, a fungus which attacks several parts of the plant may be expected to develop several different methods of penetration, each appropriate to the organ or tissue invaded. The germ tubes of some fungi produce appressoria over stomata or on intact cuticle whereas the appressoria of others appear to be confined to stomata (Flentje, 1959). More information on these aspects is clearly needed.

Hydathodes

Some bacteria, including *Erwinia amylovora* and *Xanthomonas campestris* can enter plants through hydathodes, but there are rather few reports of fungi doing so. This is surprising since hydathodes are more or less permanently open and secrete droplets containing organic and inorganic substances, including sugars and nitrogenous compounds capable of being utilized by fungi. The vascular connexions of the hydathode would seem to offer ingress to vascular pathogens. Baker *et al.* (1954) have reported that *Botrytis cinerea* colonizes necrotic tissue around the hydathodes of *Matthiola incana*, this necrosis perhaps resulting from high salts concentration due to evaporation of the hydathode exudate. Perhaps the latter contains substances which inhibit or repel fungal germ tubes. The spots caused by *Alternaria brassicicola* often develop at the margin of brassica leaves, and Ruscoe (1967) found that the germination of conidia was 22% in exudate collected from hydathodes on cauliflower leaves as compared with 60% in deionized water. The germ tubes were shorter in exudate, suggesting that the latter contains some inhibitory principle. Lesions developed when conidia were placed along the margin of cauliflower leaves but it was not ascertained whether infection actually occurred through the hydathodes.

The development of lesions at the leaf margin could be due to factors other than hydathode infection. Rain water, for example, might wash conidia to the leaf margin where they would collect, or the margin might be a more efficient trapper of conidia than are the other parts of the leaf. Hydathodes occur at the margin and tip of leaves and are few in number compared with stomata, so that the chances of spores falling on or within effective striking distance of hydathodes are correspondingly smaller – unless, that is, there are factors which favour the deposition of spores at or near hydathodes. It may be that infection through hydathodes is more widespread than is at present appreciated, a possibility which merits further investigation.

Lenticels

Lenticels are normally filled with loosely aggregated cells which allow entry of air and which would seem to offer very little resistance to fungal entry. Lenticular and wound penetration are somewhat similar, cork being involved in both, and many lenticel invaders can also enter through wounds, particularly soil borne pathogens such as *Streptomyces scabies*, *Armillaria mellea*, *Spongospora subterranea*, *Phymatotrichum omnivorum* and *Pectobacterium carotovorum*. The germ tubes or hyphae of invading fungi grow between the cells of the lenticel without, apparently, entering them or deriving nutrients from them, although there seems no reason why this should not occur in young lenticels before their cells become suberized. More infection generally occurs through young than old lenticels (as in infection of American bladder nut, *Staphylea*, by *Hypomyces ipomoeae*: Davis, 1935), and resistance of potato tubers to *Streptomyces scabies* (common scab) may be associated with rapid suberization of the lenticels, but this is discounted by some investigators. The shape, size and number of the lenticel cells may be important, those of scab resistant varieties being small and compact as compared with the irregular, loosely arranged cells of susceptible varieties (Darling, 1937, but others disagree). When the pathogen has grown through the lenticel the way to the inner tissues of the plant is clear during the growing season when the lenticels are open, but not in winter when they are usually closed by a basal layer of suberized cells formed by the phellogen, and no doubt this layer is an effective barrier.

The invasion of lenticels by *S. scabies* seems to stimulate division of the phellogen and formation of a layer of closely packed cells, presumably incipient cork cells which do not usually become suberized and so are probably not an effective barrier to the pathogen. The latter may in some way delay suberization although an effective cork barrier eventually forms and seals off the pathogen. The nature and extent of the scab thus depends partly on the rapidity with which an effective barrier develops. Little is known about the ways in which lenticel tissue and fungi interact, but the situation may be more complex than in stomatal penetration. Lenticels vary considerably in size and morphology and a number of germ tubes or hyphae may enter one lenticel. The hyphae of root invaders such as *Phymatotrichum omnivorum* grow between the loose cells of the lenticel and may then mass together to form wefts or tufts which force their way through the underlying tissue into the inner tissues, some kind of mass action perhaps occurring in such cases.

Fruits may also be invaded through lenticels, as in blue mould of apples caused by *Penicillium expansum* and brown rot of stone fruits (*Sclerotinia fructicola*). *Nectria galligena* (apple canker) can apparently enter twigs through lenticels. As previously mentioned, however, almost all these lenticel invaders have other and sometimes more important pathways into plants – through wounds, lesions caused by other fungi, and leaf scars.

Other points of entry for pathogens include leaf scars (*N. galligena*), the exit points of lateral roots (*Thielaviopsis basicola*, black root rot of tobacco; Conant, 1927), wounded oil vesicles of citrus fruits (*Penicillium digitatum*, green mould), nectaries and stigmata.

Direct penetration

Although direct penetration of the apparently intact surface of the plant has been known for many years (DeBary, 1886) its precise mechanism is

still not understood, despite much investigation. The physico-chemical
characteristics of cuticle and cell wall are important factors in this, and
further study of these aspects should increase our understanding of the
problem. These cannot be discussed in detail here and reference can be
made to the accounts by Northcote (1958), Martin (1964), and books on
plant anatomy.

Structure of cell walls and cuticle

According to Dickinson (1960) the external layer lining the intercellular
spaces and between adjacent cells (the middle lamella) consists largely
of pectic substances (p. 219), particularly calcium and magnesium
pectates, and can be disintegrated by pathogens which produce pectolytic
enzymes, notably soft rot fungi and bacteria. This is probably an over-
simplified view of its structure and other substances, including proteins,
have been reported to occur in the middle lamella. Within this layer is
the primary cell wall consisting largely of cellulose embedded in a matrix
of pectic substances and hemicelluloses, this matrix being continuous with
the middle lamella. The relative proportions of pectic substances and
hemicelluloses in the matrix are variable, but there is some evidence that
the latter often predominate. The cellulose may be present as micellae
as described on p. 225. Other substances including protein, lignin, suberin
and cutin have been reported in the primary cell wall and its structure
and composition are clearly complex.

The primary cell wall may be thick or thin, depending on the nature
of the tissue and other factors, and its composition varies in different
species of plants, in different tissues, and at different stages of maturity.
The relative amounts of the various components of the wall have an
important bearing on its strength, elasticity, permeability to water, and
resistance to penetration. In some tissues a secondary cell wall, consisting
chiefly of cellulose and perhaps small amounts of hemicelluloses and
lignins, is laid down within the primary wall. In lignified cells lignin
(p. 228) is deposited in the matrix surrounding the cellulose microfibrils,
possibly in some sort of chemical association with them, and it constitutes
almost all the central lamella of woody cells.

The cuticle is a non-cellular membrane which covers most of the aerial
parts of higher plants, and according to Wood (1960) chemically similar
layers occur on the free surfaces of mesophyll cells and on the inner walls
of the epidermis exposed to the air spaces of the leaf. It may be less than
a micrometre in thickness although considerably thicker in some plants,
especially xerophytes, and is generally thinner and less uniformly developed in young than in older tissue. The outer waxy layer is hydrophobic
and largely impermeable to water but the inner layers can absorb

moisture, swell and force the wax aggregates apart. The innermost layer of the cuticle passes gradually into a predominantly pectic layer which in turn merges into the largely cellulose outer wall of the epidermal cell. The distinction between cuticle and cell wall is often difficult to establish except in well defined cuticles, some of which can be separated off by chemical methods. The chemical composition of cuticle is outlined on p. 217.

Factors influencing formation of appressoria

Direct penetration of epidermal cells by fungi has been described by Dickinson (1960), Gaumann (1950), Butler and Jones (1949), and others. Fungal germ tubes or hyphae grow to a variable extent over the surface of the plant, this depending on the species of fungus and plant and also, probably, on the angle between the hypha and the plant surface. With a low angle of approach considerable surface growth may occur and hyphae may even grow away from the surface (Leach, 1923), whereas with a high angle penetration rather than surface growth is likely to occur. Of interest in this connexion is the report by Stakman (1915) that uredospore germ tubes of *Puccinia graminis* tended to form incipient appressoria in the depressions between epidermal cells where the angle of approach would be higher, and this is true of many fungi which penetrate the cuticle.

Forward growth of the hypha or germ tube eventually stops and appressoria are formed as described above (p. 152). This can be a thigmotropic response, as suggested by formation of appressoria by germ tubes on such artificial membranes as gold leaf, paraffin wax and collodion, and also on impenetrable surfaces such as glass. Thigmotropism may not be the whole story, and rather little is known about the physiological changes in the germ tube which bring about or accompany formation of appressoria. Other factors which stimulate or inhibit the latter process have been described. Thus appressoria of *Puccinia triticina* and *P. striiformis* were formed on artificial membranes only when leaf material of a susceptible wheat plant was incorporated (Dickinson, 1949) and volatile substances inducing appressoria were produced by uredospores of *P. graminis* (Allen, 1956).

The germ tubes of aeciospores of *Puccinia menthae* (mint rust) produced infection structures resembling appressoria when exposed to thymol at its own saturated vapour pressure on glass but not on glass in the absence of thymol. Thymol also reduced spore germination and elongation of germ tubes, possibly acting as a morphogenetic switch in bringing about the formation of appressoria (Cox, 1969). It is uncertain whether the leaf susceptibility of various labiate plants to *P. menthae*, or to the different races of the rust, depends on the presence in their essential oils of thymol or similar substances able to induce the formation of appressoria or inhibit spore germination.

Studies on different strains of *Corticium soiani* on roots, stems and leaves of several plants by Flentje and coworkers in Australia (Flentje, 1957; Kerr and Flentje, 1957) indicated that appressoria developed on susceptible but not on resistant plants. In the latter the hyphae of the fungus grew irregularly over the surface without adhering to it, or they adhered and followed the junction lines between epidermal cells. Further experiments suggested that formation of appressoria is probably affected by the nature of the surface over which the hypha is growing, and also by diffusible substances which cause arrested growth and multiple branching of side branches leading to development of appressoria.

Similar results have been obtained with radish stems attacked by *C. solani* (Flentje, Dodman and Kerr, 1963), and with strains of *Helminthosporium sorokinianum* (Van Velsen, 1957) and *Cochliobolus victoriae* (Paddock, 1953) on cereals. The germ tubes of the last two fungi grew haphazardly on the plant surface and failed to produce appressoria, produced occasional abortive ones, or functional ones, depending on the combination of pathogen race and cereal variety.

Inhibition or disruption of uredospore germ tubes and appressoria – apparently by diffusates from resistant or non-host plants – has been described by Leath and Rowell (1966) and Shipton (1966) in *Puccinia graminis tritici*, by Hilu (1965: *P. sorghi*), by Zimmer (1965: *P. carthami*), and by other workers. Localized collapse or other reaction of the plant cells around the infecting structure may occur, perhaps due to diffusible exudates from the fungus, since aqueous extracts of germinating uredospores may have similar effects (Shipton, 1966). Inhibition of the fungus is presumably due to fungitoxic diffusates from the resistant plant, possibly produced as a response to attempted invasion, and phytoalexins (p. 266) are perhaps involved.

Flentje (1959) suggests that the susceptibility of young seedlings to *Corticium solani* may be associated with incomplete cuticular development, which allows diffusible stimulants to leak out and bring about formation of appressoria. The thicker cuticle of older seedlings confines the stimulant, and appressoria thus fail to form, but they can be made susceptible by puncturing the cuticle or by partially removing it with a liquid solvent. This may be one of the factors involved in the susceptibility of young as compared with older tissue in some diseases.

Little is known about these host secretions affecting formation of appressoria, but they are perhaps analogous to the substances (hormones) involved in the initiation, development and ultimate fusion of antheridia and oogonia in *Achlya* and other fungi (Raper, 1940; Hawker, 1957), in which the ultimate formation of antheridia depends on the antheridial initials making contact with a solid substrate which may be oogonia or artificial membranes. There is increasing evidence that both chemical and contact stimuli govern the formation of appressoria and that the process is more complex than is often assumed. Although appressoria are best known in leaves and stems they may also develop during invasion of roots by some fungi, despite the absence of cuticle. Substances produced by other microorganisms on the plant surface might also influence appressorial formation but little is known about this possibility.

All plant surfaces probably secrete substances which affect to varying extents the microorganisms growing on them, and some examples of stimulation of germination, growth of germ tubes and formation of appressoria have been given. Inhibition of these processes has also been described (see above), but is probably less frequent than stimulation, as some fungi can and do penetrate to a limited extent plants which they are unable to parasitize. For example, Webb (1949) reported that zoospores of *Plasmodiophora brassicae* enter the root hairs of many non-host plants.

Penetration of the cuticle

In direct penetration of a leaf the infection hypha (peg, thread) which arises from the underside of the appressorium, as described below, has to pass through the cuticle and the underlying tissue and sometimes thickened outer wall of the epidermal cell, although it sometimes presses between the epidermal cells. The process has been studied in many fungi including *Clasterosporium carpophilum* on almond (Samuel, 1927, figure 10·2) *Venturia inaequalis* and *V. pirina* on pear (Wiltshire, 1915; Nusbaum and Keitt, 1938), *Botrytis cinerea* on broad bean (Blackman and Welsford, 1916), *Phytophthora infestans* on potato (Pristou and Gallegly, 1954), *Puccinia graminis* on barberry, *P. psidii* on pimento and *Ravenelia humphreyana* on *Caesalpinia* (Hunt, 1968). Although penetration without appressoria has been described, Dickinson (1960) considers that this could happen only with a really soft plant surface or, possibly, with a germ tube penetrating a thin cuticle at a high angle of approach. Where considerable force is required for penetration some degree of adhesion between the germ tube apex and the plant surface would seem to be necessary and this may be achieved by the appressorium. Similarly, it is thought that nematode larvae must have some kind of anchoring or adhesion mechanism for penetration to occur (Linford, 1942).

The infection hypha which arises from the underside of the appressorium is extremely fine, in some cases near the limit of resolution with ordinary light. It presumably originates as a growing point in the otherwise non-extendable appressorial wall, grows towards the plant surface and penetrates the cuticle and outer layer of the epidermal cell as a

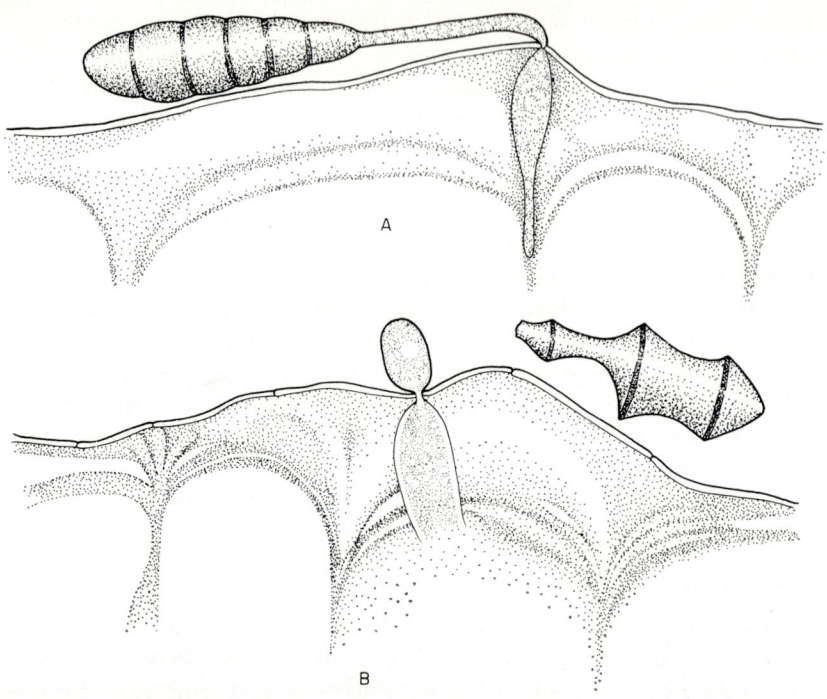

Figure 10.2   Direct penetration of the cuticle. Penetration of almond leaves by germ tubes of *Clasterosporium carpophilum*. A, the penetration hypha passing between epidermal cells. B, passing into the epidermal cell ($\times$ 950 and 800 respectively).

narrow thread which may or may not increase in diameter during its journey. Indentation of the cuticle at the point of penetration may occur. The infection hypha varies considerably; for example, in some Ustilaginales it swells before penetration, in *Botrytis cinerea* it resembles an inverted funnel (Blackman and Welsford, 1916), and irregular variations in its diameter have been described by Wiltshire (1915). Dickinson (1960), who describes the process of penetration in detail, suggests that these variations are related to the ratio of pectin to cellulose in the cell wall, to the enzymic abilities of the fungus, and to the force which the latter exerts.

Much has been written on the ways in which infection hyphae penetrate the cuticle, particularly as to whether penetration is a purely physical process or whether cuticle softening enzymes are involved; this is discussed on p. 218. It may be that slight localized softening of the cuticle occurs around the infection hypha, thus facilitating penetration.

In the presumed absence of cuticle softening enzymes it is probable that penetration is largely by physical force, and there is considerable evidence to support this. The very fine, pointed infection hypha kept rigid by high osmotic pressure (up to about 7 atmospheres, possibly higher in some cases) and fixed firmly to the plant surface would seem to be a very effective instrument for this purpose. Growth of the infection hypha by intussusception (interpolation of new macromolecules into the existing wall) perhaps exerts force in the early stages of penetration, namely the indentation of the cuticle, whereas force exerted in later stages may be due to elongation (Dickinson, 1960).

That infection structures of fungi can exert considerable force is shown by their ability to penetrate artificial membranes of paraffin wax, collodion and gold leaf, as shown by Miyoshi (1895) with *Botrytis cinerea*, and by

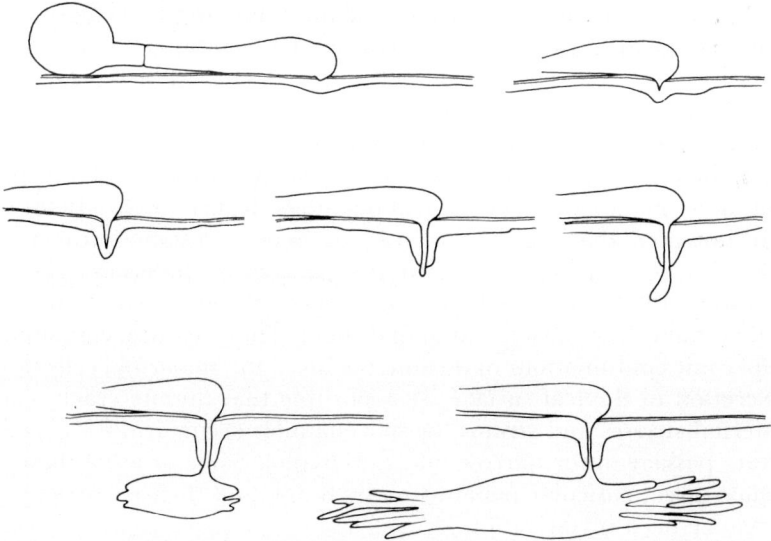

Figure 10.3 Germination of conidia of *Erysiphe graminis* on the epidermis of wheat. A fine stylar process from the germ tube (or from a small subapical appressorium) pierces the cuticle, and in its passage through the cellulose layer it is preceded by a local thickening of the layer into a papilla which it eventually pierces at the apex; inside the host cell it becomes dilated into a lobed, branched haustorium, and in doing so invaginates the lining layer of cytoplasm (× 1000).

subsequent workers. There was no penetration if the membrane exceeded a certain hardness or thickness, and similar considerations perhaps apply to plant cuticles: thus young leaves are generally more readily attacked by many pathogens than are older leaves with thicker, tougher cuticles. Hawkins and Harvey (1919) found that greater force was needed to penetrate the tissues of potato tubers resistant to *Pythium debaryanum* than those of susceptible varieties.

Resistance of *Berberis* leaves to basidiospores of *Puccinia graminis* was partly associated with their resistance to puncture by a round-pointed needle about 25 μm in diameter (Melander and Craigie, 1927). This resistance to puncture refers of course to cuticle plus outer epidermal wall, and other factors including the size, shape, wall thickness and probably turgor of the epidermal cells are also involved. A similar case obtains for resistance of tomato fruits of different ages to *Alternaria tomato* (Butler and Jones, 1949), and cuticle thickness has been related to resistance to foot rot of peas caused by *Ascochyta pinodella* (Gilchrist, 1926). Older barley leaves with cuticles 2·5–5 μm thick, as compared with 0·4–1·5 μm in young leaves, were resistant to mildew (*Erysiphe graminis*) but became infected when the outer layers of cuticle were pared off (Butler and Jones, 1949). Etiolation, excess moisture, certain deficiencies and excesses of trace elements and other factors which result in soft or thin cuticle may predispose plants to infection. Conversely, low humidity and high temperature may induce a thick, tough cuticle resistant to some fungi. For example, coffee berries are less infected by *Colletotrichum coffeanum* at high temperatures (Nutman and Roberts, 1960).

At one time it was supposed that cuticle formed a more or less continuous, intact, impermeable layer over the aerial parts of the plant, except for stomata and other natural openings. Roberts *et al.* (1948) have shown, however, that channels containing pectic substances traverse the cuticle of apple leaves and permit the passage of materials. Hall and Donaldson (1962) described cuticular pores through which wax was extruded, but others have failed to find them. There are also ectodesmata, protoplasmic continuations in the outer walls of the epidermal cells serving for excretion to the leaf surface. It is possible that minute cracks caused by internal stresses and strains, or soft channels occur in the cuticle and facilitate passage of the narrow infection hypha. Some or all of these may influence direct cuticular penetration by fungi, and their occurrence and significance need investigation.

Penetration of the cell wall

Having passed through the cuticle the infection hypha has to grow through the underlying outer wall of the epidermal cell, which consists basically of a network of cellulose microfibrils in a matrix consisting principally of pectic materials with small amounts of arabans, galactans, xylans, and other substances. The infection hyphae of some fungi pass between the radial walls of epidermal walls without actually entering them whilst in others, for example *Diplocarpon rosae*, the mycelium develops between cuticle and epidermis and enters the cells of the latter.

In contrast to cuticular penetration it appears that penetration by the fungus of cellulose and pectin – using these terms in a wide sense – is largely enzymic, the infection hyphae growing quickly through the softened materials. Pectolytic enzymes are important in this but there is doubt as to the part played by cellulases, some investigators considering them to be relatively unimportant. However, many plant pathogens can produce cellulases, and it may be that the pectic components in the cell wall are quickly degraded, thus allowing rapid progress of the invading hypha, whereas cellulose breakdown is a much slower process and proceeds for some time after invasion.

Penetration of the cell wall may occur within minutes and is probably a combination of physical pressure and enzymic softening. Swelling of the invaded cell wall and of walls some distance away may occur, presumably due to diffusion of enzymes. Such swellings vary considerably in extent, ranging from sharply localized (*Ustilago tritici* on wheat: Batts, 1955) to pronounced thickening which almost obliterates the lumen of the cell, as in *Venturia inaequalis* attacking epidermal cells of the stem (Marsh and Walker, 1932). Swelling is probably due to pectolytic enzymes

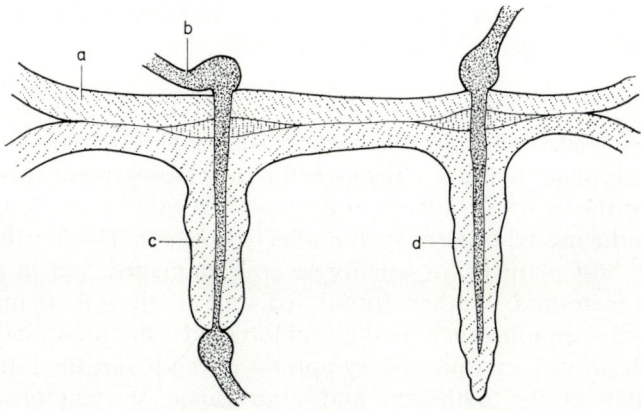

Figure 10.4 Lignituber formations in the roots of a wheat seedling after invection by *Ophiobolus graminis* (take-all and whiteheads). a, cell wall; b, invading hypha; c, lignituber perforated by a hypha; d, lignituber in which a hypha is intercepted. × 4,000.

secreted by the invading hypha, and the latter becomes sheathed by wall substances to form a composite structure or lignituber. The latter projects to a varying extent into the lumen of the cell and sometimes seals off the hypha, thus acting as an effective barrier to further penetration. In other cases the hypha grows through the investing wall material and enters the interior of the cell. Lignituber formation could thus be regarded as a defensive reaction of the cell (figure 10.4). The precise origin of the swelling is obscure. It sometimes appears to result from deposition of new wall material (Moss, 1926), whilst in other cases it may be due to swelling of pectic or cellulose wall constituents as a result of enzyme action. Dickinson (1960) has suggested that the innermost cellulose layer of the wall is not penetrated unless the hypha secretes effective cellulases and even then penetration may be a slow process; since this layer is elastic it is pushed into the cell as a sheath investing the hypha. Lignitubers are described by Fellows

(1928), Young (1926), Smith (1938), Batts (1955) and others. Gummy material formed by enzymes of *Stereum purpureum* degrading the vascular elements of the host may be a similar phenomenon (Brooks and Brenchley, 1931). Enzymic breakdown of the cell wall no doubt releases sugars and other nutrients which the invading hyphae use.

Indirect infection

Some pathogens enter and grow through organs and tissues in which they incite only slight disease symptoms or none at all, and in this way reach the parts of the plant which they normally attack. The latter then develop symptoms and the pathogen generally produces its spores. The intervening tissues through which the fungus grows may be parasitized and provide nutrients although they often appear to function as passive pathways: seedlings, root hairs, buds, leaves and flowers provide examples of this 'indirect infection' (Gaumann, 1950).

Seedlings

In many seed borne and soil borne Ustilaginales the young seedling is invaded. Hyphae then grow through the developing plant tissues, finally destroying the ovaries, stamens and sometimes other parts of the mature plant, producing teliospores in the affected organs. During the systemic phase the host plant is not usually severely damaged, but in some smut diseases it is stunted, in others stimulated, and in others there may be mild generalized symptoms such as slight chlorosis. In the final phase the host tissue is destroyed, conspicuous symptoms develop and the fungus sporulates. Entry of the pathogen and appearance of symptoms are thus separated in time (several months in some cases) and space, symptoms appearing on organs remote from the original entry point of the pathogen. If the infected plant grows rapidly it may outstrip the fungus and produce normal unsmutted seeds, but the second crop of heads produced after cutting back may be smutted, the fungus having meantime caught up. Some smuts may enter the young meristematic tissue of host plants and subsequently produce symptoms and spores in the flowers. Hyphae may perennate within infected plants, making their way each season to the flowers. It is possible that similar considerations hold for some species of Peronosporaceae which sporulate on the flowers of the host plant after the latter has been infected in the seedling stage from soil borne oospores, for example *Peronospora corollae* on *Campanula* and *Linaria* (Gaumann, 1923).

Root hairs

Among the pathogens which enter roots through root hairs are *Plasmodiophora brassicae*, *Phymatotrichum omnivorum* (Texas root rot of numerous plants), *Fusarium oxysporum f.sp. lini* (flax wilt), *F. oxysporum f.sp. conglutinans* (cabbage yellows) and probably other fungi. The delicate thin walled root hairs and the parent epidermal cells would seem to offer little resistance to invading fungi but rhizosphere effects probably exert a protective action. Many pathogens which enter through root hairs can also do so through epidermal cells and wounds. The root nodule bacteria (*Rhizobium*) of Leguminosae also enter through root hairs in the form of infection threads.

Buds

Some rust fungi, including *Uromyces pisi*, enter through unfolding buds and grow into the developing shoots which become diseased. *Taphrina cerasi* attacks cherry buds and causes them to develop into typical witch's brooms: in this case the fungus enters and attacks the buds (Gaumann, 1950).

Leaves

Basidiospores of some rusts which attack trees, including *Cronartium ribicola* (blister rust of five-needled pines; currant rust), enter the leaves and grow down into the branches and trunk where aecia are eventually produced, in some cases 2–3 years later. As in some smut diseases, infection and disease are separated in place and time.

Flowers

Several pathogens enter the stigmata and, less often, the nectaries of flowers, thence attacking the ovaries and growing down through the peduncle into the stems, for example *Sclerotinia laxa*, the cause of brown rot, blossom wilt, spur blight and wither tip of stone fruits. Conidia germinate on the stigma and the germ tubes grow down through the style into the ovary, as do pollen tubes. The fungus can also enter through wounds (cracks, frost damage) and lenticels of the fruit. Entry through nectaries is exemplified by *Erwinia amylovora* (fire blight of pear and apple) in which the bacteria are brought to the nectaries by bees and subsequently invade the ovaries and branches; entry through wounds can also occur.

These cases are to be distinguished from those in which symptoms develop in pathogen-free organs some distance from the infected tissue. In silver leaf disease of plums caused by *Stereum purpureum* the typical silvering originates from separation of the upper epidermis from the mesophyll cells with attendant accumulation of air beneath the epidermis. This separation appears to be due to substances, possibly pectolytic enzymes, produced by the fungus in the branches and carried to the leaves in the transpiration stream. In vascular wilt diseases the leaves may show wilting and browning although the causal organism is some distance away in the roots and sometimes in the stem. These symptoms are of complex origin but may be due partly to a reduced water supply to the leaves, and partly to toxins.

Other means of infection

In this account the emphasis has been largely on the entry on fungal germ tubes, or structures derived from them, into plants. There are, however, other agents of entry, some of which are discussed below.

Zoospores

Fungal zoospores are generally amoeboid and without a definite cell wall. The flagella disappear when the zoospore comes to rest on the plant surface, and the encysted zoospore may produce a germ tube which enters directly or through a stoma. Curtis (1921) has described the process in *Synchytrium endobioticum* (potato wart), the cytoplasm and nucleus of the zoospore passing through a very fine penetration tube into the interior of the host cell and rounding up again when inside. The mechanisms of entry are probably similar to those of infection hyphae produced by non-motile spores and formation of appressoria has been described. Zoospores of *Plasmodiophora brassicae* enter root hairs directly, those of *Albugo candida*, *Pseudoperonospora cubensis* and *Plasmopara viticola* normally enter through stomata, and those of *Phytophthora infestans, Bremia lactucae* and others may penetrate in either way.

Hyphae, mycelial strands and rhizomorphs

Hyphae can often enter plant tissue as readily as germ tubes can. Penetration may be by individual hyphae or by hyphae aggregated together to form mycelial strands and rhizomorphs of varying size and complexity. Some soil borne fungi, including *Armillaria mellea*, a root parasite of numerous plants, may normally spread and infect by rhizomorphs. The actively growing tip of the rhizomorph penetrates the root and spreads between bark and wood, sometimes entering the pith. It can penetrate the piliferous layer of young roots or the periderm of older ones, the rhizomorph tip becoming firmly attached to the root by a sticky mucilage which quickly hardens. The subterminal part of the rhizomorph lies in contact with the root and sends out short lateral branches which in turn adhere to and may penetrate the root. Multiple penetration thus occurs and the rhizomorph may continue to grow and repeat the process. Penetration is thought to be largely by mechanical pressure although chemical action has also been suggested, and the rhizomorph is reported by Lamphere (1934) to be rich in enzymes. No doubt the fungus also enters through wounds and at the exit points of lateral roots. In other fungi, including *Ophiobolus graminis* (take-all of cereals), superficial hyphae enter the root. The entry of viruses, bacteria, and parasitic angiosperms into plants is discussed in the chapters on these pathogens.

11 The colonization of the infected plant

When a pathogen has successfully established itself in host tissue its subsequent spread is influenced by many factors including its aggressiveness, susceptibility of the tissue, and environmental conditions. For example, the lesions caused by a pathogen may be smaller, develop more slowly and produce fewer spores in a resistant than a susceptible plant. Some viruses become systemic in certain species of hosts but remain localized in others, and temperature may affect this. The spread of some leaf pathogens is limited by veinlets, resulting in typically angular lesions, or by anatomical or chemical barriers developed by the host as a response to infection (defensive reactions).

Parasites can be grouped in various ways on the basis of their post-penetration development. They may be strictly localized thus causing the small necrotic lesions of many leaf spot diseases, they may cause more extensive blotches or a generalized necrosis of much of the shoots or roots, or they may become systemic to varying extents within the plant. The parasite may be confined to one organ or tissue although its effects may be apparent in uninvaded tissue some distance away. It may produce enzymes and/or toxins which have an immediate harmful effect on the plant tissue, often in advance of the actual parasite, or it may have little apparent effect and may indeed stimulate growth by interfering with growth regulation in the plant as discussed in Chapter 13 (p. 241).

Successful penetration of the cell wall does not necessarily mean that the parasite is able to establish itself within the tissue. If the latter is resistant the invading hyphae may fail to develop further, or they may produce apparently non-functional haustoria. There may be a hypersensitivity reaction, the plant cells in the immediate vicinity of the invading hyphae dying rapidly and sometimes preventing further progress of the latter. The subsequent colonization of plant tissue by pathogens is described in the present chapter, and the physiological, anatomical, morphological and cytological changes which accompany infection are considered in the following chapter. There is much variety in the method and extent of colonization of the infected plant but for our purposes the following patterns of postpenetration development can be considered:

Ectoparasitic development

The mycelium lies largely on the surface of the infected tissue with haustoria entering the epidermal cells, more of which are penetrated as the fungus grows. Typical circular colonies thus develop in the early stages although this pattern may subsequently be lost as the infected

(a)

Figure 11.1   Three destructive powdery mildews: (a) *Podosphaera leucotricha* on apple leaves; (b) close-up of *Podosphaera leucotricha*; (c) *Sphaerotheca pannosa* on a young rose shoot; (d) *Erysiphe graminis f.sp. hordei* on a barley leaf; cleistothecia can be seen as dark specks among the white ectoparasitic growth of the fungus.

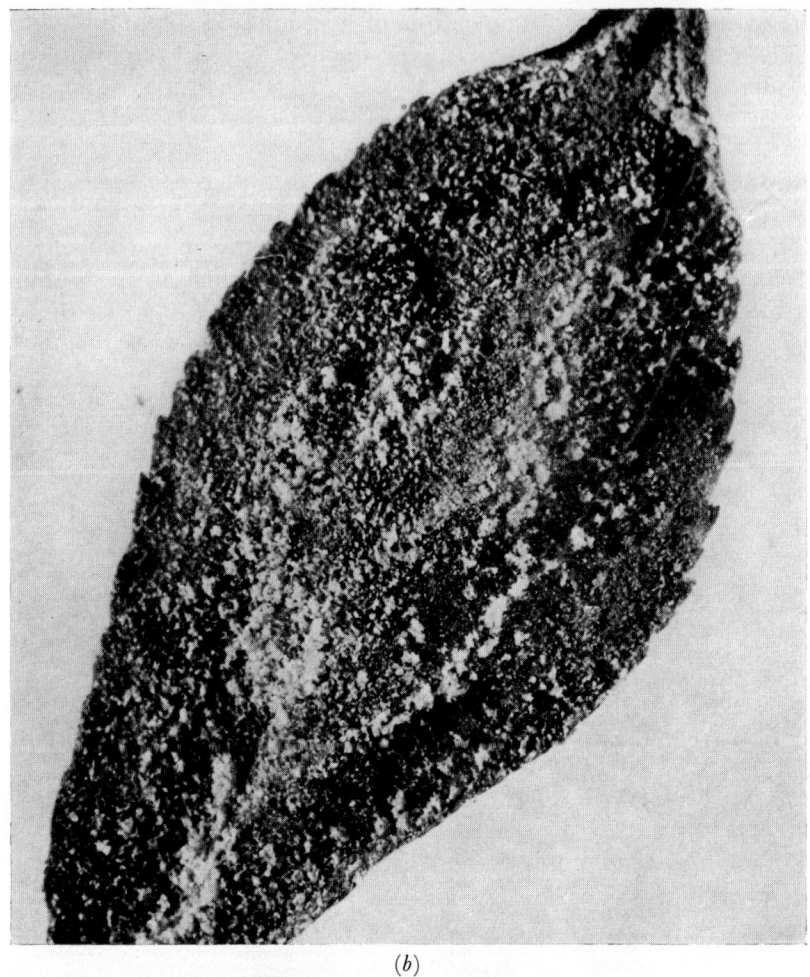

(b)

organ becomes more or less completely covered. Reproductive structures, whether asexual or sexual, develop on the superficial mycelium.

These parasitic epiphytes are to be distinguished from saprophytic epiphytes, the latter including microorganisms which normally live on exudates and debris on plant surfaces – the aerosphere and rhizosphere inhabitants – or in honeydew resulting from insect infestation. Such saprophytic 'sooty moulds' on the aerial parts of plants include species of *Cladosporium, Alternaria, Aureobasidium* and others, and often superficially resemble parasitic 'dark mildews' (Meliolaceae). In the latter family the dark mycelium grows over the leaf surface, sometimes in radiating strands, and is attached by short side branches (hyphopodia) while nutrients are absorbed by other branches (stomatopodia) which pass through the stomata

(c)

and develop haustoria in the mesophyll cells. A similar situation is seen in
some members of the Hemisphaeriales (Microthyriales) such as *Asterina*,
and in the Erysiphaceae, although in the latter only the epidermal cells
are usually entered (figure 11.1). In *Leveillula* and *Phyllactinia*, however,
hyphae pass through the stomata and form haustoria in the mesophyll cells.

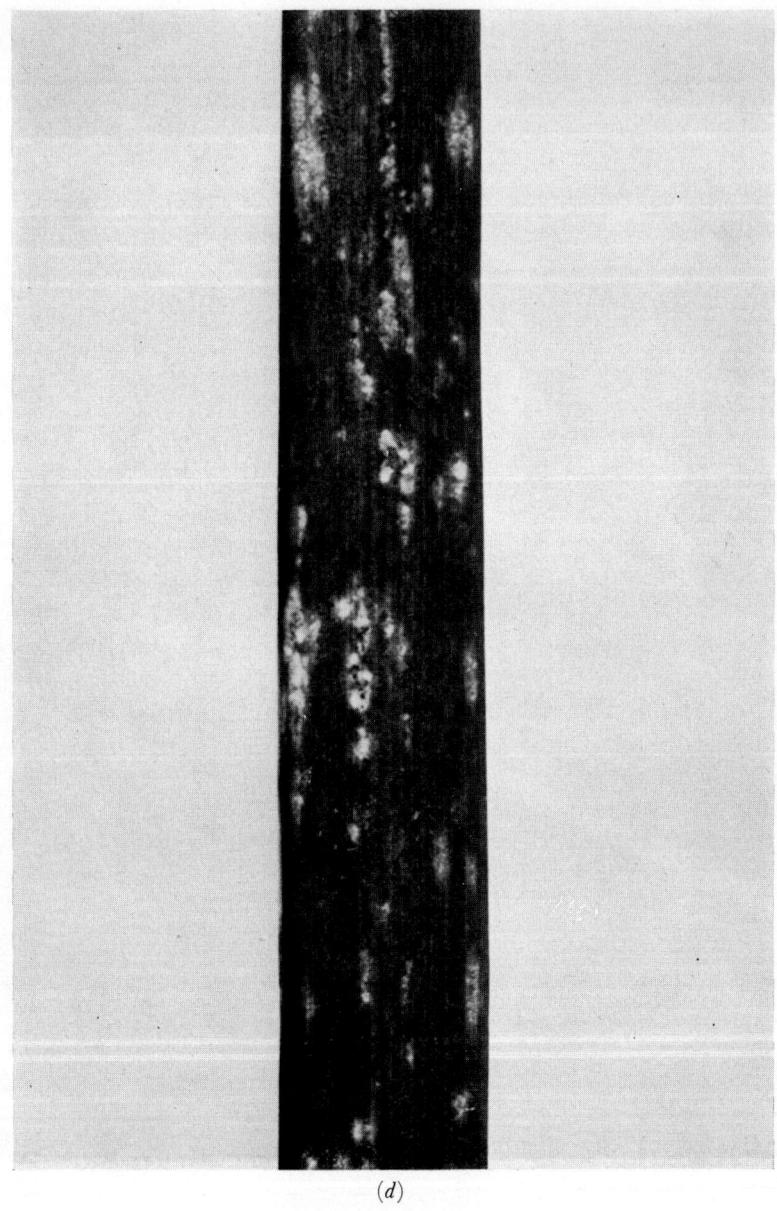

(d)

The pathogens in this group are mostly obligate parasites. Being largely superficial the mycelium is exposed to desiccation, radiation and other hazards, and many mycelia are dark, possibly a protective feature. As noted above (p. 145) the rather large amount of moisture in the conidia of

Erysiphaceae is not easily lost, and it would be interesting to know whether this also applies to the mycelium. If so this might be a means of avoiding desiccation of the superficial mycelium whose only internal source of water is the parasitized epidermal cells of the host. The fungus would then be comparable to a succulent. Since the propagules are formed superficially there would seem to be few problems in their liberation and dissemination.

Endoparasitic development with external mycelium

Some parasitic fungi colonize the interior of the plant and also produce an external aerial mycelium which grows superficially and repeatedly enters the plant, for example *Corticium solani* (stem canker of potato). The runner hyphae of *Ophiobolus graminis* (take-all of cereals) grow along the roots to the base of the culm which they enter, and *Fomes annosus* grows freely along the outside of pine roots, especially in alkaline soil (Rishbeth, 1950, 1951). Rhizomorphs may also grow along roots either superficially or between bark and wood. The production of external mycelium which grows over the host surface enables invasion to occur at several different points and no doubt leads to rapid colonization and is more likely to over-come or evade active host resistance than a single attempted penetration (Garrett, 1956). The external mycelium may also produce propagules but is to be distinguished from such well defined fruiting bodies of limited growth as ascocarps and basidiocarps which, although on the host surface, do not normally grow over it or reinvade it. In some cases, for example, *Corticium solani*, the external mycelium constitutes a loose crust which produces basidiospores and thus functions as a basidiocarp, but this is not generally the case.

Subcuticular development

The hyphae of *Diplocarpon rosae* (black spot of rose) grow mostly between the cuticle and the outer wall of the epidermal cells, forming a circular fibrillose colony with a fringed margin (figure 11.2). They also pass through the middle lamella of the epidermal cells and form a chiefly intracellular mycelium which feeds by means of club-shaped haustoria in the epidermal cells and probably in mesophyll cells in severe infections. The parasitized cells seem to be little affected but eventually chlorose and die. Subcuticular acervuli develop, rupture the cuticle and liberate conidia, and the sparse apothecia develop in dead leaf tissue. *Venturia inaequalis* (apple scab) appears to be similar and according to Gaumann (1950) both fungi colo-

Figure 11.2   Blackspot of rose caused by *Diplocarpon rosae*. Note radiating strands of subcuticular mycelium.

nize the mesophyll only after death of the leaf, but there is some doubt about this and it is likely that these subcuticular pathogens can sometimes colonize the internal tissues of the living leaf. Although not obligate parasites they are highly specialized in that they produce haustoria, have little immediate killing effect on parasitized cells, and grow only slowly in culture. The hyphae are partially protected by the overlying cuticle which has to be ruptured before the spores can be dispersed.

Development in parenchymatous tissue

Many pathogens colonize the parenchyma of mesophyll and cortex, further spread into the vascular cylinder being halted by the endodermis, although there may be entry into the pith. In a few cases, as in *Taphrina*, the hyphae are entirely intercellular, presumably obtaining nutrients through the membranes of the adjacent cells and this indirect method perhaps results in some degree of systemic development. The hyphae of less specialized fungi are often chiefly intracellular, progressing with branching from cell to cell until the tissue is more or less completely colonized. Toxins and enzymes may be secreted and bring about rapid softening and necrosis of tissue ahead of the pathogen, but other parasites seem to enter living cells which, however, may die soon after penetration. The relative amounts of intracellular and intercellular hyphae depend on

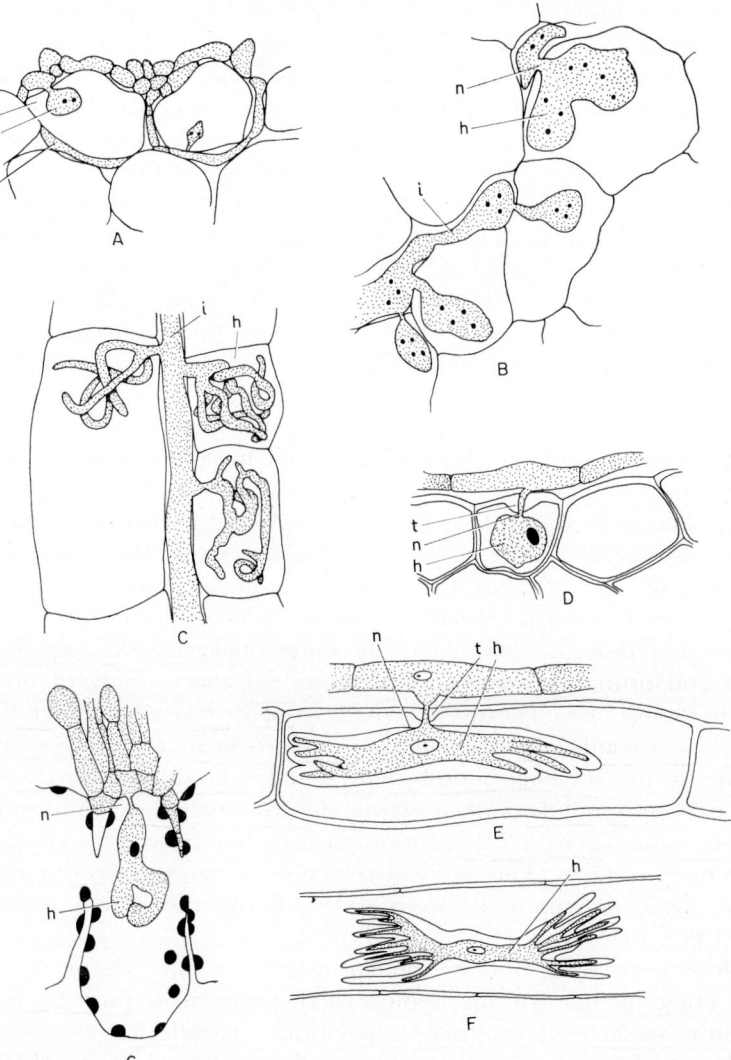

Figure 11.3 A, Simple binucleate haustoria (h) of *Coleosporium senecionis* in cell of groundsel in neighbourhood of a telium. Note intercellular hyphae (i) and narrow neck (n) of haustorium. B, Lobed, multinucleate haustoria (h) of *Peronospora parasitica* in cell of leaf of wallflower. Note intercellular hyphae and narrow neck of haustorium. C, Branched, filamentous haustoria of *Peronospora calotheca* in cells of stem of *Asperula odorata*, seen in longitudinal section (after De Bary). D, Superficial hypha of a powdery mildew, *Erysiphe polygoni*, which has penetrated and formed a simple haustorium in an epidermal cell of garden pea. Note thickening (t) of wall of host in response to attack. E, Longitudinal section of epidermal cell of oat with haustorium of *Erysiphe graminis*. Note elongated shape and fringed ends of haustorium which increase the absorbing area (after Smith). F, Similar haustorium seen in surface view. G, Forked haustorium of *Puccinia triticina* in mesophyll cell of leaf of Little Club wheat in neighbourhood of a uredium (after Allen). (× 300.)

the species of fungus, the nature of the host tissue, and other factors. Hyphae may grow in the intercellular spaces or in the middle lamella between adjacent cells. The hyphae of some fungal pathogens are at first intercellular but subsequently invade the host cells, whereas those of others, for example *Pythium debaryanum*, seem to grow freely within or between plant cells depending partly on the type and age of the tissue.

Some fungi have intercellular hyphae with haustoria which enter host cells and absorb nutrients from them. Such haustoria are often produced by intercellular or ectoparasitic fungal parasites, and especially by specialized biotrophs such as Peronosporaceae, Albuginaceae, Erysiphales and Uredinales, where they appear to cause only minimal damage to the parasitized cells. They are of varied size and shape, ranging from knob-like structures to simple, lobed, branched, coiled or coralloid hyphae, sometimes small and rather insignificant, sometimes quite extensive and almost filling the host cell (figure 11.3. Their morphology is not constant and may vary in different tissues or in different host plants. Haustoria may ramify extensively within the cell but they do not normally puncture the plasma membrane although they invaginate it. A layer of cell wall material ensheaths the haustorium at its point of entry and the whole organ is enveloped by a relatively dense layer or 'zone of apposition' (Peyton and Bowen, 1963) which becomes thicker in the region of the sheath and probably permits exchange of substances between host and parasite (figure 11.4). Haustoria provide intimate contact between the two organisms, a condition approaching symbiosis in that invaded cells may continue to live for long periods and, as noted above, haustoria seem to inflict only minimal damage. Systemic infection may develop in this way. In other cases, as with *Phytophthora infestans*, haustoria may kill the cell rather more quickly. The detailed structure of haustoria is discussed by Moore (1965), Peyton and Bowen (1963), Berlin and Bowen (1964) and Rice (1935, 1945).

Endoparasitic fungi liberate their propagules to the exterior in various ways. These include fruiting bodies which protrude or push up through the host surface at maturity (pycnidia, perithecia, sporodochia), pustules which break through the host epidermis (acervuli, sori of Uredinales and Albuginaceae), and conidiophores or sporangiophores which force their way out between epidermal cells or through stomata, as with conidiophores and synnemata of Hyphomycetes and sporangiophores of Peronosporaceae. The parasite may rapidly disintegrate the infected organ or tissue and so expose its propagules, as in many Ustilaginales, or the spores may be liberated by slow decay of the tissue. In many fungi the propagative spores are liberated above the surface of the infected tissue whereas the overwintering spores remain in the dead tissue, but there are exceptions to this, including the teliospores of many Uredinales. Bacteria

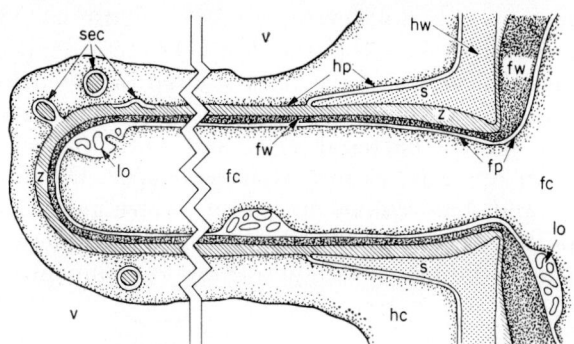

Figure 11.4 Diagram of host parasite interface in haustorial region. Fungal cytoplasm (fc) is bounded by the fungal plasma membrane (fp), lomasomes (lo), and the fungal cell wall (fw) in both the intercellular hypha (right) and the haustorium (centre). The relative positions of the host cell vacuole (v), host cytoplasm (hc) and host plasma membrane (hp) are indicated. The host cell wall (w) terminates in a sheath (s). The zone of apposition (z) separates the haustorium from the host plasma membrane. Invaginations of the host plasma membrane and vesicular host cytoplasm are considered evidence for host secretory activity (sec).

often exude from the diseased tissue or may be liberated from the latter, and the seeds of parasitic angiosperms are mostly borne on aerial shoots.

Development in vascular tissue

Vascular tissues are colonized principally by Hymenomycetes, sometimes by Ascomycetes, Fungi Imperfecti and bacteria, but more rarely by other microorganisms. In white rot the lignified heart wood is attacked by fungi secreting ligninases, while in brown rot the sap wood is chiefly attacked by those secreting cellulases. Pectolytic enzymes may also be involved and wood invading fungi spread by penetration of the cell walls and in some cases by enzymic dissolution of the middle lamella, and possibly through pits. The living cells (xylem parenchyma) may be attacked as well as the dead vessels, and the character of the rot will be related to these aspects; accounts are given by Butler and Jones (1949) and Cartwright and Findlay (1958).

Enzymic breakdown of cellulose seems to be a rather slow process, and that of lignin even slower, and wood rotting may thus progress only slowly, with the fungus producing its (usually) large fruiting bodies on the decaying wood. Some pathogens utilize the vascular tissues for transport or growth, sometimes discolouring or blocking them in so doing – for example vascular wilt fungi and bacteria in the vessels (p. 115), and some viruses in the phloem (p. 54). In these cases the contaminated conducting elements may not develop any specific disease symptoms and the pathogen eventually breaks out and attacks the ground tissues of the plant, which may meantime have been injured or killed by toxic substances secreted by the pathogen and carried upwards in the transpiration stream. Fungal spores, bacterial cells and virus particles may also be transported in this way, as in *Ceratostomella ulmi* (Dutch elm disease: Banfield, 1941) and *Agrobacterium tumefaciens* (crown gall). The latter can also be transported by tumour strands – proliferating infected host tissue which advances by sliding growth, according to Gaumann (1950).

Endobiotic development

Some pathogens, generally non-mycelial ones, are endobiotic in the sense that the thallus is entirely contained within a host cell and may be distributed to the daughter cells during cell division. Patches or sectors of infected cells are thus formed, and the propagules are released by decay of the tissue or by discharge of zoospores through an exit tube in *Olpidium*. In fungi this endobiotic condition is largely restricted to the non-mycelial Phycomycetes including Plasmodiophorales, but certain other pathogens, including some Ustilaginales, might also be distributed during cell division as suggested by Melchers (1933) for *Sphacelotheca sorghi*. Viruses are also endobiotic, as are some bacteria. Many of these endobiotic pathogens are obligate parasites and tend to stimulate rather than destroy their host cells, thus causing tissue proliferation.

Systemic development

Many pathogens are restricted to a rather sharply defined area of tissue which may range from a small lesion a few millimetres in diameter to large blotches of several centimetres. The factors influencing the size of infected areas are diverse and include not only environmental conditions and the aggressiveness of the pathogen but also chemical and morphological characteristics of the host plant. Thus lesions may be limited by veins and so assume an elongated form ('stripe') on grass leaves or an angular shape on some dicotyledonous leaves. Under favourable conditions or where numerous infections occur the individual lesions may coalesce to form large, irregular, necrotic areas, sometimes leading to a generalized infection of the organ or plant. These symptoms arise basically from numerous localized infections, as distinct from systemic infection in which the pathogen is present in much of the plant without, however, necessarily causing symptoms in all infected parts.

The extent of systemic infection varies with different pathogens. Some systemic viruses occur in most of the aerial parts of the plant although they are not present in all tissues. Vascular wilt pathogens occur in the xylem vessels of root and stem, and the hyphae of many Ustilaginales may be present in much of the meristematic tissue of the shoots. Some Uredinales spread through the ground tissues whilst others are localized; the mycelium producing aecia may be systemic, that producing uredospores localized. In perennial hosts the mycelium may perennate within the tissues, both host and pathogen dying back in the autumn and growing again in the spring. Some systemic pathogens, although present in and obtaining nutrients from, much of the host plant, produce their typical disease symptoms in a particular organ or tissue. In others, as in some systemic viruses, the symptoms may be generalized and affect many parts of the plant. There may, for example, be stunting and/or mosaic symptoms over much of the shoots, especially in cases of early infection.

Systemic pathogens are conventionally regarded as rather highly specialized parasites, often feeding by haustoria and causing slight tissue damage until completion of their life cycle. Included here are systemic representatives of the Uredinales, Peronosporaceae and Albuginaceae, all obligate parasites. There are exceptions, and not all systemic parasites are obligate, and *vice versa*. Although the smut fungi occur as parasites they are not obligate parasites in that they can be grown on culture media, nevertheless many are systemic. *Pyrenophora graminea* (barley leaf stripe) and *Taphrina deformans* (peach leaf curl) are sometimes quoted as examples of systemic non-obligate parasites but there is much doubt about this (Butler and Jones, 1949). The Erysiphales are non-systemic obligate parasites but their mycelium is largely superficial with haustoria entering the epidermal cells. Obligate parasitism is considered below (p. 186).

The speed with which a pathogen colonizes the host depends on its method of spread (for example, distribution by cell division is generally slower than by hyphal growth or conveyance in the transpiration stream), its aggressiveness, environmental conditions and the nature and susceptibility of the tissue. Invasion of lignified tissue, which is only slowly degraded by enzymes, is a slow process, whereas a pathogen secreting powerful toxins which diffuse well ahead of it can progress rapidly under favourable environmental conditions. Gaumann (1950) records as much as 18 mm daily for rhizomorphs of *Armillaria mellea*, 13 mm for *Stereum purpureum*, and about 0·5 mm daily for *Trametes pini*. Leaf lesions and fruit rots enlarge rapidly under favourable conditions, and some of the smaller leaf spots may attain normal size soon after their initial appearance.

Organ and tissue specificity

For successful colonization the pathogen must be able to enter the tissue and the latter must contain suitable available nutrients and not be or become toxic to the pathogen. Since different tissues, organs and plants differ in these respects they will also vary in their capacity to support the growth of parasites, and the latter will tend to colonize specific organs, tissues and hosts, but rather little is known about why pathogens are restricted in this way.

The reaction of a plant tissue to a pathogen may change as it matures, older tissue often, but not always, becoming less liable to attack (mature or adult plant resistance). There are many exceptions to this generalization, and Kuc (1966) points out that older tissues are principally attacked by pathogens which enter through natural openings or wounds, or which penetrate younger tissues and remain dormant until the tissue develops to the susceptible state. Thus, stems of young tomato plants are resistant to *Botrytis cinerea* but become susceptible with increasing physiological age; a sparse infection occurs in the young stem, remains latent for several weeks, and eventually develops further when the plant passes into the susceptible phase (Wilson, 1963). Such alterations in susceptibility are not well understood and are presumably associated with physiological and possibly morphological changes in the maturing tissue.

Some pathogens such as *Botrytis cinerea*, *Corticium solani* and *Xanthomonas solanacearum* (brown rot) can attack several tissues and organs, and may have a wide host range. These are usually regarded as relatively unspecialized parasites and can presumably produce enzymes enabling them to utilize as food the different substances present in different tissues, organs and plants. Most parasites do, however, have some degree of selectivity. Thus root parasites rarely attack leaves although there are some exceptions, including *Macrophomina phaseoli* which can cause leaf spotting as well as the more usual 'charcoal rot' of stems and roots in tropical and subtropical areas. Leaf pathogens often infect the young green stem and perianth segments, and some leaf smut fungi, for example *Ustilago striiformis* (stripe smut) occasionally produce sori in the inflorescences and stems as well as – more usually – on the leaves of some grasses (figure 11.5). Pathogens such as *Venturia inaequalis* (apple scab) and *Xanthomonas malvacearum* (bacterial blight of cotton) can attack leaves, stems and fruit, and similarly for many Erysiphaceae and Peronosporaceae. *Phytophthora infestans* attacks potato shoots and tubers.

These differences may be associated with such morphological features as, for example, obligate stomatal penetrators being unable to enter roots, or the absence of the susceptible tissue in a particular organ. Root-invading fungi which have acquired the capacity for saprophytic survival in soil

Figure 11.5   Leaf smut (*Ustilago striiformis*) on *Holcus lanatus*. Linear sori develop in the leaves and sometimes the fungus attacks the inflorescence.

may perhaps have lost the ability to colonize leaves. Conversely, many leaf pathogens are unable to survive for long in a free state in soil although they may survive in infected plant tissue or as resistant propagules therein. Some root-attacking fungi may, however, colonize shoots under conditions very favourable for infection; *Gibberella fujikuroi*, for example, which normally attacks sorghum roots and stems can also infect the leaves and heads during prolonged wet weather. Some root pathogens seem able to invade shoots under favourable conditions, others not.

Some pathogens are confined to a specific organ of the plant, the best known of which is perhaps *Claviceps purpurea* which attacks only the ovaries of grasses, entering through the stigmata at flowering time. Some smut fungi destroy only the ovaries, and *Ustilago violacea* (anther smut of carnation) destroys only the stamens, although in both cases the fungus may be systemic; that is, although present elsewhere in the plant it produces its spores – and typical smut symptoms – only in a specific organ. However, many species of Ustilaginales which generally infect the inflorescence may occasionally produce sori in leaves, stems and peduncles. According to Lang (1912) *U. nuda* produces leaf sori if infected barley plants are prevented from flowering. In many such cases it seems that the fungus 'preferentially' colonizes a specific organ but, if prevented from doing so or under conditions highly conducive to infection, may break out elsewhere.

Most pathogens show tissue specificity to varying extents, growing or reproducing only in certain tissues. Rust fungi generally attack unlignified ground tissue, many smut fungi invade young meristematic tissue of seedlings, ovaries and buds, most Erysiphaceae attack epidermal cells, some wood rotting fungi affect the heart wood and others the sap wood, vascular wilt pathogens make their way into the xylem vessels, some viruses affect the phloem (for example potato leaf roll – phloem necrosis), and *Phytophthora cambivora* (ink disease of chestnut) attacks the cambium (and other tissues) of roots and stems. Suberized tissue is resistant to many pathogens, and cork and endodermis may be effective barriers to their spread. Pathogens which produce a wide range of enzymes and toxins able to soften or kill cells are likely to colonize more tissues than, for example, those which can enter only young tissues. As with organs, the capacity to enter, to obtain suitable nutrients, and to inactivate toxic substances which may be present largely determine whether a pathogen does or does not colonize a tissue. Organ and tissue specificity are closely related and cannot in practice be satisfactorily separated.

Plant-parasite relationship:
obligate and facultative parasitism

As mentioned above, parasites can colonize plant tissue only if it contains or develops food materials suitable for them. Parasitism is thus basically a nutritional relationship between two organisms, and Thrower (1966) defines a parasite as 'an organism or virus existing in intimate association with another living organism from which it derives an essential part of the material for its existence'.

In becoming parasitic an organism largely avoids the competition for limited nutrients which many saprophytes have to face but the parasite, if it is to survive, must overcome the defences of the host plant and must be able to obtain sufficient food from the latter to complete its life cycle. If it attacks an annual plant it must also find ways of surviving in the absence of susceptible plants. This may be difficult since the organism is likely to have sacrificed some of its saprophytic abilities in becoming parasitic, but this difficulty can be overcome by the production of resistant propagules. The evolution of plant parasitism is an interesting if somewhat profitless subject for discussion. Some workers consider that plant parasites have evolved from forms saprophytic on senescent vegetation, and if one accepts this hypothesis there is perhaps an evolutionary progression from obligate saprophytism to obligate parasitism and, possibly, mutualistic symbiosis.

In **obligate saprophytism** nutrients are obtained only from dead organic substrates. **Facultative parasitism** includes organisms which usually live as saprophytes but which can attack living tissue under certain conditions, especially senescent or damaged tissue or storage organs, for example *Rhizopus nigricans, Botrytis cinerea*. These 'opportunist' pathogens often have a wide, rather indiscriminate host range, are rather unspecialized parasites, and can usually be cultured easily. Many appear to be wound parasites. **Facultative saprophytism** includes organisms which usually live as parasites but which can grow saprophytically, for example *Phytophthora infestans* and *Venturia inaequalis*. These generally have a narrower host range, are more highly specialized parasites, and often grow only slowly in culture. **Ecologically obligate parasitism** includes organisms which invariably occur in nature as parasites but which can be grown in culture, for example many smuts (Ustilaginales), **Obligate parasitism** refers to those organisms which occur only as parasites and which cannot be grown in axenic culture (but see below), for example Erysiphales, Uredinales, Peronosporaceae, Albuginaceae. By contrast, **symbiosis** is often regarded as a highly advanced type of parasitism in which the host is hardly damaged and may in fact benefit from the association. This is better described as mutualism since symbiosis

G

(living together) includes parasitism if the host plant is not thereby killed.

There is some confusion in the use of the terms 'facultative parasite' and 'facultative saprophyte'. The former is sometimes taken to denote a parasite which can live saprophytically, but more frequently it denotes a saprophyte which can be parasitic. Similarly, 'facultative saprophyte' may describe a saprophyte which can be parasitic or (more often) a parasite which is sometimes saprophytic. In practice the difference is one of degree only. Nor is there any rigid distinction between parasites, predators and symbionts. Some organisms can be parasitic, saprophytic or symbiotic according to circumstances and host. This is exemplified by *Armillaria mellea*, the honey fungus, which parasitizes some plants, appears to be saprophytic on others, and forms an apparently symbiotic association with the orchid *Gastroidea elata* but different strains of the fungus are perhaps involved. *Rhizobium* is normally symbiotic with roots of leguminous plants but it can become parasitic under certain conditions, and there are pathogenic strains of the bacterium.

Plant parasitism may have originated as a result of organisms normally associated saprophytically with senescent or dead vegetation acquiring the ability to attack living tissue, by mutation or possibly by a slow process of adaptation, although the latter is controversial. The pathogenicity of some parasites weakens in axenic culture, presumably due to increasing preponderance of saprophytic strains or to adaptation, but can often be restored by passage through a susceptible plant. Similarly, the pathogenicity of an obligate parasite to one host may be weakened or increased by passage through another. Some rust fungi have been reported to grow in axenic culture, presumably as non-obligately parasitic strains arising through mutation or adaptation, the latter perhaps associated with adaptive enzymes.

Parasites obtain nutrients from their host plants in different ways, but can conveniently be considered as biotrophs or necrotrophs (Gaumann, 1950), that is, parasites which obtain their energy from the living (biotroph) or from the dead (necrotroph) cells of the host plant (Munch, 1929; Link, 1936; Thrower, 1966). These two terms are often equated with obligate and non-obligate (facultative) parasites, respectively.

Obligate parasitism

Obligate parasites have been defined as those which obtain their nutrients only from living tissue and so cannot be grown on non-living (axenic) culture media in the laboratory. Although their nutritional requirements are not well understood it is generally assumed that they require complex labile substances which are present only in living cells.

In this sense an obligate parasite is one for which a suitable non-living culture medium has not yet been formulated. Many chytrids and other fungi, previously regarded as obligate parasites, have now been grown in axenic culture, and it is probable that improved techniques will eventually enable most obligate parasites to be cultured. Axenic culture of *Gymnosporangium juniperi-virginianae*, *Puccinia malvacearum* and *Uromyces ari-triphylli* from teliospores has been described by Cutter (1951, 1959, 1960, 1960*a*) and Hotson and Cutter (1951), and sporing colonies of *Puccinia graminis tritici* have recently been grown from uredospores on a medium containing yeast extract (Williams, Scott and Kuhl, 1966; Williams *et al.*, 1967; Scott and Maclean, 1969). It is clear that the definition of obligate parasitism in terms of inability to grow in axenic culture involves inconsistencies.

The term can also be used in an ecological sense, obligate parasites being those which in nature grow and reproduce only on living plants and do not occur as saprophytes, although it may be possible to grow them in axenic culture in the laboratory. This wider and perhaps more natural definition would include such parasites as the Ustilaginales, *Claviceps*, *Taphrina*, many phytopathogenic bacteria and others, as well as obligate parasites as defined in the previous paragraph. Obligate parasites do not normally kill susceptible cells which they enter, at least not in the early stages of infection and to do so would indeed be disadvantageous since such parasites obtain their nutrients from living cells. The means by which obligate and near-obligate parasites keep infected plant cells alive and functioning are uncertain, but presumably involve an interchange of materials between host and parasite, a process in which haustoria probably play a prominent role. The need to keep infected cells alive is probably less critical with facultative parasites, some of which kill the cells of the infected tissue anyway. Of greater importance to the 'killer' facultative parasite is the capacity to kill plant cells without provoking defence mechanisms likely to destroy itself.

How biotrophs such as rusts and powdery mildews obtain carbohydrate from the host plant is not well understood but it seems likely that the sucrose of the host is converted into other carbohydrates and sugar alcohols (polyols), notably trehalose, mannitol and arabitol. These are the soluble carbohydrates – using the term in a wide sense – most frequently found in the mycelium of Basidiomycetes and Ascomycetes. Polyols are said to be only poorly metabolized in higher plants, except in those which contain them, and conversion of plant carbohydrates into these fungal carbohydrates perhaps ensures that they do not move back into the parasitized plant tissue. Further details of carbohydrate metabolism in rust diseases can be obtained from Daly (1967), and the movement of carbohydrates from plants to their parasites has been reviewed by Smith *et al.* (1969).

Characteristics of obligate parasites

Apart from their invariable occurrence as parasites, obligate parasites often show other characteristics which, however, are not necessarily unique to, or shown by, all of them. They may be completely intracellular (endobiotic) or, more often, are partially so in that the intercellular hyphae bear haustoria which enter the host cells. Some facultative parasites, including *Phytophthora infestans*, also produce haustoria, and neither the latter nor intracellular development is a reliable criterion of obligate parasitism.

Obligate parasites often have a fairly mild, non-necrotic, or even stimulatory effect on host tissue, at least until sporulation occurs, and this is sometimes accompanied by systemic development to varying extents. Neither benign reaction of infected tissue nor systemic development is unique to obligate parasites since such facultative parasites as *Taphrina deformans*, *Exobasidium vaccinii* and *Agrobacterium tumefaciens* cause little if any necrosis and indeed cause proliferation of infected tissue. It is, however, true that few obligate parasites cause necrosis until sporulation sets in. Even in *Phytophthora infestans*, a facultative if specialized parasite, sporulation can occur on living green tissue under certain conditions.

Vigorous plants are often most severely attacked by obligate parasites whereas the reverse may apply with facultative parasites, although there are many exceptions. Physiological specialization is generally considered to be characteristic of obligate parasites, this conclusion being derived from the intensive study of this phenomenon in rusts (particularly *Puccinia graminis*) and smuts. Such parasites are often closely adapted to their host plants in that the latter are rarely severely damaged, but facultative parasites also exhibit physiological specialization. There are also apparent exceptions to the generalization that obligate parasites have a narrower host range. Thus, *Erysiphe polygoni* and *Leveillula taurica* attack many different species of plants but they probably comprise several host specific races. This seems to be a different situation from that found in such unspecialized facultative parasites as *Botrytis cinerea* which attack a very wide range of plants rather uncritically and with little host specificity. Many unspecialized parasites tend to invade plants through wounds, whereas specialized ones usually enter through stomata or by direct penetration of the cuticle.

Yarwood (1956) has suggested that the propagules of an organism showing complete obligate parasitism would neither germinate nor grow without continuous contact with the host plant. There is no recorded example of this and he speculates that there are grades of obligateness and that the extent to which germ tubes grow in axenic culture might be a criterion of this. On this basis he forecasts that *Peronospora destructor* with a germ tube length of 500 μm in non-nutrient culture and 2800 μm in nutrient culture will be more readily cultured than *Uromyces phaseoli* (390 μm, 1000 μm) and the latter more readily than *Erysiphe polygoni* (44 μm, 280 μm). Other factors play a part in this and, as Yarwood points out, this method of assessing the degree of obligate parasitism needs further investigation. Some rust fungi have been cultured but there appears to be no convincing account of axenic culture of Erysiphales, Peronosporaceae or Albuginaceae.

Occurrence of obligate parasitism

Obligate parasites occur in all the main groups of plant pathogens except bacteria, although many bacterial phytopathogens are invariably associated with plant tissue, do not survive long when introduced into soil, but can be grown in axenic culture and from this viewpoint they are technically not obligate parasites. Many produce necrotizing enzymes and toxins and have the characteristics of facultative parasites, but there are some – notably *Agrobacterium tumefaciens*, *Corynebacterium fascians* and *Rhizobium* spp. – which cause tissue proliferation rather than necrosis and do not seem to destroy host tissue to any marked extent, features characteristic of obligate parasites.

The Plasmodiophorales are ecologically obligate parasites, and axenic culture of *Plasmodiophora brassicae* and *Spongospora subterranea* has been reported by Jones (1928) and Kunkel (1915); this is questioned by Karling (1942), and axenic culture has not been confirmed in this order. Some chytrids (Chytridiales) appear to be ecologically obligate parasites but many have been cultured in recent years. It is likely, however, that endobiotic forms such as *Olpidium* and *Synchytrium* are obligate and there are no reports of these having been grown in culture.

An interesting series from facultative to obligate parasitism is found in the Peronosporales, in which the Pythiaceae are facultative and the Albuginaceae and Peronosporaceae obligate parasites. Species of *Pythium* often cause host necrosis, lack haustoria and are easily cultured. This also applies to some species of *Phytophthora* (for example *P. citrophthora*, brown rot of lemons) while others (*P. infestans*) develop haustoria, may cause delayed host necrosis, are less easily cultured, and might be considered as near-obligate parasites. Other species have not been grown in axenic culture. Members of the Peronosporaceae and Albuginaceae have well developed haustoria, cause little or delayed necrosis or may stimulate host tissue, have not been cultured, and are obligate parasites. Apparently transitional forms of this sort do not occur in the other two major orders of obligate fungal parasites (the Uredinales and Erysiphales), and the Peronosporales would thus seem to be suitable subject for investigations on obligate parasitism.

All members of the Erysiphales (Perisporiales), comprising the Erysiphaceae, Meliolaceae and Englerulaceae (Martin, in Ainsworth, 1963, combines the latter two families into a separate order, the Meliolales) appear to be obligate parasites. They differ from most parasitic fungi in generally being superficial on the host, with haustoria entering the epidermis (most Erysiphaceae) or mesophyll. Various substances including sucrose, copper sulphate, glutathione, liver extract and barley leaf extract increase spore germination and growth of germ tubes in the Erysiphaceae (Yarwood, 1956) and might be of potential value in axenic culture, but the latter has not been achieved and it may well be that the Erysiphaceae will prove refractory in this respect.

The Uredinales are highly specialized parasites. Many attempts have been made to grow them in axenic culture and, as noted above, success has been reported by several investigators. All rusts seem to be obligate parasites, and their nearest facultative relatives are probably the smuts (Ustilaginales), many of which have been grown in culture although occurring only as parasites in nature.

Parasitic angiosperms show varying degrees of parasitism, some being partial parasites and photosynthesizing their own organic nutrients, others entirely parasitic. Many have clearly evolved from non-parasitic forms, probably in fairly recent times. Most of them are ecologically obligate parasites, but axenic culture of some, for example *Cuscuta* (dodder: Loo, 1946), has been reported.

According to Yarwood (1956) about one quarter of the parasites attacking plants are obligate, and many cause serious crop diseases. Viruses, in as far as they can be regarded as parasites, are obligate ones as they cannot as yet be grown on non-living media.

Facultative parasitism

Facultative parasites obtain nutrients from their host plants in various ways. Some of the more highly specialized ones, such as *Venturia inaequalis*, may cause little destruction of tissue in the early stages of attack although necrosis may occur later. This has been termed 'eusymbiosis' by Gaumann (1950), and the parasitized cells may remain alive and functional for some considerable time with their metabolism perhaps modified to meet the nutritional requirements of the parasite. There is little information as to the methods by which near-obligate parasites obtain nutrients from their host plants but they may be similar to those used by obligate parasites. *Taphrina deformans, Exobasidium vaccinii* and other organisms which cause tissue hypertrophy often cause virtually no necrosis, but the functional efficiency of the severely misshapen leaves must be greatly reduced. In other diseases specific organs of the plant are destroyed although, apart from this, the infected plant does not seem to be greatly affected; a case in point is ergot of grasses (*Claviceps*) in which the ovaries are replaced by sclerotia of the fungus.

Some parasites quickly kill limited areas of host tissue by means of toxins of parasite or host origin or by harmful enzymes (Chapter 13) and thereafter live on the dead tissue. These have been termed 'perthophytes' and they include pathogens which cause leaf spotting, fruit spotting and localized root lesions. The infected plant generally survives and may be only slightly damaged, although in severe attacks there may be considerable tissue necrosis leading to shedding of the infected organs and in extreme cases to the death of the plant.

The whole plant may be killed by some pathogens which thereafter live as saprophytes on the dead remains as, for example, in damping-off of seedlings caused by *Pythium* spp. and other fungi; this situation carries an element of risk for the pathogen in that it may be suppressed by saprophytic secondary fungi which colonize the dead tissue.

By comparison with obligate parasites facultative ones are generally held to be less specialized in their parasitism. Many of the more highly specialized facultative parasites, for example *Diplocarpon rosae*, grow only slowly in axenic culture, and in this sense are often referred to as 'near-obligate' parasites. The less specialized parasites, such as *Botrytis cinerea*, tend to grow rapidly on quite simple culture media and to attack senescent or damaged tissues or plants, and some are wound parasites.

The differences between obligate and facultative parasites are not absolute. At one extreme are, for example, downy mildews (Peronosporaceae) which have not as yet been grown in axenic culture while at the other end are parasites with strong saprophytic tendencies (some fusaria), but there are intermediate types such as *Venturia inaequalis* and other near-obligate parasites. These latter fungi are not technically obligate parasites since they can be grown, albeit with some difficulty and slowly, in axenic culture, yet they have many of the characteristics of obligate parasites – under natural conditions they live as parasites, surviving in the form of resting propagules when the host plant is absent. In turn, obligate parasitism may in some cases have led to mutualism, a form of symbiosis in which plant and parasite appear to live in 'peaceful co-existence', this condition sometimes becoming obligate for one or both partners.

Some of the characteristics of specialized and unspecialized parasites are summarized in the table below; these are generalizations rather than completely accurate, and there are many exceptions.

Table 2

	Unspecialized parasites	Specialized parasites
Entry into the plant	Often through wounds	Through natural openings or by direct penetration
Development in the plant tissue	Intercellular and intracellular	Intercellular and intracellular, often with haustoria; some are endobiotic
Infection of the plant	Rarely systemic	Sometimes systemic to varying extents
Effect on the invaded tissue	Often necrosis; enzymes and /or toxins may be involved	Rarely necrotic in the early stages, sometimes stimulatory; growth hormones perhaps involved
Tissue attacked	Often senescent, damaged or immature tissue	Often mature, undamaged tissue and meristematic tissue
Plants attacked	Weakened, damaged or unthrifty plants often attacked	Vigorous plants often attacked
Nutrition	Parasitic and often saprophytic to varying extents	Parasitic
Growth in axenic culture	Often good on quite simple media	Often slow on most media, or not yet achieved (obligate parasites)
Host range	Often wide	Often narrow
Parasitic specialization	Not generally marked	Often marked
Survival outside the plant	As saprophytes or resting propagules; sometimes in soil as free-living saprophytes Some are seed borne	As perennial mycelium in the plant or as resting propagules Some are seed borne

12 The results of infection

The physiological changes in diseased plants are usually reflected in visible symptoms which may be mild or severe, depending partly on the nature and aggressiveness of the pathogen and the susceptibility of the plant. McNew (1960) suggests that there are six major vital processes in plants, and correspondingly six main ways in which pathogens adversely affect plants. These are:

1. Destruction of food reserves in storage organs, seeds, fruits, wood and other plant material. Many of the pathogens involved are wound parasites and are able to secrete a variety of enzymes which destroy the host tissue rapidly, as in soft rots, or in a more leisurely fashion, as in decay of wood, depending in part on the nature of the tissue – for example, enzymic breakdown of lignified tissue is much slower than that of parenchyma. The parasites are generally unspecialized but destructive and include certain species of *Rhizopus, Sclerotinia* and *Penicillium,* and *Erwinia carotovora.*

2. Destruction of seedlings or impairment of their growth. In these diseases the young tissues of the seedlings are destroyed, older tissues being mostly resistant. Included here are pathogens which cause damping-off and other forms of seedling blight, for example some species of *Pythium, Phytophthora, Rhizoctonia* and *Fusarium,* some of which may also be involved in root diseases. These pathogens no doubt produce necrotizing enzymes and can be regarded as slightly more advanced parasitically in that they are able to attack living, albeit usually immature, tissue. The seedling may be attacked before or after emergence, and in the latter case it may survive although weakened and checked in growth.

3. Impairment of the water absorbing capacity of the plant – principally root rot diseases. The fungi involved are more advanced in that some are able to invade mature as well as young roots and, although many are soil inhabitants, others can survive in soil only as resistant propagules or in diseased roots rather than as free-living saprophytes. Entry may be through wounds or by direct penetration, and root destruction can often be sufficiently extensive to kill the plant. Some may also cause foot rot

and stalk rot. Examples include some root attacking species of *Pythium*, *Fusarium*, and *Helminthosporium*, and *Phymatotrichum omnivorum*, *Ophiobolus graminis* and *Macrophomina phaseoli*, to mention but a few.

4. Interference with the upward transport of water and solutes – principally vascular wilt diseases. The vascular tissues are primarily colonized and the adverse effects on the plant may be due to the resulting reduced upward movement of water and/or to the production of toxins by the pathogen. The pathogens invade chiefly through wounds and may be soil borne (for example *Fusarium oxysporum*) or insect borne (for example *Erwinia tracheiphila*). They are to a considerable extent specialized as regards host and tissue attack, and in their pathogenicity mechanisms (for example toxin production). Examples are *Fusarium oxysporum*, *Verticillium albo-atrum*, *Ceratostomella ulmi* (Dutch elm disease), *Ceratocystis fagacearum* (oak wilt) and *Erwinia tracheiphila* (cucumber wilt).

5. Reduction of the photosynthetic capacity of the plant – principally pathogens which destroy photosynthetic tissue. These pathogens are extremely varied and range from poorly specialized necrotrophs which kill immediately to highly specialized biotrophs which at first have apparently little effect on the infected tissue – there may even be stimulation. The necrotrophs include such leaf spotting fungi as *Cercospora*, *Helminthosporium*, *Septoria* and numerous others. Generalized blighting may be caused by some, including *Phytophthora infestans*. Green stems may be similarly affected, also flowers and fruits. Biotrophs include downy mildews, powdery mildews, and rusts. Some viruses cause varying degrees of chlorosis of leaves, or more rarely, tissue necrosis.

6. Interference with the metabolism of the plant. The pathogens involved in this type of disease tend to be specialized, and are frequently obligate parasites which are thought to divert the host plant's metabolism into producing substances which they can utilize. Host injury is often minimal, at least until sporulation, and a state approaching mutualism may be reached. Stimulation of infected tissue may occur, leading to overgrowths of various types, as discussed below. The numerous pathogens of this sort include rusts, smuts, Peronosporaceae, *Albugo*, and powdery mildews. The extreme is perhaps seen in viruses which apparently direct the metabolism of infected cells into producing more virus particles.

Several other ways in which plants are affected by parasites could be mentioned – for example, interference with the reproductive processes as in destruction of flowers or seed by many smuts and *Claviceps*, or in sterility brought about by some viruses. These adverse effects involve physiological changes in the diseased plant which, except in symptomless carriers, result in visible symptoms of varying degrees of severity, depending on the nature and aggressiveness of the pathogen, the susceptibility of the plant, and environmental conditions. The results of infection are here considered under (1) physiological changes, (2) anatomical and morphological changes and (3) the symptoms of disease in plants.

Physiological changes in the infected plant

These have been extensively studied during recent years, with particular emphasis on respiration; information on other aspects is fragmentary. Efficient functioning and growth of a plant depend on a number of physiological processes which are so closely interconnected that change in one is likely to bring about changes in others, for example, even slight changes in the complex processes which regulate growth in plants can have marked effects. The effects of pathogens on respiration, photosynthesis, nitrogen metabolism, and transpiration are considered briefly below, but many of the conclusions must be regarded as tentative and likely to be modified as more information becomes available.

In many if not all diseases host respiration increases following infection, and changes in the type of respiration have been suggested in some instances. Much of this increased respiration occurs in the host tissue rather than in the pathogen, and similar increases have been reported in virus infected tissue, particularly in local lesions as distinct from systemic infections. Increased respiration begins soon after infection and often attains its maximum – which may be several times normal – a few days later in the case of obligate parasites. The increase is probably associated largely with increased synthetic activities of the infected tissue and as the latter is progressively colonized and killed, respiration falls off and eventually ceases with death. Similar increases may be brought about by metabolites, including toxins, produced by pathogens. Much of the work on respiration has been with obligate parasites in which infected tissues of susceptible plants may remain alive for a considerable time and often show stimulated metabolic activity including increased protein synthesis and higher auxin content. Adjacent uninfected tissue may behave similarly. Infected resistant tissue often shows similar respiratory increase but this falls off as the tissue dies as a result of hypersensitivity. Tissue attacked by toxigenic necrotrophs is likely to be killed rather rapidly so that any respiratory increase may not be detectable except in the adjacent uninfected tissue. Such increase has been reported in resistant plants and there is some indication that respiratory changes are here associated with formation of phenolic substances which may play a part in the defence mechanisms of the plant. Increased metabolic activity including respiration commonly occurs in damaged tissue whether injured mechanically, chemically or parasitically, and is associated with the processes of healing.

The biochemical aspects of these respiratory changes are imperfectly understood although there is some evidence that the hexose mono-phosphate pathway – normally not of great importance as compared with the Embden–Meyerhof–Parnas pathway and the tricarboxylic acid cycle in respiration in higher plants – becomes prominent in plants attacked by at least some rusts and powdery mildews (Wood, 1967).

In studies on the respiration of diseased tissue it has to be remembered that

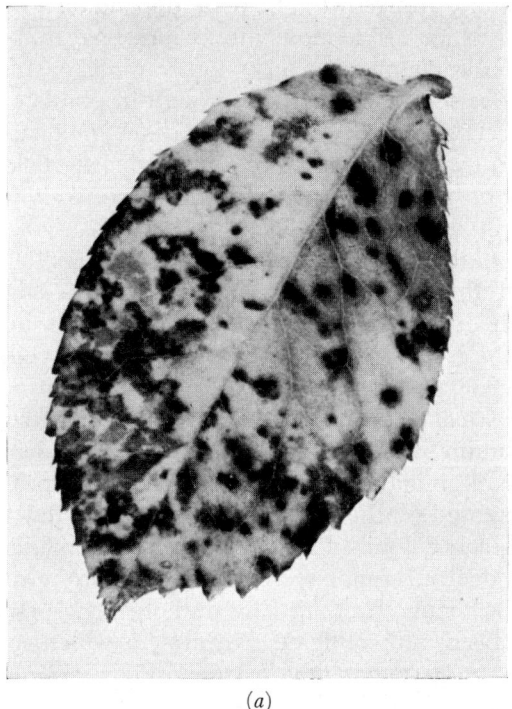

(a)

Figure 12.1   Green islands (a) on a senescing rose leaf, (b) around uredia of *Uromyces rumicis* on a dock (*Rumex*) leaf (enlarged); lesions of a leaf-spotting fungus are also present.

both host and parasite may contribute to any respiratory changes observed. This difficulty has been partly overcome by various methods, for example by inactivating the parasite without killing the host tissue, by removing the parasite (as in the ectoparasitic powdery mildews), by taking measure-ments beyond the area of tissue occupied by the parasite, or by using culture filtrates or toxins produced by the parasite. Although there are drawbacks to all these methods they have often given comparable results indicating that much of the observed respiratory increase probably originates from the infected host tissue. Respiratory changes in infected

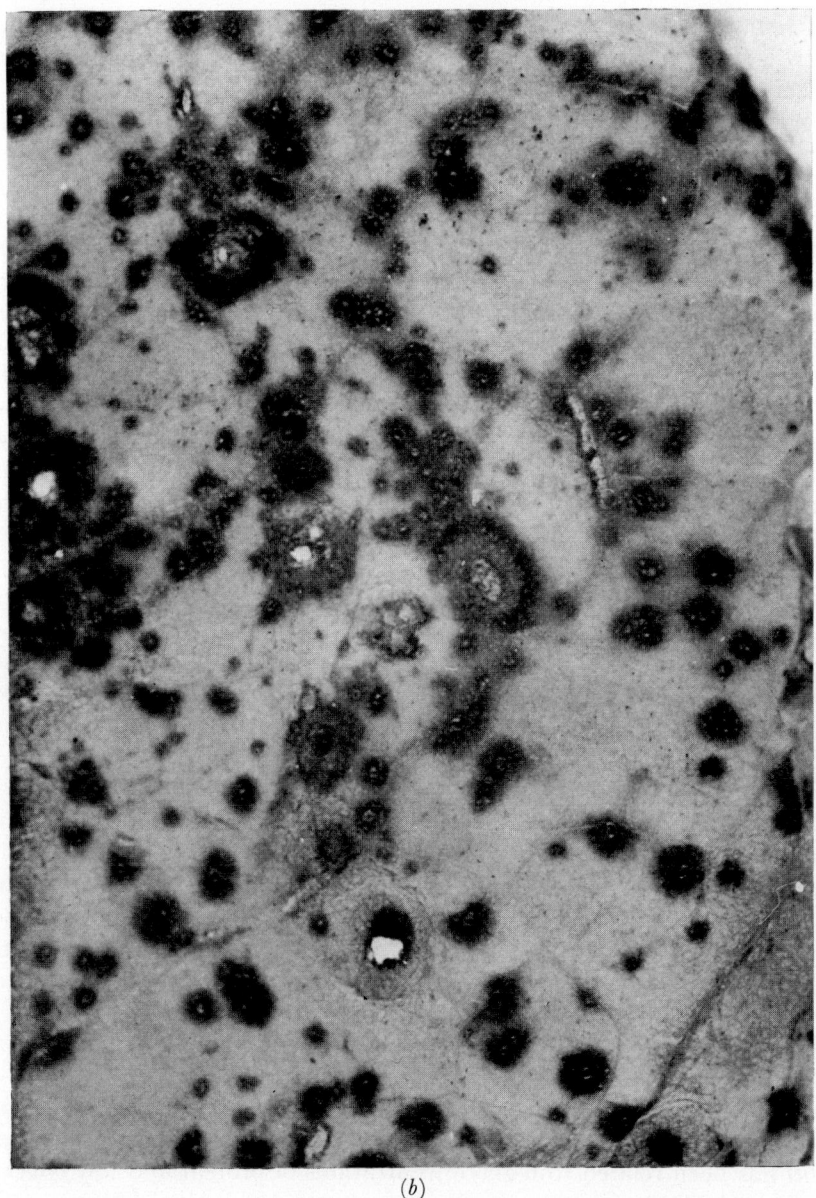

(b)

plants are discussed by Uritani and Akazawa (1959), and Millerd and Scott (1962).

Photosynthesis by infected tissue is reduced in many diseases. This can be due to rapid destruction of green tissue by necrotrophs, but it also occurs to a smaller extent in diseases caused by biotrophs in which shere is no immediate necrosis. In these cases there is sometimes a limited initial increase of photosynthesis and this effect may be prolonged in mild infections – perhaps indicating that infection is at first stimulatory as suggested by Gaumann (1950). This initial increase is followed by reduced photosynthesis after a few days, and Allen (1942) found that after 10 days it was only 10% of that of healthy leaves in wheat infected with *Erysiphe graminis*. This was due partly to reduced chlorophyll content and also probably to other changes which adversely affect photosynthesis. In some diseases, notably those caused by obligate parasites, there may be localized 'green islands' around the infected areas, whereas the rest of the leaf becomes senescent and chlorotic (figure 12.1). In such islands the photosynthetic activity of the host tissue is presumably maintained, or possibly stimulated, by the presence of the parasite, the latter diverting the metabolism of the host to meet its own nutritional requirements. These changes might be partly mediated by growth regulating substances including auxin and kinin which have the effect of delaying senescence. Rather similar green islands can be induced by water extracts of *Erysiphe graminis* conidia, *Puccinia graminis* uredospores, yeast extract, growth regulators such as indole-3-acetonitrile, wounding and chemicals (Yarwood, 1967; Wood 1967). Although often present in diseases caused by rusts and powdery mildews green islands also occur in some diseases caused by viruses, dodder and by such non-obligate parasites as *Rhytisma acerina* (tar spot of sycamore) and *Venturia*. They may also develop on naturally senescing leaves.

Metabolites including carbohydrates, amino acids and proteins tend to accumulate in green islands due to reduced translocation from the island, increased translocation to it, or to increased synthesis within it. Selective accumulation of metabolites by diseased or injured plant tissue frequently occurs and is no doubt associated with defence and repair processes. Postinfectional increases of nitrogenous compounds in susceptible tissue, usually in rust diseases, have been reported by several investigators, and also changes in nucleic acid concentration – RNA often increases in infected susceptible tissue but not in infected resistant tissue, and DNA levels are not usually affected. RNA probably increases in both host and parasite and it is possible that there is exchange of nucleic acids between the two. Resistance of wheat to *Puccinia graminis* var. *tritici* has been related to high concentrations of protein and low concentrations of soluble nitrogen and carbohydrate. There is as yet little indisputable information on these effects and their significance in the infected plant.

Changes in transpiration of infected plants have been reported. Increased transpiration could result from increased permeability of the host, while reduced transpiration might be due to stomatal closure following infection or to propagules or mycelium covering the leaf surface. Transpiration of infected leaves may be above normal at night – perhaps due to enhanced cuticular transpiration following increased stomatal closure. Transpiration by day is chiefly stomatal, that by night chiefly cuticular. Bean leaves attacked by *Uromyces phaseoli typica* transpired much more after than before the uredia opened (Gerwitz and Durbin, 1965), presumably due to increased ease of water loss through the open sori.

The physiological changes occurring in virus infected plants are not well understood. Farkas and Solymosy (1965) conclude that few of the observed symptoms can be explained in biochemical terms and that many of the metabolic alterations observed also occur in starving, senescent tissues.

Anatomical and morphological changes in the infected plant

The physiological changes occurring in the diseased plant and briefly outlined above have their counterparts in the anatomical and morphological changes ('morbid anatomy') which constitute the visible symptoms. The symptoms caused by parasites are basically comparable to those resulting from mechanical, chemical, atmospheric, insect and other injuries in that all are the expression of similar physiological responses of the plant. The visible reaction of tissues to pathogens is in part related to the pathogenicity mechanisms of the parasite, at least in the early stage of infection. Macerating enzymes which destroy the middle lamella tend to bring about separation of the component cells (soft rot) and eventually their death, although how the latter occurs is not known. Localized secretion of wall degrading enzymes permits fungal hyphae to enter the cells without immediate necrosis. Toxins may precede the pathogen and cause necrosis of tissue around the infection site and probably affect the permeability of the plasmatic membrane. Upsets in the balance of growth regulating substances can result in hyperplasia (stimulation of cell division), hypertrophy (excessive growth of the affected tissue or organ) or hypoplasia (subnormal growth), or various combinations of these, without necrosis.

More highly specialized parasites such as rusts may have little visible adverse effect on the plant until sporulation occurs, when collapse or necrosis of infected host cells may occur. This could be due to the sudden and considerable withdrawal of nutrients by the fungus from the host which must be involved in the more or less simultaneous production of large numbers of propagules. In some downy mildews, for example, numerous rather large sporangiophores and sporangia develop within hours from hyphae which grow out through the stomata, and this must entail great expenditure of energy derived directly or indirectly from the host. It is possible that other factors are involved here, including the physiological changes occurring during the change over from vegetative growth to sporulation. This sporulation injury occurs with many specialized plant pathogens and is conspicuous in some downy mildews.

Effects on cells

In a sense these constitute the internal symptoms, the 'pathological anatomy' of Gaumann (1950). Changes in cell contents and cell membrane following infection are varied and imperfectly understood. There may be necrosis or stimulation of the affected cells, or little conspicuous

Figure 12.2   Leaf spot of primula caused by *Ramularia primulae*. The chlorosis around the lesions may be due to toxin(s) produced by the fungus.

change beyond browning and death of the protoplast. Chlorophyll may be destroyed (figure 12·2), and anthocyanin pigments develop in some diseases as in peach leaf curl (*Taphrina deformans*). Phenolic substances, including tannins, often accumulate, and nuclei sometimes enlarge before degenerating. Cell walls may be breached either mechanically or, probably more often, by the action of enzymes which soften pectic substances, cellulose, lignin and other constituents of the plant cell wall. Decay of various types –

soft rot, brown rot, white rot, wet rot, dry rot, spongy rot, and so on – thus develops (see Cartwright and Findlay, 1958; Butler and Jones, 1949). Cell walls are of varied composition and even in lignified walls there may be sufficient amounts of other substances to permit penetration by fungi lacking ligninases but producing pectolytic or cellulolytic enzymes. Tissue disintegration is reviewed by Husain and Kelman (1959).

Infection by biotrophs often results in stimulation rather than necrosis of cells although the latter may occur later. Hypertrophy or hyperplasia, or both, may occur, particularly in parenchymatous tissue, leading to various types of proliferation as described in the next section. Some viruses cause abnormalities in nuclear division of infected host cells, but whether this occurs in hyperplasia due to other causes is not known. Hyperplasia may, however, result in changes of shape and structure; for example, in peach leaf curl the palisade cells multiply and become more or less isodiametric and difficult to distinguish from the cells of the spongy mesophyll. The cytology of hypertrophy, especially the details of nuclear division in hyperplastic tissue, merits much more attention than it has received in the past. Lysosome-like structures have recently been reported in plant cells (notably by Pitt, 1968), and their swelling and disruption in potato tuber tissue infected with *Phytophthora erythroseptica* (pink rot) have been observed (Pitt and Coombs, 1968). This results in the liberation of acid phosphatase and esterase accompanied by rapid death of the host cells. It is not known whether the disruption of these structures is a cause or a consequence of cell death, but such disruption apparently precedes any other histological or histochemical changes so far detected in the infected cells. These observations raise interesting possibilities as to the role of these lysosome-like structures in plant infection and merit further investigation and extension to other plant diseases. They might, for example, be involved in the cell necrosis which occurs in soft rot diseases (p. 223).

Effects on growth

Severely diseased plants generally show subnormal development because the processes on which growth depends are impaired. In addition there are the disturbances in growth and form brought about by pathogens, and termed teratology by Gaumann (1950). These are, no doubt, the outward expressions of derangements in the growth regulating mechanisms of the plant, probably due to substances produced by the parasite, the host or both. Comparable changes can be brought about not only by fungi, bacteria and viruses but also by insects, nematodes, certain chemicals, and as a wound response.

Figure 12.3 Cotton plant infected by the cotton leaf curl virus. Such plants are abnormally tall with elongated internodes, and stand well above the level of uninfected plants.

Figure 12.4 Sorghum plant infected by *Sclerospora sorghi*. Infected plants, one of which is shown, are stunted, chlorotic and sterile. Large numbers of sporangiophores bearing sporangia develop as a whitish growth on infected leaves in wet weather or when there is heavy dew. Note the extreme shortening of the internodes.

Generalized changes

Growth changes may be of a generalized nature resulting in abnormally tall or, more frequently, stunted plants. In the bakanae disease of rice, caused by *Gibberella fujikuroi*, some infected plants develop elongated internodes and become abnormally tall and somewhat chlorotic; this may perhaps be associated with production of gibberellic acid. Other infected plants may, however, be stunted and the fungus can cause seedling blight and foot rot. Similar elongation can be produced by certain rusts (aecia of *Uromyces pisi* on *Euphorbia cyperissias*), smuts (*Ustilago hypodytes*, stem smut of *Bromus*), downy mildews (*Sclerospora sacchari* on sugarcane) and viruses (cotton leaf curl virus) (figure 12.3). Internode shortening leading to a shortened and often rosette type of growth is not uncommon (figure 12.4) and occurs in, for example, dwarf bunt of wheat (*Tilletia contraversa*) and several virus diseases. Such generalized stunting or elongation is often caused by systemic parasites which may also retard the growth rate. These generalized effects are described by Braun (1959) as 'harmonious changes involving exaggerated growth responses'.

Galls, tumours and witch's brooms

Growth may be affected in a more irregular way as in hypertrophy of organs and in the formation of witch's brooms, galls and tumours. Hypertrophy is usually accompanied by some degree of distortion and is often due to highly specialized parasites. *Plasmodiophora brassicae*, for example, causes the well known club root or 'finger and toes' disease of Cruciferae in which the infected roots become greatly swollen and mis-shapen, due to enlargement and increased division of parenchymatous cells, chiefly in the cortex (figure 12.5). Some rusts cause marked hyper-trophy of stems as *Puccinia lagenophora* on *Senecio*, and the conspicuous leaf thickening and distortion produced by *Taphrina* (for example *T. deformans*, peach leaf curl) is due to stimulated division and enlargement of the mesophyll cells. Equally striking are the 'leafy galls' caused by *Coryne-bacterium fascians* on a variety of herbaceous plants. The symptoms are very varied and include fasciation (flattened stems), development of numerous short swollen shoots, misshapen leaves, and other malformations and dwarfing. The irregular vein thickenings found in some virus diseases may grow out into enations which in extreme cases, for example cotton leaf curl, can develop into small leaf-like structures.

Galls and tumours are outgrowths or excrescences from the plant, often appearing as irregularly rounded structures attached to the infected organ. They vary in size from small, soft swellings involving only a few cells (as in some species of *Synchytrium*) to large woody structures which may be several centimetres across (crown gall on woody hosts). They are often largely parenchymatous, but scattered and sometimes numerous vascular elements may be present, although these are probably not functional. Galls can be caused by fungi, bacteria, viruses (for example Fiji disease of sugarcane), insects and apparently non-parasitic agents. Gall inducing species occur in most of the main groups of plant pathogenic fungi including Chytridiales,

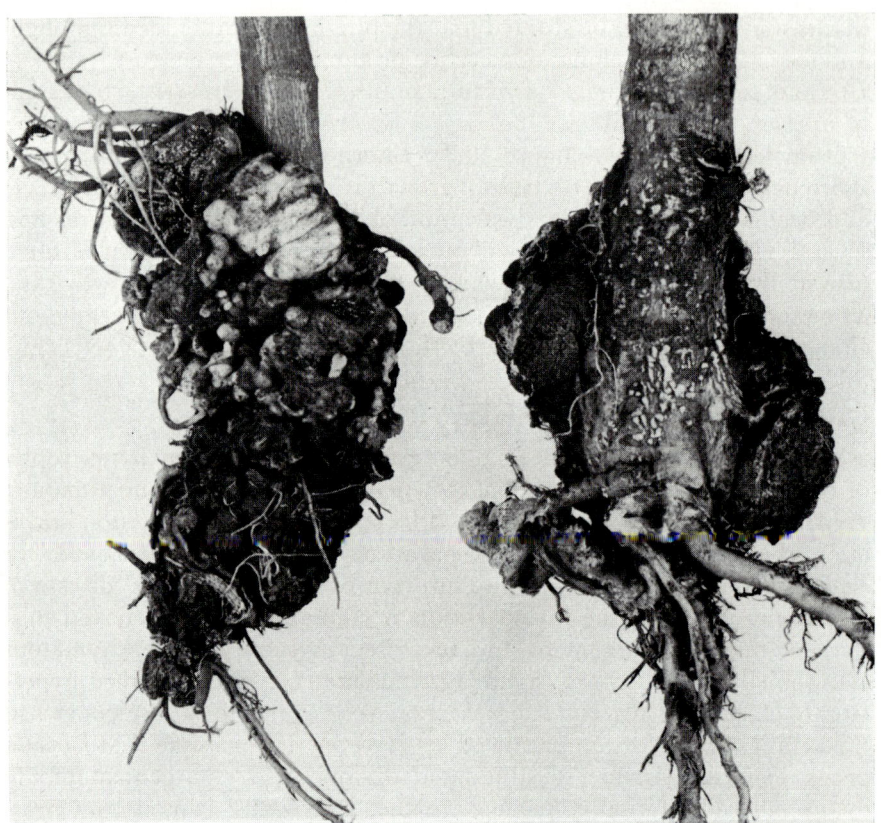

Figure 12.5   Club root (*Plasmodiophora brassicae*) on brussels sprouts; the severely swollen and misshapen tap root bears few lateral roots.

Plasmodiophorales, Taphrinales, Exobasidiaceae, Uredinales and Ustilaginales. Among others may be mentioned the root or (occasionally) stem galls of *Agrobacterium tumefaciens* (crown gall), the smaller twig tubercles of olive knot (*Pseudomonas savastanoi*) in which the internal tissues of the gall are destroyed while the outer ones proliferate, potato wart (*Synchytrium endobioticum*), 'cedar apples' of juniper (*Gymnosporangium juniperi-virginianae*), maize smut (*Ustilago maydis*) and the large galls produced by the rust *Uromycladium* on *Acacia* spp. in Australia – the latter are probably the largest known and may attain over 30 cm in diameter.

The most intensively studied is crown gall on which there is an extensive literature, although the disease itself is of no great economic importance. The bacterium causing crown gall is a wound parasite and can convert normal plant cells into tumour cells which thereafter become more or less autonomous in growth, probably due to activation of systems leading to synthesis of growth regulating factors. Tumour formation is a complex process and apparently involves conditioning of the plant cells, probably as a result of wounding, and the subsequent conversion of these susceptible cells into tumerous ones by a tumour inducing principle (TIP) produced by the bacterium. The nature of TIP is unknown but it has been suggested that it might be a specific DNA. Wounded plant cells reach maximum susceptibility to TIP in 2–3 days and become less susceptible as the normal healing processes of the tissue become effective. Little is known as to how TIP functions although several theories have been put forward (see Wood, 1967). Parts of crown gall tumours are apparently sterile as are some of the secondary tumours formed (usually) higher up the plant than the primary tumours. The origin of these secondary tumours is obscure and they have been attributed to strands of bacteria ('tumour strands') which grow through the plant, to bacteria transported in the vascular tissue, to distribution of bacteria during cell division and elongation, and to substances of bacterial origin transported from the primary tumours. The last named could well be involved in formation of sterile secondary tumours. The formation of crown gall tumours is discussed by Braun (1962) who (1959) classifies overgrowths as self limiting and non-self limiting.

The former comprise: (1) Intumescences – simple overgrowths resulting from abnormal elongation and sometimes increased division of small groups of cells. These can be induced by chemicals and wounding but are not known to be caused by pathogens. (2) Galls – localized overgrowths in which the host cells are stimulated to excessive growth, the latter being dependent upon continued stimulation: these can be caused by insects, bacteria (leguminous root nodules), fungi (*Plasmodiophora brassicae*), and nematodes (root knot, *Meloidogyne*). Overgrowths which are not self limiting (tumours) are autonomous overgrowths which are not dependent upon continued stimulation, for example crown gall, wound tumour virus (Black, 1952), and 'genetic' tumours which are apparently of non-parasitic origin. Plant tumours are described by Braun (1959).

Witch's brooms can be caused by fungi (*Taphrina*, some rusts), bacteria (*Corynebacterium fascians* can have this effect), and certain viruses, as well as by insects and mites. They arise basically from stimulation of structures which normally remain dormant, for example buds which develop into secondary shoots. There may also be some degree of leaf distortion and chlorosis, and flowers are rarely produced. The broom very often appears to be a more or less independent growth and characteristically takes the form of an upright cluster of small shoots, often contrasting sharply with the horizontal growth habit of the normal shoot.

Excessive production of adventitious roots on stems occurs in some fungal, bacterial and virus diseases, as in tomato plants attacked by *Pseudomonas solanacearum*, and is presumably related to changes in growth regulating substances following infection. They may also develop in plants attacked by vascular wilt pathogens and this has been attributed to formation of ethylene by plant or parasite. A striking example of root proliferation is hairy root of apple caused by *Agrobacterium rhizogenes*, perhaps not distinct from *A. tumefaciens*, in which numerous long fibrous roots develop. In 'frenching' of tobacco apical dominance is lost in diseased plants and numerous very narrow upright leaves develop, giving the plant a rosette or even witch's broom appearance. This condition may be due to substances produced by *Bacillus cereus*, a common soil bacterium, but its aetiology is obscure. Similar reduction of leaves and lamina occurs in some virus diseases as in fern leaf of tomato caused by cucumber mosaic virus.

Floral abnormalities

Apart from the direct damage caused by flower-infecting smuts, *Claviceps*, and similar pathogens, the floral parts may be greatly modified or transformed in some diseases. Parts which are normally rudimentary may be stimulated to develop, with striking and sometimes bizarre results including sterility. These effects may be brought about by fungi (often systemic obligate parasites), viruses, insects and mites, and sometimes appear to be genetical in origin. One of the best known is anther smut of Caryophyllaceae caused by *Ustilago violacea*. When ovulate plants of *Melandrium* are infected by *U. violacea* the normally vestigeal stamens develop and at maturity the anthers contain smut spores instead of pollen; this may be accompanied by some atrophy of the gynoecium. The normally sexless flowers at the top of the inflorescence of grape hyacinth (*Muscari comosum*) may be stimulated to produce stamens containing smut spores when the plant is infected with *Ustilago vaillantii*. Induced development of vestigeal ovaries in normally staminate flowers occurs in *Buchloe dactyloides* infected with *Tilletia buchloeana* and in *Andropogon furcatus* infected with *Sorosporium everhartii*, and various other floral abnormalities caused by smut fungi are described by Fischer and Holton (1957).

Phyllody – transformation of floral parts into leaf-like structures – is caused by various mites, insects, fungi and viruses. In other cases stamens may become petaloid, or there may be doubling of the perianth segments. Rudimentary cobs may develop into twisted, leafy shoots in maize plants attacked by *Sphacelotheca reiliana*, and phyllody of stamens can be caused by

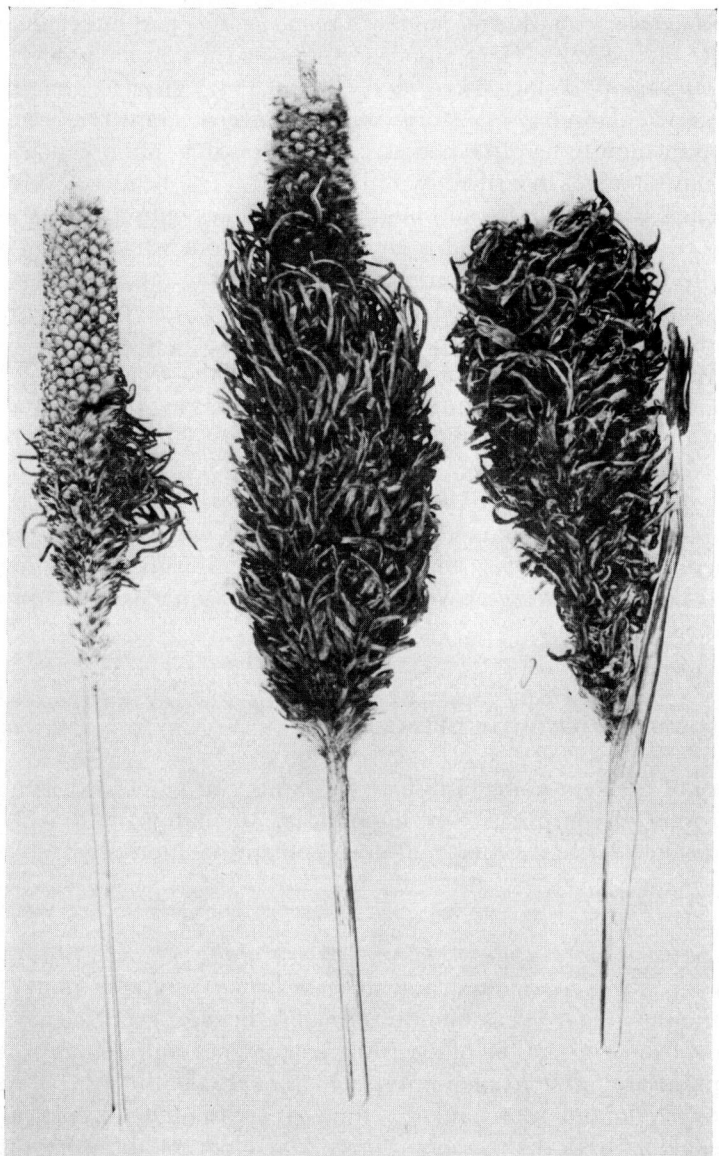

Figure 12.6   Green ear of *Pennisetum typhoides* (millet) caused by *Sclerospora graminicola*.

Ustilago bullata on *Bromus erectus*. In violet (*Viola sylvestris*) plants attacked by *Puccinia violae* the stamens are often transformed into petaloid structures, and the floral parts of Japanese plum infected with *Caeoma makinoi* develop into leaves (Braun, 1959). These abnormalities are sometimes of economic importance as in the striking floral malformations caused by

Sclerospora graminicola (downy mildew, green ear) on pearl millet (*Pennisetum typhoides*) (figure 12.6). Here, upper segments of the floral axis develop into small leafy shoots, distorted bristles of the spike may grow to a length of 2.5 cm or more, enlarged glumes sometimes turn green, stamens are often converted into minute leaf-like bodies, and the pistil is often replaced by a small leafy shoot, as described by Butler (1918). The head is severely misshapen and usually sterile, although in some cases only a part is affected and the rest produces normal grain. There are somewhat similar but less severe floral modifications in certain Cruciferae attacked by *Albugo candida* – infected radish flowers are often enlarged, green and fleshy with the stamens converted into small leafy structures. Viruses which induce phyllody and other floral abnormalities include those causing big bud of tomato, false blossom of cranberry, and spike disease of sandalwood, and viruses can result in reduced flowering and sterility of the flowers which are produced.

Some of these floral modifications are so marked that affected plants have on occasions been named as new species or varieties, as described by Fischer and Holton (1957) for smuts; plants of *Agrostis tenuis* which were dwarfed by *Tilletia decipiens* were described by Linnaeus as *A. polymorpha* var. *pumila*.

Symptoms of disease in plants

Many of the symptoms of disease in plants can be classed as necrosis, hypertrophy (hyperplasia), or hypoplasia, the latter in a wide sense including sterility and subnormal development of chlorophyll.

Necrosis

Necrosis is the commonest and most destructive type of injury and is conventionally regarded as an indication of rather unspecialized parasitism, resulting from the action of necrotizing enzymes and toxins. All parts of the plant are liable to such injury which may take the form of root rot, stem rot, stem and root cankers (limited areas of dead cortical tissue often sealed off by corky barriers) (figure 12.7), foot rot, damping-off, petal blight, fruit rot and scab, stamen blight and the numerous types of leaf lesion. The last named include spots of varying size and appearance (zonate, target board, angular, anthracnose, tar, frog eye are some of the descriptions used), blotch, streak, stripe and blight. Some leaf attacking fungi, for example *Trichometasphaeria turcica* (leaf blight of maize: Jennings and Ullstrup, 1957), cause localized wilting of infected leaves, due perhaps to plugging of the xylem vessels by the fungus or by mucilaginous

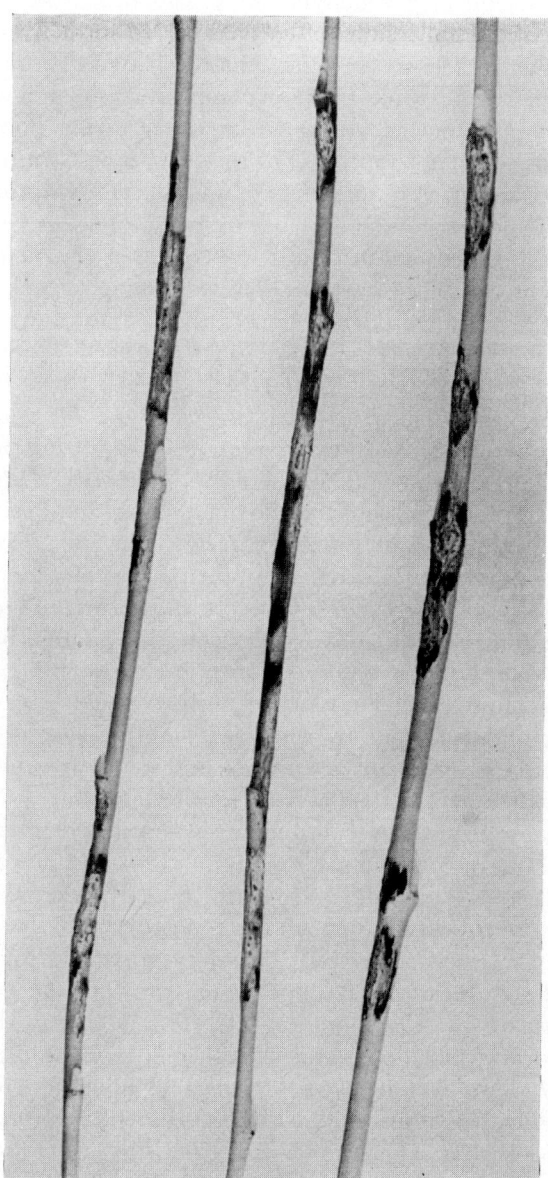

Figure 12.7   Stem cankers of willow caused by *Marssonina salicicola*. The cankers may girdle the stem and so cause die-back and leaf shedding. The leaves are also attacked and the disease can cause severe damage to golden weeping willows.

substances formed as a result of infection. Alternatively toxins may be
involved. Dissolution of parenchyma may lead to leaf shredding and to
a fibrous stem rot. Leaf lesions often coalesce to form irregular patches
of necrotic tissue and in severe infections the leaves dry up and may be
prematurely shed, the whole plant becoming brown and withered with
drying up of buds, flowers, young fruits and growing points. Different
agents may cause similar symptoms but there are usually minor differences
which enable experienced observers to diagnose from symptoms with some
degree of confidence; the lesions caused by two pathogens very often show
slight or marked differences in colour, size or other characteristics.

Tissue necrosis can be caused by chemical damage, mechanical injury,
insects, nematodes, viruses (local lesions), bacteria and fungi, and some is
apparently of genetical origin. The fungi involved are chiefly Fungi
Imperfecti and Ascomycetes – *Cercospora, Ramularia, Septoria, Phyllosticta,
Ascochyta, Alternaria, Helminthosporium, Colletotrichum, Mycosphaerella* are a
few of the numerous leaf-attacking fungi. Root-rotting fungi are less
numerous and include species of *Fusarium, Corticium, Helminthosporium,
Rosellinia* and *Fomes*. Stem cankers, particularly of small stems, are often
caused by Ascomycetes and Fungi Imperfecti such as *Nectria, Endothia,
Sphaeropsis* and *Coniothyrium*, and many of the pathogens which infect leaves
can also attack young green stems. Cankers and rotting of larger branches
and trunks are sometimes due to Ascomycetes but more often to Basidio-
mycetes, particularly Polyporaceae and, less frequently, Agaricaceae.
Petal blight is often caused by rather unspecialized parasites, notably
Botrytis cinerea, and fruit rots by such near saprophytes as *Rhizopus* and
Penicillium. Seedling pathogens are diverse and frequently include *Pythium,
Rhizoctonia, Penicillium, Fusarium* and various other fungi.

Many specialized parasites cause necrosis of infected tissue in the later
stages of attack, as in rusts, smuts, downy mildews and powdery mildews.
In these the obvious symptoms, at least in the early stages, often refer to
the appearance of the parasite itself. Thus 'powdery mildew' derives from
the characteristic superficial, white, powdery growth of mycelium, conidiophores and conidia of the Erysiphaceae, 'smut' to the masses of dark
teliospores formed by Ustilaginales, 'downy mildew' to the sporangiophores and sporangia formed on the host surface by Peronosporaceae, and
'black spot' (*Diplocarpon rosae*) of roses to the dark subcuticular mycelium of
the fungus. Other symptoms such as chlorosis or necrosis may be present
but masked to varying extents.

Hypertrophy

Hypertrophy caused by pathogens or injury involves proliferation or
enlargement of the affected cells, or both, and includes such overgrowths

as galls, tumours, witch's brooms, fasciation, thickening and curling of
leaves, and others as described above. These effects can be caused by certain insects, mites, nematodes, viruses, and chemicals as well as by some
bacteria and fungi, and apparently by physiological upsets of unknown
origin. It is thought that they result basically from imbalance of growth
regulating substances. With the exception of certain bacteria, notably
those causing crown gall and leguminous root nodules, the organisms
concerned are chiefly specialized parasites belonging to such diverse
groups as Plasmodiophorales, Chytridiales, Peronosporaceae, Albuginaceae, Taphrinales, Ustilaginales, Uredinales and Exobasidiaceae. Some
are systemic to varying extents.

Hypoplasia (*under-development*)

This in its extreme form leads to atrophy in which the organ or tissue
fails to develop at all. Included here are reduced development of the whole
plant, parts of the plant, certain tissues, flowers or fruit (sterility), or
chlorophyll (chlorosis).

Diseased plants are often subnormal in growth because of loss of photosynthetic tissue, reduced ability to take up water from the soil, or other
causes. These stunting effects can be very marked if the disease is severe,
especially in young plants, and are to be distinguished from the stunting
resulting from interference with the growth regulating mechanism of the
plant following infection by some pathogens, notably some smuts and
viruses. Individual organs, including leaves and flowers, may be reduced
in size and/or altered in shape. Reduced, misshapen leaves result from
infection by some viruses and also occur in diseases caused by such fungi
as *Exobasidium* (figure 12.8). Some viruses cause profound alterations in
leaves and flowers; for example 'fern leaf'in which the lamina may virtually
disappear, 'little leaf', and numerous modifications of the leaf shape in
which infected leaves bear little resemblance to normal ones. Flowers may
fail to develop, may be shed, may be sterile or may produce only worthless
seed.

Reduced development of chlorophyll, leading to various types of chlorosis, mosaic and mottling, occurs in many virus and deficiency diseases,
and chlorophyll breaks down during necrosis of photosynthetic tissue. The
mottling may be in different shades of green and yellow or sometimes
almost white and can also take the form of ring spot in which the chlorotic
or necrotic areas are arranged in concentric rings around a central spot.
Mottling may be rather mild and indefinite in pattern or sharply contrasted
(mosaic) and may or may not be accompanied by curling, crinkling,
blistering or other distortion of the leaf. Chlorosis sometimes takes the form
of striping or streaking, especially in grass leaves. There may be vein

Figure 12.8 Azalea leaves infected by *Exobasidium vaccinii*. Infected leaves are often so distorted and reduced as to become almost unrecognizable.

clearing – a translucent appearance of the veins – or vein banding in which dark green bands bound the veins, or a general chlorosis of the whole leaf as in the 'yellows' diseases. Infection with some viruses leads to colour breaking of the flowers, the normal colour being irregularly distributed as splashes or streaks on a paler background, giving a variegated effect which can be of horticultural value. Other floral abnormalities induced by viruses include phyllody, suppression of flowering, abscission or drying up of young flowers and fruit, malformation or reduction or abortion of fruits and seeds, sterility of the gynoecium, failure of stamens to mature, and aborted pollen. Fruits may show such symptoms as mottle or ring spot, are often of inferior quality and taste, and may fail to ripen, or ripen unevenly.

Figure 12.9 Silver leaf of plum caused by *Stereum purpureum*. The silvering is due to separation of the epidermis from the mesophyll, thus allowing air to enter the leaf. This separation has been attributed to substances – possibly pectolytic enzymes – carried from the infected woody parts to the leaves in the transpiration stream.

In some diseases symptoms are shown by organs which are not themselves infected. Some wilting, for example, is a generalized response to shortage of water which can be due to root damage by fungi, bacteria, insects, nematodes, or physical and chemical agents. The well known symptoms of silver leaf probably result from phytotoxic substances produced as a result of attack by *Stereum purpureum* of the branches and trunk of

Figure 12.10   Die-back of *Lonicera fragrantissima* caused by *Botrytis cinerea*; the fungus enters the
stem through cracks in the bark, wounds and fresh leaf scars.

the plum tree, these substances being carried to the leaves in the transpiration stream (figure 12.9). Some of the symptoms characteristic of vascular
wilt diseases – epinasty of petioles, production of adventitious roots, vein-
clearing, wilting and leaf necrosis – perhaps have a similar origin. Die-
back can be caused by pathogens attacking the apex of the shoot (figure
12.10) or by water deficiency or phytotoxic substances originating from

attack further down the plant. Although the appearance of symptoms usually indicates successful parasitism this is not invariably so; the small necrotic spots or flecks characteristic of hypersensitivity (p. 264) may be an effective resistance mechanism of the invaded tissue.

13 Mechanisms of attack

Pathogens which cause immediate and severe tissue damage to their host plant are conventionally regarded as less specialized parasites which obtain their nutrients from cells killed in advance by metabolic products. Other parasites, perhaps an intermediate group, invade and kill plant cells. Such necrotrophs are in contrast to biotrophs, more specialized parasites which at first have only a slightly adverse effect on the host although the latter is usually more severely damaged when sporulation occurs. These harmful effects are often caused by substances produced by the pathogen, or perhaps by the host as a result of infection, and include enzymes, toxins, growth regulating substances and others. There is an extensive literature on the biochemical and physiological aspects of these substances, and only a brief summary can be given here. General accounts of host/parasite interaction are given by Buxton (1964), Yarwood (1967), Mirocha and Uritani (1967: molecular and biochemical aspects) and Wood (1967).

Enzymes

Fungi can produce a great variety of enzymes, no doubt related to the nature of the materials colonized. Those normally produced have been called constitutive enzymes as distinct from adaptive or inductive enzymes whose formation appears to be stimulated by the presence of the appropriate substrate. Enzymes catalyse many of the biochemical processes of living organisms and thus play a fundamental role in the host-parasite interaction. They are concerned not only in the initial entry of the pathogen and its spread within the plant but also in the degradation of host tissue into metabolites which the parasite can utilize. The complex biochemical changes proceeding in parasitized tissue, and the enzymes involved, are now being studied using modern techniques, but knowledge of these aspects is slight. Rather more is known about some of the enzymes which affect the constituents of plant cell walls – cuticle, pectic substances, cellulose, hemicellulose and lignin. Husain and Kelman (1959) give a general account of tissue disintegration.

Cuticular enzymes

The significance of cuticle softening enzymes in plant diseases is uncertain and needs more investigation; some aspects are discussed earlier (p. 162). Much of the cuticle consists of a cutin framework with the waxes embedded within it and extruded from its surface to give a waterproof 'bloom'. The central region appears to consist largely of cutin with its hydrophobic methyl groups probably orientated towards the radially arranged layer of wax molecules which are congregated near the outer surface, and its hydrophilic hydroxyl and carboxyl groups orientated towards the interior (Martin, 1964). Basically cutin is thought to consist of esters which yield on hydrolysis fatty and hydroxy-fatty acids ('cutin acids'), such as di- and tri-hydroxystearic acids. The cuticular waxes consist typically of complex mixtures of long-chain paraffins, alcohols, ketones, esters and acids, with the paraffins and esters predominating at the outer surface.

There are considerable differences in the amount of cutin and wax in leaves of different species of plants. The cuticle may be thin, as in potato leaves, or thick, as in laurel, and fruits often have a thicker cuticle than the leaves of the same plant. Cutin rarely exceeds 60% by weight of the complete cuticle; in dessert and cider apple fruits the waxes comprised 30–45%, cutin 30-40%, and cellulose less than 10%, depending on variety and stage of maturity (Martin, 1964).

Small quantities of other substances such as proteins, carbohydrates, pigments and occluded pectin and cellulose may also be present. Further information on the cuticle can be obtained from Martin (1964), Frey-Wyssling (1953), Fernando et al. (1964), Wood (1967), Juniper (1960), Leigh and Matthews (1963), and Martin and Juniper (1969).

From what is written above it is clear that the cuticle is chemically complex and several enzymes are no doubt involved in its dissolution: (1) cutinase which catalyses the breakdown of cutin, a complex polyester which hydrolyses into fatty and hydroxy-fatty acids (cutin acids) and other substances, (2) enzymes concerned with breakdown of fatty acids, and (3) those enzymes which degrade other cuticular substances, possibly including proteins, pigments (perhaps a complex of tannin and carbohydrate: Martin, 1964), pectic substances and cellulose.

Degradation of cuticular material is brought about by some fungi (for example *Penicillium spinulosum*: Heinen and Linskens, 1961) and leaf

H

cuticle is no doubt broken down by soil fungi. Enzymes catalysing lysis of cutin, and other enzymes concerned with breakdown of fatty acids, as well as pectic and cellulolytic enzymes, have been found in *P. spinulosum*. A pathogen equipped with such enzymes should be able to degrade cuticularized epidermal cell walls, but many investigators consider that chemical degradation of the cuticle plays little if any part in penetration. Pathogenic fungi are not known to produce cutinases although this is not necessarily significant since the problem has not been adequately investigated.

Wiltshire (1915) found that infection hyphae of *Venturia inaequalis* grew in the cuticle but this might be due to channels of softer material in it. Nusbaum and Keitt (1938), although unable to confirm this, pointed out that their results did not eliminate the possibility of a slight and sharply localized solvent action of the infection hypha on the cuticle. It may be that some such cuticle breakdown occurs around the infection hypha, perhaps resulting in the formation of fungitoxic substances (for example cutin acids) which may inhabit its further growth (Martin, 1964). Such inhibition has been observed and might be due to chemical factors, although it is generally attributed to physical ones. Germinating spores of *Colletotrichum gloeosporioides* degrade the cuticle of orange leaves (Chaudhuri, 1935), and Graniti (1962) considers that cuticular breakdown can occur in olive leaves attacked by *Spilocaea oleagina*. The protoplasm of oat epidermal cells was visibly affected 12–18 hours before *Cochliobolus victoriae* passed through the cuticle (Paddock, 1953), and Hansford (1946) suggests that certain tropical foliicolous ascomycetes appear to have a chemical effect on the host's cuticle. A considerable reduction in cutin content of rose leaves infected by *Sphaerotheca pannosa*, and a smaller reduction in apple leaves attacked by *Venturia inaequalis* have been reported by Roberts *et al.* 1960, suggesting that cutin is degraded by these fungi.

The evidence of these and other reports suggests that some plant pathogens can degrade cutin. Fungal pathogens can produce enzymes able to degrade cellulose, pectic substances and lignin, and it might be expected that some would produce cutinases. However, as noted by Wood (1960), any extensive production of such enzymes would probably lead to increased permeability of the leaf surface and a consequent desiccation which might be disadvantageous to the invading fungus. Dissolution of the cuticle would also open up the leaf to secondary invaders, notably bacteria, which might crowd out the primary pathogen, especially were the latter an obligate parasite.

Infection hyphae may penetrate the cuticle in a few hours whereas the enzymic breakdown of cuticle in the soil is relatively slow, probably too slow to be of much use to an infection structure which must penetrate rapidly if it is to survive. On balance it seems likely that although some of the fungi which attack plants may produce cutinases, the latter may not be produced sufficiently quickly or in sufficient quantity to play an important role in penetration of the cuticle. A localized secretion of such enzymes by the infection structure could, however, soften the cuticle and so facilitate penetration. This is supported by the results of recent studies on the penetration of barley leaves by *Erisyphe graminis f.sp. hordei* which led Edwards and Allen (1970) to suggest that the first stage of penetration might be facilitated by a strictly localized secretion of cuticle degrading enzymes by the tip of the infection peg.

Pectic enzymes

Pectic enzymes and their significance in plant diseases have been reviewed by Bateman and Millar (1966), Sadasivan and Subramanian (1963) and Wood (1955, 1959, 1960, 1960a), who give numerous references to the extensive literature. An interesting account has recently been written by Brown (1965), one of the pioneer workers on enzymic dissolution of cell walls. Pectic enzymes and pectic substances are described by Demain and Phaff (1957), Joslyn (1962), and Kertesz (1951), and cell walls by Frey-Wyssling and Muhlethaler (1965), and Roelofsen (1959).

The capacity to produce pectic enzymes is widespread in fungi, bacteria and nematodes, and changes in the pectic components of cell walls of *Nicotiana* infected by tobacco mosaic virus have been described by Weintraub and Ragetli (1961). Although pectic substances are best known as the basic material of the middle lamella between cells they are also present to varying extents in the primary and possibly in the secondary wall, and pectic enzymes may thus be of significance in the invasion of such structures. Pectic substances are polymers consisting primarily of α-1,4 linked galacturonic acid units, and many of them have the ability to form gels at low concentrations. The carboxyl group on carbon 6 may be unesterified as in the polygalacturonic acids which, if colloidal, are known as pectic acids. Many of the latter are thought to comprise about a hundred units but there may be as little as five, and they and the pectates formed with polyvalent cations are insoluble in water.

The carboxyl groups of pectic acids may be esterified to varying extents with methyl alcohol to give pectinic acids which are estimated to contain 100–200 units probably arranged as in pectic acids (Davies, Giovanelli and Rees, 1964). Pectins are pectinic acids of high methoxy content (75% or more of the carboxyl groups methylated: Bateman and Millar, 1966) which form gels with sugar and acid. Pectinic acids from different plants show different degrees of methylation, and this affects their stability and solubility, the latter increasing with methylation and falling off with increasing molecular size. Pectic acids and pectinic acids both form colloidal solutions, and the former are fairly stable whereas the latter readily depolymerize, especially under alkaline conditions. Water soluble pectic substances may occur in cell vacuoles but little is known about this.

Pectic substances which are insoluble in water are generally termed protopectin, a material which appears to be present in the matrix of the primary cell wall, is soluble in dilute acids, and yields pectinic acids of different methoxy content in different plant species and tissues. Pectic substances in the middle lamella are reported to be insoluble in dilute acids but soluble in dilute alkalis and may be complexes in which chains of pectic acid are linked through calcium and possibly magnesium and other polyvalent cations.

Pectic preparations vary in composition according to species of plant, type and age of tissue, and method of extraction. They generally contain considerable amounts of such non-uronide substances as galactans, arabans, mannans, xylans and other polysaccharides known collectively as hemicelluloses and are perhaps linked in some unknown way with other cell wall constituents. Hemicellulose preparations from different plants and tissues vary in the numbers and type of constituent compounds. Cell walls consist basically of a complex, interwoven network of cellulose microfibres in an amorphous matrix containing mainly pectic substances, lignin and hemicelluloses, the relative proportions of which vary according to the type and age of the cell.

From this brief and simplified account it is clear that the chemistry of pectic substances and their relations to other components of the cell wall are complex and imperfectly understood: further information can be obtained from Kertesz (1951), McCready and Owens (1954), and Deuel and Stutz (1958). No doubt the enzyme systems which bring about degradation of cell wall constituents are equally complex.

The pectic enzymes at present known fall into two major groups:

Pectinesterases (PE), or pectinmethylesterases, catalyse hydrolysis of the methyl ester groups of pectinic acids to methyl alcohol and pectinic acids of reduced methoxy content and eventually to pectic acid, although de-esterification is rarely complete. They appear to be widely distributed in plants and microorganisms, those of fungal origin generally having a lower optimum pH for their activity.

Polygalacturonases (PG), or pectic glycosidases and lyases, are chain splitting enzymes which break the links between adjacent galacturonic acid units in pectic substances. This can occur by a hydrolytic mechanism (hydrolases) or an eliminative mechanism (lyases), and Bateman and Millar (1966) further classify these pectic glycosidases and lyases into eight types based on whether cleavage occurs terminally or randomly in the chain and whether pectin or pectic acid is 'preferentially' attacked. There is some terminological confusion and the names pectinase, depoly-merase, protopectinase, pectin depolymerase and others have been used.

Wood (1959) adopts the classification proposed by Demain and Phaff (1957) *viz.*, polygalacturonase (PG) when the 'preferred' substrate is pectic acid, polymethylgalacturonase (PMG) when it is pectin. If chain splitting is at random the enzymes are endo-PG and endo-PMG, whereas if only terminal linkages are attacked they are exo-PG and exo-PMG.

Enzymic degradation of protopectin has been ascribed to protopectinase, probably a collection of enzymes which degrade insoluble protopectin into soluble pectinic acids and so play a part in maceration of plant tissue by soft rot organisms.

The capacity to produce pectic enzymes seems to be widespread among living organisms, especially higher plants, microorganisms and animals feeding on plants, and is thus not necessarily indicative of phytopathogenicity. Pectinesterases occur in most parts of plants (particularly fruits), endopolygalacturonase develops during ripening of certain fruits, and endo-pectin methyl-trans-eliminase is present in healthy pea tissue (Bateman and Millar, 1966), but relatively little is known about other pectic enzymes in higher plants.

Many fungi and bacteria produce pectic enzymes, especially pectinesterase, in culture, and this may be stimulated by the presence of the specific substrate. Different microorganisms or even different isolates of the same species may form different pectic enzymes. Less is known about production of the chain splitting galacturonases. Production of pectic enzymes by a pathogen in culture does not necessarily indicate that they are produced in the host plant or that they play a part in pathogenesis. Murant and Wood (1957), for example, found that *Erwinia aroideae* caused much more rotting of potato tubers than did *Pseudomonas syringae*, *P.* sp., and *Flavobacterium* sp. although culture filtrates of all four bacteria had similar macerating activity. Production of pectic enzymes in culture was reported to be about the same in non-pathogenic and phytopathogenic bacteria although pectin methyl esterase was produced only by the soft rot *Erwinia* spp. (*carotovora, atroseptica, aroideae, phytophthora*), by *Xanthomonas campestris*, and by one strain of *X. vasculorum* (Smith, 1958).

Many factors, including *p*H, affect the type and amount of enzymes produced, and conclusions derived from *in vitro* studies may not be a reliable indication of what happens in the plant. The possibility that some of the pectic enzymes detected in diseased tissue are of host or contaminant origin has to be borne in mind, and a further complicating factor is the possible inactivation of enzymes by natural inhibitors present in adjacent healthy tissue or perhaps formed after death of the host cells.

Pectic enzymes are generally most active in the early stages of infection and are best studied at that time. For these and other reasons the significance of these enzymes in pathogenesis is uncertain but there is much circumstantial evidence of their importance. Thus, microchemical tests indicate the disappearance or changed nature of pectic substances from the middle lamella in some diseases, and the amount and type of pectic substances may differ in infected as compared with nearby healthy tissue. Comparative estimates of the quantity and types of pectic enzymes present in diseased and healthy tissue may yield valuable information, although the results are often difficult to evaluate. Some plant pathogens can utilize pectic substances as a sole source of carbon but it is not known how widespread this ability is.

Pectic enzymes are apparently of prime importance in soft rot diseases in which parenchymatous tissue is rapidly invaded with accompanying dissolution of the middle lamella to give a mass of soft, disorganized, water-soaked tissue which dies and is likely to be colonized by secondary invaders. If contamination does not occur the affected tissue may remain more or less colourless without the discolouration which normally accompanies death. Although soft rot organisms often produce pectic enzymes in culture it is likely that other enzymes are also involved in maceration of plant tissue, as discussed below. Tissue of high water content seems to be particularly prone to soft rot, and the availability of calcium and boron influences susceptibility, no doubt through their effect on the cell wall. Growth-regulating substances may have a similar effect. Different species and tissues vary in their pectic composition and so in their susceptibility to enzymic degradation; for example, pectinic acids of *Beta* contain a high proportion of acetyl groups and those of young peaches are almost completely esterified, and enzyme inhibitors may be present. Soft rot diseases are thus more complicated than often appears at first glance. The microorganisms involved include *Pectobacterium carotovorum* (possibly including *Erwinia aroideae*), *Pseudomonas marginalis*, *Botrytis cinerea*, *Penicillium expansum*, *Sclerotinia fructigena*, *Rhizoctonia solani*, and various Phycomycetes (*Pythium, Phytophthora, Rhizopus*). Many of these are wound parasites or attack chiefly debilitated plants.

Pectic enzymes may be secreted by some of the pathogens involved in spotting and blotching of leaves, although the macerating effect may be masked by necrosis caused by toxins. Some such pathogens cause small translucent lesions in the early stages of infection, or the lesion may have a translucent border. These effects may be due to pectic enzymes or they could be due to toxins or other causes. Weintraub and Ragetli (1961) have reported that the walls of cells adjacent to lesions caused by tobacco mosaic virus on *Nicotiana* leaves contain predominantly calcium pectate as compared with pectic acid interspersed with calcium pectate in normal tissue. Calcium pectate is apparently more resistant to pectinase, and this perhaps limits spread of the lesion and prevents systemic development of the virus. Similar considerations may apply to leaf spot diseases caused by other pathogens.

The role of pectic enzymes in vascular wilt diseases is uncertain. They may play a part in invasion of the extravascular tissues and in obstructing the movement of water through the xylem vessels, this obstruction perhaps being due to large molecules of pectic substances released from the walls of vessels or adjacent cells by pectic enzymes, but toxins may also be involved and the situation is complex. Many vascular wilt pathogens produce macerating enzymes in culture and these may be important in the final stage of this type of disease when the pathogen moves out of the vascular cylinder and invades the adjacent tissues. The typical silver leaf symptoms caused by *Stereum purpureum* have been attributed to pectic enzymes carried up to the leaves in the transpiration stream.

In parenchymatous tissue exposed to pectic enzymes the cells separate along the middle lamella which consists principally of pectates, and chain splitting polygalacturonases are probably involved. However, the middle lamella is continuous with the matrix of the primary wall so that maceration could result from enzymic degradation of pectic substances in the outermost layers of the matrix. After separation further enzyme action leads to breakdown of the protopectin of the primary cell wall, and enzymes not yet characterized are concerned in this. The cells of macerated tissue soon die although the reasons for this are obscure and are discussed by Brown (1965) who distinguishes a 'macerating principle' from a 'lethal principle'. Since mere separation of cells would probably not kill them and the products of enzymic pectolysis are unlikely to be toxic he postulates colloidal proteolytic, lipolytic or polysaccharide attacking enzymes which kill by destroying the permeability regulating mechanism of the protoplasts. Such a colloidal toxin would be unable to reach the protoplast until the cell wall had been breached by appropriate enzymes. It is of interest that a hemicellulase, probably α-L-arabinofuranosidase, able to macerate tissue and kill protoplasts, has been isolated from culture filtrates of *Sclerotinia fructigena* by Byrde and Fielding (1962, 1965), and that a similar enzyme was found in cultures of *Botrytis cinerea*, *Penicillium expansum*, *Rhizoctonia solani* and *Sclerotinia sclerotiorum* on potato media. Enzymic dissolution of the cell wall no doubt facilitates the entry of substances, including toxins, into the cell and the outward movement of substances, including nutrients useful to the pathogen. It also exposes other components of the cell wall to enzyme action.

Another possible explanation for the death of protoplasts in soft rot diseases is put forward by Wood (1967). He points out that, once certain physical barriers in the cell wall have been removed by macerating enzymes, the limiting external membranes of the protoplasts might burst following their rapid expansion on absorbing water. This is borne out by the results of plasmolysis experiments reported by Tribe (1955), in which the cells in discs of potato tuber exposed to macerating enzymes of

Erwinia aroideae and *Botrytis cinerea* remained alive much longer when plasmolysed than when unplasmolysed, although maceration was only slightly affected by plasmolysis. Microscopical examination failed, however, to support the 'bursting' theory.

Although pectic enzymes have been studied chiefly in soft rot diseases it is likely that more specialized pathogens also produce them, as has been shown for germinating uredospores of *Puccinia graminis tritici*. They are likely to be involved in the growth of hyphae between host cells and in penetration of the epidermal cell wall which has a pectic matrix. Pectic enzymes interact, sometimes synergistically, with other enzymes and metabolites, as in *Cladosporium cucumerinum* in which maceration of cucumber hypocotyl tissue was most rapid with a crude enzyme preparation containing pectic enzymes and protease (Kuc, 1962). Enzymes which catalyse the breakdown of hemicelluloses in the cell wall may have a similar effect, and also substances which produce a pH suitable for pectolysis, as reported by Bateman and Beer (1965) for oxalic acid in beans attacked by *Sclerotium rolfsii*.

There may be antagonistic effects in which pectic enzymes are inactivated, notably by phenols or tannins, or their synthesis inhibited, as discussed by Byrde (1963). Thus, oxidation of phenols in certain apple varieties produced tannin-like substances which inactivated macerating enzymes and so reduced infection (Byrde, 1956, 1957) and polygalacturonase of *Verticillium albo-atrum* was inhibited by oxidation products of polyphenols (Patil and Dimond, 1967). There are many reports of pathogenicity being related to ability to produce pectic enzymes, and Friedman and Ceponis (1959) found that mutants of *Pseudomonas marginalis* of low pathogenicity to lettuce and chicory had a reduced ability to produce pectic enzymes and to utilize pectic substances. Mann (1962), however, concluded that production of pectic enzymes by *Fusarium oxysporum f.sp., lycopersici* was not essential for development of wilt symptoms although these enzymes might play some part in pathogenicity.

High sugar concentrations may reduce production of enzymes and this may be of significance in some diseases. Horsfall and Dimond (1957) have pointed out that certain pathogens tend to be associated with tissues of high sugar content, others with those of low sugar content, and Keen and Horton (1965) suggest that high sugar content of onion roots imparts resistance against *Pyrenochaeta terrestris* (pink root) by suppressing production of pectic enzymes by the pathogen. High calcium content often appears to confer disease resistance, possibly due to enhanced resistance to attack by certain polygalacturonases resulting from increased formation of calcium pectate.

There are many cases in which pathogenicity shows no relationship to production of pectic enzymes, and it is important to recognize that the latter is only one of the factors operating in pathogenesis. Many others such as entry of the pathogen into the plant, environmental conditions, water content of the tissue (Brown, 1965), and the defensive reactions of the host are involved. Pectic enzymes appear to be important in some diseases, notably soft rots of parenchymatous tissue, but are probably less so in others, and more investigation of their significance in pathogenesis is needed.

Other enzymes are probably involved in maceration of plant tissues although pectic enzymes are at present thought to be most important in this respect. Among them are the arabinofuranosidase described above, 'phytolysin' from culture filtrates of *Dothidea ribesia* (Naef-Roth, Gaumann and Albersheim, 1961) and possibly proteolytic enzymes, although there is some doubt about the last named. Doubtless there are other enzymes involved in the breakdown of other components of the cell wall.

Cellulolytic enzymes

These have been studied in relation to deterioration of textiles and wood but comparatively little is known about their significance in plant diseases. The cellulose molecule consists basically of a long chain of several thousand *D*-glucose residues joined by β-1,4 linkages. The molecules are arranged in parallel bundles of about 2000, these forming the microfibrils, which are in turn grouped in larger bundles of about 400 to form the macrofibrils (Davies, Giovanelli and Rees, 1964). Some investigators, for example Preston (1961), have suggested that cellulose is a mixed polysaccharide, others that it is chemically linked to encrusting materials such as lignin. Within the microfibrils the molecules are not uniformly arranged, there being crystalline areas where the chains are more or less parallel, and amorphous areas where they are more randomly arranged. The fibres are intertwined to form a lattice-like structure with the inter-fibrillar spaces filled with an amorphous matrix composed chiefly of pectic substances, hemicelluloses and lignin. Cellulose thus forms the basic framework of cell walls in plants. It is insoluble in water but can be made soluble by substituting the hydrogen of the primary and secondary hydroxyl groups with groups such as methyl and ethyl, and such soluble derivatives (for example carboxymethylcellulose) have been extensively used in enzyme studies.

Enzymic degradation of cellulose is imperfectly understood. Whitaker (1953, 1957) working with *Myrothecium verrucaria* concluded that a single enzyme converts cellulose into glucose by random cleavage of the molecule. Others, including Aitken *et al.* (1956), consider that it is converted to the disaccharide cellobiose by one enzyme and thence to glucose by a second one, cellobiase. Reese (1956) and others postulate a series of enzymes: Cl enzymes loosen or release the chains from the cellulose molecules which then take up water and are hydrolysed by Cx enzymes to cellobiose or glucose. These aspects are discussed by Norkrans (1963), and other accounts of microbial degradation of cellulose are given by Siu (1951), Gascoigne and Gascoigne (1960), Siu and Reese (1953) and Greathouse and Wessel (1954).

In contrast to some pectolytic enzymes which are often constitutive, cellulases are usually adaptive in that their formation is stimulated by the presence of cellulose, and the products of enzymic hydrolysis of the latter may reduce further enzyme secretion (Siu and Sinden, 1951). Cellulases are produced by many organisms including higher plants (particularly germinating seeds), certain insects and nematodes, and many fungi and bacteria. Although many microorganisms degrade soluble cellulose a smaller number have been shown to attack native insoluble cellulose, which would seem to be important in pathogenesis. However, cellulases have been obtained from diseased tissue in some cases and apparent degradation of cellulose occurs in some plant diseases, especially in the later stages.

Cellulases are no doubt involved in decay of wood, and many of the fungi responsible are able to break down cellulose and hemicellulose. This is true of the brown rot fungi whereas those causing white rot break down lignin and also, to some extent, cellulose. Many other factors are also involved, including the ability to inactivate or withstand fungitoxic substances in the wood, and the power to destroy encrusting substances which protect the cellulose. Of the many species of fungi, mostly Basidiomycetes, which cause wood decay only a few attack the heartwood of living trees, and few of these cause decay of wood in service or attack the living sapwood – indeed, many cease to develop further once the tree has been felled although they may remain alive for several years. The fungi which rot dead timber are generally not those which attack the wood of the standing tree. Submerged wood is commonly rotted by aquatic Ascomycetes and Fungi Imperfecti, and presumably these produce cellulolytic and lignolytic enzymes.

It is generally thought that cellulases are of little significance in the early stages of pathogenesis, perhaps because cellulose is at first protected by the enveloping matrix. Many soft rot organisms produce cellulases as well as pectic enzymes, and degradation of cellulose is probably an essential phase in these diseases. Some of the fungi causing damping-off of seedlings appear to be unable to produce cellulases *in vitro* (for example many Pythiaceae) whereas others (for example *Rhizoctonia solani, Fusarium moniliforme*) are reported to produce both cellulolytic and pectic enzymes and, perhaps associated with this, have a greater capacity to attack older tissue. Similarly, *Sclerotium rolfsii* can cause soft rot and can also attack mature, hardened tissue, and is reported to produce a cellulolytic enzyme (Husain, 1957). This may also apply to canker forming fungi such as *Botryosphaeria ribis* which produces much cellulase in culture, grows well on native cellulose, and invades the woody tissue as well as the bark (Husain and Dimond, 1958; Husain and Kelman, 1959). Some of the fungi causing root rot and foot rot are cellulolytic, and it is possible that cellulases are involved in leaf spot and blight diseases although little is known about this.

Pseudomonas solanacearum (Husain and Kelman, 1957, 1958), *Verticillium albo-atrum* (Talboys, 1958) and *Fusarium oxysporum lycopersici* (Husain and Dimond, 1958a) cause wilt diseases and also produce cellulolytic enzymes in culture, and a solution of partially purified enzymes of the last named fungus caused wilting of tomato cuttings whereas a similar but heat inactivated solution had no effect. It has been suggested by Wood (1960a) that conditions within the tracheae favour production of cellulases by vascular wilt pathogens, and that local action of these enzymes might result in the formation of compounds of high molecular weight which could impede the transpiration stream. There is growing evidence that cellulolytic as well as pectolytic enzymes and toxins are involved in vascular wilts but the situation is at present obscure.

Rather few cases have been studied in detail and this perhaps partly accounts for the widely held view that cellulolytic enzymes are of less importance than pectic enzymes in plant diseases. It appears that the former develop or act more slowly than the latter and they are perhaps important in breaking down cellulose into sugars, thus providing nutrients for the pathogen in the later rather than the early stages of attack. They may be of greater importance in diseases in which the host tissue is only slowly colonized but more completely degraded, as in dry rot of potatoes caused by *Fusarium caeruleum* and, possibly, vascular wilt diseases (Wood, 1960a). It may be, however, that the slow colonization of the host is due to the defence mechanisms of the latter.

Production of cellulolytic enzymes *in vitro* is often reduced by sugars and by various inhibitors such as polyphenols (Mandels and Reese, 1963). As with pectic enzymes it is uncertain whether the frequently reported association of disease resistance with phenolic compounds in the host tissue results from enzyme inhibition. Thus Deese and Stahmann (1962) suggest that the damaged, invaded tissue releases phenols which in the presence of high oxidase activity form quinones inhibitory to enzymes produced by the pathogen. The cellulolytic powers of more specialized parasites is uncertain although germinating uredospores of *Puccinia graminis tritici* produced a cellulase able to hydrolyse soluble derivatives of cellulose (Sumere *et al.*, 1957).

Hemicellulases

Hemicelluloses are important constituents of plant cell walls, particularly mature and thickened ones. They are complex, insoluble polysaccharides consisting of mixtures of such pentosans as xylans (especially in secondary walls), mannans (especially in gymnosperms), galactans, arabans and others. Many microorganisms, saprophytic and parasitic, produce hemicellulases and can presumably convert hemicelluloses into pentoses and uronides. It seems that some cellulolytic enzymes can degrade hemicellulose components, as with hydrolysis of xylans by cellulase produced by *Myrothecium verrucaria* (Bishop and Whitaker, 1955). It is surprising that so little attention has been given to cellulolytic and hemicellulolytic enzymes in plant diseases, as compared with the intensive investigation of pectolytic enzymes. There are, however, some reports of hemicellulases being implicated in plant diseases. These include xylanase and arabinase in sunflower hypocotyls attacked by *Sclerotinia sclerotiorum* (Hancock, 1967), arabinofuranosidase in culture filtrates of *S. fructigena* (Byrde and Fielding, 1962, 1965), and at least two extracellular xylan degrading enzymes were produced by *Diplodia viticola* growing on autoclaved grapes (Strobel, 1963). Van Etten and Bateman (1969) found that *Sclerotium (Corticium) rolfsii* produced exogalactanase, endomannanase, galactosidase and endoxylanase in culture and that these enzymes also occur in bean tissue infected by the fungus. Hemicellulases will no doubt be found to be implicated in other plant diseases.

Lignolytic enzymes

Lignin, probably the major component of plant cell walls after cellulose, is a complex polymer consisting predominantly of substituted phenyl propane units, but its structure is obscure. It occurs chiefly in the matrix surrounding the cellulose fibrils and possibly in some sort of chemical association with the latter. In woody cells lignin constitutes almost all of the middle lamella and forms its own framework in the walls so that the latter are strengthened and remain intact even after cellulose and hemicellulose are removed. Deposition of lignin is normally followed by death of the cell so that fungi which attack lignified tissue may be described as perthophytes.

White rot fungi, chiefly Basidiomycetes, break down lignin by means of enzymes (ligninases, lignases) which are apparently polyphenoloxidases of the laccase type. Such enzymes may be present in culture filtrates of white rot fungi grown in media with lignin as sole carbon source (Gottlieb and Pelczar, 1951). The chemistry and breakdown of lignins are described by Brauns (1952), Brauns and Brauns (1960), Kremers (1959), Neish

(1960), Pearl (1967), Davies *et al.* (1964), and Lawson and Still (1957), and decay of wood by Campbell (1952) and Cartwright and Findlay (1958). Brown (1966) gives a recent review of lignins.

Except in wood decay, lignolytic enzymes are probably of only minor importance in plant diseases, although further study is needed. Lignin is a resistant material and is thought to be attacked by only a few microorganisms and then only slowly. Husain and Kelman (1959) point out that many of the monocotyledons subject to foot rot have a fairly high lignin content and that lignolytic enzymes might be involved. In this connexion the report by Fischer (1953) that certain species of *Fusarium*, including *F. lactis* and *F. nivale* (conidia of *Griposphaeria nivalis*, the cause of snow mould of turf) can readily break down lignin is of interest.

Other enzymes possibly involved in degradation of cell walls

Suberin, present in corky tissue, is of course degraded in nature, presumably by microorganisms. It is a complex of substances including several fatty acids (suberogenic acids) and is apparently similar to cutin. A layer of suberized cells often develops as a response of the tissue to wounding or to invasion by parasites. Corky layers can be effective barriers against invading pathogens, suggesting that most plant pathogens are unable to break down suberin, or to break it down sufficiently quickly for suberin degrading enzymes to be of much significance in the degradation of cell walls.

Proteins are present in some cell walls and some fungi produce proteolytic enzymes in culture and in the infected plant. Hancock and Millar (1965), for example, detected protease activity in alfalfa leaf tissue infected by *Stemphylium botryosum*. There is little information as to whether proteases play any part in the degradation of cell walls. Tsung-Che Tseng and Bateman (1969) have pointed out that several plant pathogens, including *Sclerotium rolfsii*, can produce phosphatidases and they suggest that these enzymes and proteases might affect cell membranes, since phospholipids and proteins are the major components of plant membrane systems. These enzymes may be involved in the necrosis of cells which occur in soft rot diseases (p. 223).

Toxins

In plant pathology this term is used loosely to connote substances, usually but not invariably of pathogen origin, which are injurious to plants and which may or may not play a role in disease. This wide interpretation includes harmful enzymes and indeed there is no sharp demarcation between these and toxins.

The significance of toxins in plant disease is uncertain. It is generally accepted that symptoms which develop in advance of the pathogen, often as a chlorotic or translucent zone, are likely to be due to diffusible metabolites secreted by it, but whether all pathogens produce toxins is not known, and the position of obligate parasites in this respect is obscure. Gaumann (1954) considered that microorganisms are pathogenic only if they are toxigenic, this applying to plant and animal diseases, but symptoms can originate from other causes such as withdrawal of nutrients from the host. The production of typical disease symptoms in a plant inoculated with a cell-free filtrate from a pure culture of the pathogen suggests, but does not prove, that toxins are involved. However, some saprophytic fungi produce phytotoxic metabolites in culture and there has been an uncritical tendency to ascribe a role in pathogenesis to such metabolites without adequate investigation. Hence there are many reports of toxins causing disease symptoms but few proven cases. In an attempt at rationalization the following terminology has been proposed:

Vivotoxin is 'a substance produced in the infected host by the pathogen and/or its host, which functions in the production of disease' (Dimond and Waggoner, 1953). Three minimal criteria were suggested: reproducible separation of the toxin from the 'sick' plant, purification or chemical characterization, and induction of at least a portion of the disease syndrome by placing the toxin in a healthy plant. A later amendment (Dimond, 1955) specified that the toxin should not be present in the healthy plant but this seems illogical and would exclude, for example, ethylene.

Pathotoxins are 'those toxins which have been shown to play an important causal role in disease' (Wheeler and Luke, 1963), comprising those produced by pathogen, host, or interaction between them. On this basis fungitoxic substances of host origin, such as phytoalexins, should be included. 'Pathogen' is used for living organisms which cause disease and it has been suggested that 'chemopathogen' be used for toxic substances which cause disease.

Other types of toxin are: **phytotoxin,** a general term for phytotoxic substances produced by living organisms; **endotoxin,** intracellular toxins formed in bacterial cells and not liberated until the latter die; and **exotoxin,** extracellular toxins which diffuse from the living bacterial cell. Antibiotics produced by microorganisms and involved in antagonism, and phytoalexins and other fungitoxic substances present in or produced by plants can also be regarded as toxins. Phytoncide is a misleading word used to denote toxic substances produced by plants. There are also phytotoxins produced by insects and possibly by nematodes and parasitic angiosperms although some of these are no doubt enzymes.

Symptoms of many of the bacterial diseases of man and animals are due to complex proteinaceous toxins produced by the bacteria in the host tissue and often distributed in the blood stream. These toxins are antigenic and specific antitoxins can be prepared, thus facilitating investigation. Toxins produced by plant pathogens have small molecules compared with those produced by animal pathogens, the molecular weight running into hundreds as compared with thousands and with this is associated the diffusibility of plant toxins and their ability to pass through cell walls. Many parasitic and saprophytic microorganisms produce phytotoxic substances in culture, but proof that they are produced in the infected plant and cause the disease symptoms is rarely forthcoming.

Ideally, for a toxin to be proven as the cause of a specific disease it should fulfil the following conditions (Wheeler and Luke, 1963): (1) When applied to a susceptible plant in low concentrations, such as might be expected to occur in the diseased tissues, it should produce all or nearly all of the symptoms characteristic of the disease. It should be remembered, however, that several toxins each causing different symptoms may be involved in some diseases. (2) Toxin and pathogen should have a similar host range, and immune or highly resistant plants should be largely unaffected by the toxin, and *vice versa*. This may be complicated by defence reactions of the plant which prevent entry of the pathogen or its multiplication. (3) The pathogenicity of the organism should be correlated with its capacity to produce the toxin – weakly pathogenic strains should be less toxigenic. Many factors, however, govern pathogenicity, and the conditions of culture may affect production of toxins.

These are rigorous conditions and few toxins scrupulously fulfil them. As Pringle and Scheffer (1964) point out, each case must be considered on its own merits rather than rigidly adhering to what is in effect a set of Koch's postulates for toxins.

There is an extensive literature on toxins in plant disease, and reviews are given by Brian (1955, 1958), Gaumann (1954), Ludwig (1960), Braun and Pringle (1959), Deverall (1964), Wheeler and Luke (1963) and Pringle and Scheffer (1964). See also *Phytotoxins in Plant Diseases*, edit. by Wood, R. K. S., Ballio, A. and Graniti, A. (Academic Press, London and New York) 1971. Some of the better known toxins are now briefly described.

Host-specific toxins

Victorin is probably the best authenticated fungal toxin. It is produced by *Cochliobolus (Helminthosporium) victoriae*, the cause of Victoria blight of oats in the USA, a destructive and rather unspecialized pathogen which causes foot and root rot and leaf blight. It is soil- and seed-borne and produces a highly potent toxin which acts at some distance from the original infection and is described in detail by Pringle and Scheffer (1964) in their account of host specific plant toxins. Victorin, the toxic principle in culture filtrates, reproduced the symptoms and physiological effects of the fungus – including increase in respiration and tissue permeability – when inoculated into susceptible plants, and both pathogen and toxin affected plants of susceptible but not resistant varieties of oats. Victorin is exceedingly phytotoxic, refined preparations being toxic even at 1 part in 5 thousand million, and it has been shown that the fungus produces these minute amounts in susceptible hosts. Thus, extracts of diseased plants produced typical blight symptoms when inoculated into susceptible ones. It appears to be a fairly low molecular weight pentapeptide linked to a tricyclic amine which was named victoxinine. The latter, but not victorin, is also produced by non-pathogenic strains of *C. victoriae* and indeed by other species of *Helminthosporium* (Nishimura *et al.*, 1966).

Victorin is fairly stable in acid solution but becomes less stable on purification. The refined product is a white, water soluble powder which degenerates at room temperature but retains its toxicity *in vacuo* at $-20°C$. In culture some strains of the fungus readily produce victorin, others not, and what may have been virus infected cultures grew poorly and produced less victorin (Lindberg, 1960). This toxin appears to be specific to Victoria varieties of oats. Many species of plants are insensitive to it (Luke and Wheeler, 1955) and others may undergo limited invasion by the pathogen; for example, *Phaseolus vulgaris* developed a slight fleck-like necrotic spotting with little or no sporulation (Winstead and Hebert, 1956). Some grasses were affected by the fungus and developed leaf lesions, but the symptoms were different and perhaps due to other causes (Nelson and Kline, 1961, 1962). Both pathogen and toxin appear to have a limited and similar host range.

The way in which victorin kills susceptible tissue is not understood. According to Pringle and Scheffer (1964) it may act at a specific receptor site, possibly on the outer surface of the plasma membrane (Luke, Warmke and Hanchey, 1966). As in many plant diseases respiration increases, possibly by uncoupling oxidative phosphorylation (Sanwal, 1961), but mitochondria are apparently insensitive. Permeability of the cell membranes is affected leading to loss of cellular contents, and leachates from victorin treated tissue contained several forms of nitrogen, carbohydrates, amino acids and various minerals (Black and Wheeler, 1962; Wheeler and Black, 1962; Black, 1963). Victorin inhibits root growth, transpiration and auxin induced cell elongation (Litzenberger, 1949; Wheeler, 1969). That the fungus does not appear to be present in the leaves until some time after death of the tissues suggests that the toxin moves ahead. Susceptible plants react relatively slowly to the fungus in the early stages of invasion whereas resistant ones react more quickly, the affected cells and the fungus dying rapidly (Paddock, 1953). It is uncertain whether victorin in some way delays host reaction.

There are reports of several other apparently host specific toxins which have not been as well investigated as victorin. **Periconin,** probably a polypeptide of fairly low molecular weight, is present in culture filtrates of *Periconia circinata* which causes seedling blight, crown rot and root rot (milo disease) of some dwarf milo sorghums in the U.S.A. Like *C. victoriae* it appears to be a destructive but rather unspecialized soil borne parasite. The refined toxin preparation and the pathogen incite similar symptoms and have a similar host range (Scheffer and Pringle, 1961; Pringle and Scheffer, 1963, 1966, 1967); two distinct toxins have recently been reported by Pringle and Scheffer (1967). Culture filtrates of *Alternaria kikuchiana*, the cause of black spotting of leaves and fruits of *Pyrus serotina* in Japan, contain toxins provisionally named **phytoalternarin** A, B and C, of undetermined chemical nature. Fungus and filtrate had a similar host range and caused similar symptoms (Hiroe, 1952; Hiroe and Aoe, 1954; Hiroe, Nishimura and Sato, 1958; Mori, 1962).

Toxins produced by bacterial plant pathogens

Most of the toxins produced by plant pathogens seem to be pleiotropic, that is, they have multiple effects on the host cells, but the 'wildfire' toxin produced by *Pseudomonas tabaci* is reported to be monotropic, as are many of the toxins produced by bacteria which attack animals. This bacterium causes leaf lesions with characteristic chlorotic halos, and a single unstable toxin (**tabtoxinine**), apparently the lactone of a complex amino acid (Woolley, Pringle and Braun, 1952; Woolley, Scheffer and Braun, 1952, 1955), has been isolated from culture filtrates and causes typical wildfire symptoms. Strains deficient in tabtoxinine do not produce the chlorotic halos around the leaf lesions, but tabtoxinine is non-specific and causes wildfire symptoms not only on resistant tobacco plants but also on many species of plants which are not susceptible to the pathogen (Braun, 1959). Possibly, the defence mechanisms of resistant plants prevent rapid multiplication of the bacteria (Diachun and Trautman, 1954).

P. tabaci and *P. angulata* (angular leaf spot of tobacco, lesions without a halo) are similar except in the symptoms they produce, and the latter may be a tabtoxinine deficient strain of the former (Braun, 1937). The inhibitory effect of the toxin on *Chlorella* was overcome by methionine (Braun, 1950, 1955), and methionine sulphoxime, an antagonist of methionine, produced wildfire symptoms. This suggests that the toxin is an antimetabolite of methionine, although this has yet to be proved. Possibly other bacterial plant pathogens produce toxins which act as antimetabolites, and Patel and Walker (1963) found marked changes in the amounts of some amino acids in chlorotic but bacteria-free leaves of bean plants inoculated with *P. phaseolicola* (halo blight), a bacterium reported to produce a toxin (Skoog, 1952). *P. mors-prunorum*, the cause of bacterial canker, leaf spot and gummosis of stone fruits, is thought to produce a proteinaceous endotoxin since cell-free filtrates of old, but not of young, cultures caused typical symptoms when infected into the bark of susceptible plum trees (Erikson, 1945; Erikson and Montgomery, 1945). Toxins and enzymes are probably produced by many of the bacteria which cause necrosis of plant tissue, but few have been investigated in this respect.

Other toxins

Those described above are perhaps the best authenticated examples of toxins but many others have been reported, some of which are briefly discussed below. **Picularin**: *Pyricularia oryzae* causes the destructive blast disease of rice involving leaf spotting and collar and culm rot. The seedling symptoms and leaf browning of mature plans have been attributed to two toxins one of which (α-picolinic acid) is non-specific and apparently produced in quantity in the later stages of the disease (Tamari and Kaji, 1954, 1955). The other, picularin, is more active and semi-specific in that it affects blast susceptible rice plants more than resistant ones. Low concentrations of picularin inhibit the germination of the conidia of *P. oryzae*, and the fungus has been shown by Ogasawara, Tamari and Kaji (1957, 1961) to produce a protein ('picularin-binding protein', possibly a copper oxidase: Tamari and Kaji, 1954, 1955) which binds picularin and destroys its fungitoxicity but not its phytotoxicity. The ways in which picularin affects plant tissue are not understood but it induces increase of polyphenols and oxidases (Sanwal, 1961) and its toxicity is counteracted by chlorogenic acid, one of the principal poly-phenols of the rice plant; these aspects are discussed by Toyoda and Suzuki (1957, 1960), Togashi *et al.* (1960), Wheeler and Luke (1963) and Sanwal (1961). It increases respiration and growth at low concentrations and inhibits them at higher ones.

Alternaric acid occurs in early blight of tomato and potato, caused by *Alternaria solani*. Some of the lesions appear to be devoid of the fungus under certain conditions, suggesting that a mobile toxin is involved (Pound and Stahmann, 1951). Cultures of *A. solani* produced a dibasic acid, alternaric acid, which caused necrotic lesions similar to those caused by the fungus. The toxin also inhibits or severely restricts growth of fungal germ tubes without actually preventing germination. Alternaric acid is thought to be fairly non-specific and its significance in early blight is uncertain. Thus some highly pathogenic strains of the fungus failed to produce it in culture and it is clear that other factors and possibly other toxins are involved (Brian *et al.*, 1949, 1951, 1952).

Colletotin is produced by *Colletotrichum fuscum* (anthracnose of *Digitalis*). It is apparently similar to alternaric acid and perhaps acts by disrupting cell permeability or by affecting pectic enzymes (Goodman, 1960; Lewis and Goodman, 1962).

Hydrogen cyanide is considered by Lebeau and Dickson (1955) to be implicated in winter crown rot (snow mould) of alfalfa caused by an unidentified Basidiomycete in the U.S.A. Symptoms develop in winter when snow and ice might prevent escape of the gas, and application of hydrogen cyanide caused typical symptoms of the disease.

Fumaric acid is thought to be responsible for the symptoms of hull rot of almonds, probably caused by *Rhizopus* spp., but it has not been found in more than trace amounts, possibly because of its conversion to other acids. The toxin is translocated from the affected fruit and causes blighting of adjacent leaves and twigs. Cultures on water extracts of mesocarp tissue produced fumaric acid and other metabolites but only the former incited blight when inoculated into shoots (Mirocha and Wilson, 1961; Mirocha, De Vay and Wilson, 1961).

Oxalic acid is produced by some fungi and may function as a toxin in some diseases, as in crown rot of groundnut seedlings caused by *Aspergillus niger* in which the pathogenicity of isolates was correlated with their capacity to produce oxalic acid in culture (Gibson, 1953). This acid is also produced by *Sclerotinia sclerotiorum* (Overell, 1952) and may be implicated in several other diseases, but its significance is uncertain. There are also reports of toxins produced by *Helminthosporium sativum* (Ludwig, 1957), *Ophiobolus miyabeanus* (Orsenigo, 1956, 1957), *Rhizoctonia solani* (Kerr, 1956), and other plant pathogens.

Many of the other reports of toxins produced by plant pathogens, for example by *Pythium* (possibly enzymic: Brandenburg, 1950) and *Botrytis cinerea* (Gentile, 1951) are not well documented. Some pathogens probably bring about changes in host tissue which result in the formation of phytotoxic substances. For example in chocolate spot of beans (*Vicia faba*) caused by *Botrytis* sp. the characteristic lesions are thought to be due to a bean phenolase enzyme which is in some way activated by the fungus. Extreme pH, ammonium sulphate, anionic wetting agents and others also activated the latent phenolase (Kenten, 1957, 1958), and germ tubes from *Botrytis* spores quickly caused leaf lesions (Deverall and Wood, 1961, 1961a). The possible occurrence of indirect effects of this sort in other diseases is worth investigating.

Toxin production by parasitic angiosperms

This possibility is rarely investigated although mistletoe berries (*Viscum*) may contain a toxin which causes necrosis in the bark of apple trees (Paine, 1950). It is possible that *Striga asiatica* (witchweed) secretes substances which adversely affect growth and transpiration of the host plant, since extracts of witchweed roots caused wilting and death of rice seedlings in the laboratory (Hattingh, 1954; Uttaman, 1950). Few parasitic angiosperms cause necrosis of the host and it appears that their toxins, if any, are somewhat different from those considered above.

Toxins in vascular wilt diseases

These have been extensively investigated, especially in tomato wilt caused by *Fusarium oxysporum f.sp. lycopersici* in which Gottlieb (1943, 1944) showed that toxins might be involved; accounts are given by Brian (1955), Dimond (1955), Ludwig (1959), Subramanian and Saraswathi-Devi (1959), Sadasivan (1961), Beckman (1964) and others.

The symptoms of vascular wilt diseases include vein clearing, epinasty, plugging and browning of the vascular elements, development of adventitious roots on the stem in some cases, wilting, necrosis, and death in severe infections. Enzymes, toxins and probably growth regulating substances are thought to be involved in this complex of symptoms, but there is little agreement as to their significance. Epinasty and possibly development of adventitious roots are probably due to ethylene produced by pathogen and/or host, and vascular browning may result from the oxidation of phenolic substances to melanins by polyphenoloxidases. Plugging of the xylem vessels has been attributed to the activity of pectic and possibly other enzymes which degrade cell walls and result in deposition of gummy substances in the lumen of the vessels. Formation of tyloses, perhaps related to disturbances of growth regulating mechanisms, may also be involved.

The late Professor Gaumann and his associates in Zurich have isolated three toxins from culture filtrates of *F. oxysporum f.sp. lycopersici* – **lycomarasmin, fusaric acid,** and **vasinfuscarin.** Unfortunately it is not known to what extent these are involved in the diseased plant as distinct from the laboratory, an objection which can be applied to much of the work on toxins in plant diseases. Lycomarasmin is a dipeptide which brings about wilting and yellowing of tomato cuttings, and its phytotoxicity is increased in the presence of iron, perhaps due to formation of a complex. The permeability of the mesophyll cells is probably affected and lycomarasmin may at first cause excessive transpiration, but water uptake subsequently falls off more rapidly than water loss, leading to desiccation and wilting. Its significance is uncertain and evidence for its formation in the plant is not strong – in fact it may be a product of senescence, appearing only when hyphae begin to autolyse.

Fusaric acid, a butylpyridine carboxylic acid, appears to be present in infected plants in several wilt diseases caused by *F. oxysporum f.sp. lycopersici* (tomato), *vasinfectum* (cotton), and *cubense* (Panama disease of banana). It is phytotoxic, causing intercostal necrosis of leaves, permeability changes, reduction of respiration and growth, necrosis of cortical tissues overlying the vascular bundles (leading to furrowing of the stem), and epinasty of petioles (Gaumann, 1958), but there is doubt as to whether the rather high concentrations of fusaric acid needed to bring about these effects occur in the plant (Sanwal, 1961). The latter author (1961) described the physiological effects of this toxin and suggested that it could cause a partial uncoupling of oxidative phosphorylation. Its role in pathogenesis remains problematical, and Deverall (1964) concludes that it plays no part in development of wilt symptoms although it might act in conjunction with other metabolites. Vasinfuscarin is apparently a protein with enzymic properties (Gaumann, 1954) and it is reported to produce the vascular browning typical of vascular wilts. Phytonivein, present in culture filtrates of *F. oxysporum f.sp. niveum*, may be involved in wilt of water melons caused by the fungus (Hiroe and Nishimura, 1956).

Diffusible toxins may be implicated in several other wilt diseases including 'sleepy disease' of tomato (*Verticillium albo-atrum*: Bewley, 1922; Green, 1954), wilt of Michaelmas daisy (*V. vilmorinii*: Dowson, 1922, 1923), pea wilt (*Fusarium orthoceras* v. *pisi*: Linford, 1931, 1931a), brown stem rot of soya (*Cephalosporium gregatum*: Chamberlain and McAlister, 1954), tobacco wilt (*Pseudomonas solanacearum*: Hutchinson, 1913), maize wilt (*Xanthomonas stewarti*: Harris, 1940), and cucumber wilt (*Erwinia tracheiphila*: Harris, 1940). There is rarely conclusive evidence that toxins or enzymes are directly responsible for the symptoms of vascular wilt diseases. Very often the toxin is not as host-specific as the pathogen, it may not produce all the symptoms of the disease, and few toxins have been demonstrated in the infected plant in sufficiently high concentrations. Wilting of tomato cuttings, the experimental material often used, can be brought about by, for example, high molecular weight compounds and pectic and cellulolytic enzymes as well as by the toxins mentioned above, although they probably act in different ways. Gaumann and Obrist (1960) list a number of wilt-inducing substances obtained from culture filtrates of fungi.

Vascular wilt diseases of woody plants have been less well investigated, but enzymes and toxins may be involved. The pathogen often enters through wounds and breaks in the twigs and invades the vascular tissues, causing browning, gum-formation, tyloses, and wilting and death of leaves. Examples include silver leaf of plum and other trees (*Stereum purpureum*: Brooks and Brenchley, 1929, 1931a), coral spot of currants (*Nectria cinnabarina*: Kobel, 1951), oak wilt (*Ceratocystis fagacearum*: Beckman, Kuntz and Riber, 1963; Beckman *et al.*, 1963), Dutch elm disease (*Ceratostomella ulmi*: Feldman *et al.*, 1950; Frederick and Howard, 1951), chestnut blight (*Endothia parasitica*, producing diaporthin and skyrin: Bazzigher, 1954; Gaumann and Naef-Roth, 1957; Boller *et al.*, 1957), and others. In many of these diseases, culture filtrates of the causal fungus incite similar symptoms, suggesting but not proving that toxins may be implicated.

Certain complex organic compounds, particularly polysaccharides such as glucosans, may cause disease symptoms by reason of a physical effect associated with the large size of their molecules rather than by chemical toxicity. They seem to be of importance in some bacterial wilts and may be present in the slime produced by many phytopathogenic bacteria (Leach *et al.*, 1957). Synthetic compounds with large molecules, such as polyethylene glycols and polyvinyl alcohols, can induce wilting of tomato cuttings, and their effectiveness in this respect is said to be correlated with their molecular weight (Braun and Pringle, 1959). Little is known about the way in which these toxins operate, but it is likely that their large sluggish molecules impede upward passage of water by partially occluding the vascular elements and/or by increasing the viscosity of the fluid in the vessels. Localized leaf wilting might also result from similar blocking of the small vessels in the leaf veinlets. This type of wilting is apparently reversible and ceases when the toxin is removed. Pectic and possibly cellulosic and other polysaccharide-like substances may perhaps function in this way. Hodgson, Peterson and Riker (1949) investigated the toxicity of polysaccharides and other substances with large molecules to tomato cuttings and concluded that wilting was due to mechanical blocking of the vessels rather than chemical toxicity. Wilt-inducing poly-saccharides are also discussed by Feder and Ark (1951), Hodgson, Riker and Peterson (1947), and McIntire, Peterson and Riker (1942).

Toxins of obligate parasites

The toxins mentioned above are those produced by rather unspecialized parasites which obtain their nutrients from host cells killed or injured by the toxin. As might be expected there is little evidence that obligate parasites, which obtain their food from living host cells, produce necrotiz-ing toxins although they probably produce substances which render the host tissue more suitable for their growth and development; and in some cases growth of the host tissue is stimulated. Phytotoxic substances, possibly of host origin, may be involved in resistant plants showing hypersensitivity, and Silverman (1960) found toxic substances in infected wheat leaves at high temperatures (when the plant was susceptible to *Puccinia graminis tritici*) but not at low temperatures (resistant, that is hypersensitive). Millerd and Scott (1955) have reported a toxic substance in barley infected with powdery mildew. Toxins might also be involved in the later stages of attack by some biotrophs, when sporulation and tissue necrosis occur, but it is probable that growth stimulating substances are involved in the earlier stages. Whether such substances should be termed toxins is doubtful although they do enhance the food supply of the pathogen.

Kirkham and Hignett (1966) report that pigmented proteins (**melano-proteins**) from culture filtrates of *Venturia inaequalis* stimulated growth of the fungus in apple leaves, and the lower molecular weight components of the extract greatly enhanced pathogenicity. These melano-proteins might affect either the water balance of the tissues or the efficiency of the vascular system, perhaps by altering the permeability of the cell wall. These compounds could be regarded as toxins in the sense that they render the host more susceptible to colonization by the fungus.

Effects of toxins on plant tissue

The changes in host tissue brought about by phytotoxic substances are varied and imperfectly understood. Many stimulate host respiration, at least in the early stages, but this occurs in most types of tissue injury. Most toxins have multiple effects but the wildfire toxin produced by *Pseudomonas tabaci* is thought to be monotropic. Some toxins are fairly host specific, more are probably toxic to a range of plants susceptible and resistant to the toxigenic pathogen. The ways in which toxins kill plant cells are complex with many interactions between toxin and tissue, the latter no doubt sometimes releasing necrotizing enzymes and other toxic materials (including phenolic substances) when injured. The task of disentangling these effects is a difficult one and it is not surprising that information on these aspects is fragmentary. Possible mechanisms of phytotoxicity include the following:

1. **Permeability changes:** some toxins probably kill plant cells by altering the semipermeability of the plasma membrane, thus permitting loss of water and metabolites and also unrestricted entry of substances, including toxins. The plasma membrane consists largely of lipid substances and proteins, and any substance able to destroy these or to disrupt the processes involved in membrane organization or formation are likely to result in increased permeability. Lycomarasmin, fusaric acid, α-picolinic acid, oxalic acid, victorin and other toxins affect permeability. Fusaric acid and picolinic acid increase water permeability at low concentrations (for example 10^{-6}M), reduce it at higher concentrations

($10^{-3}M$), and bring about coagulation of the protoplasm at yet higher concentrations (Sanwal, 1961).

Wheeler and Luke (1963) point out that the ability of susceptible tissue to respond to victorin seems to depend on some property of the living cell, suggesting that the primary effect of this toxin is on cell permeability and that the other physiological changes and symptoms of the disease stem from this. Hanchey (1969) has recently reported that treatment of susceptible oat leaves with uranyl acetate before or at the same time as treatment with victorin led to reduced electrolyte loss from the treated leaves. This might be due to formation of a complex between victorin and uranium ions, but uranyl salts did not prevent root inhibition caused by the toxin, and it would seem that factors other than permeability changes are also involved.

2. **Disruption of normal metabolic processes:** this could result from coagulation or hydrolysis of protoplasmic proteins, from blocking of enzyme systems, or from the toxin acting as an antimetabolite to some vital metabolite (for example, tabtoxinine for methionine described above). Piricularin inhibits the polyphenoloxidase system of susceptible rice plants, and Sanwal (1961) suggests that victorin acts by uncoupling oxidative phosphorylation. Fusaric acid and α-picolinic acid can form chelate-ring complexes with heavy metal ions and could, therefore, inhibit enzyme systems which require such metals for their action. It may be significant that these two toxins can reduce the activity of iron-dependent enzymes such as catalase and peroxidase and that this inhibition can be neutralized by addition of an excess of ferric iron. Toxin-resistant tissue can presumably inactivate the toxin in some way or perhaps bypass the blocked enzyme system by making use of alternative metabolic pathways.

3. **Other mechanisms of toxicity:** these include (a) the physical 'blocking' effect of large molecules as described above; (b) possible osmotic effects, about which there is little information; (c) stimulation of host growth, presumably by interference with the growth regulation systems of the plant – this increased growth may be controlled or uncontrolled, as described in Chapter 12; and (d) some toxins, including victorin, inhibit root development; Futrell and Kilgore (1969) attribute the inhibition of root growth in maize seedlings attacked by *Gibberella fujikuroi* (*Fusarium moniliforme*) to a thermostable toxin produced by the fungus, the infected seedlings subsequently developing chlorosis, necrosis and blighting. Other mechanisms of toxicity have been suggested, but more research in this fundamentally important aspect of pathogenesis is needed.

Despite extensive investigation there is no general agreement as to the significance of toxins in the diseased plant. There are those who attribute most of the symptoms of disease directly to toxins produced by the pathogen, but there is increasing evidence that many symptoms are due largely to host metabolites or physiological changes occurring as a result of infection, as discussed by Allen (1966). It may be that the latter is true for diseases caused by biotrophs and other pathogens which do not immediately cause tissue necrosis in the host plant, but there is considerable circumstantial evidence that toxins are involved in necrotic diseases caused by rather unspecialized necrotophic fungi and bacteria.

Growth-regulating substances

In some diseases the growth habit of the infected plant is altered in various ways. There may be increased growth (controlled or uncontrolled), shortening or lengthening of the internodes leading to rosetting or to abnormally tall plants, conversion of perianth members into leafy structures (phyllody), vein thickening and formation of enations, witch's brooms, premature leaf abscission and so on. These symptoms can be caused by some fungi, bacteria, viruses, nematodes, insects, and mites and by application of growth-regulating substances, and it is tempting to conclude that the latter are in some way involved, especially since changes in them may occur in some diseases. The main growth regulators involved are **indolylacetic acid** (IAA) and **gibberellin.** The former is produced by several fungi and bacteria in the presence of tryptophan, probably its most important precursor, and some fungi are able to produce oxidases which destroy IAA, but most of the pathogens so far tested seem to produce only fairly small quantities of IAA. However, as pointed out by Sequeira (1963), different organisms may have evolved different pathways of IAA synthesis involving precursors other than tryptophan. It is also probable that as yet uncharacterized growth regulators other than IAA, gibberellins and kinins are involved in pathogenesis. Although the term auxin is sometimes restricted to IAA it is frequently used in a broader sense to include all growth regulators of the hormone type. The ways in which auxins regulate plant growth are not clear, and it is not surprising, therefore, that even less is known about their significance in diseased plants.

There are numerous reports of hyperauxiny in diseased plants, especially where tissue hypertrophy occurs, as in crown gall (*Agrobacterium tumefaciens*), the voluminous literature on which has been reviewed by Braun (1954, 1962) and Klein and Link (1955). Auxins and fungi are reviewed by Gruen (1959), and Stowe and Yamaki (1957) and Brian (1957) discuss the gibberellins. Hyperauxiny in infected tissue could be due to production of auxin by the pathogen, to its increased production by the host, or to its reduced destruction in the diseased tissue. It has been reported in smuts (for example, maize smut, *Ustilago zeae*: Turian and Hamilton,

1960), rusts (for example *Uromyces pisi* on *Euphorbia cyparissias*: Zimmerman, 1936: Pilet, 1960; *Endophyllum sempervivi* on *Sempervivum tectorum*: Pilet, 1952; *Puccinia carthami* on safflower: Daly and Inman, 1959; *Puccinia graminis tritici* on wheat: Shaw and Hawkins, 1958), powdery mildews (*Erysiphe graminis* on wheat: Shaw and Hawkins, 1959) and white blister (*Albugo candida* on *Brassica napus*: Srivastava, Shaw and Vanterpool, 1962). These are all diseases in which hypertrophy of host tissues occurs or, at least, there is no immediate necrosis, the pathogens all being biotrophs.

There is evidence that auxin accumulates through inhibition of IAA oxidase activity, and it is possible that this also occurs in non-obligate parasites such as *Pseudomonas solanacearum*, in which enzyme inhibition appeared to be correlated with accumulation of IAA and with increase of scopoletin, a competitive inhibitor of IAA oxidase (Sequeira and Kelman, 1962; Andreae, 1952). The premature leaf abscission occasioned by very mild infections – sometimes a single leaf lesion – of such pathogens as *Omphalia flavida* (coffee blight: Sequeira and Steeves, 1954; Ray, 1958) and *Diplocarpon rosae* (Kazmaier, 1960) suggests that degradation of IAA by the fungus occurs in the infected leaves since both fungi can produce IAA destroying enzymes in culture. Increased IAA is reported in tomato stems and leaves infected by *Verticillium albo-atrum* and is considered by Pegg and Selman (1959) to be responsible for most of the symptoms including petiole epinasty, tyloses, hyperplasia of the pith and formation of adventitious roots, but it is likely that enzymes and toxins are also involved.

Changes in auxin concentration also probably occur in some bacterial diseases, as in *P. solanacearum* mentioned above. The auxin situation in crown gall is confused. There appears to be a higher concentration of IAA in the galls and the bacterium produces this growth regulator in culture, but it seems that host cells are first transformed into tumour cells by some as yet uncharacterized tumour inducing principle and that IAA or other regulators then stimulate these tumour cells to divide and form galls (Braun and Laskaris, 1942). It may be that increased auxin occurs in other bacterial diseases involving hypertrophy – for example *Corynebacterium fascians* (leafy gall of various herbaceous plants) and *Rhizobium* (leguminous root nodules).

There are several reports of reduced auxin concentration in plants attacked by viruses causing stunting, but the evidence is conflicting and other investigators have been unable to find such reductions. According to Sequeira (1963) there are increases in scopoletin in solanaceous hosts infected by several viruses and this substance may be of considerable significance in pathogenesis. Auxin deficiency may occur in the later stages of some virus diseases, but further investigation is clearly needed. Some types of virus-induced dwarfing can apparently be overcome by gibberellin

(Maramarosch, 1957), and the latter may perhaps be involved. It would be interesting to study auxin concentrations in plants attacked by viruses which cause hypertrophy, for example enation diseases, to ascertain whether hyperauxiny occurs. Some nematodes, including root knot nematodes of the genus *Meloidogyne*, cause hypertrophy of host plant tissue, and it is possible, although it has not been demonstrated, that growth-regulating substances are involved. Several of the latter have been extracted from nematode galls; Yu and Viglierchio (1964), for example, found IAA, IAN (indolylacetonitrile) and IAE (ethyl ester of IAA) in tomato galls caused by *M. hapla* and in the nematode eggs and larvae, and a substance similar to IAA was extracted from roots of *Abelmoschus esculentus* (okra) galled by *M. javanica* (Balusubramanian and Rangaswami, 1962). This nematode is reported to induce giant cells and hypertrophy, possibly by formation of auxin-like substances. Other growth regulators may be involved in nematode hypertrophy, for example IBA (indolyl butyric acid: Yu and Viglierchio, 1964). Further information can be obtained from Sayre (1960) and Webster and Lowe (1966).

Some insects which cause plant galls produce substances with growth promoting activity (for example the sawfly *Pontania*: McCalla, Gentile and Hovanitz, 1962), and Maxwell (1961) has reported the presence of IAA and other auxins of host origin in aphid honeydew. The withdrawal of such auxins from the plant might be partly responsible for the stunting of infested plants. It is likely that insect and also, probably, mite infestation can result in disturbances of the growth-regulating systems of the plant, but little work seems to have been done on this.

A comprehensive account of the stimulating effects of pathogens, nematodes and insect on plant growth is given by Braun (1959), and by Braun and Pringle (1959). Plant galls are described by Felt (1940) and Mani (1964).

Gibberellic acid and gibberellins, of which twenty-nine have so far been reported, are growth-regulating substances which affect cell extension and certain other processes such as flowering, and breaking of dormancy in some seeds and tubers. In his recent review of gibberellins Lang (1970) notes that chemically unidentified gibberellin-like substances have been found in eight fungi other than *Gibberella*, as well as in bacteria, algae, mosses, ferns and gymnosperms. Gibberellic acid is a tetracyclic di-hydroxylactonic acid of formula $C_{19}H_{22}O_6$. There appears to be a close relationship between gibberellins and auxins in plants (Brian, 1958*a*; Brian and Hemming, 1958), and tissues treated with gibberellic acid may develop higher auxin concentrations. Both substances, perhaps acting synergistically, seem necessary for maximum stem elongation – it may be that gibberellic acid neutralizes some growth-inhibiting system, possibly auxin destroying enzymes, which normally regulates plant growth.

Gibberellins and gibberellic acid are produced by *Gibberella fujikuroi* (conidia, *Fusarium moniliforme*), a fairly unspecialized parasitic fungus causing root rot, foot rot, stalk rot, mouldy heads and seedling diseases of cereals and grasses in warmer regions of the world. It causes bakanae (foolish seedling) disease of rice in which young plants, if not too severely infected, tend to become etiolated and abnormally tall. This increased height results from rapid elongation of stems and leaves, in turn due to cell extension leading to longer internodes. There are other symptoms including reduced tillering, and Kurosawa (1926) in Japan found that cell-free culture filtrates of *G. fujikuroi* could cause all the symptoms of bakanae disease when watered over rice seedlings, thus opening the way to discovery of the gibberellins and related compounds. The pathogen probably causes elongation of stem and leaves by increasing the gibberellin concentration of the infected plant, and it could be that the abnormal plant elongation characteristic of certain other diseases has a similar origin. Pathogens of this type include *Endophyllum sempervivi* (leek rust), *Uromyces pisi* (aecia on *Euphorbia cyparissias*), *Puccinia suaveolens* on *Cirsium*, *Calyptospora geoppertiana* on *Vaccinium*, *Ustilago hypodytes* on *Bromus*, and *Sclerospora sacchari* (sugarcane downy mildew).

Carrot plants infected with tomato big-bud virus bolted and flowered prematurely (Kunkel, 1951), and cotton plants attacked by cotton leaf curl virus may be abnormally tall (Tarr, 1951). There is marked stunting in some smut, bunt and virus diseases, and Maramorosch (1957) was able to reverse this by applying gibberellic acid to plants infected with aster yellows virus (China aster), corn stunt virus (maize) and wound tumour virus (clover). Similarly, Chessin (1958) reported reversal of stunting of tobacco plants infected by severe etch virus. These and other cases of abnormal elongation or stunting might be associated with changes in gibberellin and/or auxin concentration in infected plants. Thus leguminous root nodules caused by *Rhizobium* are reported to contain gibberellin-like substances (Radley, 1959), and stunting of uninoculated *Psychotria bacteriophila* is apparently overcome by both gibberellin and *Klebsiella*, the endophytic nitrogen fixing bacterium which forms nodules on the leaves (Silver *et al.*, 1963).

Gibberellin-like substances have been found in angiosperms, gymnosperms, ferns, algae, fungi and possibly bacteria, and are probably widespread in the plant kingdom. In fungi they are known with certainty only from *Gibberella fujikuroi* but similar substances have been found in other fungi. There is a very extensive literature on gibberellins, and reviews are given by Stowe and Yamaki (1957), Phinney and West (1960, 1961), Stuart and Cathey (1961), Brian and Grove (1957), Paleg (1965) and others.

Kinins (cytokinins) are thought to induce rapid cell division in the presence of auxin. The best known is kinetin (6-furfuryl-amino-purine), but other synthetic 6-substituted purines are active in this respect, and the stimulatory activity of some plant extracts has been attributed to such substituted adenine derivatives as, for example, zeatin in maize kernels. The significance of kinins in pathogenesis is uncertain, but Kiraly, Hammady and Pozsar (1967) have reported increase of kinin-like substances in *Phaseolus vulgaris* and *Vicia faba* leaves attacked by *Uromyces phaseoli* and *U. fabae* respectively. They suggest that increased kinin(s) leads to the formation of 'green islands' around the infection centres, nutrients accumulating in the green tissue and becoming depleted in the general leaf tissue which then becomes senescent. This may be associated with diversion of the host's metabolism by the fungus in such a way that the adjacent leaf tissue remains or becomes a suitable habitat for it. Cytokinins are perhaps involved in movement of nutrients within the plant (Pozsar and Kiraly, 1966), and Thimann and Sachs (1966) reported that the disease caused by *Corynebacterium fascians* could be imitated by treatment with kinetin; they consider that the synthesis of cytokinins may be important for many plant pathogens. Kinins are reviewed by Miller (1961), Skoog and Armstrong (1970), and in Shantz (1966).

From this brief summary it will be apparent that various growth factors including auxins, gibberellins, kinins and probably others not yet characterized, are involved in the complex systems which regulate the growth of plants, and that normal growth results from the correct balance of these factors. Conditions or pathogens which derange the balance will tend to cause abnormal growth, and this will be reflected in the symptoms shown by the affected plant. The extent to which such derangements are involved in plant disease is not known. Although some growth-regulating substances have been chemically defined their mode of action is obscure and this applies even more forcibly to the role of these substances in pathogenesis. For further accounts of growth-regulating substances in plants reference may be made to Shantz (1966), Audus (1963), Galston and Purves (1960), Bentley (1958), Thimann (1963) and the papers cited above.

The mechanisms of pathogenicity discussed above comprise chiefly the production of such substances as enzymes, toxins and growth regulators by pathogen and/or host plant. Many other attributes of pathogens are involved in successful colonization of the host, for example the rapidity with which fungal propagules germinate and invade the plant, and the rate at which the pathogen spreads through the tissues and thus avoids, or otherwise, the chemical or morphological defences of the host. This rate of spread will depend partly on the formation of the metabolites described above and also on the inherent growth vigour of the pathogen as well as on the speed of reaction of the invaded tissue. The osmotic pressure of the pathogen influences its ability to take up water and nutrients from the parasitized cells. The mechanical pressure exerted by the penetration structures of parasitic angiosperms partly determines whether successful host invasion occurs, and this no doubt applies to penetration hyphae of fungi. The ability to produce effective appressoria, to withstand or neutralize toxic metabolites of host origin, and to compete successfully with other pathogens or secondary invaders in colonizing the affected tissue can all be regarded as mechanisms of pathogenicity. The physical presence of the parasite, especially if extensive, can have injurious effects on the cells of the invaded tissue and large masses of intercellular mycelium may force apart mesophyll cells, disrupt their normal functioning and sometimes bring about their disorganization. The epidermis is ruptured by fungal fructifications, such as acervuli, which push up through it. Mechanical damage of this sort is not infrequent but rarely seems to be the sole cause of injury. Bacteria and possibly some fungi may have to attain a certain minimum population level before they become able to invade the plant, in which case speed of multiplication may be critical. To be effective, pathogenicity mechanisms must not only have the required effect on the host tissue, they must also exert that effect sufficiently quickly to evade or neutralize the counter-active reactions of the plant – these are discussed in the next chapter.

14 Mechanisms of defence

On coming into contact with a plant a pathogen may behave in several ways. As an example let us consider a spore of a fungal plant pathogen alighting on a leaf under environmental conditions favourable for its germination: (1) The spore and leaf may appear to have no effect on each other. If the spore germinates the germ tube does not penetrate and the spore eventually dies. Whatever it is that causes fungi to invade plants is not operating or is in some way neutralized. (2) Germination of the spore and/or growth of the germ tube may be depressed or stimulated. Depression is likely to reduce infection, stimulation to enhance it. These effects are probably due to substances either in the leaf, or secreted by it as a result of contact with the pathogen. (3) The germ tube or, more often, a structure derived from it may enter the leaf but fail to develop further; that is, penetration occurs and also, to a limited extent, temporary infection. Many pathogens enter non-host plants in this way, and are presumably checked by the penetrated tissue becoming unsuitable for their further growth. (4) Limited invasion of the host tissue may occur, host reaction or other factors thereafter restricting spread of the pathogen in the leaf tissue. Tissue reaction may be so violent that a zone of dead and possibly fungitoxic cells surrounds the pathogen and prevents its further development (hypersensitivity). Slight flecking or necrotic spotting may develop. (5) There may be extensive invasion of host tissue, the plant's resistance being overcome and typical disease symptoms developing.

There are many variations of these possibilities; for example, the invading fungus may produce a superficial mycelium from which multiple infection subsequently occurs (p. 151) or it may survive in an attenuated state and fail to produce spores. Which of these possibilities is realized will depend partly on the effectiveness of the pathogen's attack and the plant's defence, both of which are genetically determined. Environmental conditions and such factors as the amount and effectiveness of the inoculum (p. 315) and the numbers and efficiency of vectors often play a decisive role in influencing the outcome of the struggle, and can sometimes be manipulated to favour the plant and discourage the pathogen (disease control by cultural practices).

Although resistance to pathogens is usually a process of response (Allen, 1959a) rather than a pre-existing state, there are reports of so-called passive or static defence mechanisms present in the plant before infection: these are in contrast to active reaction of the plant to the pathogen. Pathogenesis is a dynamic process and the intensive investigations carried out in recent years have indicated how complex host-parasite interaction can be. Resistance has sometimes been attributed to specific properties or reactions of the plant but more often it is probably the result of several interacting processes whose relative significance may be modified by environmental factors.

Most pathogens are unable to attack most plants, and disease susceptibility is thus, in the overall view, rather infrequent. Unspecialized parasites such as *Botrytis cinerea* may colonize numerous species of plants, but parasitism here appears to be rather crude and more specialized parasites usually have fairly narrow host ranges. The latter are also often characterized by minimal damage to the host, at least until completion of the parasite's life cycle, and a state bordering on more or less peaceful co-existence or mutualism may be attained. Indeed, Yarwood (1967) considers that disease, as distinct from infection, occurs when microorganism and host plant get out of step. This imbalance is often caused by man applying successful but unnatural methods of crop production, as in the introduction of new species of plants into his cultivated areas. In natural populations of plants the more susceptible strains tend to die out so that the species as a whole becomes more resistant or tolerant, but this is not so to the same extent in crop plants in which natural genetical variation is greatly reduced by man.

Allen (1959a) points out that compatibility relationships are widespread in organisms, as in fusion of gametes, fungal anastomoses, grafting in plants and animals, and other biological processes. The extent to which these are related to compatibility (susceptibility) or incompatibility (resistance) in plant/parasite associations and immunological phenomena in animals is an important and interesting problem.

When plant tissue is injured it usually reacts in such a way as to repair the damage, and substances ('hormones') from the injured cells probably trigger off the processes which lead to cell division and repair, often associated with formation of cork. It is possible that somewhat similar processes occur as a reaction to infection by pathogens, phenolic substances being released in both cases – hence caution must be exercised in interpreting the results of inoculation experiments in which the plant tissue is damaged. As Allen (1959a) states, 'In the evolution of a mechanism of defense against pathogenic organisms, it is probable that the general potentialities for coping with injury have been applied to the special job of coping with parasitic injury.' Successful parasites are presumably able to inhibit, circumvent or neutralize this natural reaction of wounded tissue, and the report by Keyworth and Dimond (1952) that wounding may enhance host resistance is interesting in this context.

Defence mechanisms are considered below as 'preinfectional' or 'post-infectional'. This is a convenient arrangement provided it is realized that the distinction is sometimes more apparent than real and that in some cases it is difficult to decide which category is involved.

Preinfectional defence mechanisms

Broadly speaking these comprise pre-existing properties of the plant which either prevent the pathogen from entering, or prevent its further development if it does enter. Examples are the physico-chemical and 'protoplasmic' factors such as nutritional status, presence or otherwise of fungitoxic compounds, osmotic pressure, permeability, water content, and pH. These static or passive resistance mechanisms constitute what Gaumann (1950) terms 'the material bases of axeny'.

The cuticle and other layers as defence mechanisms

The cuticle covers much of the aerial parts of higher plants and has been regarded as a principal obstacle to entry of pathogens. This view has been questioned in recent years. Martin (1964) concludes that its contribution to the protection of plants is not great and that the nature of the cuticle is such that it does not constitute a serious barrier to invasion except, perhaps, for hard, thick cuticles. The fact that more pathogenic fungi penetrate directly through the cuticle than through stomata would seem to substantiate this.

Cases have, however, been reported in which the cuticle acts as a physical or chemical barrier to infection. Disease resistance has been related to physical resistance of the outer epidermal wall to needle puncture in *Berberis* attacked by *Puccinia graminis* (Melander and Craigie, 1927), in flax attacked by *Melampsora lini* (Sharvelle, 1936), in potato tubers attacked by *Pythium debaryanum* (Hawkins and Harvey, 1919), and to cuticle differences in coffee attacked by *Colletotrichum coffeanum* (Nutman and Roberts, 1960), in strawberry leaves attacked by *Sphaerotheca macularis* (Peries, 1962), and in various plants attacked by *Botrytis cinerea* (Louis, 1963). The susceptibility to pathogens of young plant tissue has been attributed to its thin or uneven cuticle, and the cuticle may be particularly important in protecting fruits whose internal tissues offer little resistance to pathogens.

A waxy cuticle reduces the adherence of water to sloping plant surfaces and so impedes the formation of infection droplets, which tend to run off. Suberized external layers prevent entry of some pathogens, and Wild (1929) correlated periderm thickness of potato tubers with resistance to powdery scab (*Spongospora subterranea*). In such cases the underlying plant tissue protected by the cuticle or periderm may be susceptible to the pathogen and may become infected if wounded. Deposition of silicic acid on the lignocellulose walls of epidermal cells increases resistance of rice leaves to infection by *Pyricularia oryzae* (rice blast); this fungus often invades through motor cells which remain unlignified longer than the other epidermal cells (Yoshii, 1936). Measures which promote deposition of silicic acid, such as planting in flooded soil or application of silicic acid, reduced incidence of the disease (Yoshii, 1941).

As well as hindering invasion a tough epidermal layer may prevent an established pathogen from breaking out of the host tissue and liberating its propagules, thus reducing the amount of effective inoculum produced.

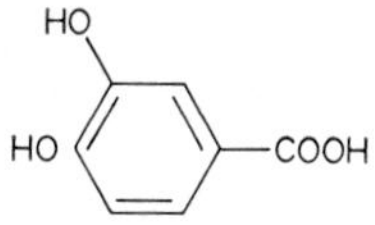

Figure 14.1   Protocatechuic acid

Pathogens which invade through stomata may be held back if the latter are insufficiently open. Thus *Xanthomonas citri* (citrus canker) enters the wide open stomata of susceptible grapefruit, but not those of resistant mandarins in which the stomata are narrow and slit-like with broad lips which project over and nearly cover the stoma (McLean, 1921). The stomata of some rust resistant wheat varieties are closed much of the time and prevent entry of infection structures produced by germinating uredospores of *Puccinia graminis* (Hart, 1929). Lenticels which suberize rapidly may prevent entry of pathogens as reported in potato scab (*Streptomyces scabies*), and successful pathogens perhaps delay this suberization.

Tissues may act as chemical barriers to pathogens and this effect is often difficult to disentangle from the physical effect. It is possible that some cuticles contain fungitoxic substances and might thus act as chemical as well as physical deterrents to pathogens. Fungitoxic substances have been detected in plant waxes, and cutin acids of *Citrus* lime are toxic to

Gloeosporium limetticola (wither tip). Possibly there is localized breakdown of the cuticle, resulting in formation of fungitoxic substances, as the infection hypha penetrates it. The high resistance of *Ginkgo biloba* leaves to disease may be associated with the cuticular waxes (Johnstone and Sproston, 1965). J. C. Walker and his colleagues at Wisconsin showed that the resistance to smudge (*Colletotrichum circinans*) of onion varieties with pigmented outer scales is related to the presence of catechol and protocatechuic acid (figure 14.1), phenolic compounds which diffuse from the dead coloured scales and prevent spore germination. They are formed when the scales die, the latter not being fungitoxic when alive. Fungi such as *Aspergillus niger*, which can withstand protocatechuic acid, are able to attack the pigmented onions, as can those which penetrate through other routes.

Root exudates have been implicated in protective mechanisms, exudates from resistant roots being more highly toxic to pathogens and/or less toxic to antagonistic soil inhabitants such as *Trichoderma*, as was claimed by Timonin (1940) for hydrogen cyanide in resistance to flax wilt (*Fusarium oxysporum f.sp. lini*). Root diffusates also play a part in the resistance of peas to *F. oxysporum f.sp. pisi* (Buxton, 1957), and no doubt they are involved in defence against other root-attacking pathogens, although the ways in which this occurs are varied and not well understood. Exudates from resistant roots might repel or be toxic to the pathogen, might lack some substance needed by it, encourage antagonistic microorganisms, or might in some other way (for example, by altering the pH) sufficiently modify the delicate microbiological balance in the rhizosphere to prevent infection.

Roots probably excrete larger quantities of metabolites than do the aerial parts of plants, and rain is likely to remove solutes from the latter. However, Topps and Wain (1957) found that extracts of, but not washings from, the leaves of several plant species, especially *Sambucus nigra* (elder) and *Ligustrum vulgare* (privet), reduced the germination of *Botrytis cinerea* spores and retarded germ tube growth. Reduced germination of fungal spores on disease resistant leaves has been attributed to leaf exudates but more often, probably, exudates stimulate the germination of fungal spores, thus resulting in increased disease liability, and they may also effect growth of germ tubes and formation of appressoria.

These chemical and morphological barriers prevent the pathogen from entering the plant and are often not very highly specific, although resistance has been fairly convincingly attributed to them in a few diseases.

Further progress of pathogens which have successfully penetrated may be prevented by the tissues of the plant – indeed this must frequently happen since many pathogens enter plants which they do not parasitize. This inhibition may be due to the presence of pre-existing toxic substances in the tissue (postinfectional ones are discussed later), to the lack of a substance or substances required by the pathogen, or to some unfavourable factor such as pH, osmotic pressure, or water content.

Spread of an established parasite within the plant may also be restricted by layers resistant to penetration, for example the endodermis, or the parasite may be confined to a particular type of tissue because only the latter constitutes a suitable substrate for its growth. A parasite may lack the enzymes necessary for successful penetration or colonization of some tissues, or inhibitory substances may be present. Deficiency of nutrients or moisture may be factors limiting full development of the pathogen.

Thus, many pathogens show tissue specificity to varying extents. Thickened cell walls may reduce the spread of pathogens within a tissue and lignification will tend to exclude those pathogens unable to produce ligninases. 'Barricade tissues' (Gaumann, 1950) which limit the spread of some pathogens include suberized layers, such as cork and endodermis, and sclerenchyma. The position of such confining layers partly determines the distribution of the pathogen within the plant; for example, many rust sori and lesions of leaf spotting fungi are confined to parenchymatous ground tissue and in grass leaves are elongated parallel to and between the veins, giving a striped or striate appearance. Oospores of *Sclerospora sorghi* (downy mildew of sorghum) develop in and disorganize the mesophyll between the vascular bundles, thus reducing the leaves to masses of tangled fibres – the characteristic leaf shredding symptoms of the disease. Wheat varieties in which extensive sclerenchyma encloses the susceptible parenchyma may show only a sparse and often sterile development of black stem rust (*Puccinia graminis*) on the haulms (Hart, 1931). The amount and distribution of resistant tissues in the plant can thus influence susceptibility to some pathogens. The development of histological barriers as a response to infection is considered later.

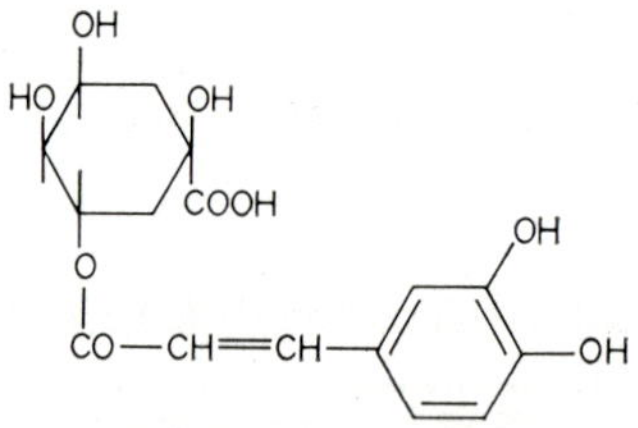

Figure 14.2   Chlorogenic acid

Inhibitory substances in plants

Many plants contain substances which can inhibit fungi, bacteria and viruses, and disease resistance has frequently been attributed to such substances, sometimes on rather inadequate grounds. Forty years ago the resistance of wheat to stem rust was attributed to phenols (Newton,

Lehmann and Clarke, 1929; Newton and Anderson, 1929).* Chlorogenic acid (figure 14.2) has been implicated in the resistance of potato tubers to scab (*Streptomyces scabies*), perhaps by stimulation of protective cambium activity (Johnson and Schaal, 1952), and Martin, Baker and Byrde (1966) suggest that the furocoumarin, isopimpinellin, is present in citrus lime leaves and protects them against *Gloeosporium limetticola*. The same authors (1966a) point out that furocoumarins may be an important class of natural defensive agents in plants. Thus the leaves of some (for example *Skimmia*, *Escallonia*), but not all, plants rarely attacked by foliage pathogens tend to contain relatively large amounts of these substances. A fungitoxic isocoumarin has been isolated from carrot (Condon and Kuc, 1962) and Virtanen and his colleagues have reported on the possible role of oxazolinones as fungitoxic protectants (Virtanen and Hietala, 1955).

Inhibition of polyphenolases by substances derived from polyphenols has been reported, and phenolics such as chlorogenic acid, caffeic acid, catechol and phloridzin can be inhibitors of various enzymes. Byrde (1957) has suggested that the activity of macerating enzymes produced by *Sclerotinia fructigena* (brown rot) is reduced by oxidation products of polyphenols in resistant cider apples, and there was a strong correlation between decreasing chlorogenic acid and increased susceptibility of ageing potato roots to *Verticillium albo-atrum* (Patil, Powelson and Young, 1964; Patil, Zucker and Dimond, 1966). Chlorogenic acid is a competitive inhibitor of IAA oxidase and may be involved in diseases where resistance is associated with high IAA content of the plant.

Resistance of some varieties of black mustard (*Brassica nigra*) to *Plasmodiophora brassicae* has been attributed to allyl isothiocyanate and phenyl isothiocyanate, fungitoxic substances derived from the glucoside sinigrin, but recent work has not confirmed this (Walker and Stahmann, 1955). Peroxidase activity and field resistance to *Phytophthora infestans* in potato appear to be correlated although Tomiyama (1963) questions this. The sap of oat seedlings stimulated spore germination in *Ustilago avenae* and *Pyrenophora avenae*, which attack oats, but inhibited it in several nonpathogens of this plant; avenacin, a glucoside of oats, may be involved (Tomiyama, 1963). The resistance of carrot roots to *Pythium aphanidermatum* has been attributed to an unidentified, apparently preformed, phenolic substance (Chakravarty and Srivastava, 1967).

A correlation between phenolic content of rice and resistance to *Pyricularia oryzae* has been reported by Wakimoto and Yoshii (1958). Polyphenols are probably implicated in resistance to *Venturia inaequalis* (apple scab) and *V. pirina* (pear scab) as discussed by Kirkham (1957,

---

* Seevers and Daly (1970), however, were unable find any differences in total phenolic compounds between healthy or resistant and susceptible wheat plants when inoculated with race 56 of *Puccinia graminis* var. *tritici*.

1957*a*, 1959), Kirkham and Flood (1956), and Flood and Kirkham (1960). The situation appears to be complex, and resistance might depend on the relative amounts of various phenolics rather than on the presence of a single fungitoxic one. The relative freedom of balsam (*Impatiens balsamina*) leaves from fungus diseases may be associated with an abundance of phenolic substances or precursors (for example glycosides) which are oxidized to fungitoxic quinones which destroy both the invading fungus and the adjacent host cells (Sproston, 1957). There are other reports of resistance based on preinfectional fungitoxic substances but, as in the balsam case just described, their preinfectional status is in doubt. It is probable that some phenolic compounds are converted into more highly fungitoxic substances, such as quinones, as a response to infection. On the other hand, some phenolics can be utilized as nutrients by some fungal pathogens. The possible significance of phenolic compounds in pathogenesis is discussed later (p. 262).

There is some recent evidence that sterols may be involved in defence mechanisms. The steroid glycoalkaloids α-solanine and α-chaconine were the major fungitoxic substances in potato peel, being present in concentrations at least eight times that necessary to inhibit by 50% the growth of *Helminthosporium carbonum*, a fungus which does not attack potato (Allen and Kuc, 1968). Tomatine, another steroid glycoalkaloid of solanaceous plants, was more toxic to non-pathogens than to pathogens of tomato, and *Septoria lycopersici* (tomato leaf spot) was able to detoxify α-tomatine whereas other *Septoria* spp., non-pathogenic to tomato, were unable to do so (Arneson and Durbin, 1967, 1968). These results provide some circumstantial evidence that tomatine may protect tomato leaves against some pathogens and further investigation is needed. The mode of action of these fungitoxic steroid glycoalkaloids is discussed by Arneson and Durbin (1968*a*); possibly they bring about disruption of permeability in fungi as suggested by Hendrix (1970) in his review on sterols in growth and reproduction of fungi.

Absence of nutrients required by the pathogen

Unless plant tissue supplies all the nutrients necessary for growth of a pathogen the latter will not be able to colonize it successfully. This is, of course, an over-simplification in that fungi and bacteria generally have considerable and varied biosynthetic abilities, and many can synthesize the nutrients they require provided suitable raw materials are available. Resistance might thus be due to the absence of such nutrients in the tissues combined with the inability of the pathogen to synthesize them. This is most likely to apply to obligate or near-obligate parasites whose nutritional requirements are thought to be highly specialized. Walker and Stahmann

(1955) suggest that in such pathogens the availability of highly elaborated growth factors such as vitamins, polypeptides, amino acids and proteins, and the presence of complex enzyme systems may be essential for success-ful parasitism, and that resistant plants may lack one or more of these factors. Similarly, different races of a pathogen may differ in their re-quirements of these factors. This is clearly a complex situation, and few cases have been convincingly demonstrated, although some mutants of *Venturia inaequalis* which were deficient in choline and riboflavin were unable to cause scab unless these substances were supplied (Kline, Boone and Keitt, 1957).

It has been suggested that a balance between growth-inhibiting and growth-promoting substances in the plant determines whether the latter shall be resistant or susceptible (Lewis, 1953). It is often difficult to ascer-tain whether the failure to develop further of a pathogen which has entered a plant is due to the absence of essential nutrients or to the presence of inhibitory substances. Thus Butler and Jones (1949) cite the case of potato wart caused by *Synchytrium endobioticum* in which zoospores of the fun-gus can enter the epidermal cells of immune potatoes but fail to develop further and apparently die within a few days. Whether this is due to toxicity or deficiency of the host cells is not known.

Nutritional aspects of host-parasite interaction are discussed by Garber (1961) who suggests three possible mechanisms to interpret the loss of pathogenicity of nutritionally deficient mutants for specific hosts: (1) the concentration of the nutrient in the plant tissue may be inadequate (Garber and Shaeffer, 1957); (2) other compounds may inhibit uptake of the nutrient by the pathogen (Garber, 1958); and (3) other substances may be required for uptake of the nutrient and these may be absent or in-adequate (Garber, 1959). There is little convincing evidence on this and some investigators have been unable to link resistance with inability of the resistant variety to supply the factors necessary for growth of the pathogen – for example Burrows (1960) with oat stem rust (*Puccinia graminis f.sp. avenae*).

There are, however, some reports of resistance being related to nutri-tional factors – for example Leach (1919, 1923) with *P. graminis* on wheat and *Colletotrichum lindemuthianum* on beans, and Wellensiek (1927) with *P. sorghi* on maize. More recently Lukezic and De Vay (1964) have correlated the resistance of plum varieties to *Rhodosticta quercina* (canker) with the amount of myo-inositol in the bark of the trees. This fungus is naturally deficient in myo-inositol, and more of this substance was present in bark of the susceptible cultivar President than in the bark of the two resistant cultivars Beauty and Duarte; further, the resistance of Duarte was reduced by adding myo-inositol to the bark tissue.

Resistance has also been attributed to the concentration of nutrients in plant tissue, as distinct from the absence of specific nutrients needed by the pathogen. Sugar content is perhaps the best known example of this. High sugar content of the tissues favours some pathogens such as certain rusts and powdery mildews, whereas the reverse holds for others including *Alternaria solani* (early blight of tomato), and *Ceratostomella ulmi* (Dutch elm disease), as discussed by Horsfall and Dimond (1957). Plants presumably become resistant to high sugar pathogens when the sugar content of their tissues falls to a certain level, and this may be brought about, for example, by treatment with certain growth-regulating substances. Boron facilitates translocation of sugars so that these tend to accumulate in the leaves of boron deficient plants and the latter are apparently resistant to *Cochliobolus sativus* (barley leaf spot), a low sugar pathogen, but susceptible to *Erysiphe graminis*, a high sugar pathogen (Eaton, 1930). This is an interesting hypothesis and Grainger (1956, 1962) has associated resistance with a low ratio of total carbohydrate to residual dry weight of the plant in several diseases, notably potato blight and *Pyrenophora avenae* on oats. Resistance is perhaps related to changes in carbohydrate concentration as plants mature or when they are grown under different environmental or nutritional conditions but they are probably not as important as the more specific resistance mechanisms such as production of phytoalexins.

In his study of *Stereum purpureum* in New Zealand, Beever (1970) found that the xylem sap of susceptible trees (peach, plum) contained more nitrogen and carbohydrate and was more favourable for growth of the fungus than was the sap of resistant trees (apple, pear). There were also qualitative differences in that the main sugar and sugar alcohol in the sap from resistant trees were sucrose and sorbitol, neither of which supported good growth of *S. purpureum*, whereas the sap of susceptible trees also contained glucose and fructose which were more favourable for growth of the fungus. As in most cases in which resistance to a pathogen is ascribed to a specific nutritional factor the evidence is largely circumstantial and the connexion, if any, difficult to prove.

*p*H

Closely linked with nutritional factors and often difficult to disentangle from them are such aspects as *p*H, osmotic pressure and permeability of the host cell. The *p*H of the plant tissue influences many physiological processes in both plant and parasite, notably enzyme activities, and resistance to certain *p*H sensitive pathogens might be related to unsuitable *p*H of the plant tissue. Most phytopathogenic fungi seem to be fairly tolerant of hydrogen ion concentration, and those which colonize acid tissues, such as citrus fruits, can often assimilate limited amounts of the organic acids present. There are few convincing cases of disease resistance directly attributable to pH, although the resistance of ripe tomatoes to *Bacterium vesicatorium* (*Xanthomonas vesicatoria*) may be due to their high acidity (pH 4–4·6), as described by Gardner and Kendrick (1921).

Osmotic pressure and permeability effects

According to Lilly and Barnett (1951) the cells of parasitic fungi usually have a higher osmotic pressure than that of the surrounding host cells, this being necessary for absorption of water from the latter. The osmotic pressure of the haustoria of such phanerogamic parasites as *Lathraea squamosa* (toothwort) and *Orobanche crenata* (broomrape) was considerably greater than that of the parasitized plant tissue (Bergdolt, 1927). Again, the haustorial osmotic pressure of *Striga asiatica* (witchweed) was much higher (up to 7 atm.) than that of the cortical cells of the parasitized maize plant (2–3 atm.: Saunders, 1933), and severity of attack on sorghum plants was greatly reduced when the osmotic pressures of parasite and host were approximately equalized by growing the latter at high nutrient concentrations (Solomon, 1952).

Osmotic pressure has also been implicated as a resistance mechanism against some fungal pathogens, notably *Erysiphe cichoracearum* (lettuce mildew) in which cells of resistant tissues or varieties had a higher osmotic pressure than that of susceptible ones. Further, resistance could be modified by altering the mineral nutrition of the plant, and shaded leaves or those cultured on distilled water became susceptible, whereas young lettuce seedlings with high osmotic pressure were resistant (Schnathorst, 1959). Similar considerations possibly apply to *Uncinula necator* (grape mildew: Delp, 1954; Goheen and Schnathorst, 1963) and *Sphaerotheca pannosa* var. *persicae* (peach mildew: Weinhold and English, 1964). Thatcher (1939, 1942) studied the osmotic and permeability relations of certain fungi and their hosts and found that the osmotic pressure of the fungus invariably exceeded that of its host, being about 44 and 22 atm. respectively in the germ tubes and haustoria of *Uromyces fabae*, 19 atm. (in the haustoria of *U. caryophyllinus*), 30 atm. (in the hyphae of *Botrytis cinerea*), and 23 atm. (in hyphae of *Sclerotinia sclerotiorum*) as compared with about 8–13 atm. in the host tissue. The permeability of the plasma membrane of host cells to water, urea and dextrose was increased, thus no doubt enabling the pathogens to absorb water and nutrients from them. This increased permeability was thought to be due to secretions of the fungi, and many of the toxins produced by plant pathogens increase the semipermeability of host cells. The permeability of Mindum wheat leaf cells was, however, reduced on infection with race 36 of *Puccinia graminis f.sp. tritici*, to which it is resistant, although narcotization resulted in increased permeability and susceptibility. It seems likely that high osmotic pressure of host cells, or reduction in their permeability, tends to render nutrients and water unavailable to the invading pathogen, but only a few instances of disease resistance based on this appear to have been described. Permeability in relation to plant disease is discussed by Wheeler and Hanchey (1968).

The importance of the water content ('wateriness') of plant tissue as a factor in infection has recently been emphasized by Brown (1965). Some diseases, including many but not all caused by biotrophs, are encouraged by high water content of the tissues, and subturgidity could thus be a resistance mechanism. Brown suggests that subturgor of the tissues results in free water being withdrawn from the infected area, thus leading to desiccation of the pathogen. Many organisms can grow saprophytically on dead cells whereas comparatively few can attack the same cells when alive, and this may be associated partly with the ability of living cells to withhold water and nutrients. Only organisms able to overcome this control – for example by osmotic and permeability effects or by killing the tissue by means of toxins and enzymes – may be able to become parasitic. These aspects have been inadequately studied.

Postinfectional defence mechanisms

The mechanisms of resistance discussed above are essentially passive or static, being present in the plant before infection occurs ('preinfectional'). They constitute, as it were, the plant's first line of defence, and tend to be rather non-specific although ineffective against pathogens able to attack the plant. Many fungi can enter non-host plants to a limited extent, indicating that other defensive reactions come into operation when the external fortifications have been breached. These active dynamic post-infectional mechanisms are now generally considered to be of greater significance than preinfectional ones in protecting plants against pathogens and are considered below.

Tomiyama (1963) points out that growth of a disease lesion in resistant tissue is at first rather rapid, gradually decreases and finally ceases (Akai, 1959), indicating that resistance is an active biochemical process. Disease resistance can often be reduced by narcotics and in some cases by inhibitors of oxidative metabolism such as 2,4-dinitrophenol, suggesting that such inhibition is involved. Infection is commonly accompanied by increased respiration of the host, and resistant plants frequently show a greater temporary increase (Farkas and Kiraly, 1955).

Gaumann (1950) classifies postinfectional resistance mechanisms into (1) anti-infectional or antiparasitic defence reactions which affect the pathogen itself, including plasmatic and necrogenous reactions; (2) anti-toxic defence reactions which affect the metabolic products of the pathogen, including histogenic and gummous demarcations; (3) induced tolerance in which the plant, although infected, is desensitized and no longer visibly responds to the pathogen: examples of this occur in virus diseases of plants.

The literature on resistance mechanisms is extensive, especially on biochemical aspects, and no attempt is made here to cover it. Among the many reviews are those of Brown (1934, 1936, 1955), Brown, Brooks and Bawden (1948), Hart (1949), Barnett (1959), Savulescu (1960), Kuc (1966) and Hare (1966). Obligate parasitism is discussed by Allen (1954, 1959, 1959a) and Yarwood (1956); host-parasite interaction in rusts by Shaw (1963); biochemical aspects by Walker and Stahmann (1955), Tomiyama (1963), Woolley (1959), Kiraly and Farkas (1959), Farkas and Kiraly (1962: phenolics), and Rich (1963); disease immunity by Chester (1933), Butler (1936) and Dufrenoy (1936); metabolic resistance by Sempio (1950); host factors by Kirkham (1959) and Allen (1966); and response to parasites by Yarwood (1967). The biochemistry and physiology of plant immunity are discussed by Rubin and Artsikhovskaya (1963), and Wood (1967) and Goodman, Kiraly and Zeitlin (1967) give excellent accounts of the physiology of parasitism.

Histological barriers

The histology of defence in plants has been reviewed in some detail by Akai (1959), and some of the preinfectional barriers have been mentioned above. More important, probably, are the histological and chemical changes which occur as a result of infection. It is often difficult to determine whether the effectiveness of a histological barrier is due to its physical, chemical, or both attributes. A cork layer may develop around the infection site and if formed quickly enough effectively seals off the invading pathogen. In other cases, as in some foliicolous species of *Alternaria*, the corky barrier is penetrated by the fungus and a second barrier develops and is in turn breached, and so on, leading to lesions with characteristic concentric ridges. A shot hole effect results from development of an abscission layer which extends from the upper to lower epidermis around the infected tissue and causes the latter to drop out, as in shot hole of peach caused by *Clasterosporium carpophilum*. Shot hole symptoms can result from wounding or from sprays containing, for example, copper, suggesting that this response is a generalized one to tissue damage rather than to attack by pathogens as such. Similar sealing off by cork layers occurs in roots and stems attacked by some pathogens, formation of cork being involved in canker diseases caused by some Ascomycetes. These processes are described in some detail by Gaumann (1950) and Akai (1959).

Although mature cork is resistant to many fungi it is less resistant when young, and its effectiveness as a barrier may thus depend on its speed of formation as related to the growth rate of the invading pathogen. When *Streptomyces scabies* (common scab of potato) infects tubers of the variety Menominee it is effectively confined by rapid cork development, whereas in the susceptible variety Smooth Rural cork development is slower and ineffective (Vaughn, 1948). It has been suggested that some pathogens can delay suberization and possibly others hasten it. Successful formation of cork barriers results in localized scabs surrounded by a ring of scar tissue (cicatrice), as in the scab diseases caused by species of *Sphaceloma* (often conidial states of *Elsinoe*), *Streptomyces scabies* (potato scab) and others. Considerable destruction of plant tissue may occur, and it seems, therefore, that this type of resistance mechanism is at best only partially successful. A cork barrier might prevent diffusion of toxins from the diseased tissue, while elimination of diseased lesions which occurs in shot hole diseases and, indeed, premature abscission of diseased leaves as in black spot of roses (*Diplocarpon rosae*) might be regarded as defence mechanisms in that the plant thereby rids itself of diseased tissue. Although the plant loses some of its substance further spread of the pathogen may be reduced. The significance of cork barriers is open to question and it may be that the barrier does not itself halt the pathogen, some other factor being responsible for this. If so, the barrier 'is of no greater significance than a monument on a battlefield; it merely marks the place where an issue was decided' (Brown, 1955).

The limited development of lesions caused by many leaf spotting pathogens has been attributed to several causes. In some cases hypersensitivity is probably involved, particularly so when lesions are minute. Formation of an effective cork barrier around the lesion prevents its further development, or limitation of the lesion may mark the point at which the defensive reactions of the parasitized tissue are able to halt the pathogen. The fungus generally produces its reproductive structures in the dead tissue of the lesion, and its confinement to a small lesion might lead to its rapid sporulation – it has been suggested that there is perhaps an antagonism between the vegetative and reproductive phases of fungi. The reverse, however, might be true, namely that the fungus is confined because it starts to produce spores and thus its vegetative growth weakens and the lesion ceases to expand, thereby enabling the resistance mechanisms of the tissue to become effective. Barriers to growth stimulate sporulation in some fungi, but in culture many fungi produce spores in the absence of barriers (Van der Plank, 1959). Vegetative growth of systemic fungal pathogens in the host plant is less restricted and sporulation is often delayed. The lesions caused by some pathogens are not delimited by cork but merge gradually into the adjacent uninfected tissue, and extensive irregular blotches of necrotic tissue (leaf blotch) may be produced by others. Coalescence of individual lesions may, of course, confuse the situation.

Gums, resins and tannin-like substances are often produced when plant tissue is damaged, whether mechanically or by pathogens or insects, and these exudates may be effective barriers against some pathogens, especially in woody plants. They may be somewhat fungicidal and become a physical barrier on solidifying. Resistance to *Stereum purpureum* (silver leaf disease) in plums was reported by Brooks (1928) to be associated with ability to produce gum – the susceptible Victoria variety produced only small quantities compared with Pershore, whose trunks rarely become diseased. The infection is sealed off by a mass of gummy tannin materials and tyloses which prevent further growth of the pathogen and dissemination of its toxins. Similar gummosis occurs in beach wood attacked by S. *purpureum* and probably explains why this tree rarely develops silver leaf symptoms although it is not infrequently attacked and sometimes killed. Resistance has been attributed to gums and resins in several other diseases, the amount and rate of formation being important factors. Gummy exudates from plants are generally not colonized by microorganisms, suggesting that they are perhaps somewhat fungitoxic.

The role of tyloses in vascular wilt diseases is not well understood and is discussed elsewhere (p. 115). Blocking of the xylem vessels by tyloses impedes the upward flow of water and if sufficiently extensive could result in wilting. If formed sufficiently rapidly tyloses might restrict spread of the pathogen or its toxins and so constitute a defence mechanism, but it is doubtful whether tyloses behave in this way (p. 116). The problem is complicated by formation of gelatinous pectic materials and gummy substances in the vessels, and Beckman (1964) suggests that resistance may in part be associated with enhanced gel formation and persistence, and increased development of tyloses.

Individual cells when invaded by pathogens react in various ways, some of which could be regarded as defensive reactions which sometimes effectively prevent further spread of the pathogen. The cell wall being penetrated by the infection peg may swell and sometimes becomes lignified or suberized (see Yoshii, 1948, and Tisdale, 1917), thus hindering penetration. Callosities (lignitubers) may develop as protuberances on the inner wall opposite the site of penetration, and may ensheath the invading infection peg to varying extents. The lignituber sometimes seals off the invading hypha while in other cases the latter grows through the investing material and enters the cell. Callosities of this sort are probably a generalized reaction to wounding since apparently similar structures can be induced by pricking the cell wall with a needle (Ito, 1949).

Phenolic substances

Resistance to several fungal plant pathogens has been ascribed to higher concentrations of fungitoxic phenolic substances and their oxidation products and to increased polyphenoloxidase (PPO) activity, generally but not invariably resulting from infection. More than 30 years ago Dufrenoy (1936) observed that when the progress of some pathogens is checked, phenolic compounds, mostly 'tannins of the gallic group', developed in abundance within the vacuoles of adjacent cells whereas in specialized parasites, tending to become systemic, tannin was formed very slowly, in small amounts and only in vacuoles close to the parasite. Subsequently, it was suggested that the establishment of *Puccinia coronata* in oat leaves depended on a supply of phosphorus from the host tissue; on depletion of this element relatively innocuous host phenolic compounds were dehydrogenated by tyrosinase into toxic quinones, leading to localized necrosis of the tissue (hypersensitivity).

The activity of PPO would seem to be important in that it can oxidize phenolics to quinones which may be more fungitoxic. Polymerization to dark coloured melanins may then occur. In tomato wilt (*Fusarium oxysporum f.sp. lycopersici*) conjugated phenols such as glucosides, tannins and lignin may be hydrolysed by enzymes to polyphenols, in turn oxidized by PPO, possibly an induced enzyme, to toxic quinones which then polymerize to cause the characteristic vascular discolouration, as suggested by Davis and Dimond (1954) and Davis, Waggoner and Dimond (1953). PPO produced by the pathogen might oxidize host polyphenols to more highly fungitoxic substances which prevent further development of the pathogen. For example a PPO inhibitor reduced the toxicity of catechol to *Cochliobolus miyabeanus* (leaf blight of rice) and prevented development of melanin, presumably by preventing enzymic conversion of catechol into fungitoxic quinones (Oku, 1960). The melanin was apparently fungitoxic although in other cases these insoluble pigments are relatively non-toxic to fungi. Self-inhibition could thus result from production of PPO by pathogens.

Germinating uredospores of *Puccinia graminis* released phenols and PPO (Farkas and Ledingham, 1959), and resistance of barley plants to *Erysiphe graminis* appeared to be associated partly with collapse of the mesophyll cells with accompanying release of a phenolic substance which accumulated around the haustoria and inhibited further development of the fungus (Scott, Millerd and White, 1957). Hare (1966) points out that aromatic substances such as polyphenols, phenolic glucosides, flavonoids, anthocyanins, aromatic amino acids and coumarin derivatives tend to accumulate in and around infected plant tissue and also in tissue adjacent to wounds where, presumably, they might exert a fungistatic effect. This is perhaps a reflection of the fundamental similarity between resistance to parasites and capacity to repair mechanical damage in plants.

Kuc (1963) described two types of reaction in apple varieties resistant to *Venturia inaequalis*. The first was a hypersensitivity reaction in which minute reddish-brown lesions appeared 36–48 hours after inoculation; this involved rapid collapse of the host cells around the penetration site and virtually no further growth of the fungus. In the second type of reaction the fungus grew to some extent beneath the cuticle but the underlying host cells collapsed in 7-10 days, the fungus ceased to grow, and restricted, non-sporing, necrotic lesions developed. In susceptible leaves the fungus showed abundant subcuticular growth, broke through the cuticle and sporulated after 10–14 days; the lesions were large and the host cells did not collapse until some time after sporulation. The difference between susceptible and resistant varieties was thought to lie in the capacity of host cells to react to some metabolite produced by the pathogen. Phloridzin, a polyphenolic glucoside present in the bark and leaves of apple, was hydrolysed to glucose and phloretin by a β-glycosidase, and the phloretin was oxidized by PPO to fungitoxic intermediate compounds, and the latter to melanins. These intermediate compounds, possibly quinones, may have been responsible for resistance to the fungus. They were produced in susceptible and resistant apple leaves but their formation was much quicker in the resistant ones, thus leading to rapid inhibition of the invading pathogen. There are other cases of this sort in which resistance has been related to phenolic substances with varying degrees of plausibility, and there is some evidence that resistance may be associated with phenolic inactivation of the extracellular enzymes which help the pathogen to colonize the plant.

The significance of these effects is uncertain, but reports linking phenolic substances with disease resistance in various ways are increasing. Kuc (1963) suggested that the great variety of phenolic compounds occurring in plants might provide a partial explanation for the specificity of host-parasite interaction. For example, certain plant species (resistant) might contain or produce phenolic substances toxic to a particular pathogen whereas others (susceptible) lack them. Other workers, however, are sceptical and point to the paucity of adequately documented cases. Cruickshank (1963) notes that there is little direct evidence that the brown pigments (broadly described as polyphenol oxidation products) often associated with infection are of any great significance in pathogenesis – they may be 'a diffuse secondary attendant phenomenon of defense reactions which has no causal relationship to resistance *per se*'. The significance of phenolic compounds in host/parasite interaction undoubtedly has many facets and needs more critical investigation. Recent accounts are given by Farkas and Kiraly (1962), Baldacci and Locci

(1965), Rohringer and Samborski (1967), Kosuge (1969), and Rich (1963).

Hypersensitivity

This term, first used by Stakman (1915), denotes increased sensitivity as in the rapid death of a host cell in the immediate vicinity of the site of infection. The invading parasite may thus find itself surrounded by a zone of dead host cells and if it is a biotroph its further growth may be prevented. Resistance here is in fact due to extreme sensitivity of the plant tissue, and characteristic small necrotic lesions develop. One would expect this resistance mechanism to be of greatest significance with obligate parasites such as rusts and powdery mildews, and this is to some extent the case. Hypersensitivity is also of significance with some necrotrophs which obtain their nutrients from dead tissue and it seems likely that it is not simply a matter of starving the pathogen: presumably the dead tissue becomes toxic to the invading pathogen, perhaps related to development of phenolic or other compounds toxic to both plant and pathogen. Scheffer (1961) suggests that in normal tissue phenols are kept in a reduced state by reducing agents such as ascorbic acid or dehydrogenases, whereas in hypersensitivity they are converted to toxic quinones due to the tissue having insufficient reducing agents. In some cases the fungus may be confined to the hypersensitive lesion in an attenuated state, neither growing nor producing spores and eventually dying. The capacity of some fungi to remain dormant in growing tissue and to resume development at a later date may perhaps be included here although little is known about such latent infections.

Hypersensitivity is discussed in detail by Klement and Goodman (1967), and by Muller (1959) who describes the process in diseases caused by fungi, bacteria and viruses. It is possible that hypersensitivity is also associated with resistance to some insects and nematodes. Interactions leading to rapid death of the host cell and inactivation of the parasite are called parabiotic as compared with eusymbiotic in which host cell and parasite remain alive for a longer time (Gaumann, 1950). Hypersensitivity has been studied chiefly in rusts, powdery mildews, potato blight (*Phytophthora infestans*) and wart (*Synchytrium endobioticum*), barley stripe (*Pyrenophora graminea*), apple scab (*Venturia inaequalis*), *Pellicularia filamentosa* (*Rhizoctonia solani*) on various plants, several bacterial plant pathogens, and in viruses. The rapidity and intensity of the reaction vary in different host-pathogen combinations as do the cytological changes, as described by Allen (1923, 1927), Humphrey and Dufrenoy (1944), Rice (1935), Smith (1938), Stakman (1915), Stakman and Levine (1922) and others. There was, for example, an immediate reaction in red clovers resistant to *Erysiphe polygoni*, with rapid disorganization of the invaded cells and of occasional surrounding cells; infected cells and the invading hyphae soon died whereas this did not happen in susceptible varieties (Smith, 1938). Resistant barley leaves attacked by *E. graminis* showed collapse of mesophyll cells near the infected epidermal cells, perhaps caused by toxin to which susceptible plants were tolerant (White and Baker, 1954). Essentially similar results have been reported for other diseases in which resistance appears to be related to hypersensitivity. In many cases it seems that the infected host cell is killed before the parasite.

Klement and Goodman (1967) point out that hypersensitivity is associated with loss of cell turgor and suggest that it might result from cleavage of S—S bonds in the proteins of cellular membranes leading to increased permeability and leakage of polyphenols and polyphenoloxidase from the cells; in this connexion it may be significant that sulphydryl (SH) containing substances, such as thioglycolic acid and mercaptoethanol, produced a typical hypersensitivity reaction.

Although the precise sequence of events is uncertain Tomiyama (1963) suggests the following hypothesis for the hypersensitivity reaction in resistant tissue. (1) The metabolism of the infected cells temporarily increases, becomes abnormal and the cells die; this occurs more rapidly in metabolically active cells and resistance is directly correlated with the rate of dying. (2) The metabolic activity of adjacent uninfected cells may increase and phenolic and other substances may accumulate, some of these perhaps being transported into the lesions; phytoalexins may be formed and also, possibly, self-toxic substances produced by the parasite. (3) Phenolic and other compounds develop in the lesions, completing the death of the infected cells and also (but probably later) of the pathogen. (4) Adjacent uninfected cells may start repair action by formation of cork barricade layers and in some cases the lesions may be sloughed off. Many aspects of hypersensitivity are obscure and, as Barnett (1959) points out, it is not clear whether the toxic phenolic compounds which accumulate in the lesion cause the death of the host cells and pathogen or whether they are a result of necrobiosis.

Time is an important factor in the effectiveness of hypersensitivity as a resistance mechanism. If the host reaction is too slow the invading pathogen may be established and out of reach by the time that the mechanism attains a fungistatic level. Similarly, if the reaction is too mild the pathogen may be able to withstand it. The infected cells of resistant tissue may begin to collapse after only a few hours, but the process takes several days in some rust infections. Cells of resistant potato tubers die 1–2 days after infection by *Phytophthora infestans* whereas those of susceptible tubers remain alive for up to 3 weeks. That there is a strong connexion between hypersensitivity and respiration is suggested by the fact that treatment with respiratory inhibitors reduces hypersensitivity of potato tubers to

P. infestans, as discussed by Muller (1959) who considers that increased respiratory activity occurs. Treatment with narcotics, such as chloroform, may also reduce hypersensitivity and resistance, and Tomiyama (1963) suggests that inhibition of oxidative metabolism may be involved.

Jhooty and Yarwood (1967) have recently made the interesting observation that the normal resistance of cowpea (*Vigna sinensis*) leaves to certain powdery mildews could be reduced by appropriate heat treatment (for example 50°C for 20–70 seconds) before inoculation; such treatment induced necrotic lesions on cowpea leaves inoculated with *Erysiphe polygoni* from clover.

There are many reports of hypersensitive collapse of infected host cells in resistant tissue, and the idea of a causal relationship between hypersensitivity and resistance has become widely accepted. Nevertheless there are cases in which the two do not seem to be causally related, and it would be wrong to conclude that the mere occurrence of hypersensitivity is in itself proof that the latter is the mechanism of resistance. Brown, Shipton and White (1967) were unable to find any consistent relationship between the colony size of *Puccinia graminis f.sp. tritici* on wheat leaves and the rate of increase of collapsed tissue. They concluded that hypersensitivity was neither the only nor necessarily the most important factor in resistance to this fungus, and suggested that hypersensitive necrosis of host tissue is not the cause of resistance but rather a consequence of infection in the resistant hosts used.

Hypersensitivity is a complex phenomenon involving in some cases at least the formation of phenolic compounds and sometimes of phytoalexins. It appears to be an effective resistance mechanism against some pathogens but not against others, being only one of the defensive reactions of the plant against invading pathogens.

Phytoalexins

The importance of fungistatic compounds produced by the plant in response to injury or infection has been emphasized by many workers, and Muller (1956) used the term phytoalexin for such compounds. Phytoalexins are now being increasingly investigated and have been detected in several diseases, but more investigation of their overall significance as a resistance mechanism is needed. Among other papers are those by Muller and associates (for example, Muller and Borger, 1939; Muller, 1956, 1961), Kuc and associates (see Kuc, 1966), and Cruickshank (1963). Phytoalexins can be described as antibiotics which arise from metabolic interaction of host and parasite and which are inhibitory to microorganisms attacking plants. They may be associated with host cell necrosis (hypersensitivity) at the infection site but not necessarily so when induced by chemicals (Cruickshank and Perrin, 1963) or spore-free water in which germination has previously taken place. Various methods have been used to demonstrate their formation (see Cruickshank, 1963), in most of which a spore suspension of the pathogen is placed on resistant host tissue for a variable time and then removed and assayed for fungitoxicity after removal of the original spores. This technique detects only the phytoalexin which has diffused out into the inoculum drop and this is likely to be considerably less than that present in the infected tissue.

The host-parasite interaction which results in formation of phytoalexins appears to occur only in living cells and is generally considered to be restricted to the immediate neighbourhood of the infection site although there might conceivably be translocatable phytoalexins (p. 283). Formation of phytoalexins is perhaps associated with necrobiosis of the affected host cells, at least in parasitic diseases. They are produced by, and are characteristic of, the host rather than the pathogen, and are probably rather unspecific although different pathogens show differences in sensitivity to them. The phytoalexin responses of both resistant and susceptible host varieties are apparently similar but the former produce phytoalexin more quickly and possibly in larger quantities. As with hypersensitivity the speed of host reaction is important in determining whether the tissue is colonized or not.

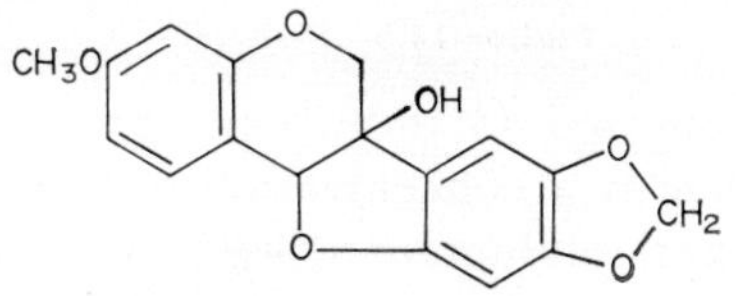

Figure 14.3   Pisatin

Postinfectional antifungal substances have been demonstrated in such widely different plant species as potato, pea, sweet potato, barley and carrot, and a few have been chemically characterized. These include: pisatin, a chromanocoumarane from pea (figure 14.3); trifolirhizin, a glucoside from red clover roots; an isocoumarin from carrot roots (figure 14.4); orchinol, a phenanthrene from orchid tubers; ipomeamarone, a tetrahydrofuran from sweet potato roots; phaseollin from French bean (figure 14.5); and viciatin from broad bean whose structure does not appear to have been identified.

Other diseases in which there is evidence suggesting the formation of phytoalexin-like substances include black spot of rose (*Diplocarpon rosae*: Saunders, 1967), leaf spot of wheat caused by *Septoria trictici* (Baker, 1969), leaf spot of brassicas (*Alternaria brassicicola* and *A. brassicae*: Ruscoe, 1967), and the leaf diseases of *Primula* caused by *Ramularia primulae* and *Cercosporella primulae* (Adebayo, 1969), to mention but a few.

Some of these antifungal substances are perhaps present in low concen-

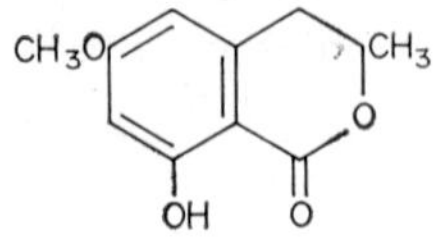

Figure 14.4 Isocoumarin

trations in normal tissue, their formation being intensified by infection or some other stimulus. Pisatin, for example, is formed when dilute solutions of certain metallic salts (especially those of mercury, silver and copper) are placed on pea pod endocarp tissue, and it is possible that phytoalexins are produced when metallic fungicides are applied to crops. Certain metabolic inhibitors such as sodium fluoride and sodium monoidoacetate are reported to have a similar effect (Cruickshank and Perrin, 1963; Perrin and Cruickshank, 1965).

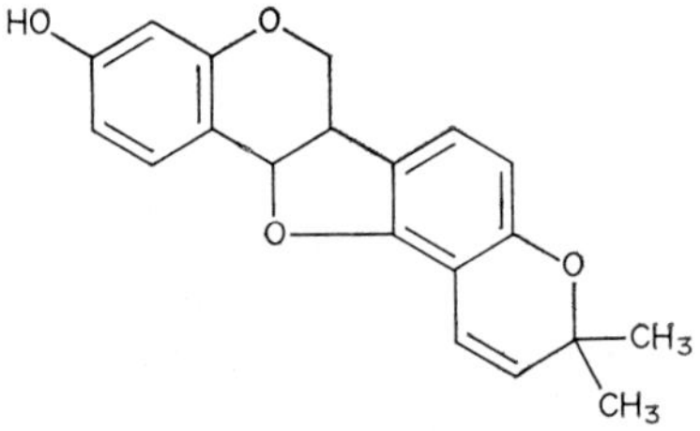

Figure 14.5 Phaseollin

Other substances reported to induce pisatin formation by pea pods include ethylene, which at a concentration of 1 p.p.m. induced a slight production (Chalutz and Stahmann, 1969). At certain concentrations a number of antibiotics (actinomycin D, cycloheximide, chloramphenicol and others) and ribonuclease stimulated pisatin formation, although they failed to do so at higher concentrations (Schwochau and Hadwiger, 1969); many of these substances interfere with protein synthesis in the plant. Auxins, or antiauxins and polyphenols are reported by Bell and Presley (1969a) to induce the formation of phytoalexins in cotton plants resistant to *Verticillium albo-atrum*.

Phytoalexins do not appear to be fungus specific in that several or possibly many parasitic fungi, which may or may not be pathogens of the plant, can induce formation of the phytoalexin produced by that particular plant. However, fungi which successfully attack a plant are generally less sensitive to its phytoalexin than those which do not attack it; for example, *Ascochyta pisi*, which attacks peas, is relatively insensitive to pisatin whereas it is much more sensitive to phaseollin from French bean, a plant which it does not attack.

Phytoalexins are probably fungistatic rather than fungicidal, but this no doubt depends partly on the quantity present. As well as reducing spore germination they frequently retard the growth of those germ tubes which are produced, so that the latter are stunted and feeble and less likely to infect the plant. Phytoalexins can thus discourage infection by reducing both the percentage germination of the spores and the subsequent growth of the germ tubes and in some cases the latter effect may be as important as the former in preventing infection. Young tissue seems to be more active in their formation than old tissue, and the latter is often more susceptible to pathogens. Thus phytoalexin production by cauliflower leaves which had been inoculated with *Alternaria brassicicola* and *A. brassicae* was greater in young (resistant) leaves than in old (susceptible) leaves, as reported by Ruscoe (1967). Bailey (1969) found that the production of pisatin decreased as pea leaves became senescent, and suggested that the increased susceptibility of such leaves to some fungi stems from the inability of senescing leaves to produce effective amounts of phytoalexin. The finding that treatment of leaf discs with benzyladenine reduced senescence and also maintained pisatin production would seem to support this conclusion. It may be that the increased resistance of leaves to some pathogens which follows application of benzimidazole and kinetin – substances which maintain protein synthesis and so delay senescence – is due to continued production of phytoalexin. Such treatments might have potentialities in delaying senescence in plants and thus in reducing their liability to infection by pathogens, such as *Botrytis*, which often attack senescent tissue.

Formation of phytoalexin can begin a few hours after the spores of the inciting fungus start to germinate, and often reaches a peak a day or so after inoculation, depending on the plant-pathogen combination. Aerobic conditions are thought to be required for synthesis of phytoalexins, and narcotics are reported to be inhibitory, suggesting that the formation of phytoalexins is dependent on living plant tissue. Spore-free water in which spores of *Fusarium* sp. had been incubated for a day at 23°C induced production of phytoalexin when placed in the seed cavities of soyabean pods, but this capacity was destroyed by heating at 60°C for 10 minutes (Uehara, 1959), indicating that thermolabile substances (possibly enzymes) produced by the germinating spores are involved. This is supported by results obtained by Bell and Presley (1969a) working with *Verticillium albo-atrum*. A conidial suspension of this fungus, killed by exposure to 50°C for 10 minutes, induced synthesis of phytoalexins (thought to be compounds related to gossypol) by cotton plants and also caused water soaking and discolouration in the vascular tissue which, according to Bell and Presley, is usually attributed to polygalacturonase activity. In this disease phytoalexin may be induced by an enzyme which causes cell injury, rather than by gene activation as suggested by Hadwiger and Schwochau (1969) and discussed below (p. 303).

According to Cruickshank (1963) the rate of phytoalexin formation is probably critically important in combinations of host variety–parasite strain (as in the reaction of different varieties of potato to different races of *Phytophthora infestans*) but probably less so where combinations of pathogens and non-pathogens of specific host are involved. Host specificity of phytoalexins occurs between genera but probably not within a species or even between related species. Gene-for-gene relationships might be interpreted on the phytoalexin characteristics of the plant and the phytoalexin sensitivity of the pathogen, both being genetically determined; a range of host-parasite interaction types might thus arise. Susceptibility could be related to failure of the invading pathogen to stimulate formation of phytoalexins, or to its tolerance of the amounts produced, in turn related to its ability to degrade the phytoalexin. Environmental and/or nutritional factors might affect these processes and so modify the resistance of the plant.

There is increasing evidence that some of the fungi which attack a plant are able to do so because they can degrade its phytoalexins, and that non-pathogens are unable to do this. Thus Christensen (1969) found that, in liquid culture, the two pea pathogens *Fusarium solani pisi* and *Ascochyta pisi* completely degraded pisatin in 3 days whereas with *F. solani phaseoli* and *Monilinia fructicola*, which do not infect pea, about 33–53% of the pisatin remained. *Stemphylium botryosum* and *Helminthosporium turcicum* both induced formation of a phytoalexin by alfalfa. The former fungus, a pathogen of alfalfa, rapidly degraded the phytoalexin but *H. turcicum* – which does not attack alfalfa – did not do so (Higgins and Millar, 1969). Other similar cases will no doubt be found; for example, the ability of *Alternaria brassicicola*, but not *A. brassicae*, to infect *Matthiola* (stock) leaves (Ruscoe, 1967) could be associated with the capacity – which has not, however, been demonstrated – of *A. brassicicola* to degrade the *Matthiola* phytoalexin, a capacity not possessed by *A. brassicae*.

Kuc (1966) points out that the production of several phytoalexins by a plant might be advantageous in that it would afford protection against a larger number of potential pathogens, and the probability of a specific pathogen overcoming this defensive reaction would be lessened if several inhibitors were present. Thus chlorogenic acid inhibited such non-pathogens of carrots as *Helminthosporium carbonum* and *Venturia inaequalis* but did not inhibit *Ceratocystis fimbriata*, which was, however, inhibited by isocoumarin also produced by carrot roots. Postinfectional increase in fungitoxic compounds which are normal plant metabolites, for example chlorogenic acid and caffeic acid, is considered here to be phytoalexin in nature although this is widening the concept.

Phytoalexins probably play a part in resistance to bacterial plant pathogens. Thus, multiplication of certain bacteria non-pathogenic to beans was inhibited by a postinfectional reaction of the plant whereas that of bacteria pathogenic to beans was not affected (Klement and Lovre-kovich, 1962). Phytoalexins in plants have been compared to anti-bodies in animals and are similar in developing as a response to infection. Phytoalexins, however, are thought to be mostly restricted to the in-fection site and are comparatively simple compounds of low molecular weight, amounting to several hundred. Some, but not all, are phenolic-like whereas antibodies are proteinaceous. Although the importance of phyto-alexins has been convincingly demonstrated in several host-pathogen combinations phytoalexins have not been detected in others, perhaps due to inadequate techniques.

Much of the work on phytoalexins has been done with storage organs (especially potato tubers), seed pods or leaves, and its extension to other organs including roots is desirable. Phytoalexins are very probably involved in the resistance of roots to some fungi, as in the resistance of cotton roots to *Verticillium albo-atrum* (vascular wilt). In this disease the rate of formation of phytoalexins was reported by Bell (1969) to be related directly to the resistance of the plant and inversely to the pathogenicity of the fungus. Certain cotton varieties which were susceptible at 22–24°C were apparently resistant at 30–32°C, and production of phytoalexin – believed to be substances related to gossypol – was greatest at 27–35°C, suggesting that phytoalexins are involved in this reversal of susceptibility at the higher temperatures (Bell and Presley, 1969). Possible induction of phytoalexin production by obligate parasites also merits investigation in that non-obligate parasites such as *Phytophthora infestans* and *Monilinia fructicola* have hitherto been chiefly used in phytoalexin investigations. Cruickshank (1963) considers that these postinfectional antibiotic sub-stances of low molecular weight play an important role in disease resist-ance of plants, and more work on them is clearly needed.

Detoxification

Interaction of plant and parasite may lead to the formation of substances (for example, phytoalexins) which inhibit the parasite or which facilitate its development; the latter category includes toxins, enzymes and growth-regulating substances. There is some evidence that resistant plants may be able to contain or neutralize such harmful substances in various ways, these processes being collectively known as detoxifications ('antitoxic defence reactions' of Gaumann, 1950). Victorin, a toxin produced by *Cochliobolus victoriae* (victoria blight of oats), is inactivated in resistant plants (Romanko, 1959) and is absorbed by certain resistant varieties of oat, rye grass and sorghum (Doupnik and Wheeler, 1965). The mechanism of victorin inactivation is unknown. Wheeler (1969a) found that it disappeared from sealed hollow segments of resistant oat coleoptiles floating in water much more quickly than from similarly treated suscept-ible coleoptiles. The latter became flaccid after 12 hours and leaked large amounts of victorin into the surrounding water. The resistant coleoptiles remained turgid for the duration of the experiment (24 hours) and only traces of the toxin were detected in the water. It was concluded that victorin is in some way firmly bound or otherwise inactivated by resistant tissue. Possibly, susceptible and resistant oat tissue inactivate the toxin at about the same rate but, whereas inactivation continues in resistant cells, it ceases in susceptible cells which are severely damaged. Oat tissue is thus resistant because it tolerates victorin, presumably by virtue of its greater capacity to inactivate the toxin. Toxin formation by *Verticillium albo-atrum* is reduced in wilt resistant tomato plants although these are invaded by the fungus (Blackhurst, 1963). Little is known about inac-tivation of toxins but the processes may be similar to those involved in microbial tolerance to toxic agents or in toxin neutralization by certain substances (p. 530).

In some host-parasite combinations resistance may be related to in-activation or reduced or inhibited synthesis of enzymes by the parasite. These effects have been attributed to phenolic substances which react with sulphydryl groups, amino acids, or metals involved in enzyme activity (Byrde, Fielding and Williams, 1960). Phenols and their oxi-dation products inhibit a wide range of enzymes and their effects on pectic enzymes have been studied by several workers. Byrde, Fielding and Williams (1960) suggested that the resistance of cider apples to *Sclerotinia fructigena* (brown rot) was due to their ability to inactivate the pectic enzymes produced by the fungus, and Cole and Wood (1961) reported that oxidized phenols inactivated its polygalacturonase. Other metabolites of host or parasite origin may affect the enzymic potentialities of the latter, and absence of a substrate required for the induction of enzymes necessary for successful colonization of the plant might be another resistance mechanism.

Changes in pH as a result of host-parasite interaction might reduce or enhance enzyme synthesis or activity, and oxalic acid favours polygalact-uronase activity and binds calcium previously present in the pectates of cell walls, thus permitting destruction of kidney bean hypocotyl tissue by *Sclerotium rolfsii* (Bateman and Beer, 1965). Polyvalent cations, notably calcium, barium and magnesium, may affect the activity of pectic and possibly other enzymes and so play a role in resistance. Castor bean cap-sules resistant to *Botrytis ricini* contained less water soluble pectin and more calcium and magnesium, but less sodium and potassium than susceptible ones, and resistance was thought to be related to the inability of the extracellular fungal pectinases to break down the capsules (Thomas and Orellana, 1963, 1964). The greater resistance of older kidney bean hypocotyls to *Rhizoctonia solani* may be associated with conversion of pectin to calcium pectate, so that the pectic compounds of the cell walls become less liable to degradation by polygalacturonase; thus older hypocotyls showed higher calcium and lower methoxy contents (Bateman and Lumsden, 1965). There is growing evidence that resistance may be related to inactivation by phenolics (of host or parasite origin) of the extracellular enzymes which enable pathogens to colonize plants.

Repressed synthesis of the polysaccharide-degrading enzymes which enable some pathogens to enter plants is proposed as a possible resistance mechanism by Albersheim, Jones and English (1969) in their discussion on the involvement of plant cell walls in the infection process. This repression might be brought about by carbohydrates resulting from the action on the plant cell wall of polysaccharide-degrading enzymes of pathogen origin. It is suggested that small changes in the composition, structure or accessibility of the plant's carbohydrates could alter qualitatively and/or quantitatively the polysaccharide-degrading enzymes secreted by an invading fungus or bacterium, and in this way might impart resistance to the plant. On this view, a plant is resistant to infection if its cell walls can be degraded by a pathogen to provide sufficient carbohydrate to repress the synthesis by the pathogen of the enzyme (or enzymes) which enable infection to occur. Carbohydrates apparently regulate the production of polysaccharide-degrading enzymes, especially those involved in the breakdown of pectic substances, by a number of plant pathogens in culture media, and virulence has in some diseases been correlated with the capacity of the pathogen to produce these enzymes. Thus, a correlation between the virulence of isolates of *Colletotrichum lindemuthianum* (anthracnose of bean, *Phaseolus vulgaris*) and their ability to produce α-galactosidase has been demonstrated by English and Albersheim (1969). The hypocotyl cell walls of 5-day-old bean plants, which are susceptible, yielded more than half their neutral sugars as galactose when treated with the enzymes secreted by *C. lindemuthianum*. This suggests that degradation of galactose-containing polymers in bean hypocotyl cell walls is required for infection to occur. In further experiments, each of three strains of the fungus secreted a greater amount of α-galactosidase when grown on hypocotyl cell walls of a bean variety susceptible to the individual strain than when grown on cell walls from a resistant bean variety – indicating that cell walls in some way control the production of this enzyme by *C. lindemuthianum*.

Albersheim, Jones and English (1969) consider that molecular interactions between the carbohydrate constituents of plants and the polysaccharide degrading enzymes produced by pathogens could account for the inherent resistance of most plants to most microorganisms and also for the comparatively rare instances in which microorganisms infect plants. This hypothesis, discussed further on p. 304, concerns only the initiation of infection and not any subsequent defence mechanisms which may develop in the infected plant.

Auxin reduces the growth of some pathogens and high auxin concentration in the plant may be associated with resistance (Shaw and Hawkins, 1958), but the significance of this is uncertain. Maleic hydrazide, a growth inhibitor, reversed the resistance of cotton plants to *Fusarium* wilt when applied before but not after inoculation (Sadasivan, 1961), perhaps by some indirect action on the metabolism of the host. Certain polyphenols, such as chlorogenic acid and caffeic acid, are inhibitors of IAA oxidase, an enzyme produced by some fungal pathogens. Such polyphenols might thus bring about resistance by neutralizing the auxin destroying abilities of the pathogen, in this way maintaining a high auxin concentration in the host tissue and so promoting resistance. No doubt other growth-regulating substances including kinins and gibberellins are involved in resistance, and indeed it seems likely that resistance and susceptibility mechanisms are closely bound up with regulation of protein and nucleic acid synthesis. Flotation of detached leaves on water containing small amounts of kinetin or benzimidazole often prevents the loss of resistance to certain rusts which occurs when the leaves are floated on sugar solutions or water (Samborski, Forsyth and Person, 1958), and similarly for powdery mildew (*Erysiphe cichoracearum*) of cucumber (Dekker, 1963). This maintenance of resistance may result from prevention by kinins of protein breakdown in the host tissue, thus starving the fungus of amino acids normally originating from such breakdown. This explanation presupposes that resistant plants are deficient in these amino acids, and other hypotheses are possible. There are reports that gibberellic acid increases susceptibility to some pathogens, for example by Lucas and von Ramm (1963) with brown spot (*Alternaria longipes*) of tobacco, and Sinha and Wood (1964) with *Verticillium* wilt of tomato. This and other studies of the detoxification processes in the host-parasite interaction are an interesting and little explored field of research.

Changes in the protein metabolism of host and parasite

Production of postinfectional inhibitors and the other effects discussed above involve considerable metabolical changes in host and parasite mediated by such regulators as nucleic acids, proteins and enzymes. Infection often results in increased respiratory and enzymic activity, and in the appearance of 'new' enzymes, proteins and probably other substances not previously present in host or parasite. Such postinfectional changes in protein pattern have been described in bean plants attacked by *Uromyces phaseoli* (Staples and Stahmann, 1963, 1964), and by *Pseudomonas phaseolicola* (Rudolph, 1964). Quantitative and qualitative differences in protein make-up following infection have been reported by several investigators, and compounds with different antigenic properties may thus arise. These alterations in protein synthesis are generally greater in resistant than in susceptible plants (Stahmann, 1963). The antigenic constitution of varieties of cotton resistant to *Xanthomonas malvacearum* (bacterial blight) differed more from that of the bacterium than did the antigenic make-up of susceptible ones, suggesting that antigenic compatibility may play some part in varietal reaction (Schnathorst and De Vay, 1963). In sweet potato infected by *Ceratocystis fimbriata* (black rot) Weber and Stahmann (1964) described changes in the activity of several enzymes which suggest that the fungus modifies the protein metabolism of the tissue even at a distance of millimetres from the infection site.

These changes are presumably due to toxins (in the wide sense of the term), and toxin from culture filtrates of *Pseudomonas tabaci* (tobacco wild fire), when injected into tobacco leaves, caused chlorosis, protein break-down and changes in the activity of a number of enzymes, some of which were activated, some reduced and others apparently unaffected (Farkas and Lovrekovich, 1965). Apparently 'new' bacterial dehydrogenases, oxidases, acid phosphatases and esterases were found in bean plants attacked by *Pseudomonas phaseolicola*. There was also a catalase of bacterial origin which, it was suggested, might suppress host peroxidases in suscep-tible plants since peroxidase activity increased in resistant (hypersensitive) varieties but not in susceptible ones (Rudolph, 1964). Certain varieties of wheat are susceptible to *Puccinia striiformis* at higher temperatures and resistant at lower ones, and several extra proteins were present at higher temperatures. Two varieties not undergoing this temperature mediated change in susceptibility did not show these protein changes – possibly the extra proteins were essential for the pathogen or perhaps they inactivated fungitoxic compounds arising during infection (Strobel and Sharp, 1965).

The mechanisms underlying these changes are not understood. Kuc (1966) suggests that enzyme induction and repression may be involved. For example infection of, or injury to, plant tissue might bring together hitherto separated enzymes and substrates, with consequent formation of substances able to entrap repressor molecules which normally prevent synthesis of a messenger RNA; the latter is thus formed and brings about synthesis of the corresponding protein. The formation of postinfectional compounds such as phytoalexins, proteins and enzymes might be inter-preted on this sort of basis.

Increase in the size of nuclei and RNA content may occur in infected tissue and has been investigated in some rust diseases, notably *Puccinia graminis f.sp. tritici* (Allen, 1923; Person, 1960; Bhattachayara, Naylor and Shaw, 1965). RNA tends to decline with age in normal green leaves, and the greater amount in leaves infected by biotrophs could be due to delay in this decline. In bean leaves an area of 3–4 mm around the uredia of *Uromyces phaseoli* – which later becomes the 'green islands' – contained more RNA than the intervening tissue or that of uninfected leaves (Heitefuss, 1966). In other cases there may be decrease in RNA and DNA, as in soya leaves infected with *Peronospora manshurica* in which the extent of decrease depended on the age of the plant (Millikan, Wyllie and Pickett, 1965). Decrease of histones in nuclei following infection has been reported. Histones are thought to be important in nuclear activity including the regulation of protein synthesis (Goodwin and Sizer, 1965), and their removal could unmask host DNA and so activate RNA mediated synthesis of specific proteins. Decrease in histones and increase in RNA and total proteins can occur very soon after infection, suggesting that gene activation through removal of histones could be an early phase in host-parasite interaction.

Qualitative as well as quantitative changes in nucleic acids possibly accompany infection, but there is little information on this. Knowledge about postinfectional changes in the bases which compose the RNA and in the relative amounts of the different types of nucleic acids such as ribosome RNA, transfer RNA and messenger RNA is needed. Such changes in host physiology induced by the invading pathogen may determine whether the plant is resistant or susceptible. According to Shaw (1963), susceptibility to rusts is characterized by increased amounts of auxin, RNA and protein in the plant. As he points out, the view that susceptibility depends on the controlled induction of enzymes involving an orderly diversion of synthetic process in the host is attractive but unproven. To what extent these considerations apply to other plant parasites, obligate and otherwise, is at present largely a matter for speculation. Apparently similar increase in the size of nuclei and nucleoli occurs in plant tumours due to various causes (Owens and Specht, 1964), including some nematodes, *Agrobacterium tumefaciens* (crown gall) and in tissue adjacent to wounds – in fact such hypertrophy is probably characteristic of cells of high metabolic activity. Treatment of plant tissue with kinetin may have a similar effect. This substance may enhance or reduce resistance of tissue to different pathogens depending on the plant and pathogen involved, age of the tissue, amount of kinetin applied, and other factors.

Increases of soluble nucleotides have also been demonstrated in tissue infected by *Puccinia graminis* and other obligate parasites and viruses, and there is evidence that some parasites may secrete RNA into the infected tissue. Bison, a variety of flax susceptible to *Melampsora lini*, became resistant when ribonuclease was applied to the cotyledons before but not after inoculation, presumably due to interference with the protein metabolism of the pathogen (Hadwiger and Fulger, 1967). *Phytophthora infestans* can degrade RNA, and such breakdown might occur in parasitized host cells (Page, 1965). Nucleic acid metabolism in obligate parasitism is reviewed by Heitefuss (1966) who, while observing that 'metabolic events in connexion with nucleic acid can be interpreted to explain almost every phenomenon in host-parasite relations', also points out that nucleic acids, although important, are only one of the numerous factors in the host-parasite complex.

It has been suggested that the host may modify the protein metabolism of the parasite. Resistant varieties of tomato, potato and banana were able to suppress synthesis of pectic enzymes by *Fusarium* and *Verticillium*, and rust infection of bean leaves was accompanied by suppression of two isoenzymes of malate dehydrogenase and one of acid phosphatase in the germinated uredospore (Stahmann, 1963).

There has been much speculation as to the possible roles of amino acids in the resistance of plants to pathogens. In his review Andel (1966) suggests that some might be fungicidal, fungistatic or might in some way reduce the pathogenicity of parasites, although there is little evidence for these possibilities. It seems more likely that the metabolism of the host plant is in some way involved, perhaps resulting in the formation of fungicidal or fungistatic substances or in nutritional changes which render the tissues less congenial to the pathogen. In this context the stimulation of pisatin production by certain amino acids, but not by others, is of interest (Perrin and Cruickshank, 1965). The chemotherapeutic activity of some amino acids might be related to their ability to act as antimetabolites in the metabolism of the pathogen or of the host plant.

Acquired immunity

When an animal recovers from attack by a pathogen it may become immune for varying lengths of time to subsequent infection by that pathogen. Such acquired immunity is the basis of protective vaccination and there has been considerable controversy as to whether this phenomenon occurs in plants. Chester (1933) reviewed the subject and thought that increased resistance to reinfection could occur despite the doubtful validity of some of the supporting evidence. This view was questioned by Butler (1936), particularly in diseases caused by fungi and bacteria, although he noted that mutualistic associations between the latter and higher plants (as in mycorrhiza, and bacterial root nodules of Leguminosae) might result from an induced immunity to the originally parasitic organism. Since then many plant pathologists have accepted that a modified type of acquired immunity can occur in plants although somewhat different from that found in animals.

The most convincing cases are in diseases caused by viruses and this may perhaps be related to their intracellular nature, as discussed by Price (1940, 1964). Immunity following recovery is often of the carrier type in which the virus is still present although the plant is symptomless. In cross-immunity, infection by one virus strain protects the plant against closely related strains of the same virus, and this immunity may be of the carrier type or of the 'chronic disease' type (Price, 1940) in which virus and symptoms are both present, with the latter mild and chronic, rather than acute. The 'sterile' type of immunity, that is apparent absence of virus and symptoms, probably occurs in plants but there do not appear to be any authenticated cases of formation of animal-type antibodies in plants which have recovered from virus attack; claims to this effect have, however, been made and the possibility should be borne in mind. In plants, acquired immunity is of the active type in that it results from interaction of plant and parasite ('antigen'). Passive immunization resulting from introduction of antibodies does not seem to have been demonstrated in plants although rabbit serum which agglutinated *Agrobacterium tumefaciens* protected pelargoniums from the pathogen (Gaumann, 1950).

In recent years it has been suggested that recovery from virus diseases in animals is mediated by interferon, a protein apparently non-specific in its action, which helps eliminate the virus from infected tissue. The antibody mechanism is specific to the infecting virus and is thought to prevent reinfection. Although animal-type antibodies have not been convincingly demonstrated in plants there are reports of protective substances which may play a part in acquired immunity, as described by Wallace (1944), and Gilpatrick and Weintraub (1952). The latter authors (1952) found that the upper leaves of a *Dianthus* plant, whose lower leaves had been inoculated with carnation mosaic virus, were resistant to infection although they did not apparently contain the virus. Several other similar cases have been reported, as discussed by Loebenstein, Rabina and Praagh (1966) who extracted an interferon-like agent which interfered with infection by tobacco mosaic virus from leaves of *Datura stramonium* showing acquired resistance after infection with TMV or tobacco necrosis virus. It seems that some degree of resistance to virus infection can be induced not only by related viruses, but also by fungi, non-infectious TMV protein and ultraviolet inactivated virus (Loebenstein, 1960, 1962, 1963). Thus inoculation of *Peronospora tabacina* into stems of tobacco plants resulted in increased resistance of the leaves to TMV as well as to the fungus (Cruickshank and Mandryk, 1960; Mandryk, 1960, 1963).

Atanasoff (1964) includes phytoalexins within his concept of interferon, a substance thought to be of protein or polypeptide nature and of much higher molecular weight. On this basis interferon is considered to be formed by all kinds of host organisms including Protozoa, bacteria, plants, insects and higher animals including man, and its formation can be stimulated by widely different pathogens – viruses, fungi, bacteria, parasitic angiosperms, Protozoa and possibly nematodes.

Yarwood (1967) suggests that acquired resistance to parasites may be related to that of plant ovules to secondary fertilization and possibly to acquired tolerance of plants to heat, cold and chemicals. Exposure of plants to certain agents such as heat can sometimes predispose them to subsequent infection by a pathogen, and this could be considered as acquired susceptibility. This can sometimes be reversed by varying the dosage of the predisposing agent (Yarwood, 1964, 1964a with heat and *Uromyces phaseoli* on beans), but whether this phenomenon is related to the mechanisms involved in acquired resistance is not known.

The self-limiting lesions produced by many leaf spotting pathogens are considered by some to be examples of acquired immunity, sometimes associated with hypersensitivity and production of phytoalexins, but there are other possible explanations (p. 260).

Interactions of pathogens

On inoculating two pathogens simultaneously or successively into a plant susceptible to both, and under conditions favourable for infection by both, there is often no observable reaction between them – both develop as they would have done had they been inoculated singly. Thus, lesions caused by *Alternaria brassicicola* and *A. brassicae* coalesced to form a single mixed leaf spot when cauliflower leaves were inoculated with the two fungi in the laboratory. Such mixed lesions were not observed in the field although some leaves bore separate lesions caused by both of these fungi, and a large old lesion bearing *A. brassicae*, *A. tenuis* and *A. tenuissima* was found (Ruscoe, 1967). There was no evidence of reaction between *A. brassicicola* and *A. brassicae* and indeed, several pathogens often occur on the same leaf without apparently interfering with each other. A pathogen may enter a plant through the lesions caused by another pathogen, in which case there is clearly no antagonism between the two. In other cases there is observable interference between pathogens attacking the same plant organ, resulting in synergism or, more often, antagonism.

Synergistic effects

These are best known in viruses. Some virus diseases are caused by a mixture of two viruses, neither of which alone has much effect on the plant, but has marked effects when the two are combined, and which may cause symptoms different from those caused by either of the component viruses. Tomato streak disease is caused by tobacco mosaic plus potato virus X, and other similar cases are known (Ross, 1959; Kassanis, 1963). Synergism is perhaps less frequent with fungal pathogens but some cases have been recorded – for example, that described by Moseman and Greeley (1964) in which prior infection of wheat plants with *Erysiphe graminis f.sp. tritici* predisposed them to infection by *E. graminis hordei*. Another example has been reported by Manners and Gandy (1954) who found that simultaneous inoculation of five wheat varieties with *E. graminis tritici* and *Puccinia triticina* (brown rust) led to increased rust in two varieties, diminished rust in one variety, and had no consistent effect in the other two varieties. In most cases, however, rust tended to be reduced in plants which had been inoculated with *Erysiphe* before being inoculated with *Puccinia*. Infection and invasion of detached cabbage cotyledons by *Alternaria brassicicola* was enhanced by the presence of *Peronospora parasitica* (Channon, 1970).

Other cases in which previous or simultaneous infection by one pathogen predisposes plants to attack by a second one are mentioned by Yarwood (1959). They include the predisposition of peach to *Sphaerotheca pannosa* and *Sclerotinia fructicola* by *Taphrina deformans*, of wheat to root-rotting fungi (mostly *Fusarium culmorum* and *Cochliobolus sativus*) by *Urocystis tritici*, of wheat to *Puccinia striiformis* by *Tilletia caries*, of oats to *P. coronata* by *Ustilago kolleri* and *U. avenae*, and of potato tubers to *Fusarium caeruleum* by *Phytophthora infestans*. Several cases involving smuts are discussed by Fischer and Holton (1957). In some of the cases mentioned above the second pathogen enters the plant through lesions caused by the first pathogen, as with *F. caeruleum* and *P. infestans* in potato tubers, but in others the first pathogen apparently induces changes in the plant which render it more susceptible to the second one.

A synergistic reaction between *Leptosphaeria nodorum* (glume blotch) and *Puccinia recondita f.sp. triticina* (brown leaf rust) on wheat in the Netherlands has been described by Van der Wal, Shear and Zadoks (1970). Wheat plants in a growth chamber were inoculated at the 50% heading stage with uredospores of the rust and 3 weeks later were exposed to a massive inoculum of *L. nodorum* conidia. Except for lesions or rust pustules, the leaves inoculated with either fungus alone remained green and turgid whereas those inoculated with both fungi died. Head symptoms caused by *L. nodorum* were more severe on rust infected plants than on non-rusted plants, and the loss in yield of plants infected by both fungi was significantly larger than the calculated sum of the losses caused by each fungus alone. Production of uredospores was reduced, and that of teliospores was stimulated, in plants infected by *L. nodorum* as compared with plants not infected by the latter fungus. This effect was possibly associated with senescence induced by *L. nodorum*, although senescent rust infected plants not attacked by *L. nodorum* bore fewer telia than plants attacked by both fungi, suggesting that factors in addition to senescence may be involved.

Antagonistic effects; cross-protection

Antagonism is more frequent than synergism and has been studied chiefly among viruses. It often, but not invariably, occurs between apparently related viruses and presumably arises through interference with virus multiplication or from competition for receptor sites (p. 52). One virus may completely suppress another, as with tobacco severe etch virus which prevented multiplication of potato virus Y and henbane mosaic virus, and replaced them even in plants in which the latter viruses were established (Bawden and Kassanis, 1945).

There are other cases in which infection by one disease-inciting agent protects against a second one, although the mechanisms involved have seldom been investigated in detail, the reports usually recording the results of experiments in which two pathogens are inoculated simultaneously or successively into susceptible plants. These interactions take various forms and are of considerable potential importance in crops which are attacked by several pathogens. Interactions may be between different races of a pathogen, different species of a genus, different genera, or different types of disease-inciting agents.

Protection against a more aggressive isolate of a pathogen by previous inoculation of the plant with a less aggressive or avirulent isolate has been reported by Schnathorst (1966), who found that a mild strain of *Verticillium albo-atrum* protected cotton plants against a more aggressive strain of the fungus. Similar protection has been described among some of the bacteria which attack plants and is discussed as 'premunity' by Klement and Goodman (1967). Premunity is defined as 'a non-specific acquired immunity which manifests itself in plants pretreated (inoculated) with one bacterium which "immunizes" or protects the plant from infection by another bacterial pathogen'. It is a less specific, slower, and weaker reaction than hypersensitivity and may be of importance as a defence mechanism of plants against bacteria. Premunity can be brought about not only by pretreatment with avirulent strains of the bacterium but also by killed pathogenic bacteria, ribonuclease and other agents. Hadwiger and Schwochau (1969) consider that alteration in the repression level of resistance genes of the plant may be involved in premunity.

Cross-protection between different species of a genus has been reported in *Fusarium solani* (sprout rot) which protects sweet potato plants against *F. oxysporum* (wilt) (McClure, 1951; Bega, 1954), and in the strains of these two species which attack pea (Buxton and Perry, 1959; Perry, 1959). In these two examples the two pathogens involved cause different types of disease – vascular wilt (*F. oxysporum*) and root rot (*F. solani*) – and the latter fungus perhaps invades the plant first and slows up colonization of the root by *F. oxysporum*, as discussed below.

K

282   PRINCIPLES OF PLANT PATHOLOGY

Several examples of cross-protection between different genera of plant pathogens have been described. Mantle (1962) found that inoculation of wheat with a mixture of *Ustilago nuda* (loose smut) and *Tilletia tritici* (bunt) resulted in suppressed sporulation of the latter in some varieties, whereas both fungi produced spores in the same ears in other varieties, with *Tilletia* usually towards the top of the ear. *Uromyces phaseoli* (bean rust), which does not infect sunflower, protected the latter against *Puccinia helianthi*, the cause of sunflower rust, and *vice versa* (Yarwood, 1956b). Antagonism between *Erysiphe graminis f.sp. tritici* and *Puccinia triticina* occurred in some varieties of wheat (Manners and Gandy, 1954).

Cross-protection has also been described between widely different disease-inciting agents. Preinoculation of tobacco plants with *Peronospora tabacina* (blue mould) protected them against infection with tobacco mosaic virus, the latter protected beans against *Uromyces phaseoli*, previous infection of bean plants with *U. phaseoli* and of sunflower plants with *Puccinia helianthi* protected them against smog damage (Yarwood and Middleton, 1954), and other examples are given by Yarwood (1967). It seems logical to conclude that the first applied disease agent brings about changes in the tissues of the plant which in some unknown way make the plant less susceptible to the second disease-inciting agent, but the nature of these changes is not understood.

What appear to be interactions of pathogens are not infrequently observed in the field. Plants infected by pathogen A are not attacked, or are less severely attacked, by pathogen B than are plants free from pathogen A. Very few cases have been reported in detail despite the potential importance of such cross-protection in disease control – it might, for example, be possible and worthwhile to protect crop plants against a destructive pathogen by infecting them with a pathogen which causes only slight damage.

There are several mechanisms of cross-protection. A pathogen may bring about structural and/or metabolic changes in the infected plant which discourage the development of a second pathogen. Thus Perry (1959) found that *Fusarium solani f.sp. pisi* (root rot) colonized the epidermis and outer cortex of pea roots more rapidly and more extensively than did *F. oxysporum f.sp. pisi* (vascular wilt), and brought about changes in the physical nature and metabolic activity of the cortex which delayed the progress of *F. oxysporum* to the stele of the root, thus reducing the incidence of wilt.

It may be that there are localized antagonistic effects between pathogens, resulting in one pathogen reducing infection by another. Thus, inoculation of wheat seedlings with uredospores of *Puccinia coronata* (crown rust of oat) reduced the number of leaf rust sori produced on subsequent inoculation of the seedlings with *P. recondita* (wheat leaf rust), and the sori formed were of a different infection type (Johnson and Huffman, 1958). These effects could be due to the formation of substances inhibitory to *P. recondita* when the wheat seedlings were inoculated with *P. coronata*.

Phytoalexins are often considered to play a part in cross-protection. Chamberlain and Paxton (1968) carried out ingenious experiments in which phytoalexin produced by inoculated resistant soyabean plants was conveyed through string wicks into susceptible plants, and the latter were thereby protected against *Phytophthora megasperma* var. *sojae* (stem rot). In other experiments wick tips containing phytoalexin prevented infection when placed with the fungus in wounds in the hypocotyls of susceptible plants. Inoculation of *Peperomia* leaves with avirulent isolates of *Phytophthora nicotianae* var. *parasitica* resulted in hypersensitivity lesions which could not be colonized by virulent isolates, and this protective effect extended beyond the lesion to the tissue immediately adjacent (Siradhana *et al.*, 1969). Although phytoalexins are generally considered to be restricted chiefly to the inoculation site some might be translocated within the plant, thereby conferring resistance to other parts of the plant. It is tempting to ascribe the increased resistance of tobacco leaves against *Peronospora tabacina*, following stem inoculation with this pathogen, to phytoalexins translocated to the leaves from the inoculated stems. Indeed, extracts of resistant leaves reduced germination of the conidia of *P. tabacina* (Cruickshank and Mandryk, 1960). There is increasing evidence, at present largely circumstantial, for movement of phytoalexin in the plant although this has yet to be demonstrated conclusively, and little is known of the ways in which such movement might occur.

There are other ways in which infection of plant tissue by one pathogen might be prevented or reduced by the presence of a second pathogen – for example, by secretion of toxic substances, by competition for limited available nutrients, or – with stomatal invaders – by one pathogen monopolizing the stomata. Indeed, many of the defence mechanisms elicited in plants by pathogens, as described earlier in this chapter, could be involved in cross-protection.

It is interesting that the interaction of two pathogens can be of a different nature in different varieties of the host plant, as described by Manners and Gandy (1954). Of the five wheat varieties simultaneously inoculated with a mixture of *Erysiphe graminis tritici* and *Puccinia triticina* the latter rust was increased in two varieties, reduced in one variety, and there was no consistent effect in the other two varieties. All five varieties were 'semi-resistant' to the race (66) of *P. triticina* used and susceptible to the *Erysiphe* inoculum used. Whatever the reasons it is clear that in this case the genotype of the plant affected the type of interaction which occurred.

Most studies on the interactions of pathogens have been undertaken with obligate or highly specialized parasites such as rusts and powdery mildews which probably alter the metabolic pattern of the infected and adjacent tissue but do not kill it for some time. Less specialized parasites often kill the infected tissue rather quickly and any cross-protection which develops is likely to be associated with this; for example, obligate parasites are unlikely to colonize tissue killed by a necrotrophic pathogen. This, however, is almost certainly not the whole story, and cross-protection among fairly unspecialized parasites needs further investigation.

Disease escape

A plant or tissue may remain disease-free because it passes through its susceptible phase at a time when the pathogen is absent, present in insufficient amount to achieve infection, or when environmental conditions are unfavourable for infection; by the time the pathogen is ready and able to attack it the plant is no longer susceptible. *Sphacelotheca sorghi* (covered smut) invades sorghum seedlings during the few days between germination and emergence, and if conditions at that time are not conducive to infection the plants remain uninfected despite the presence of the fungus on the seed. Conditions which delay emergence will prolong the period of susceptibility and so increase the likelihood of infection. Similar considerations apply to some other pathogens which are able to attack the plant only in the seedling stage. According to Gaumann (1950) wheat and barley are less liable to attack by *Claviceps purpurea* partly because their flowers have usually fertilized themselves by the time they open and are consequently in a less susceptible state. Rye, on the other hand, is cross-pollinated and the stigmas are fully receptive when the glumes open, and the latter may remain open for several days if fertilization does not occur. Hence ergot infection is more likely in rye than in wheat. These and other similar cases are examples of disease escape due to insufficient synchronization between pathogen and plant, rather than to mechanisms of resistance.

Although what has been written in this chapter refers primarily to mechanisms of resistance against fungal plant pathogens it is likely that much of it also applies to bacterial pathogens and, to a lesser extent, viruses. The last named, however, show special features in that they are within, and very intimately associated with, the host cell, and are composed largely of nucleic acids and proteins having some affinities with the genetical material of the host. The metabolism of the infected plant is diverted by the virus to producing more virus particles, a process which seems to have no counterpart in fungal infections although highly specialized fungi probably modify the host's metabolism to suit their own nutritional requirements, perhaps by pathogen RNA directing the synthetic processes of the plant. The defence mechanisms of plants against viruses are discussed in Chapter 4.

The importance of postinfectional resistance mechanisms, notably the production of fungitoxic phytoalexins and phenolic compounds, has become evident in recent years and has tended to replace the older view that resistance is often a preinfectional condition of the plant. Information on host-parasite interaction at the molecular level is now becoming available, particularly as concerns the role of nucleic acids and their possible interchange between host and parasite. The extent to which highly specialized parasites may be able to direct the metabolism of the host plant to suit their own requirements is an interesting field of investigation as yet barely touched. The intensive investigations of the past 20 years or so have shown that host-parasite interaction is a complex and dynamic process, and that the means of defence at the disposal of the host plant are more varied than hitherto realized.

Deverall (1969) suggests that some form of 'recognition' involving matching of information of, perhaps, surface proteins and probably mediated by nucleic acid or proteins occurs between fungal and plant cells. Recognition leading to successful parasitism occurs in a few cases but more often there is rejection brought about by hypersensitivity, phytoalexins or cellular antibodies. On this view successful parasites are those which can colonize the plant without provoking its resistance mechanisms or which can suppress the latter if provoked.

The essential similarity of the metabolic changes involved in pathogenic and cellular injury to plant tissue have been emphasized in recent years. Improved techniques for assaying phytoalexins in plant tissue have shown that these substances are probably produced as a generalized response of plant tissue to injury. Thus phaseollin was formed in brown, necrotic bean leaf tissue infected by tobacco necrosis virus (Bailey and Ingham, 1971) and this case would seem to be an exception to the induction hypothesis (p. 303) proposed by Hadwiger and Schwochau (1969) – TNV is unlikely to produce phaseollin-stimulating substances such as monilicolin A (a non-phytotoxic and non-fungitoxic polypeptide produced by *Sclerotinia fructicola* in culture: Cruickshank and Perrin, 1968). The way in which phaseollin is formed is uncertain but Rathmell and Bendall (*Physiol. Pl. Path.*, **1,** 351, 1971) consider that its production may represent a specific stimulation of isoflavonoid metabolism which is separate from any general increase in phenol metabolism associated with cell necrosis.

15 The genetics of plant-pathogen interaction

The attack and defence mechanisms described above are genetically determined in the pathogen and host plant, respectively. Genetical variation results in new races of pathogens, some of which have different pathogenic abilities and may be able to attack hitherto resistant plants. Similarly, new varieties of host plants arise, some of which are more resistant to pathogens. In both organisms the more effective races and varieties tend to survive, the less effective ones to disappear. Effective disease develops when a virulent race meets a susceptible variety but not when the pathogen is avirulent or the plant resistant. This may, however, be modified by environmental factors in that, for example, the normally effective resistance of a plant may be overcome under conditions highly favourable to the pathogen and/or unfavourable to the plant. The distinction between immunity and resistance, although theoretically valid and sometimes practically useful, can be of doubtful significance in the field, where high resistance is often equated with immunity ('field immunity'). The outcome of plant/parasite interaction depends on the relative effectiveness of the plant's resistance and the parasite's pathogenicity as mediated by the prevailing environmental conditions, and a knowledge of the genetics of both resistance and pathogenicity is clearly necessary for intelligent disease control by plant breeding methods.

The mechanisms which bring about variation in plants – principally hybridization and mutation – will not be considered here. Those which bring about variation in fungi are perhaps more diverse and include mutation, hybridization, heterokaryosis, parasexual recombination and possibly adaptation; accounts are given by Johnson (1960), Day (1960), Christensen *et al.* (1947) and others.

Mutation

Gene mutation occurs in all living organisms and can often be accelerated by treatment with chemical or physical mutagens. The pathogenic abilities of parasites as well as their morphological and other characteristics can be changed in this way and there is evidence that these are of importance in the development of new strains. In a haploid fungus such mutation should have immediate expression but this may be modified by epistatic or other effects. If the cell in which gene mutation occurs contains more than one nucleus the expression will be modified by the other nuclei present and in such heterokaryotic fungi, pathogenicity – and other characteristics – will be a composite effect.

New races attributed to mutation have been reported in *Cladosporium fulvum* (tomato leaf mould) where 'step' mutation (each mutation overcoming the protective effect of a single gene) is thought to have occurred (Bailey, 1950), and similar mutations have been achieved experimentally by ultraviolet irradiation (Day, 1957). Pathogenic variation due to mutation has also been reported in *Phytophthora infestans, Puccinia graminis, Melampsora lini*, and various smuts, to mention but a few. Many of these mutations are likely to be recessive and their expression will be dependent on sexual reproduction with accompanying recombination of pathogenicity factors. Anastomosis between hyphae (and germ tubes) may be followed by exchange of nuclei and this may also permit expression of recessive pathogenicity mutations.

This could be of considerable significance in Fungi Imperfecti and in those Phycomycetes, Ascomycetes and Basidiomycetes in which the perfect stage is rarely formed, as in some Erysiphaceae in which cleistothecia fail to develop under certain climatic conditions. Although the inadequate information available suggests that mutations affecting pathogenicity are fairly rare they are doubtless an effective mechanism for variation when the enormous numbers of spores produced by many pathogens are taken into account; for example, Watson (1957, 1957a) reported increased pathogenicity due to mutation in *Puccinia graminis* when large numbers of uredospores were involved. Mutation can also bring about reduced pathogenicity or other changes disadvantageous to the pathogen, and there is some evidence that these occur more frequently than mutation to increased pathogenicity.

The practical implications of mutation in aggressiveness of pathogens are difficult to assess. The sudden appearance of new races of increased pathogenicity in a pathogen which has hitherto been of only moderate pathogenicity has been ascribed to mutation and this may well be true. The recent (1970) appearance of a new, highly destructive race of *Helminthosporium maydis* (southern leaf blight) on maize in the United States may be an example of this (*Pl. Dis. Reptr*, **54,** 1099; 1970). Mutations also provide the basic pathogenicity changes which are subsequently brought out by hybridization or similar recombination mechanisms, and without mutation the latter would be of more restricted scope.

Hybridization

Hybridization between genetically different races is a fruitful and important source of variation in pathogens which undergo sexual reproduction involving nuclear fusion with subsequent meiotic division and reassortment of genes. Fungi such as Fungi Imperfecti, which fail to produce a sexual stage, possibly find a substitute process in parasexuality, described below. Hybridization is likely to be encouraged by incompatibility mechanisms which prevent or reduce inbreeding, and many pathogens are heterothallic. The origin of new pathogenic races by hybridization has been studied chiefly in rusts, smuts and certain Ascomycetes, especially *Venturia inaequalis*. New races have been synthesized experimentally by crossing pre-existing smut races and there is little doubt that this occurs in nature.

Hybridization can be intraspecific, interspecific or even intergeneric, and the resulting hybrids may have pathogenic abilities different from the parental races. Often the hybrids are intermediate in pathogenicity between the two parental races, but some may be more and others less pathogenic, and similar considerations apply to other inherited characteristics. Some hybrids show a tendency towards lysis, perhaps due to inherited lethal factors, or may fail to develop normally or to form spores, and such abnormal behaviour may limit the numbers which survive, thus to some extent imposing a natural check on the formation of new races by hybridization – particularly so in interspecific or intergeneric crosses.

Several different races or species of rusts and smuts may be present in a field of cereals and the opportunities for hybridization must in such cases be considerable. Elimination of the sexual stages of pathogens minimizes this type of variation as well as reducing overwintering of some fungi. Destruction of barberry bushes in control of black stem rust is a case in point, and there are often more races of the rust in the vicinity of such bushes. Extensive recombination of genes occurs in autoecious rusts, such as *Melampsora lini* (flax rust), in which all spore stages occur on the same plant. Interspecific hybridization in fungi is discussed by Nelson (1963).

Heterokaryosis

This term has been used with somewhat different meanings by different authors, as discussed by Parmeter, Snyder and Reichle (1963) who give a useful account of heterokaryosis as a mechanism of variation in plant pathogenic fungi. A heterokaryotic cell is one which contains two or more genotypically different nuclei, the condition of dikaryosis – that is, two nuclei per cell – being a special case obtaining in the secondary mycelium of many Basidiomycetes. It is possible that some cells of a fungus may be heterokaryotic, others homokaryotic, the organism as a whole then being considered heterokaryotic. Heterokaryosis can originate through mutation in one of the nuclei of a cell or through interchange of nuclei following fusion of hyphae or germ tubes. Apart from dikaryosis in smuts, rusts and Hymenomycetes, heterokaryosis has been reported in pathogens belonging to the Fungi Imperfecti, Ascomycetes and, to a lesser extent, Phycomycetes, but not all these reports are entirely convincing (Parmeter, Snyder and Reichle, 1963). Heterokaryosis appears to be necessary for pathogenicity in heterothallic smuts and in uredospore and aeciospore infections in heterothallic rusts, but not in infection by basidiospores as the latter are normally uninucleate and hence necessarily homokaryotic. There is much evidence that heterokaryosis not only conditions pathogenicity but also enables the effects of mutation to pathogenicity (often recessive) to be expressed.

The significance of heterokaryosis in the production of new pathogenic races of Phycomycetes, Ascomycetes and Fungi Imperfecti is less well understood. Buxton (1956) produced nearly avirulent races of *Fusarium oxysporum f.sp. pisi* by ultraviolet irradiation, and showed that heterokaryons between such avirulent races could be as virulent as wild-type races; the heterokaryons were recovered by culturing from the diseased plants. He (1960) concluded that some of the increases in virulence of pathogens in nature may be due to heterokaryosis between weakly virulent strains.

Nutritional deficiencies can affect pathogenicity as shown by Hrushovetz (1957) who demonstrated that repeated culturing of *Helminthosporium sativum* on media supplemented with certain amino acids led to a progressive loss of pathogenicity in some cases. The mechanism involved is uncertain but such repeated culturing may have led to selection for deficient nuclei, thalli containing the latter being less pathogenic. The increased pathogenicity due to heterokaryosis in the mycelium would not be inherited by the spores unless the latter contained a full complement of parental nuclei, and would not obtain with uninucleate conidia. Heterokaryosis is thus unlikely to bring about any permanent inherited change in pathogenicity which would persist after sporulation, although parasexual recombination (see below), in which heterokaryosis is a first step, could do so. Heterokaryons in Fungi Imperfecti and Ascomycetes tend to be unstable – at least in the laboratory – and their occurrence in these groups has not been adequately investigated. According to Caten and Jinks (1966) heterokaryons occur chiefly between homokaryons with similar genotypes and this would reduce the importance of heterokaryosis in producing variation. Heterokaryosis is discussed by Davis (1966).

Parasexual recombination

This process in which genetical recombination occurs in the vegetative thallus in the absence of a sexual stage has been investigated chiefly in species of *Aspergillus* and *Penicillium* in the laboratory by Pontecorvo and his coworkers (Pontecorvo, Roper and Forbes, 1953; Pontecorvo and Sermonti, 1954; Pontecorvo, 1956; see also Bradley, 1962). Although the details are obscure the essential features of the parasexual cycle are: (1) production of diploid nuclei in a heterokaryotic mycelium containing haploid nuclei, presumably by nuclear fusion of some sort; (2) multiplication of the diploid nuclei along with the haploid ones; (3) development of a diploid mycelium, that is a diploid strain; (4) mitotic crossing-over resulting in recombination of genes; and (5) haploidization of the diploid nuclei in which recombination of whole chromosomes occurs, unbalanced combinations being eliminated. The results are similar to those achieved by meiosis, a much more precise and regular process. The frequency of these events appears to be low and there is little information as to the significance of this somatic recombination in nature, especially as concerns the fungi which attack plants. Parasexuality, however, produced new races of *Fusarium oxysporum f.sp. pisi* (Buxton, 1956) and has also been reported in *Ascochyta imperfecta* (black stem of alfalfa: Sanderson and Srb, 1965), *Verticillium albo-atrum* (Hastie, 1962, 1964; Fordyce and Green, 1964), *Fusarium oxysporum f.sp. cubense* (banana wilt: Buxton, 1962), *Cochliobolus sativus* (Tinline, 1962) and others. There is evidence that somatic recombination may occur in smuts and rusts, as in *Ustilago maydis* (Rowell, 1955), *Puccinia graminis* (Watson, 1957) and *P. recondita* (Vakili and Caldwell, 1957). This is based partly on observations that more new races may develop from heterokaryons between two germinating uredospores than would be theoretically expected, and has been attributed to some kind of parasexual recombination. Somatic recombination in rusts does not occur in single dikaryons, but only when several dikaryons are present; the reasons for this are not understood.

Somatic recombination by parasexual methods has been demonstrated in the laboratory but its significance in producing new races of pathogens in the field has yet to be established. One would expect it to be of importance in fungi lacking sexual reproduction, and it may well be so in the Fungi Imperfecti, many of which are very variable fungi; it is discussed by Roper (1966) and Tinline and MacNeill (1969).

Adaptation

The possibility that pathogens might adapt themselves to their host plants has been debated for many years. There seems to be no incontrovertible evidence that this occurs although the evidence for adaptation to chemicals is stronger. Apparent adaptation to host plant might be due to mutation or to selecting out of pre-existing strains better able to attack the host. Changes in the enzymic capabilities of a pathogen may be mediated by the presence of appropriate substrates ('adaptive' enzymes) and this might modify its pathogenicity. Many years ago Ward (1903) suggested the concept of 'bridging hosts' by means of which a pathogen becomes able to pass from a susceptible to a hitherto resistant host, as in *Puccinia dispersa* becoming 'adapted' to resistant species of *Bromus* after propagation in some species of this grass. Somewhat similar changes were reported by Salmon (1904) in powdery mildews, and more recent work indicates that passage through some host plants can sometimes affect pathogenicity. Repeated passage through a resistant plant sometimes enhances the aggressiveness of the pathogen, and *vice versa*, as has been demonstrated in several fungi and bacteria, for example *Phytophthora infestans* (Ferris, 1955) and *Xanthomonas stewarti* (Lincoln, 1940). In other cases (for example *Venturia inaequalis*: Keitt and Langford, 1941) this has not been demonstrated. Changes in pathogenicity of *Fusarium oxysporum f.sp. pisi* brought about by exudates from pea roots have been described by Buxton (1957, 1958). Although there is increasing evidence in favour of parasitic adaptation the mechanisms involved remain obscure. Host selection of more aggressive biotypes from a mixture of biotypes, together with adaptation, mutation (perhaps by some mutagen in the host), and cytoplasmic variation may be involved in different cases. Loss of pathogenicity by fungi in culture might also be interpreted in a similar manner. The extent to which these adaptive changes are temporary (as in those due to heterokaryosis) or permanent and inherited needs further study.

Saltation

This phenomenon, also described as dissociation or sectoring, refers to the appearance of morphologically different sectors in fungal colonies. It occurs frequently in some fungi, including some isolates of *Fusarium* and *Helminthosporium*, but infrequently in others. Some such sectors remain fairly stable when subcultured while others are unstable. Saltation may be influenced by the composition and thickness of the culture medium and can affect such characteristics as colony colour and topography, rate of growth and sporulation, and size and shape of the spores. Pathogenicity might also be affected and this has been studied in *Fusarium* spp. by several investigators including Haymaker (1928), Wellman (1943), Weindling (1939), and Oswald (1949). Results have been somewhat conflicting; saltants tended to be less aggressive than the parent cultures, but occasional ones were more aggressive and these might be of significance where the saltation rate is high. No new pathogenic races with altered host ranges have been reported in saltants. The mechanisms involved in saltation are varied and not well understood. Some are probably due to gene mutation, others to heterokaryosis – particularly so in cultures derived from inoculum containing several genetically different nuclei, as in some multinucleate spores. Nevertheless, saltation has been reported in colonies derived from single uninucleate spores or from homokaryotic multinucleate spores and this is presumably due directly or indirectly (*via* heterokaryosis and possibly parasexuality) to gene mutation. Other explanations, including cytoplasmic inheritance, have been suggested and saltation remains in some ways an obscure phenomenon.

Cytoplasmic variation

There is much evidence for the existence in fungi of genetical determinants located in the cytoplasm outside the nucleus. Inheritance of such cytoplasmic determinants differs from that of the nuclear genes. Cytoplasmic inheritance has been attributed to plasmagenes (Darlington and Mather, 1949), cytoplasmic RNA (possibly some ribosomes), or genetical material detached from the chromosomes (episomes). There is little information as to the possible significance of cytoplasmic factors in bringing about variation in pathogenicity of plant pathogens, although Johnson (1954) has described cytoplasmic control of pathogenicity of *Puccinia graminis f.sp. tritici*; this is a subject which needs investigation. Cytoplasmic inheritance is discussed by Jinks (1966).

Variation in bacteria and viruses

Much of the foregoing has referred to fungi, and the mechanisms of variation described are not necessarily applicable to bacteria and viruses. There is an extensive literature concerned with mutation in bacteria but relatively little on its effects on the pathogenicity of those bacteria which attack plants. Mutation occurs in bacteria and is probably of importance in producing variants of increased or reduced pathogenicity; such variants have been artificially produced by irradiation and chemical mutagens. Old colonies originating from single cells comprise several different pathogenic strains, probably arising by mutation (for example, in *Xanthomonas stewarti*: Lincoln, 1940), and passage of the bacterium through resistant and susceptible hosts tends to result in increased (or maintained) or diminished pathogenicity, respectively, presumably by selection of the host adapted mutants. Possibly some sort of sexual process similar to that demonstrated in *Escherichia coli* occurs in plant pathogenic bacteria and could result in genetical recombination, and transformation – in which one bacterium acquires some of the characteristics of a second one by growth in its extract or filtrate – has been reported in *Xanthomonas phaseoli* by Corey and Starr (1957, 1957*a*).

Tumour inducing ability has been transferred to avirulent strains of *Agrobacterium tumefaciens* and certain non-pathogenic bacteria from virulent *A. tumefaciens*, and culture filtrates of the last named contained DNA which was thought to be the tranforming principle (Klein and Klein, 1956). The term transduction has been applied to transfer by a bacterio- phage of a segment of chromosome from the parent bacterial cell to the cell infected by the phage. In some way this introduced segment replaces the homologous segment in the recipient cell and so becomes a part of its genetical material. Such processes may occur in plant pathogenic bacteria although there is little information on this.

Viruses also show considerable variability in such characters as in- fectivity, longevity, symptoms produced on the host plant, host range and specificity to vectors. These variations are presumably due to some sort of mutation process and are inherited in that they are perpetuated in transferring the virus from plant to plant. The mechanisms involved in these changes are not well understood. In virus resistant plants the relation- ship is, in effect, between the nucleic acid of the resistance genes of the plant and the RNA of the virus particle. Variation in plant viruses is discussed by Kunkel (1947) and the genetics of viruses by Gordon (1950). Bacterial variation is reviewed by Lederberg (1949), and bacterial gen- etics by Ravin (1958), Cavilli-Sforza (1957), and Hartman and Goodgol (1959).

Genetical determination of resistance/susceptibility

The genetical basis of resistance/susceptibility to disease-inciting agents has been investigated in several cases. The early literature on this is reviewed by Wingard (1941), and a useful account of sources of disease resistance and its inheritance in crop plants is given by Stevenson and Jones (1953).

The inheritance of disease reaction in plants may be fairly simple or complex. One or a few genes may be involved (monogenic, oligogenic resistance) or several genes together with modifiers and other complicating factors (polygenic resistance) may be involved. Vertical (differential) resistance is highly effective against certain races of a pathogen but ineffective against others, whereas horizontal (uniform) resistance operates against all races of the pathogen but is less effective and more likely to break down under conditions favourable for disease development; these are discussed below.

As with other genetically determined characteristics the mode of inheritance of disease resistance varies in different host-parasite combinations, and each case has to be determined individually. The situation may be further complicated by polyploidy in the host plant, different physiological races of the pathogen, the effect of environment, complex and irregular patterns of inheritance, and the fact that different organs of the plant and tissues of different ages may show differences in reaction to the same pathogen. In genetical analysis of this sort there has to be a satisfactory definition as to what is a resistant and what is a susceptible plant, and these standards are necessarily arbitrary except in immunity. There will probably be intermediate grades of resistance/susceptibility and cases in which some symptoms of the disease are marked, others virtually absent. Vertical and horizontal resistance may occur in the same plant species, as in potatoes towards *Phytophthora infestans*. These and other factors make the study of pathogenicity and resistance a complex one.

One of the earliest studies was that of Biffen (1907) who found that resistance of wheat to *Puccinia striiformis* (yellow rust) was controlled by a single recessive gene. *P. graminis f.sp. tritici* has been intensively investigated in North America (Stakman and Harrar, 1957), and several hundred physiological races of this fungus have been distinguished; resistance has been reported as monogenic or polygenic and recessive or dominant in crosses between different varieties of wheat in relation to different races of the pathogen.

The different races of this rust are distinguished by using twelve standard differential varieties of wheat – one of *Triticum compactum* (Little Club, abbreviated to L.C.), three of *T. vulgare* (Marquis, MA; Reliance, REL; Kota, KO), one of *T. monococcum* (Einkorn, ENK), five of *T. durum* (Arnautka, ARN; Mindum, MND; Spelmar, SPM; Kubanka, KUB; Acme, AC), and two of *T. dicoccum* (Vernal, VER; Khapli, KPL). Several supplementary ones can be used to differentiate certain races, and seven infection types are recognized. (1) Immune – no uredia (sori) or other indications of infection; infection type 0 (2) Nearly immune – no sori but hypersensitive flecks present; type 0; (3) Very resistant – sori minute and surrounded by distinct necrotic areas; type 1 (4) Moderately resistant – sori small to medium and usually in green islands surrounded by a decidedly chlorotic or necrotic border; type 2 (5) Moderately susceptible – sori of medium size, infrequently coalescing, without necrosis but there may be chlorotic areas especially under unfavourable growing conditions; type 3 (6) Very susceptible – large sori often coalescing, no necrosis, but there may be chlorosis under unfavourable growing conditions; type 4 (7) Heterogeneous (mesothetic) – sori variable and sometimes including all infection types and intermediate forms on the same leaf; on reinoculation small sori may produce large ones and *vice versa*, hence no consistent separation is possible; type x.

This method of identifying races of *P. graminis* var. *tritici* must be carried out under standardized conditions since changes in temperature and light can affect the symptoms produced; these are described in detail by Stakman, Stewart and Loegering (1962). As Flor (1959) has pointed out, the marked diversity of infection types on different varieties of wheat suggests complex inheritance. The problem of breeding resistant wheats has been further complicated by an apparent dearth of resistant biotypes in bread wheat (*Triticum vulgare*) and the occurrence of sterility and undesirable linkages in some crosses between this species and resistant durum wheats (*T. durum.*)

The resistance of flax to *Melampsora lini* has been intensively studied by H. H. Flor who concluded that the hypersensitivity reaction of seedlings was conditioned by multiple allelomorphs in five loci, of which K (one gene identified), L (eleven genes), and M (six genes) are independently inherited whereas the other two, N (three genes) and P (four genes), are linked with a cross-over percentage of 26 (Flor, 1959). Resistance was dominant and virulence recessive. It is possible that other forms of inheritance may apply to other types of resistance of the flax plant to rust but these have not been investigated. Detailed study of the interaction of different pathogen races with different flax varieties led to the gene-for-gene hypothesis discussed below. There is a considerable literature on the inheritance of pathogenicity and resistance, including smuts (Holton, 1959), *Venturia inaequalis* (Keitt, Boone and Shay, 1959; Williams and Kuc, 1969) and *Phytophthora infestans* (Gallegly and Niederhauser, 1959). In the last named Black (1952) in Scotland identified four major dominant genes, R_1-R_4 (about nine are now known), controlling resistance, and also resistance, possibly recessive, due to multiple genes – this polygenic resistance is apparently conditioned by different factors in the case of tuber rot as compared with foliage blight.

Favret (1967) concludes that 'reactions of host plants in the presence of different pathogenic races are controlled by a high number of genes, and within them a still higher number of alleles for resistance exist', for example, in wheat five genes (*Erysiphe graminis*), seven (*Puccinia recondita*), seven (*P. graminis tritici*) and ten (*Tilletia* spp.); in maize three (*P. polysora*) and five (*P. sorghi*); in barley five (*P. hordei*), three (*Septoria passerinii*) and fifteen–sixteen (*Erysiphe graminis*). These figures are considered by Favret to be underestimates.

Resistance is often dominant over susceptibility in inheritance in the plant diseases so far investigated.

Vertical and horizontal resistance

When a host plant variety is more resistant to some races of a pathogen than to others the resistance has been termed vertical or differential, whereas resistance which is evenly spread against all races is horizontal or uniform (Van der Plank, 1963, 1969). Resistance can also be classified as monogenic (determined by one gene), oligogenic (a few genes), or polygenic (many genes), but what constitutes 'a few' is uncertain. Monogenic and oligogenic are sometimes equated with 'major gene' resistance and polygenic with 'minor gene' or 'field' resistance. This usage seems inadvisable since not all oligogenes are necessarily major genes in the sense of imparting high resistance to the plant which has them, and similarly

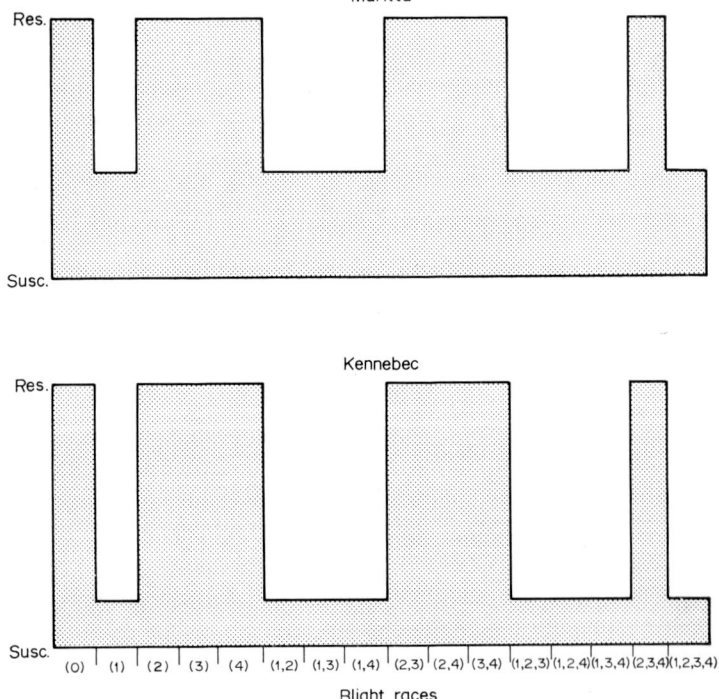

Figure 15.1   Vertical and horizontal resistance in two varieties of potato. For explanation, see text.

not all polygenes are necessarily minor genes in this sense. Nevertheless it is likely that vertical resistance is often determined by monogenes or oligogenes, and horizontal resistance by polygenes, although there may be exceptions to this generalization.

Vertical and horizontal, as applied to resistance, are mathematically derived concepts, and refer respectively to the vertical and horizontal axes of a graph. This is shown in the accompanying diagram (figure 15.1), taken from Van der Plank (1963), which indicates the foliage resistance (shaded) of two potato varieties to sixteen races of *Phytophthora infestans*. Both varieties show vertical (complete) resistance to races (0), (2), (3), (4), (2, 3), (2, 4), (3, 4), and (2, 3, 4), while resistance to the other eight races is horizontal and greater in Maritta than in Kennebec. Vertical resistance is probably always accompanied by some degree of horizontal resistance since, as Van der Plank (1968) points out, it is difficult to visualize a plant completely lacking in resistance to a pathogen. Such a completely susceptible plant would lack the ability to oppose the pathogen in any way and would be completely overrun by it.

It is suggested by Van der Plank (1968) that vertical resistance operates mostly after the pathogen has penetrated the plant and that it may involve such active defence mechanisms as hypersensitivity, production of phytoalexins, and possibly other reactions of the plant. Although these mechanisms do not entirely prevent penetration they do prevent the subsequent spread of the pathogen in the tissue, so that the plant is for most practical purposes immune. Hypersensitivity, for example, is often involved in the vertical resistance of plants against obligate and near-obligate parasites.

Horizontal resistance protects against all races of a pathogen to varying extents, but the protection it affords is usually less than that given by vertical resistance against specific races. It may operate before or after infection through defence mechanisms which reduce or delay infection, colonization of the plant, and/or production of spores by the pathogen. It seems that the tissues of horizontally resistant plants are, or become, less suitable for growth of the pathogen. The defence mechanisms involved appear to operate by reducing the germination of the spores of the pathogen or by inhibiting or disrupting the formation of appressoria or other infection structures. As a result, infection and sporulation of the pathogen are reduced and retarded rather than completely suppressed, and the rate of spread of the pathogen in the field is thereby diminished.

Genetical determination of pathogenicity

Less is known about the genetical factors which condition pathogenicity than about those which determine resistance of the plant. Most pathogens probably comprise several biotypes which show differences in virulence to different host species and varieties, these variants arising as discussed above. *Puccinia graminis*, for example, comprises several varieties or special forms (*Formae speciales*) such as *P. graminis f.sp. tritici* specialized to wheat, and *f.sp. avenae* to oats. Within the variety are physiological races specialized to one or several varieties of the host plant, as in the several hundred races of *P. graminis tritici*. These races are differentiated on their ability or otherwise to attack a set of twelve standard differential varieties of wheat, and on the symptoms produced (Stakman, Levine and Loegering, 1944). Use of a wider range of differential varieties would no doubt enable further races of the rust to be distinguished. Each race comprises a number of slightly different biotypes or individuals.

Although there may be exceptions, virulence is often recessive to avirulence in the few diseases that have been investigated. In some cases virulence is apparently inherited as a unit, due perhaps to the virulence genes being closely linked or to virulence being conditioned by multiple alleles.

Results of crosses between *Cochliobolus carbonum* and *C. victoriae* suggested that certain of the genes for pathogenicity are independently inherited (Nelson and Kline, 1963). Little is known about the numbers of genes involved in pathogenicity and there seems to be considerable variation in this. In crosses between races of *Puccinia graminis tritici* pathogenicity was considered to be governed by one pair of alleles in Kanred and Mindum and by two pairs in the variety Vernal (Johnston and Newton, 1940). Up to thirteen gene pairs are said to condition pathogenicity in *Venturia inaequalis* on apple (Williams and Shay, 1957), while pathogenicity is apparently monogenic and recessive in *Ustilago avenae* (Halisky, 1965). Genes at seven loci conditioned pathogenicity in an isolate of *Erysiphe graminis hordei* (Moseman, 1966). The fact that many species of fungi which attack plants comprise several races distinguished by qualitative or quantitative differences in their host spectrum may indicate that pathogenicity in such fungi is governed by several genes. Nelson (1961) suggests that pathogenic fungi have gene pools which include not only genes for pathogenicity to specific host plants but also additional genes for pathogenicity to other plants. Interspecific hybridization perhaps facilitates recombination between genes present in different species of the fungi, but there is little information as to the extent to which this occurs in nature.

In Van der Plank's (1969) view there are two kinds of pathogenic race. There are those which interact differentially with varieties of the host plant and which can thus only be differentiated and identified by using more than one host genotype, that is, by using a set of differential varieties. Such races are said to differ in virulence. There are also races which do not react differentially with different host genotypes but which can be distinguished by their reaction on a single host variety. These differ in aggressiveness. These two types of race correspond with the two types of host resistance – vertical and horizontal (see below) – and the terms 'vertical pathogenicity' and 'horizontal pathogenicity' have been suggested by Robinson (1969) for virulence and aggressiveness, respectively. Watson (1970) suggests that virulence/avirulence of the pathogen is controlled by specific genes which interact with corresponding resistance genes of the host in a relatively simple genetical system, whereas characters related to pathogenicity (growth rate of the pathogen, lesion size, spore output, aggressiveness) are controlled by a polygenic system.

There are several reviews of the genetics of individual pathogens or groups of pathogens. They include Moseman (1966): powdery mildews; Holton (1959) and Halisky (1965): smuts; Flor (1959): rusts; Keitt *et al.* (1959): *Venturia inaequalis*; Gallegly and Niederhauser (1959) and Gallegly (1968): *Phytophthora infestans*; and general accounts are given by Johnston (1959) and Day (1966).

Gene-for-gene hypothesis

After detailed study of the genetics of host-parasite interaction in flax rust (*Melampsora lini*) H. H. Flor concluded that for each gene determining resistance in flax there is a specific and related gene determining virulence in the rust; that is, for each gene in the host capable of mutating to give resistance there exists a gene in the pathogen capable of mutating to overcome that particular resistance (Fincham and Day, 1965). A more elaborate definition is given by Person, Samborski and Rohringer (1962). Such gene-for-gene relationships have also been proposed for potato blight (Black, 1952), apple scab (Boone and Keitt, 1957), wheat bunt (Metzger and Trione, 1962), wheat loose smut (Oort, 1963), powdery mildew of barley (Moseman, 1959), and others.

Person (1959) put forward reasons why gene-for-gene relationships are to be expected in most host-parasite systems. Mutation to increased resistance is of survival value to the host while mutation to increased pathogenicity benefits the pathogen, and the reverse mutations are probably disadvantageous. Resistance genes are of value only in a susceptible population of plants, so that the increase in frequency of resistance genes is likely to occur first and to be followed by an increase in virulence genes able to overcome the effects of the new resistance genes. One practical effect of this is that the resistant plant variety probably eventually succumbs to a new race of the pathogen which the variety has in a sense called into being.

A mutation which brings about effective resistance tends to spread through the host population and results in selection pressure at all loci in the pathogen which may be able to mutate to produce an effective counteracting gene for virulence. The latter is related in its action to the specific resistance gene whose effect it can neutralize or overcome, and a gene-for-gene relationship thus develops. New resistance genes are likely to arise and in turn be overcome by new virulence genes, so that a continuous genetical interaction between host and parasite is theoretically to be expected. An individual plant will be attacked only by those parasites which have virulence genes related to and able to overcome the action of each resistance gene of that plant. The 'universal suscept' is the host variety with no effective resistance genes, and the race of the pathogen that attacks only the universal suscept is the 'avirulent' race (Person, 1959). The properties of an ideal gene-for-gene system are discussed by the latter author (1959). From analysis of Flor's data it was concluded that many of the supposedly single-gene differential varieties of flax used contained two or more resistance genes. Mutant genes which modify the action of existing genes could also arise, in which case several genes in the parasite or host will be related to a single gene in the other member.

These genetical considerations enable predictions of the likely occurrence and characteristics of new races to be made. Black (1952) was able to do this with *Phytophthora infestans,* basing his predictions on genetical data and on the observed changes in cultures of the fungus when these were inoculated into potato varieties having new combinations of resistance genes. Six host genotypes and six related pathogen races were correctly forecast. The detailed analysis of the data is given by Person (1959) who concludes that Black's results are identical to those which would be expected from an ideal gene-for-gene system with four interacting loci. This confirms that such a system is involved in potato blight, as suggested by Toxopeus (1956).

The extent to which gene-for-gene relationships occur in plant diseases has yet to be investigated. As Oort (1963) points out the known cases all comprise pathogens such as rusts, smuts, powdery mildews, *Phytophthora* and *Venturia* which are biotrophic parasites or nearly so and which are dependent on the living host plant, outside which they can survive only as resistant propagules. They are commonly regarded as highly specialized parasites and the host range of their physiological races is rather restricted. Being ecologically obligate parasites their survival depends on the ability to overcome the protective effects of new resistance genes arising in the host plant. From his mathematical study of host-parasite genetical systems involving obligate parasites, Mode (1958) concluded that such systems might be 'relics of ancient systems of polymorphism' stemming from the time when the host plants reproduced by outbreeding, and that such balanced systems were necessary for the coevolution of obligate parasites and their hosts. Perthophytes, on the other hand, cause localized necrosis of the host and obtain their nutrients from the dead tissue. They are less specialized parasites in that their saprophytic ability is greater and they are thus less dependent on the host plant. For them increased saprophytic ability may be as important as increased parasitic potential, and gene-for-gene relationships might be expected to occur more rarely. Horizontal resistance – that which is effective against all races of the pathogen – might be of more importance in plants attacked by perthophytes, but this type of resistance can also occur in plants attacked by ecologically obligate parasites, as in the polygenic 'field' resistance of potatoes which is effective against many races of *Phytophthora infestans*.

Gene-for-gene relationships probably occur in parasitic interactions but not in mutualistic symbiosis where antagonism is absent, and the presence of such relationships might be taken as an indication of antagonistic symbiosis, that is parasitism (Person, Samborski and Rohringer, 1962). The latter authors (1962) also consider that there is no reason to postulate any structural specificities between genes for host resistance and the corresponding genes for pathogen virulence (as suggested, for example, by Flangas and Dickson, 1961). A successful attack mechanism must, however, be complementary to the resistance mechanism which it overcomes. For example Turner (1961) considers that *Ophiobolus graminis f.sp. avenae* may be able to parasitize oats by virtue of its ability to produce avenacinase which inhibits the fungitoxic glucoside avenacin of the oat plant. Mutation enabling it to produce this enzyme may have enabled *O. graminis* to extend its host range. It is likely that genetical factors determine the host plant's phytoalexin potentialities while the sensitivity of the pathogen to the latter is also genetically controlled, a system conforming to the gene-for-gene hypothesis (Cruickshank, 1963).

The gene-for-gene hypothesis offers a satisfactory genetical basis for the genetical interaction of host and parasite in many cases, but it should perhaps be mentioned that the data could also be interpreted on the assumption that some of the unit differentials in host or parasite have a more complex basis than a single gene, provided that they act independently of each other (Fincham and Day, 1965); complementary or duplicate genes might be involved. Nevertheless, the gene-for-gene relationship provides the simplest explanation and seems to be generally accepted.

Mechanisms of genetical control of resistance and virulence

Despite much discussion as to how genes bring about resistance in the plant and virulence in the pathogen many aspects of this interesting problem remain obscure. The fact that plant resistance is often dominant over susceptibility in inheritance has led some investigators to suppose that resistance implies the presence of a substance, and susceptibility its absence. Similarly, avirulence (dominant) implies the presence or production of a substance, and virulence (recessive) its absence. If this is so the resistant variety of the plant and the avirulent pathogen race would both produce substances, and Catcheside (1951) has made the interesting suggestion that these substances might be related in the manner of antigen and antibody, the presence of both together inducing incompatibility (immunity). This was investigated by Doubly, Flor and Clagett (1960) who found that a race of *Melampsora lini* was virulent to flax varieties containing its specific rust antigen as a minor constituent, and avirulent to varieties lacking that antigen. This suggests that susceptibility depends on the plant containing, as a minor antigenic component, a protein serologically related to one of the proteins of the parasite – namely, that resistance perhaps depends on some sort of recognition of a specific fungal protein which may fail if the latter resembles too closely one of the host's own proteins (Fincham and Day, 1965). An alternative explanation suggested by Johnston (1960) is based on the assumption that a specific substance is necessary for successful parasitism. The absence of such a substance from the plant would prevent parasitism unless the pathogen itself could synthesize it; that is, strains lacking this ability would be avirulent except to plants containing the substance.

A more attractive induction hypothesis has recently been put forward by Hadwiger and Schwochau (1969). Briefly this postulates that, where plant resistance and pathogen avirulence are both dominant in inheritance (as is usually the case), pathogen genes direct the synthesis of substances which activate or derepress the resistance genes of the host plant. These activated genes then bring about a hypersensitive type of response which renders the plant resistant to the pathogen. Resistance responses in the host can be invoked by microbial metabolites of various kinds and seem to depend on high metabolical activity associated with increased protein synthesis. Studies on the induction of phytoalexins by these metabolites have shown that certain concentrations of the latter bring about high metabolical activity and increased protein synthesis by interfering with the gene control mechanisms in the plant. It seems logical to suppose that microorganisms may induce host resistance by eliminating certain gene control mechanisms, bringing about an alteration in the level of gene repression in the cells.

The metabolites involved include actinomycin D, mitomycin C, ribonuclease, phytoactin B, gliotoxin, cycloheximide, puromycin and chloramphenicol. These induced formation of the phytoalexin pisatin at certain concentrations and were inhibitory at higher concentrations; for example, actinomycin D gave maximum pisatin production at 0·01 mg/ml per gramme of pea pod whereas no pisatin was detected above 0·2 mg/ml (Schwochau and Hadwiger, 1969). Most of these metabolites, although chemically diverse, in some way interfere with protein synthesis and so may be expected to change the gene repression pattern of the plant cell.

According to the induction hypothesis, the genes (P, dominant) of an avirulent isolate of a pathogen bring about the production of a substance (or substances) which activates or derepresses host resistance genes; the latter, in turn, so change the plant tissue that it becomes unsuitable for further development of the pathogen, that is resistant. The genes (p, recessive) of virulent isolates, however, do not bring about the formation of this activating substance in effective amounts, if at all, so that the tissue remains suitable for growth of the pathogen, that is susceptible.

	Host	Inducer production and gene in pathogen	
Gene pair	Potential for induction	High production, P	Low production, p
RR or Rr	High	Resistance	Susceptibility
rr	Low	Susceptibility	Susceptibility

Figure 15.2   For explanation, see text.

The gene(s) (R, dominant) for resistance in the host plant can be activated by the activating substance produced by avirulent isolates of the pathogen and, when so activated, initiates a response inhibitory to the pathogen. The genes (r, recessive) for susceptibility in the plant presumably cannot be so activated. These interactions are summarized in the accompanying diagram (figure 15.2) modified from Hadwiger and Schwochau (1969). There are, however, apparent exceptions to this hypothesis (see p. 285).

Resistance results only when the plant has the (dominant) gene for induction (RR or Rr) and the pathogen contains the dominant gene (P) for inducer production.

Although based chiefly on work with phytoalexins this hypothesis is believed by its propounders to be applicable to most resistance responses of the host plant, but is not considered to be relevant to preinfectional defence mechanisms, such as the presence of substances toxic to the pathogen in the tissue or the absence of nutrients needed by the pathogen.

The hypothesis that molecular interactions between the carbohydrate

constituents of plants and the polysaccharide-degrading enzymes produced by pathogens in part determine the initiation of infection has been
mentioned (p. 273). A model of a gene-for-gene system based on this
hypothesis is described by Albersheim, Jones and English (1969) for
anthracnose of bean (*Phaseolus vulgaris*) caused by *Colletotrichum lindemuthianum*. In this model it is assumed that the fungus is virulent only when it
produces large amounts of α-galactosidase which enable it to invade the
plant, and that synthesis of this enzyme is repressed by glucose. The
salient features of the model are summarized as follows:

The bean variety Genefer Market contains a resistance gene, assumed
to encode an enzyme which adds glucose side chains to a polysaccharide
in the cell wall through α-glycosidic linkages. The alpha strain of the
fungus does not produce α-glucosidase and is consequently unable to
release glucose from the cell walls of Genefer Market, so that when this
strain attacks the latter variety the synthesis of α-galactosidase is not repressed and infection takes place. The alpha strain can, however, synthesize β-glucosidase and thus is unable to infect the variety Red Kidney,
which contains a second resistance gene assumed to encode an enzyme
which adds glucose side chains to a polysaccharide in the cell wall through
β-glycosidic linkages; the β-glucosidase produced by the alpha strain
hydrolyses the β-glucosides of Red Kidney cell walls and thus releases
glucose which represses the synthesis of α-galactosidase and so prevents
infection. The beta strain of *C. lindemuthianum* produces α-glucosidase and
so is able to infect Red Kidney but not Genefer Market. The variety
Perry Marrow contains both α- and β-glucosides in its cell walls and so
is resistant to both alpha and beta strains of the fungus, but is susceptible
to the gamma and delta strains, neither of which can synthesize either
α- or β-glucosidase. Due to the number of polymer constituents and the
variety of linkages through which they are joined, the number of possible
variations in cell wall polysaccharide structure in plants is very great.
Analogous cells of different varieties within a plant species are likely to
have walls of identical or very similar sugar composition, but slight
differences in the nature of the glycosidic linkages might be enough to
cause differing interactions with pathogen-produced enzymes and so to
bring about gene-for-gene systems.

The stage in invasion of the plant at which resistance genes begin to
operate has been investigated in *Erysiphe graminis* on wheat by Ellingboe
(1968) and Slesinski and Ellingboe (1969). In this disease some of the
resistance genes inhibit the formation of haustoria by the fungus and have
no detectable effect on spore germination, formation of appressoria, or
initiation of penetration. These genes apparently operate at some time
between early penetration and haustoria formation, the development of
the fungus being halted when it comes into contact with the plasma

membrane of the epidermal cell. Other resistance genes operate in different ways – by bringing about hypersensitivity or by inhibiting the growth of the fungus in some other way – and become effective at different times after penetration. The extent to which these conclusions apply to other pathogens, particularly facultative parasites, is uncertain since there appear to be relatively few reports on the stages at which resistance genes become operative in plants.

Host range of pathogens

Resistance of plants to pathogens is often dominant, virulence of pathogens is often recessive, and most plants are immune to most pathogens although there may be limited entry into the plant. Most parasites thus have a limited host range and this is particularly true of highly specialized ones which are closely adapted to their hosts, as in *Puccinia graminis* which is specialized into numerous races each of which attacks only a narrow spectrum of host varieties. In such cases the metabolical systems of parasite and host are probably delicately balanced and a slight change in either may convert compatibility (susceptibility) to incompatibility (resistance). There appear to be exceptions such as *Erysiphe polygoni* which occurs on a wide and diverse range of hosts. This, however, is probably an aggregate species and it has been divided by Blumer (1933) into several species most of which are restricted to one family. Similar considerations no doubt apply to other highly specialized parasites of apparently wide host range.

Many pathogens are restricted to certain genera within a family as in *Puccinia malvacearum* (Malvaceae) and *Peronospora parasitica* (Cruciferae), but there may be generic specificity as in *Diplocarpon rosae* on *Rosa* spp. Genera such as *Puccinia* and *Cercospora* comprise numerous species which between them attack a wide range of host species, whereas others are restricted to one family or even one genus; for example, all known species of *Phragmidium* attack only Rosaceae, and *Schroeteria* (smut) is restricted to *Veronica*. Many heteroecious rusts have two markedly dissimilar alternate hosts, one of which may be annual and the other perennial; thus the uredospores and aeciospores of *Puccinia graminis* attack only certain Gramineae whereas the basidiospores attack only *Berberis*. In autoecious rusts, however, all three types of spore are able to infect the same host species as in *P. menthae* on *Mentha*. The aeciospores of most heteroecious rusts do not infect the species which bears them but this does happen in a few, for example, *Cronartium coleosporioides* and *C. flaccidum*, but not *C. ribicola*, all three of which produce aecia on *Pinus* spp. The reasons for these differences in parasitic behaviour are not understood, especially in species like *Cronartium ribicola* in which the two alternate hosts are widely different (*Pinus* and *Ribes*). The differences are presumably associated with the nuclear complement of the spores in that uredospores and aeciospores are normally dikaryotic whereas basidiospores are monokaryotic, but the way in which this operates and why it holds good in some rusts but not in others is puzzling.

The host range of less highly specialized parasites is often relatively wide and many are facultative saprophytes able to persist in a vegetative state for variable periods in the absence of host plants. Parasitism here seems to be rather crude, the infected tissue being quickly destroyed, often by action of toxins and/or enzymes. Such 'opportunist' or 'debility' pathogens are usually favoured by a weakened or damaged condition of the plant and many are, or can be, wound parasites. Their host range can sometimes be experimentally widened by providing very favourable conditions for infection in the glasshouse, so that not all plant species shown to be susceptible in the laboratory will necessarily become infected in the field. These unspecialized parasites probably have rather unspecialized nutritional requirements – many of them can be grown easily in axenic culture – and so are able to colonize different kinds of host plants and host organs. Even so there is sometimes a slight degree of specialization, as in *Botrytis cinerea* which is commonly associated with the aerial parts of plants rather than with roots and which does not appear to survive long as a free-living saprophyte in soil.

In these unspecialized parasites a weakened or damaged state of the plant tissue together with an environment favourable to the pathogen are likely to be the critical factors in infection, rather than the host genotype. Such parasites may attack hundreds of plant species in widely different taxa and rarely show parasitic specialization to any marked degree. Gaumann (1950) terms them 'omnivorous' as distinct from 'plurivorous' for pathogens with a definite and more limited, but still wide, host range. He points out that pathogens of wide host range which attack normal, that is not weakened, plants tend to be plurivorous, for example *Verticillium albo-atrum* and *Corticium solani*. However, some obligate parasites such as the uredospore and teliospore stages of *Cronartium flaccidum* (*C. asclepiadeum*) are also plurivorous. This rust is unusual in that it attacks isolated species in such diverse families as Ranunculaceae, Scrophulariaceae, Asclepiadaceae, Balsaminaceae and others (Wilson and Henderson, 1966).

Some plurivorous parasites show a slight degree of host specialization, but in others, such as *Verticillium albo-atrum*, this seems not to occur. Another interesting aspect concerning host ranges of pathogens is the reaction of plant species, related to susceptible species, to pathogens which they have not previously encountered. In some such cases the introduced species proves to be susceptible, in others resistant. In the case of resistance this is clearly inherent in the plant, rather than due to prolonged interaction between parasite and plant selecting out the more resistant or tolerant strains of the latter.

16 The factors which influence infection

Infection of plants by pathogens is influenced by many factors which may play a decisive role not only in the initial invasion but also in the subsequent spread of the disease; hence these factors are of critical importance in epidemiology. Their effects on the spread of pathogens are discussed elsewhere (p. 399), while their effects on the initial infection of the plant are briefly considered below. This may conveniently be done under four headings: plant factors, pathogen factors, environmental factors, and biotic factors.

Plant factors

The most important of these is the inherent resistance of the plant to the pathogen as determined by its defence mechanisms. Resistance, as distinct from immunity, can be overcome if conditions are highly favourable to the pathogen, especially in cases of horizontal resistance. It may change as tissues or plants become older, or if the nutritional state of the plant alters, as in a trace element deficiency. Climatic factors, notably temperature, may affect resistance, as shown by certain wheat varieties which are susceptible to *Puccinia striiformis* at higher, and resistant at lower, temperatures.

The vigour and general condition of the host plant may apparently affect its susceptibility – unthrifty, weakened, senescent or damaged plants are usually more prone to attack by unspecialized parasites such as *Botrytis cinerea*, whereas many highly specialized parasites appear to thrive on vigorous plants. This is to be distinguished from the condition in which a vigorous plant is able to tolerate attack because of its ability to replace tissues and organs destroyed by the pathogen. Such plants survive, albeit to some extent incapacitated, whereas less vigorous plants might succumb. Application of certain fertilizers might, for example, directly increase tissue resistance *per se* and might also have an indirect beneficial effect by increasing the vigour of the plant. These effects are sometimes difficult to distinguish.

Predisposition

This term has been used in slightly different ways by different authors. Walker (1950) defines it as 'the effect of one or more environal factors which makes a plant vulnerable to attack by a pathogen. It is a process which antedates penetration and infection'. In his detailed discussion Yarwood (1959) extends its scope to include reduced as well as increased susceptibility, although the term is commonly used in the latter sense. He defines it as 'the tendency of nongenetic conditions, acting before infection, to affect the susceptibility of plants to disease'. Some workers include genetically determined susceptibility in predisposition, and Chester (1947) defines it very widely as 'liability, susceptibility, or tendency to contract disease'. Other similar terms include disease proneness, acquired disposition, induced susceptibility, and preconditioning. The essential points about predisposition are that it operates before infection, and it affects the susceptibility of the host rather than directly affecting the pathogen; for example, deposition of moisture on leaves, thus enabling spore germination and penetration to occur, would not be predisposition. There are some cases in which it is difficult to decide whether or not predisposition is involved, and the same factor may directly affect the pathogen as well as predisposing the plant. Thus, Kendrick, Middleton and Darley (1954) found that as well as acting as a fungicide, zineb could reduce smog injury, presumably by its affect on the plant. The many and varied predisposing factors are discussed by Yarwood (1959), whose outline is partly followed here.

Age of the plant (ontogenic disposition)

The reaction of tissues to pathogens may change with maturation and many factors are probably involved. In different diseases resistance may increase or decrease with age, or resistance may reach its peak or its nadir in the middle-aged plant. These changes in resistance are no doubt associated with changes in the effectiveness of the plant's defence mechanisms. Younger tissues may produce more phytoalexin or produce it more quickly, or biochemical changes in the maturing tissue may make it a more or a less suitable substrate for the pathogen. These are to be distinguished from disease escape in which, for example, the maturing plant is less severely attacked because climatic conditions are unfavourable to development of the pathogen.

Seasonal and diurnal effects

The resistance of some trees to certain pathogens appears to follow a seasonal periodicity, for example, plum trees are more resistant to *Stereum purpureum* in summer (Brooks and Moore, 1926). This also applies to various trees attacked by *Nectria cinnabarina*, and Gaumann (1950) attributes the summer resistance to a direct or indirect protective effect of increased water content during the summer months. This is probably an over-simplification of the situation – Beever (1970) has correlated the seasonal variation in susceptibility of stone fruits to *S. purpureum* with the capacity of the xylem sap to support growth of the fungus. The latter grew best in sap collected in the late winter and early spring when nitrogen and carbohydrate concentrations in the sap were highest. Many fungi show a diurnal periodicity in such processes as production, discharge and germination of spores. These are probably responses to environment, although Yarwood (1959) suggests that they could be partly an adjustment by selection to the periodicities of the host plant. Maximum susceptibility at the time of maximum stomatal opening has been reported in some bacterial diseases (for example Anderson and Powell, 1950, with *Xanthomonas pruni* on peach), and Matthews (1953) obtained the greatest infection with four viruses when the plants were inoculated in the afternoon, at about the time of maximum accumulation of sugars; the factors involved, however, are not known.

Environmental effects

Increased susceptibility following preinoculation heating of the plant occurs in several diseases caused by fungi, bacteria and viruses (Kassanis, 1952, 1957; Yarwood, 1956a). A range of combinations of temperatures and exposure periods has been effective – even one second at 55°C with tobacco mosaic virus on *Phaseolus vulgaris*. Heat treatment applied as much as 4 days before inoculation was effective in beans inoculated with tobacco mosaic virus. There are few convincing cases of heat treatment increasing resistance or of low temperature affecting susceptibility except where plant injury has resulted from the treatment. Humidity seems to have little significance as a predisposing factor, although high water content of the tissues before inoculation is reported to favour infection by several fungi and (especially) bacteria, presumably by encouraging growth of the pathogens rather than by predisposition as such. In fewer cases reduced moisture content appears to favour infection. Similarly, high soil moisture increases infection by some pathogens but has the opposite effect in others. Low light intensity before inoculation apparently increases the susceptibility of some plants to some pathogens, and among other preinoculation factors said to influence infection are day length, ultraviolet radiation, X radiation, and gamma radiation. Mechanical pressure before inoculation favoured infection of bean leaves by several pathogens but not by others, and similar postinoculation pressure reduced development of some pathogens but not virus infection (Yarwood, 1953).

Nutritional factors and pH

Results of numerous experiments on the effects of fertilizers on disease susceptibility suggest that high nitrogen concentrations often favour infection, high potassium often reduces it, while the effects of phosphorus are varied, but there are exceptions to these generalizations. Nutrients applied to soil may affect soil borne pathogens as well as plants but are unlikely to have any direct effect on pathogens attacking the aerial parts of the plant; in the latter case any effect on infection will be through modification of the plant's susceptibility. Several cases of increased susceptibility at high nutrient concentrations have been attributed to osmotic effects, and the possibility that such nutrients enhance the vigour of the plant and so predispose it to infection or otherwise (depending partly on the type of pathogen involved) should also be borne in mind. Thus, deficiency of several nutrients led to increased susceptibility of soya to *Rhizoctonia solani* (Castano and Kernkamp, 1956), a fungus liable to attack weakened plants. The evidence for micronutrients as predisposing agents is conflicting and no doubt the situation is complex. Similarly there are reports of soil pH affecting the susceptibility of leaves to pathogens, notably powdery mildews, but here again the results are not clear-cut.

Wounding as a predisposing factor

Plants wounded before inoculation often become more susceptible to pathogens, especially wound parasites, in that entrance of the parasite is thereby facilitated. Wounding has a marked effect on the physiology of the plant and, as might be expected, there are reports of it being involved in predisposition. Removal of leaves or other parts apparently increases subsequent susceptibility in some diseases but has the opposite effect in others. These results have been attributed partly to changes in the carbohydrate balance of the plant brought about by wounding or removal of plant parts, and as Horsfall and Dimond (1957) point out some pathogens are favoured by low sugar content of the plant tissues, others by high sugar content (p. 256).

Much experimental work on predisposition has been carried out with viruses, and Yarwood (1959) suggests that the slight wounding necessary for the entry of some viruses into plant tissue may be a predisposition effect. Thus, wounding (by rubbing) of bean leaves followed by application of tobacco mosaic virus (without further wounding) at timed intervals resulted in an initial decrease of susceptibility within 1 minute, followed by increased susceptibility which reached its maximum in about

8 minutes and thereafter increasing resistance which became complete in about 100 minutes (Yarwood, 1959; see also Jedlinski, 1956). Yarwood (1959) speculates that the increased infection obtained by rubbing leaves with virus plus abrasive might be due to exposure of the plasmodesmata by partial removal of the cuticle. The pressure involved in rubbing may force sap up through the plasmodesmata and a mixture of sap and virus is then drawn back into the cells on relaxation of the pressure. Pressure would on this interpretation act as a predisposing factor.

Other predisposing factors

There is considerable evidence that application of some chemicals to plants affects their susceptibility to pathogens as well as affecting the pathogens themselves. Such chemical predisposition may be towards increased or decreased susceptibility. Some fungicides appear to have a beneficial effect on plant growth in the apparent absence of pathogens, presumably by affecting the physiology of the plant, and can thus be regarded as predisposing agents. Predisposition to increased susceptibility is perhaps more frequent and could sometimes be due to chemical injury to the tissues or to the chemical delaying the processes of healing in the case of wound parasites. Various pesticides increase susceptibility to different pathogens, for example 2,4-D to *Claviceps purpurea* on wheat, dichlone to *Agrobacterium tumefaciens* on cherry, and maleic hydrazide, DDT, and other chemicals to *Puccinia graminis* on wheat (see Yarwood, 1959 for a detailed list). Some of these substances are known to have specific effects on plants – for example maleic hydrazide is a growth inhibitor – and their predisposing effects no doubt arise from some indirect action on the metabolism of the plant.

Plant vigour in relation to attack by pathogens has been mentioned above. It is frequently said that highly specialized parasites tend to attack vigorous plants while unspecialiezd ones often attack weakened or damaged plants, but there are exceptions to this generalization. Howard (1940) and others have taken the view that the use of natural manures and composts promotes resistance to pathogens and insect pests. This may be true in respect of certain unspecialized parasites or in the sense that vigorous plants may be able to tolerate attack better than weak ones, but there is little evidence that manures and composts are any more effective in this respect than balanced artificial fertilizers, and it is unlikely to apply to diseases in which vigorous plants are attacked as much as, or more than, less vigorous ones. Experiments on disease susceptibility in relation to plant vigour have given conflicting results. Tapke (1951), for example, reported a positive correlation between the two factors in barley attacked by *Erysiphe graminis* whereas Trelease and Trelease (1928) had found no such correlation with the same pathogen on wheat.

Infection with one pathogen may predispose the plant towards increased or reduced susceptibility to a second pathogen. Reduced susceptibility is often described as cross-protection or acquired immunity and is discussed on p. 281. In other cases the second pathogen may colonize tissue damaged by the first, or the latter may provide an entrance for it, as in the case of *Nectria galligena* infecting apple twigs through injury caused by *Venturia inaequalis*. These effects are likely to be of importance in the ecological succession of microorganisms which colonize diseased plant tissue.

Grafting has occasionally been reported to predispose plants to disease, and in some cases this could be due to reduced vigour of the scion. Rawlins and Parker (1934) showed that cherry trees on Malaheb (*Prunus malaheb*) stocks in some way escaped or resisted natural infection by buckskin virus whereas they become very chlorotic after grafting with diseased Napoleon scions.

Plants can be predisposed towards increased or decreased susceptibility to pathogens by various preinoculation treatments, but there appears to be less information as to whether pathogenicity can be similarly altered. Germination of some fungal spores can, however, be stimulated by a limited preliminary exposure to a higher temperature, and it seems possible that their ability to infect might also be modified in this way. The pathogenicity of some plant pathogens, notably bacteria, can be modified by cultural treatments, for example by growth on a medium containing certain amino acids, but the extent to which this is due to selection of more or of less pathogenic strains already present in the inoculum used is not known.

The discussion so far has concerned mainly parasitic diseases due to parasites, but any preinoculation treatment which brings about physiological changes in the plant could influence its response to injurious agents whether parasitic or otherwise. Among the reported examples are the protective effects of certain rusts and of zineb against smog injury, and predisposition to the latter by high soil moisture (Koritz and Went, 1953). Of interest is the report that pea plants grown under sterile conditions suffered little injury from frost or *Botrytis cinerea* alone whereas the two together caused severe injury (Kerling, 1952).

The study of predisposition in plants is important for several reasons. One is that it is likely to throw light on the physiological processes which govern susceptibility of plants not only to pathogens but also to injurious environmental agents such as excessive heat, cold and atmospheric pollutants. Second, it may become possible in due course to make use of factors predisposing to plant resistance for the purposes of disease control. This is unlikely to occur in the immediate future and many practical difficulties will have to be overcome, but this method of control, if practicable and effective, would be preferable to widespread and repeated use of pesticides. Third, predisposition can be a useful method of obtaining increased infection in inoculation experiments with 'difficult' pathogens which otherwise give only low or inconsistent infection, and such methods as preinoculation shading or heating are being used in the study of viruses.

Plant exudates

Plant tissues often secrete substances which collect on the surface and which may affect the propagules of pathogens lying thereon. The amount and nature of such exudates depend on the organ involved (roots seem to be particularly active in this respect), the age and vigour of the plant or organ, the growing conditions, and on the species or variety of plant. Whether exudates accumulate will depend partly on environmental conditions – rain, for example, will tend to remove them from the aerial parts of plants. Presumably these substances exude through the ectodesmata or breaks in the cuticle as well as through such specialized structures as hydathodes and nectaries. In roots they may be derived from dead root hairs and other cells as the root grows through the soil, but there is evidence that the surface cells themselves secrete metabolites, especially from root tips, damaged tissue and indeed from most areas of high metabolical activity. Many of the substances so far identified in plant exudates would seem to be suitable for the growth of microorganisms, and include mineral salts, carbohydrates, amino acids, nucleotides, nucleic acid derivatives, enzymes, vitamins, alkaloids, and various aromatic compounds such as coumarin. Accounts are given by Rovira (1965), Borner (1960), Woods (1960) and Schroth and Hildebrand (1964) for root exudates, and by Ruinen (1961) for leaf exudates.

Metabolites produced by other microorganisms are also present on the plant surface, as is miscellaneous débris deposited from the air or from moving water in the soil, and the dead bodies and secretions of insects and other plant inhabitants.

Plant exudates may enhance or depress the germination of propagules on the plant surface, and may influence the growth of the germ tubes or formation of appressoria, as discussed elsewhere (p. 160). Exudates can also exert chemotropic or chemotactic effects on fungal hyphae, germ tubes and zoospores, particularly the last-named. Other factors no doubt influence the movement of zoospores in relation to plant roots; apparently, zoospores of *Phytophthora parasitica* are positively charged and are perhaps attracted to root areas which have a weak negative charge (Troutman and Wills, 1964). Inorganic ions, sugars, proteins and amino acids all attract zoospores but the attraction is often rather non-specific. Chemotaxy has been reviewed by Ziegler (1962).

L

Many of the fungi which attack roots are of only slight competitive saprophytic ability and survive in soil as resting spores or sclerotia which may, in some cases, remain dormant in the absence of a suitable host root. Some such propagules may germinate satisfactorily only when a plant root grows near them, presumably due to root exudates, although non-susceptible as well as susceptible roots can have this stimulatory effect. The stimulatory effect of root exudates may be due to the latter over-coming the natural fungistatic effect of many soils, perhaps by supplying the spore with nutrients which increase its germination power. There is evidence that soil fungistasis and availability of exogenous nutrients (as in root exudates) are both involved. Various nutrients are known to change or neutralize the effects of fungitoxic compounds on fungi, and Cook and Schroth (1965) suggested that toxic metabolites produced by rhizo-sphere microorganisms affected fungal spores in such a way as to raise their carbon and nitrogen requirements for germination. This effect could be overcome by supplying extra nutrients or by root exudates containing carbon and nitrogen compounds, especially sugars and amino acids. The effects of these on other – and possibly antagonistic – soil microorganisms have also to be considered, and if the root exudates favour antagonists the net result may be protection rather than infection. There are other ways in which rhizosphere inhabitants may influence infection, for example by supplying roots or pathogens with organic substances which stimulate their growth.

Pathogen factors

Infection and successful colonization of a plant by a pathogen depend not only on host and environmental factors but also on the parasitic abilities of the pathogen, and in particular on its **aggressiveness**. This is an indefinite term but can be described as the capacity to invade the plant, to obtain nutrients from it, and to reproduce in or on it (Gaumann, 1950). Suggested criteria for aggressiveness include the number of spores necessary to bring about infection (see inoculum potential below), the percentage of plants successfully attacked, the time required for infection and successful establishment of the parasite in the host (this may range from several hours to several days), and the rapidity with which the disease symptoms develop. Two other terms with somewhat similar and indefinite meanings are **pathogenicity** and **virulence**. Pathogenicity is the ability of a parasite to cause disease, while virulence is often used in a qualitative sense, races differing in virulence when they attack different varieties of the host plant. Thus pathogens often comprise several races of different virulence. Since aggressiveness primarily concerns the ability of a parasite to enter and colonize its host, and pathogenicity concerns its disease reaction (symptoms) one may find high aggressiveness combined with low pathogenicity, as in some obligate parasites which invade the host plant very efficiently but cause only minor tissue damage.

There are also fungi which can be pathogenic in that they damage the plant on or near which they grow, sometimes by producing phytotoxic metabolites or by their physical presence. The 'sooty mould' fungi (chiefly a mixture of *Alternaria, Cladosporium, Aureobasidium, Botrytis* and others) which live saprophytically on insect honeydew or débris and plant exudates on the shoots of plants, adversely affect photosynthesis by reducing the amount of light reaching the green tissues and also by restricting gaseous exchange; in no sense are they parasitic on the leaf yet they can sometimes cause appreciable damage. Some of the fungi which cause damage to roots probably do so by producing toxins which act before 'infection'. Thus *Periconia circinata*, the cause of a serious root disease (milo disease) in certain varieties of *Sorghum*, is basically a soil-inhabiting fungus which is thought to colonize roots after they have been killed by toxin (periconin, p. 233) which it secretes. It is possible that other soil-inhabiting fungi, such as *Thielaviopsis basicola*, behave similarly.

Inoculum potential

With some pathogens, no doubt the more aggressive ones, a single spore or a few spores can achieve infection under optimum conditions. Monospore cultures of some obligate parasites can thus be prepared on living plants. Other fungi, presumably less aggressive, may require larger numbers of spores for successful infection – several hundred or several thousand – and similarly with bacterial plant pathogens under natural conditions. In seed borne smuts a small number of teliospores on the individual seed may not be able to cause infection whereas a larger number will do so, and within certain limits heavily contaminated sowing seed will produce more diseased plants than lightly contaminated seed. Self-inhibition of germination occurs in concentrated suspensions of the spores of some fungi, probably due to inhibitory substances present in, or produced by, the spores, and in such fungi the capacity of small numbers of spores to infect will be advantageous. High concentrations of spores are infrequent in nature except for those which are held together by mucilage, or those contained in spore-producing structures where self-inhibition would reduce the risk of the spores germinating before their liberation and dispersal. Where high spore concentrations occur on plant surfaces any inhibitors formed might be washed away or diluted to an ineffective level by rain or dew, or they might perhaps be neutralized by plant exudates.

The minimum concentration of spores necessary for infection under optimum conditions has been termed the numerical threshold of infection (Gaumann, 1950), but for a high percentage of successful infection, or when conditions are suboptimal, a considerably greater number of spores has to be used. A low threshold is often considered indicative of high aggressiveness, but it will also depend on the susceptibility of the inoculated plant and on the environment. The threshold concept has been questioned by Van der Plank (1967a) on the grounds that it implies a synergistic interaction of propagules for which there appears to be no evidence.

A more sophisticated concept is that of inoculum potential, used by Horsfall (1932) to denote the number of infective particles present, and subsequently elaborated by Garrett (1956) as 'the energy of growth of a parasite available for infection of a host at the surface of the host organ to be infected'; a detailed discussion is given by Garrett (1960) and Wood (1967). The concept of inoculum potential was first used for soil borne pathogens and has been applied by Garrett (1956, 1960) to mycelial strands and rhizomorphs which, in his view, are collections of individual hyphae which thereby achieve the required inoculum potential for successful infection of the host root – especially when growing from a food base which keeps them adequately supplied with nutrients. The cells of phytopathogenic bacteria and the spores of some fungi are often disseminated in clumps held together by mucilage, particularly so in insect transmission, and this may represent a kind of collective pooling of the inoculum potential of numerous propagules, perhaps enabling infection to occur whereas single propagules would be ineffective. This may also apply to vector transmitted viruses.

Inoculum potential has also been used in the sense of the number of spores produced by a population of diseased plants. Dimond and Horsfall (1960, 1965) describe it as 'the number of independent infections that are likely to occur in a given situation in a population of susceptible healthy tissues', and consider it as the resultant of environmental effects, the infective ability of the pathogen, the susceptibility of the plant, and the amount of inoculum. Inoculum potential thus includes not only the number of infecting propagules per unit area of host tissue but also their aggressiveness.

For successful penetration the invading fungal structure needs to exert a minimal force, the energy for which must come from the inoculum until such time as the pathogen is sufficiently established to obtain it from the parasitized tissues. Inoculum potential can in fact be increased not only by increasing the concentration of spores but also by increasing their individual infective ability, for example by supplying extra nutrients. Under natural conditions nutrients may sometimes be provided by plant exudates, but where they are absent the inoculum must be sufficiently concentrated to attain the inoculum potential required for infection; such inoculum has been termed 'effective inoculum' (Garrett, 1956).

It is difficult to measure inoculum potential in the sense of the energy of growth available for infection at a plant surface and, as noted above, the term is used in different ways by different authors, which limits its usefulness; additional sources of information include Baker (1965) and Dimond and Horsfall (1965).

Latent infection

The infective ability of a pathogen depends not only on its aggressiveness but also on the resistance of the plant tissue, and this may change with maturation and senescence. Some pathogens are apparently unable to colonize vigorous tissue unless it is damaged or has a poorly developed cuticle, but can successfully invade senescent tissue. This inability can be overcome, at least in the case of *Botrytis cinerea* on lettuce leaves (Brooks, 1908) and on broad bean leaves (Brown, 1922*a*), by using spores suspended in a nutrient solution rather than in water, or by using more concentrated spore suspensions (Wilson, 1937). The first method no doubt increased the number of potential infective units by stimulating germination as well as by providing extra energy for infection. The pathogen may enter the tissue, colonize it to a very limited extent, and then remain quiescent and unnoticed until such time as the tissue matures or senesces and thereby becomes more susceptible. Such latent infections have been investigated in several diseases, particularly in fruit rots where they can have important economic consequences. The skin of green apricot fruits contains substances inhibitory to *Sclerotinia fructicola* (brown rot) which are not present in the skin of ripe fruit (Wade, 1956), and similarly for *Gloeosporium musarum* (anthracnose) of banana fruits (Chakravarty, 1957).

A detailed investigation of tropical fruit rots caused by *Colletotrichum* spp. in Australia was carried out by Simmonds (1963) who concluded that latent infection is due to inhibitory substances in unripe fruit and also to the absence or unavailability of suitable energy sources for the fungi involved, these conditions not occurring in the ripe fruit. Latency also occurs in leaf diseases as in Sigatoka disease of banana caused by *Mycosphaerella musicola*; Goos and Tschirch (1963) found that the fungus could be isolated from resistant leaves as much as 12 weeks after inoculation, and there were numerous localized infections although leaf spots failed to develop.

Microorganisms entering plants which they do not parasitize can also be regarded as examples of latent infection which, however, fail to develop further, and even in hypersensitivity the pathogen may survive for some time in the necrotic tissue. Recent investigations suggest that apparently healthy plant tissue can contain microorganisms, particularly bacteria, and more refined methods of investigation might also reveal fungi. There are reports of such bacteria becoming parasitic under certain conditions although the extent to which this occurs is uncertain. In many cases they appear to be non-pathogens such as *Aerobacter cloacae* and *Bacillus megatherium*, but there are reports of plant pathogenic bacteria within apparently healthy tissue. These include *Corynebacterium sepedonicum* (ring rot of potato tubers) in apparently normal potato tubers (Bonde and Covell, 1950). Some of the vascular wilt fusaria (*Fusarium oxysporum*) are said to invade the steles of susceptible plants without causing any noticeable symptoms, and more detailed investigation might well reveal yet other types of latent infection, as discussed by Wood (1967).

Environmental factors

The effects of the more important environmental factors – moisture, temperature, light and *p*H – on germination of spores have been discussed (p. 143). It should be borne in mind that the optimum for any particular factor is sometimes different in respect of germination, growth of the germ tube, and penetration – and perhaps different again in respect of colonization of the plant and sporulation.

These differences are normally related to the environmental conditions under which these various events occur. Thus, the germination of uredospores of *Puccinia graminis* var. *tritici* on wheat leaves required darkness and surface wetness and occurred over a wide range of temperature whereas penetration of the leaf required light and a slightly higher temperature than was needed for germination. In line with these requirements, uredospore germination occurred during the night when dew was condensing on the leaves and was followed by leaf penetration as the temperature rose and light became available (Burrage, 1970). These environmental factors may also affect the resistance of the plant, and some may act as predisposing factors, as discussed above. Furthermore, results obtained on glass may be different from those obtained on living plants, and the constant conditions of the laboratory rarely obtain in the field where all these factors tend to be fluctuating simultaneously, sometimes within quite wide limits. Laboratory experiments on the effects of environmental factors on infection should take these considerations into account if the results are to be extrapolated to the field.

Speed of infection is often critically important, more so perhaps than the percentage of spores which germinate, although the latter can be important with pathogens in which large numbers of germinating spores are necessary for successful infection (inoculum potential, as discussed above). Rapid infection enables the pathogen to take maximum advantage of what may be only a short period of weather favourable for infection, and may also enable it to become firmly entrenched in the host tissue before the resistance mechanisms of the latter become fully effective. This is particularly true of pathogens which require exacting conditions of temperature and/or moisture for infection, as in some downy mildews, but less so of pathogens which are more tolerant in these respects.

The pathogen is at its most vulnerable in the period between spore germination and infection, but is less vulnerable when firmly established in the host tissue, although environmental factors may still affect its development and, particularly, its sporulation. Thus, many downy mildews produce sporangiophores and sporangia only in high humidity, and the disease appears to remain static in prolonged dry weather only to become active again under wet conditions. Associated with this is nocturnal sporulation, as in some species of *Sclerospora*; this is probably a temperature-humidity effect, but host factors are no doubt also involved. In some powdery mildews, on the other hand, growth and sporulation are favoured by dry weather although high humidity may be necessary for spore germination: these aspects are discussed elsewhere (p. 144). Furthermore, the environment within the crop and at the plant surface can be appreciably different from that outside (microclimate, p. 409); for example, the light within the crop can be different in quantity and possibly in quality from that outside, and there is increasing evidence that light, through its effects on the growth of germ tubes and on penetration, can influence infection.

Meteorological factors have a marked effect on pathogens which attack the shoots of plants, and a slighter and more indirect effect on root pathogens. Heavy rain and prolonged drought or cold or heat, however, eventually affect soil conditions and hence pathogens in the soil. Substances added to the soil (fertilizers, manure, irrigation water) affect not only the plant but also soil borne pathogens and any vectors they may have. Soil additives have a direct effect on infection by root-attacking pathogens but their effect on shoot-infecting pathogens is more indirect, often as predisposing agents.

Biotic factors

This is a very extensive subject including such microbial interactions as synergism, antagonism (competition, overgrowing, mycoparasitism), rhizosphere and aerosphere effects, multiple infections, soil fungistasis, vectors, self-inhibition and stimulation of spore germination, and symbiotic associations between pathogens and other organisms. In a sense it also includes the efforts of man to prevent infection occurring, as when he applies fungicides to plants. These can be considered only briefly here; control of plant disease by the use of antagonistic organisms is discussed by Wood and Tveit (1955) and Darpoux (1960).

Rhizosphere

The rhizosphere is generally taken to include the root surface and the soil immediately adjacent to it, although 'rhizoplane' has been suggested for the actual surface. There is no strictly comparable term for the shoots of plants except perhaps 'aerosphere', and 'phytosphere'.

Most roots are completely surrounded by soil which contains numerous microorganisms, and the rhizosphere is commonly a region of intensified microbial activity; hence the microorganisms in the immediate vicinity of the root as well as those on its surface are likely to influence the infection of roots by pathogens. Although roots are reported to have a 'cuticle' this is not known to contain wax (Scott, 1965), and young (unthickened) roots might thus be expected to be vulnerable to soil fungi and bacteria. That this is not so is probably due to rhizosphere effects bound up with root exudates and the activities of other rhizosphere microorganisms, although evidence on this is sometimes contradictory. One of the best known cases is that of flax wilt caused by *Fusarium oxysporum f.sp. lini* (Timonin, 1941). The rhizosphere of Bison (a resistant variety) was reported to contain hydrocyanic acid which apparently favoured the growth of such saprophytes as *Mucor, Cladosporium, Penicillium* and *Trichoderma*, whereas that of Novelty (susceptible) contained only a trace of HCN and allowed growth of such potential pathogens as *Alternaria, Cephalosporium, Fusarium, Verticillium* and *Helminthosporium*. From these and other experiments it was concluded that the resistance of Bison was due to the protective effect of *Trichoderma viride*, a known antagonist and parasite of other soil fungi. There is, however, considerable doubt about this, and Trione (1960) was unable to correlate the resistance of flax plants with the amount of HCN (as the β-glucoside linamarin) they contained.

Somewhat similar protection due to antagonistic effects by several microorganisms has been reported in some other root diseases, for example by *T. viride* in pine attacked by *Fomes annosus* (Rishbeth, 1950, 1951). In some cases the selective encouragement of antagonists appears to be due to substances of host origin, but soil or plant additives including fertilizers and manures may have a similar effect and so reduce disease. Such additives could, however, increase resistance by affecting the nutrition and growth rate of the plant as well as through antagonism, and these effects are often difficult to distinguish. Heavy dressings of green manures or other plant residues might be slightly phytotoxic and so favour

root disease, but this might be overcome by antagonism and/or more vigorous growth of the plant. The suggestion by Eaton and Rigler (1946) that
the well known immunity of monocotyledons to *Phymatotrichum omnivorum*
(Texas root rot of cotton and other plants) is due to their rhizoplane
microflora is an interesting one, and the fact that inoculated maize plants
were apparently unaffected when grown in an unsterilized sand-bentonite
mixture but were quickly killed when the latter was sterile appears to
bear this out.

The hypothesis that certain soil amendments or root exudates protect
roots against soil fungi by encouraging the development of antagonistic
microorganisms, including *Trichoderma* and possibly some Actinomycetes
and bacteria, which fend off soil pathogens by producing antibiotic
substances, is an attractive one and merits further investigation. In many
cases, however, the situation is probably more complex and there are few,
if any, proven examples. The subject is discussed by Garrett (1956) who
suggests that the rhizosphere may be the root's outermost defence against
pathogens, and by Sanford (1959) and Lockhead (1959). Among the
many papers on the rhizosphere are those of Katznelson (1965), Katznelson *et al.* (1948) and Starkey *et al.* (1961).

The beneficial effects of mycorrhizas on plant growth are generally
attributed to nutritional factors, but the fungus may also protect against
soil pathogens to some extent. Zak (1964) in his review suggests several
possible ways in which this might come about: (1) by the mycorrhizal
fungus utilizing surplus carbohydrates and thus reducing the attractiveness of the root to pathogens – presumably this could also include other
nutrients produced by the root; (2) by the fungus acting as a physical or
chemical (antibiotic) barrier to potential root invaders – particularly so
in ectotrophic mycorrhizas in which the fungus forms a coherent mantle
around the root; and (3) by encouraging protective rhizosphere microorganisms. Mycorrhizal fungi might also induce the formation of phytoalexins or other antifungal substances which are believed by some to
preserve the balance between root and fungus in the mycorrhiza, and also,
possibly, reduce infection by pathogenic fungi present in the soil.

In their studies on the ectotrophic mycorrhizal fungi of pine roots Marx
(1969, 1969*a*) and Marx and Davey (1969) found that, in culture, several
of these mycorrhizal fungi inhibited to varying extents the growth of about
half of the forty-eight fungal root pathogens tested. *Leucopaxillus cerealis* var.
piceina (*Clitocybe piceina*) inhibited about 92% of the test fungi to different
degrees, being particularly effective against *Phytophthora* spp. but ineffective
against *Armillaria mellea* and several other root pathogens. *L. cerealis*
produced antifungal/antibacterial antibiotics, identified as diatretynes
(polyacetylenic antibiotics produced by several Hymenomycetes: Anchel
et al., 1962), in culture; 2 p.p.m. of diatretyne nitrile inhibited the

germination of zoospores of *P. cinnamomi* but 10 p.p.m. or more were toxic to aseptic pine seedlings. Mycorrhizal fungi probably protect absorbing roots against root-attacking fungi in the soil through the ectotrophic mantle of the mycorrhizal fungi acting as a physical barrier and also, possibly, by antibiotic substances which they produce. In further experiments, Marx (1970) found that mature mycorrhizas formed aseptically on roots of *Pinus echinata* seedlings by *Thelephora terrestris* and *Pisolithus tinctorius* were resistant to invasion by *Phytophthora cinnamomi* whereas non-mycorrhizal roots were heavily infected. Thus both the fungal mantle and the Hartig net (the hyphal network within the cortex of the root) appeared to act as barriers to infection by the pathogen. There is little information on these aspects but they merit investigation in view of the fact that mycorrhizal rootlets seem to remain functional for a longer period and to be less susceptible to some pathogens than non-mycorrhizal ones.

Phyllosphere

This term, proposed by Last (1955) and Ruinen (1956), denotes the leaf surface and the immediately adjacent area. Foliosphere is a similar term and the actual surface of the leaf has been named the phylloplane.

Leaves and other aerial parts of the plant are invariably colonized by a variety of epiphytic microorganisms, and the significance of this in relation to infection by pathogens is being investigated. Leben (1965) classifies these epiphytes as (1) epiphyllae – chiefly macroscopic forms such as lichens, liverworts, ferns and angiosperms, prominent in rain forests, and (2) microbial epiphytes – chiefly bacteria, fungi and algae, present in both temperate and tropical areas although often more conspicuous in the latter. These can be grouped as 'residents' which live and multiply on the plant surface, and 'casuals' which are present by accident or growing on extraneous débris. There are also the numerous microorganisms which grow on dead or dying leaves, or on dead parts of living leaves, and these are often referred to as saprophytes, although some degree of parasitism might be involved in some cases. Others live on insect honeydew (some sooty moulds). Residents which grow on leaf exudates are in a sense parasitic in that they obtain nutrients from the living plant. The distinction between epiphytes and parasites is here rather vague and a pathogen may have a resident stage living as an epiphyte on the plant surface (phytoplane). Some bacterial plant pathogens can apparently multiply on the surface of seemingly healthy leaves.

Accounts of the leaf microflora are given by Leben (1965), Last and Deighton (1965), Ruinen (1961, 1963), and others;* only a brief descrip-

* See also *The Ecology of Leaf Surface Microorganisms*, edit. by Preece, T. F. and Dickinson, C. H. (Academic Press, London and New York), 1971.

tion can be given here. Actively growing tissue is first colonized by bacteria and subsequently by fungi, there being an ecological succession rather than haphazard development. The bacteria are often pigmented, aerobic, non-sporing and gram-negative, and it is interesting that many of the bacteria which attack the leaves of plants are also of this type. Compared with soil bacteria, bacteria epiphytic on leaves can often more readily utilize glucose than lactose or lactic acid, and this may be of significance in relation to leaf exudates which commonly contain simple sugars.

Among leaf-inhabiting bacteria are *Pseudomonas trifolii*, *P. fluorescens*, and various other pseudomonads and xanthomonads which are difficult to distinguish in the present state of bacterial taxonomy. Apparently non-parasitic bacteria may also be present in stomatal cavities and within the tissues of plants, and nitrogen-fixing bacteria (*Beijerinckia*) occur on leaves in the wet tropics. Yeasts and yeast-like fungi are common on plant surfaces, but true yeasts (Endomycetaceae) are characteristic of sweet fruits (grapes, apples and so on) rather than leaves, their place on the latter being taken by members of the Sporobolomycetaceae and Cryptococcaceae, two families of Fungi Imperfecti characterized by budding ('false yeasts'). The Sporobolomycetaceae, possibly imperfect states of Tremellales, often produce ballistospores, and foliicolous forms include species of *Sporobolomyces*, *Itersonilia* (also pathogenic), *Tilletiopsis* and *Bullera*. Foliicolous Cryptococcaceae include *Rhodotorula*, *Torulopsis*, *Cryptococcus* and *Candida*, the last two genera also containing species pathogenic to man. Many Hyphomycetes also occur on leaves, particularly mature or senescing ones, but some can perhaps be weak parasites. They include *Cladosporium herbarum*, *Alternaria tenuis*, *Epicoccum nigrum*, *Aureobasidium* (*Pullularia*) *pullulans* (which has a yeast-like phase) and, less frequently, *Botrytis*, *Fusarium*, *Penicillium* and unidentified mycelial fungi. Many of these colonize moribund plant tissue and are common components of the air spora. Casual spores of a wide range of other fungi, including rusts, powdery mildews and downy mildews are also likely to be deposited on leaves, and algae and lichens can be present under conditions of high humidity and shading. In tropical areas fairly large epiphytic fungi, usually Ascomycetes such as Micropeltaceae and Chaetothyriaceae, develop on leaves, and some may occur on only a restricted range of plants.

Microbial epiphytes are generally favoured by prolonged, warm, humid conditions and tend to develop in the depressions between epidermal cells and perhaps more frequently on the lower leaf surface, although this depends on the species of epiphyte. Different plant species may have different microfloras and so may young and old leaves, and leaves at different seasons of the year. According to Last and Deighton (1965) most of the bacteria and yeast-like fungi which grow on plant surfaces are able to colonize a wide range of plants, are widely distributed in similar climatic

zones, are rarely as frequent in soil as on leaves, and are usually pigmented. Carotenoid pigments possibly afford some protection against
radiation and, being energy receptors, perhaps permit better use of available sources of energy.

Leaf epiphytes probably live on plant exudates which, as previously discussed, contain substances supporting growth of saprophytes. Where
exudates are copious and environmental conditions favourable there may
be a considerable development of epiphytes – about a million or more
bacterial cells per gramme fresh weight of leaf in some cases – and probably
similar numbers for yeast-like epiphytes, although precise figures are
lacking. Some epiphytes probably live on miscellaneous débris, and
numbers of Sporobolomycetaceae are considerably larger on diseased
plant tissue where exuded nutrients may be more plentiful, as with
Itersonilia perplexans which was more plentiful on marigold leaves infected
by *Entyloma calendulae* than on healthy ones (Brady, 1960).

Many leaf epiphytes produce antibiotic substances in culture but
whether this occurs on the plant is uncertain. There are several reports of
epiphytes reducing disease when mixed with the inoculum. Thus, saprophytic bacteria from cherry leaves decreased infection by *Pseudomonas
mors-prunorum* (Crosse, 1959), and there was some control of lettuce grey
mould (*Botrytis cinerea*) by antagonistic microorganisms (Wood, 1951).
Apart from antagonism there are other possible ways in which leaf
epiphytes could reduce infection, for example by taking up substances
(exudates) of host origin and so rendering them unavailable to pathogens,
or by physical occupation of the leaf surface. Although nutrients are
thought to be relatively plentiful on plant surfaces generally, Leben (1965)
suggests that seedling surfaces may be an exception to this – addition of
small amounts of glucose and yeast extract enhanced the antagonistic
powers of a bacterium isolated from cucumber leaves (Leben, 1964;
Leben and Daft, 1964, 1965). Epiphytic microorganisms might also pro-
voke defensive reactions in the plant which are effective against the
pathogen, rather as infection is sometimes reduced when a mixed inoculum of virulent and avirulent strains of a pathogen is used.

Many workers have investigated the superficial microflora of seeds and
Simmonds's (1947) experiments have yielded interesting results. It was
found that the microflora present on wheat plants and seed was inhibitory to *Cochliobolus sativus* and could control the disease under some conditions. Keeping seed moist for a day before inoculation resulted in less
disease than keeping it dry before inoculation, whereas seed which had
been sterilized with formalin before inoculation produced severely diseased seedlings. Seedlings grown from inoculated seed of plants kept under
conditions favourable to epiphytic microorganisms were significantly less
diseased than those from inoculated seed of plants kept under normal

conditions, and the latter seed produced less disease when kept moist prior to inoculation (Ledingham, Sallans and Simmonds, 1949). It is possible that control of some seed borne pathogens by soaking or moistening methods is due partly to encouragement of microorganisms present on the seed (Leben, Scott and Arny, 1956), although in some cases it could be due to premature germination of seed borne spores of the pathogen and subsequent death of the sporelings, to fungitoxic substances which develop during soaking, or to more rapid seed germination following soaking. There is considerable evidence that the epiphytic microorganisms on germinating seeds can give some degree of protection against pathogens but further work on this is needed.

Epiphytes living on plant exudates are to be distinguished from the fungi which colonize the honeydew produced by insects feeding on plants. These form a dark, often conspicuous layer of 'sooty mould' comprising species of *Cladosporium*, *Alternaria*, *Aureobasidium*, *Epicoccum*, and smaller numbers of *Fusarium*, *Botrytis*, and others (*'Fumago vagans'* is often included here, but as Friend, 1965, has shown this name refers chiefly to a mixture of *Cladosporium herbarum* and *Aureobasidium pullulans*). The fungi present in these composite sooty moulds vary according to plant species and environmental conditions, and often include species which occur as epiphytes. In tropical areas various Ascomycetes, notably Capnodiaceae, also occur as sooty moulds in insect honeydew, usually that of aphids, scale insects and whitefly; these are to be distinguished from the parasitic 'dark mildews' (Meliolaceae) which attack many plants in warmer areas. Honeydew epiphytes may indirectly damage the plant by reducing its light supply and possibly by producing phytotoxic metabolites. They could also reduce infection by restricting the access of pathogens to leaves, by competing for a limited supply of nutrients and by producing metabolites inhibitory to pathogens, but there is little information on these aspects.

The study of the interactions between saprophytic and parasitic microorganisms on and near plant surfaces is one which may well yield information which could be used to devise more rational disease control measures, for example, by cultural practices which encourage the development of antagonists able to inhibit development of pathogens. The rhizosphere can be thought of as the root's first line of defence against soil borne pathogens, and it is likely that the microflora of shoots and seeds also exercises a protective effect.

Antagonism and synergism

Antagonism is a rather loose term for microbial associations which are harmful to one or more of the associates, and is often used for cases in which toxic metabolites (antibiotics) are involved. It has been studied principally in relation to the rhizosphere, and competition between micro-organisms in the soil. Similar antagonism no doubt occurs on the aerial parts of plants although probably on a much smaller scale since the leaf microflora and air usually contain fewer microorganisms than the root microflora and soil. There are also fungi which are actively parasitic on other fungi, and such hyperparasitism (mycoparasitism) occurs with several soil fungi as well as with air borne ones. Hyperparasitism is wide-spread in fungi, particularly in certain orders such as the Hypocreales and Chytridiales, although not all reported cases have been adequately investigated. Some, for example *Rhizoctonia solani*, are facultative, others, for example *Eudarluca australis* on rusts, are obligate hyperparasites, and *Trichoderma lignorum* and some others can be antagonistic or hyperpara-sitic although different strains are perhaps involved. Hyperparasitic and phytoparasitic fungi show many similarities in host-parasite interaction. Some, for example, are biotrophs (obtaining food from living cells often *via* haustoria) whilst others are necrotrophs and obtain nutrients from host cells killed before invasion. It is interesting that soil fungi are attacked chiefly by necrotrophic hyperparasites or at least by those which quickly kill the invaded host cells, whereas fungi which attack the shoots of plants tend to be parasitized by biotrophic fungi. Hyperparasitism as a possible disease control measure is discussed later, and reviews are given by Boosalis (1964), Boosalis and Mankau (1965), Madelin (1968), and Barnett (1963).

It is doubtful whether antagonism and hyperparasitism can logically be separated – antagonists might be compared with many necrotrophic plant parasites in that both destroy the host tissue by toxic metabolites which they produce (antibiotics, toxins) and both directly or indirectly utilize the nutrients so released. *Papulospora stoveri* parasitizes *Rhizoctonia solani* and also produces toxic effects on it before contact (Warren, 1948), and *Trichoderma*, which also attacks *R. solani*, has been reported to produce the antifungal antibiotics viridin and gliotoxin. Webster and Lomas (1964) were, however, unable to demonstrate the production of gliotoxin or viridin by *Trichoderma viride* (*Hypocrea rufa*) although these antibiotics were produced by *Gliocladium virens*. They suggest that, since *Trichoderma* is abundant in soil whereas *G. virens* is not particularly common, many of the reports of antagonism by *Trichoderma* are true but it may be that *Trichoderma* produces an antibiotic other than gliotoxin or viridin. The extents to which hyperparasitism and antagonism occur in nature and their significance in plant infection remain subjects for future study.

The full development of some fungal structures may be prevented by overgrowing fungi and infection thereby reduced. In warm areas the young sclerotia of *Claviceps* may be covered by a profuse dark growth of

Cerebella (*Epicoccum*) which grows on the sugary fluid in which the *Claviceps* conidia (*Sphacelia*) are produced. Development of the sclerotia is thereby often inhibited, but it is not known how this occurs – possibly *Cerebella* is antagonistic to, or parasitic on, the young ergots.

Vectors which spread or inoculate pathogens into plants may also be affected by microorganisms. Predacious fungi can appreciably reduce populations of nematodes under favourable conditions and so might reduce infection by nematode transmitted viruses and fungi, and fungus transmitted viruses might be similarly reduced by microorganisms which inhibit the fungal vectors. Numbers and/or activity of bacterial and fungal pathogens might diminish as a result of virus attack, or beneficial antagonistic microorganisms might be reduced in this way. Microorganisms and viruses which cause disease in insects could reduce the incidence of diseases due to insect transmitted pathogens. Little is known about these aspects although they could be important in biological control of plant pathogens.

Self-inhibition and stimulation

Spores grouped together in clumps often germinate less than isolated ones and this has been attributed to shortage of oxygen or high carbon dioxide concentration. Germ tubes often grow away from other germ tubes but the basis of this negative tropism is not understood. There may be self-inhibitory effects, and self-inhibition of germination may be widespread in fungi. It has been investigated in some rusts, smuts and downy mildews, and probably occurs also in non-obligate parasites. Self-inhibition has been attributed to trimethylethylene (Forsyth, 1955) and to glutamic and aspartic acids (Wilson, 1958). Fatty substances are important in spore germination, and inhibitors might be derived from such substances. Bell and Daly (1962) consider that oxygen and water are necessary for their formation in *Uromyces phaseoli*. Self-inhibition also occurs among the conidia of *Peronospora tabacina* (blue mould of tobacco: Shepherd, 1962; Shepherd and Mandryk, 1963), and the aeciospores of *Puccinia purpurea* (sorghum rust: Le Roux and Dickson, 1957). It can be demonstrated by the improved germination of washed spores, and by the inhibitory action on spore germination of the water used in the washing.

The biological significance of inhibitors is uncertain. They may prevent germination of spores congregated together in the sorus or other structure before dissemination, and perhaps discourage infection in places already occupied by the fungus. The specificity of inhibitors merits investigation, and Pritchard (1965) reported that those from the uredospores of one species of rust may inhibit uredospore germination in other species but that they were not apparently present in the aeciospores tested nor in the teliospores of *Ustilago nuda* (barley loose smut) or *U. avenae*. Inhibitors produced by *U. nuda* from wheat did not affect the two other smuts. It is possible that hyphae also produce germination inhibitors, as described in *Botrytis cinerea* by Carlile and Sellin (1963), and this not infrequently occurs in culture (Robinson and Park, 1966).

Germination stimulants such as pelargonaldehyde and certain other aldehydes and some phenolic compounds (notably coumarin) are also known, and these can apparently neutralize the adverse effect of inhibitors. Little is known about these stimulators, but some have been detected in uredospore extracts and they appear to be relatively nonspecific.

These inhibiting and stimulating substances can greatly affect germination of propagules and so may be expected to have a considerable influence on the infection of plants by pathogens, and their significance in this respect deserves further study as does their possible relationship with substances of host origin which have similar effects on germination.

17 Epidemiology: the seasonal carry-over of plant pathogens

Epidemiology is primarily concerned with epidemics (more correctly termed epiphytotics in the case of plant diseases), but the term has a wide meaning and has come to include most field aspects of disease. In a sense it is the interaction of crop, pathogen and environment, populations of plants and pathogens rather than individuals being involved. These are the aspects of plant disease which, with control, are of vital interest to all concerned with growing plants for food or commercially. The epidemiology of plant diseases tends to receive less attention than pathogenesis, but a proper understanding of epidemiology is necessary for formulation of intelligent control measures. It covers the seasonal persistence and spread of pathogens, and the effects of environmental factors on their incidence, and is of great importance in disease forecasting. Disease control is an extensive subject and is usually considered separately from, although closely interwoven with, epidemiology. Mathematical analysis has been applied to epidemiology in recent years, notably by Van der Plank (1963), and this promises to be an interesting and rewarding approach to the subject, especially when combined with computer analysis of disease outbreaks. As yet, however, such analysis is based on rather few diseases and its further extension may necessitate revision of some of the conclusions reached.

Seasonal carry-over of pathogens

With plants which are perennial, able to survive the winter, or grown throughout the year, pathogens may be permanently present although not necessarily active all the time. With annual plants grown for a few months of the year and with an intercrop period during which the crop is absent, some means of overwintering are clearly necessary for pathogens of that crop; these are considered below, chiefly with reference to fungi and bacteria (for viruses see Chapter 4). In temperate areas the intercrop period is during the cold winter months, but in the tropics it usually occurs during the dry months when cultivation may be possible only under irrigation.

Perennial infection

Broadly speaking this comprises all forms of overwintering of pathogens in or on infected living plants. It includes symptomless carriers able to survive the intercrop period – and these are particularly important in some virus diseases – also tolerant varieties which are infected but show such mild symptoms as to pass almost unnoticed. Mycelium in or on infected tissue may remain dormant during the winter and start to grow and sporulate with regrowth of the host in the spring, then infecting the new 'growth. Some mildews, including *Podosphaera leucotricha* on apple, can overwinter on the bud scales, as can *Venturia inaequalis* in scabbed branches of apple trees. Roots may remain more or less permanently infected, and perennating structures such as bulbs may harbour the pathogen over the winter months. Some pathogens overwinter in or on seeds

Figure 17.1 Ring spot of brassicas caused by *Mycosphaerella brassicicola* on leaf of brussels sprout. This disease can be found on brassicas throughout much of the year in parts of Britain. The fungus spreads by means of ascospores produced in perithecia arrangeb in concentric rings in the lesions; no conidial stage is as yet known.

or other planting material (for example tubers), and so pass to the next generation; these are discussed below. *Uromyces pisi* (pea rust) establishes a perennial mycelium in the rhizomes of *Euphorbia cyparissias* which produce systemically infected shoots bearing aecia. Some heteroecious rusts have a systemically infected perennial alternate host – for example, the aecial stage of *Cronartium ribicola* (currant rust) on five-needled pines. Such systemically infected perennial plants are particularly dangerous as they constitute a permanent source of inoculum.

Spores or spore containing structures such as pycnidia may survive on perennial infected plants, especially if produced in or on twigs and branches. Resistant spores and fruiting bodies may overwinter in sheltered places such as buds or cracks in the bark, particularly in areas with mild intercrop weather where certain types of propagative spore might also survive in this way, but the extent to which this occurs is not known. No doubt the phenomenon is seasonal and depends partly on the mildness or otherwise of the intercrop period.

Some plants, notably brassicas, can be found throughout the year in parts of Britain and pathogens may be present to varying extents at all times, passing from diseased plants to the newly sown ones, as in ring spot caused by *Mycosphaerella brassicicola* (figure 17.1). Spread is likely to be limited in cold weather, and more rapid in warmer wet weather. Pathogens may pass from infected residues of spring sown cereals to autumn sown cereals and overwinter on the latter, especially if there are only a few months between harvesting the spring cereal and sowing the autumn one. Infected winter hardy weeds may harbour pathogens during the winter months and become dangerous sources of inoculum in the spring. Some plants are cultivated under glass during winter as well as outside during the summer months, and overwintering can occur in this way.

Infected crop residues

During harvesting, especially mechanical harvesting, some scattering of leaves, twigs, fruits and seeds inevitably occurs. Roots may be left in the soil, and very often so may the stubble of cereals. All these, if infected, can constitute sources of inoculum even if partially buried by ploughing, as can seedlings developing from scattered seed. The extent to which they do so depends on several factors, climatic and agricultural. Weather conditions during the intercrop period partly determine the extent to which infected crop residues ('trash') rot away and so become less dangerous as inoculum sources. Warm wet conditions which favour microbiological activity tend to rot residues more effectively than dry ones, and possible antagonistic effects and the activity of termites and other insects which destroy plant material in the soil have to be considered.

The water-holding capacity of the soil may also have an effect, and this can be of considerable practical importance. In some areas of Africa, for example, residues of cotton plants tend to persist more or less unaltered during the fairly dry months between successive crops and so can play an important role in survival of *Xanthomonas malvacearum* (bacterial blight), whereas in wetter areas the residues rot away much more quickly and are less important in seasonal persistence of the pathogen. In extreme cases very low or very high temperature during the intercrop months might destroy some pathogens although these are often partially protected by the enveloping plant tissue or by forming resistant propagules. The latter include sclerotia, oospores, pycnidia, perithecia, chlamydospores, many teliospores, and others, some of which are apparently unable to germinate without a dormancy period which may in part coincide with the intercrop period.

Climatic factors can directly affect the longevity of overwintering structures. The sclerotia of some root-infecting fungi are quite sensitive to desiccation and tend to die in dry soil, and low soil temperatures are thought to limit the geographical distribution of such warm region pathogens as *Macrophomina phaseoli*, *Corticium rolfsii* and *Xanthomonas solanacearum* (Miller, 1953). Conidia usually survive much longer in dry than moist soil, and flooding eliminates some soil borne pathogens, possibly through anaerobiosis (see Newhall, 1955). The *p*H and organic content of the soil also affect persistence of plant pathogens. It should be remembered that all these factors influence not only the pathogen but also the other microorganisms present, and antagonistic effects may develop. Survival of fungi is discussed by Sussman (1968).

Most of the pathogens which attack the shoots of plants have apparently lost the ability to survive saprophytically in soil except as resistant propagules or when established in infected host tissue which persists in soil. They are also faced with the problem of passage from the soil to the aerial part of the plant, and burial of infected tissue will make this even more difficult – deep ploughing can thus be an effective control measure in such cases. Many bacterial plant pathogens survive in a dormant condition in infected host tissue and are unable to survive as free-living saprophytes in soil, although some of the root-attacking bacteria appear to do so, including *Agrobacterium tumefaciens*. Some can apparently survive on the surface of roots of non-host plants and weeds; seasonal carry-over no doubt occurs in this way but its extent is not known.

Pathogens usually persist longer in woody residues than in leaves which disintegrate much more rapidly. Burial in soil, especially moist soil, hastens rotting, and ploughing which effectively achieves this can be useful in reducing seasonal carry-over of pathogens. Survival is often prolonged in crop residues remaining in dry, sheltered places such as barns and under hedges. Residues lying on the soil surface, particularly in dry areas, may be blown considerable distances by wind and by 'dust-devils', the latter being able to scatter even woody residues over a wide area. The bacteria which attack plants are not known to produce spores and the vegetative cells are not particularly resistant to adverse environmental conditions. Some can, however, overwinter in dead plant tissues and others secrete slime which dries to form a protective coat. In this protected dormant state bacterial cells may survive unfavourable conditions, the slime dissolving away when conditions for growth become favourable again. Some viruses can survive for years in dried plant tissue, others disappear rather quickly, and many survive only in living plant tissue.

Infected crop residues may be removed, legally or otherwise, from fields and used in villages for a variety of purposes – cotton for domestic spinning, twigs for firewood, millet and maize stalks for fences, to mention but a few – and outbreaks of disease have been traced to such inoculum sources. During removal some of the material is inevitably scattered, inoculum thus in some cases being deposited on next season's fields. These are dangerous practices and it may be necessary to legislate against them, although they are difficult to eliminate.

The pathogens which overwinter in crop residues are usually relatively unspecialized parasites able to survive in dead plant tissue, but obligate parasites may so survive in the form of resistant propagules, such as oospores, formed in the host tissue at the end of the season. Some such propagules may survive for several years, perhaps showing progressive maturation. There is little information as to how long the vegetative stages of pathogens can remain viable in plant residues under natural conditions, and no doubt this is greatly influenced by the climatic conditions during the intercrop period. Several fungal and bacterial plant pathogens survive for several years in infected plant tissue kept in the laboratory, and field observations indicate that many can survive the period – anything from about 3 to 8 or 9 months depending on the plant – between harvesting and the next sowing. Pathogens which colonize dead plant tissue tend to survive longer than more rapid colonizers as the latter will use up the available food more quickly, but this depends on the size of the tissue and the activity of competing microorganisms (Garrett, 1956). There are other possible ways in which infected crop residues might survive. These include compost which has not properly fermented, and resistant propagules which are distributed in the droppings of animals feeding on the plants, but there is little information on these possibilities.

Fields cropped in the previous season can act as inoculum sources in several other ways. Self-sown ('volunteer') seedlings may grow from seeds scattered during harvesting after remaining dormant over the winter.

Such seeds may be contaminated or infected with the pathogen and so germinate into infected seedlings, or the latter may become infected from adjacent diseased twigs or leaves. These infected seedlings can be a very dangerous inoculum source since in them the pathogen is likely to be in an active state of growth and possibly sporulation. Furthermore the diseased leaves or other parts are raised above soil level and perhaps above the accompanying growth of weeds, thus facilitating dispersal of any spores produced. Self-sown seedlings are often difficult to detect if there is a weed cover, and ploughing at the appropriate time may be necessary to destroy them, that is, when most of the scattered seed has germinated but before the new crop is up. If allowed to survive, diseased self-sown plants can be permanent sources of inoculum during the crop season; they may appear during the late autumn or early winter and persist over the winter months.

'Ground-keepers' – plants which are missed during harvesting – can also be dangerous sources of inoculum. In mild winters or sheltered areas some such plants may survive the winter and produce abundant inoculum during the following spring, especially in plants with perennial tendencies. They may develop often unnoticed at the margins and, especially, the corners of fields likely to be missed by harvesters and where the sheltered conditions are conducive to their survival. Regrowth ('ratoons') of plants which have died down in the winter or which were cut out at harvest time may occur in perennial plants grown as annuals (for example cotton). In these the roots remain alive in the soil and produce new shoots when conditions become favourable for growth during the following spring, these shoots becoming infected from nearby crop residues or self-sown seedlings. Ground-keepers and ratoons can be prolific inoculum sources of certain systemic viruses, and in some they are the main means of seasonal persistence – especially those which do not survive in crop residues, in seed, or in alternative hosts. They are also likely to be infested by insect vectors of the virus; cotton ratoons in the Gezira area of the Sudan are frequently infested with whitefly (*Bemisia gossypiperda*) which feed on the infected ratoon leaves and thereafter migrate to the newly sown cotton fields and infect them. Survival of ground-keepers and roots is related to weather conditions during the intercrop period and if these are severe the percentage survival may be small. They are often well above soil level and spore dispersal of any pathogens present will thus be facilitated. Unless destroyed they may persist as inoculum sources for a considerable time.

Subsidiary host plants

Some pathogens have a narrow host range, others a wide one, and some of those which attack cultivated plants may also attack wild ones. The latter, especially if perennial or growing throughout the year, can be important in seasonal persistence of some pathogens. Such subsidiary hosts may include symptomless carriers or tolerant plants in which symptoms are so mild as to pass unnoticed (these are particularly difficult to detect) and infected weeds or cultivated plants in gardens and glasshouses. Alternate hosts of rusts can be dangerous, particularly when the secondary host is a perennial wild plant. Elimination or prohibition of subsidiary hosts of a destructive pathogen attacking an important crop may be necessary, but difficult or impossible if they are numerous. In all cases it has to be ascertained whether the infected subsidiary host is a source of effective inoculum for the crop plant. The fact that a pathogen attacks several different species of plant does not necessarily mean that it will pass from one to the other although it is advisable to assume that it does so unless there is evidence to the contrary. As discussed above (p. 298), many pathogens comprise several different varieties and races, each adapted to one or a few host varieties, species, or genera and showing only limited intertransmissibility, the extent of which can only be determined by cross-inoculation experiments and field observations.

If the existence of subsidiary host plants is suspected a search should be made in and near the infected crop for other plants showing similar symptoms. The possible presence of known hosts of the pathogen should be checked, and cross-inoculation experiments between infected crop plants and possible subsidiary hosts may be necessary. Many, but not all pathogens tend to attack taxonomically related plants, and the latter should be investigated first, that is, other species of the same genus as that of the crop plant, other genera of the same family, and so on. It should be remembered that the results of inoculation experiments in glasshouse and laboratory are not always a reliable guide to what occurs in the field. In experimental inoculations the environment is usually made as conducive to infection as possible, more so than generally occurs in the field, and species may remain uninfected under natural conditions although shown to be susceptible when experimentally inoculated, so that a false picture of the field host range of the pathogen may be obtained. This emphasizes the importance of knowledge not only of the host range of the pathogen but also of its transmissibility between the various hosts.

A few fungal and bacterial pathogens overwinter in their insect vectors, including *Xanthomonas stewarti* (maize wilt) in flea beetles, and rice stunt virus and several others which can pass through the eggs of viruliferous leafhoppers (transovarial transmission), such viruses being able to multiply within the insect (see Maramorosch, 1964). Prolonged survival in vectors could enable pathogens to persist in the absence of their host plants, and this appears to be so with *X. stewarti* in the U.S.A. where a cold winter destroys the flea beetles carrying the bacteria and is likely to be followed by only slight bacterial wilt. Some of the 'blue stain' fungi which attack wood probably survive in the insects with which they are associated.

Infected and contaminated planting material

Some fungal spores, sclerotia, pycnidia and hyphae, seeds of phanero-gamic parasites, bacteria, viruses, and nematodes can be seed borne in various ways, and similarly for other types of planting material – tubers, bulbs, cuttings and others. The pathogen may be mixed with the seed but not attached to it, as with ergot sclerotia and with dodder seeds, or it may be present on, or attached to, the seed coat as with some smut telio-spores, bacteria, viruses, rust uredospores, and conidia. Attachment may be facilitated by a sticky or roughened spore wall and by a rough, hairy or sticky seed coat. Propagules may be present between the seed coat and structures, for example glumes, investing the seed. All these are generally referred to as contamination. Seed and pathogen can sometimes be separated by mechanical methods such as flotation or sieving, or seed treatment can often be used to destroy the propagules of the pathogen. In seed infection the seed coat and internal tissues may be penetrated to varying extents or, as in some smuts, the embryo itself may be penetrated. Heat treatment which inactivates the pathogen without unduly harming the seed may be possible in some cases of seed infection.

The relationships between pathogens and seeds are very varied and range from what appears to be almost symbiosis to rapid destruction of the seed by the pathogen. Seed borne pathogens have been classified into those which do not injure the seed, those which injure it to a certain extent, and those which kill it (Noble, 1957). During dormancy the pathogen and seed often coexist but on germination the former may become active and kill or damage the young seedling, either before or after emergence. Wallen (1964) suggests that germination may result in liberation of nutrients which stimulate the growth of seed borne pathogens. Apart from pathogens such as *Claviceps* and some smuts which destroy and replace the internal tissues of seeds, there are those which kill the seed before germination, for instance *Podosporiella verticillata* in wheat seed, which perhaps produces a toxin (Wallace, 1959). Many other pathogens can cause a combination of seed death and seedling disease which may persist into the mature plants, as in leaf and pod spot of peas caused by *Ascochyta pisi* (figure 17.2). Infected seeds tend to be shrivelled, light and sometimes discoloured, and although often incapable of germination, may act as inoculum sources for seedlings growing from uninfected seed.

Seeds become contaminated or infected in various ways – during threshing (inflorescence smuts), by spores produced on the diseased parent plant, by admixture of fragments of diseased plant tissue, by

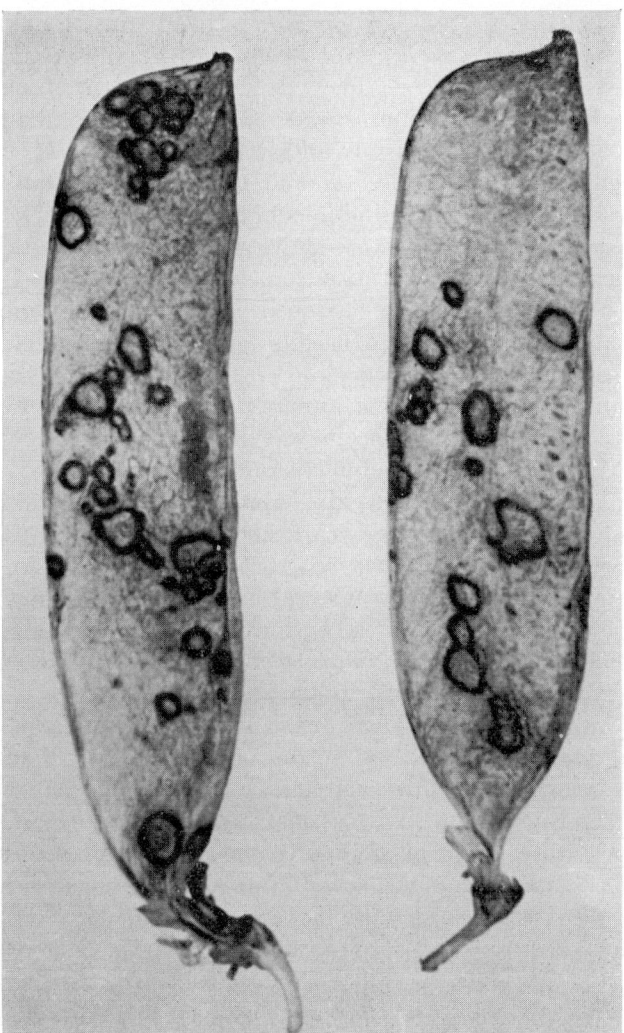

Figure 17.2 *Ascochyta pisi* on pea pods; the fungus enters the seeds through these lesions in the pod wall.

invasion of the fruit and thence of the seeds therein, by direct invasion of young exposed seeds, or by invasion of the embryo through the pistil as in *Claviceps*, some viruses and smuts, *Gloeotinia temulenta* (blind seed disease of rye grass) and *Botrytis anthophila* (anther mould of clover). The latter is an interesting and exceptional *Botrytis* in that it is said to be systemic in the clover plant without apparently causing much damage until flowering, when the anthers are largely replaced by spores. Embryo infection may occur during fertilization by pollen from an infected plant, and vascular pathogens such as *Xanthomonas campestris* (black rot of cabbage) and *Fusarium oxysporum* are said to enter seeds through the vascular system. Some spread from seed to seed is likely to occur during threshing, cleaning, packing, and other operations, particularly so with pathogens whose propagules are dry and not firmly adherent to the seed.

The longevity of propagules on and in seed varies considerably in different pathogens and according to conditions of storage. The seed often outlives the pathogen but there are many reports of the reverse occurring, and *Colletotrichum linicola*, *Polyspora lini*, *Botrytis cinerea* and *Phoma* sp. survived for about 4 years on flax seed which lost its germinability in half that time (Colhoun and Muskett, 1948). Pathogenicity, vigour or ability to produce spores often decline during prolonged storage, quickly in some pathogens but slowly in others. Some samples of *Ustilago nuda* could still infect after storage of infected barley seed for 9 years (Russell, 1961) and teliospores of this smut were found by Tapke (1953) to survive in a pathogenic state longer (14 years) when stored *in vitro* at 28–32°F than as mycelium in infected seed (7 years) kept under similar conditions, but they quickly perished when kept *in vitro* at room temperature. In their study on the longevity of fungi on cereal seed Machacek and Wallace (1952) recovered *Pyrenophora avenae* (oat seed) and *P. teres* (barley seed) after as long as 10 years whereas *Alternaria tenuis*, *Cochliobolus sativus* and *Leptosphaeria nodorum* died out rapidly in wheat seed.

Generally speaking, thin walled propagules on the seed coat can be expected to die out more rapidly than thick walled ones or than mycelium remaining dormant and protected inside the seed. Some bacteria can survive for several years in seed, or on seed if protected by dried resistant slime. Some viruses have been reported to survive for several years in infected seed without loss of virulence but tobacco mosaic declined rapidly on tomato seeds after storage for a year (Alexander, 1960). Prolonged storage can sometimes be used to free seeds from infection without seriously impairing their germinability, particularly with hard coated seeds in which gaseous and moisture exchange is largely prevented. *Ascochyta pisi*, for example, disappeared from pea seed after storage for 7 years and no adverse effects on emergence were observed (Wallen, 1955).

Many of the considerations outlined above apply also to planting material other than seed. Pathogens may be present on or in bulbs, corms, tubers, cuttings and other vegetatively propagated material, or in the soil particles adhering to them. Such material is especially dangerous in carry-over of systemic viruses but some fungi, bacteria, insects and nematodes can also persist in this way, and fungicidal or heat treatment may be necessary. Pathogens may be carried on the surface of the planting material or may be present within the tissues, as in potato tubers infected by *Phytophthora infestans* or in onion bulbs containing mycelium of *Peronospora destructor*. They may remain dormant or spread during storage so that considerable inoculum can be present at planting time. Severely infected tubers are likely to be of reduced viability and to give rise to unthrifty, diseased plants which are a source of inoculum for others.

A pathogen on the seed coat will probably not be distinguishable except in a heavy contamination with propagules of different colour from that of the seed coat, as with dark smut spores on light coloured cereal seed causing appreciable darkening of the latter. Infected seed may be lighter in weight, smaller, and sometimes shrivelled and discoloured, and there may be both infection and contamination of the same seed. A contaminated seed does not necessarily develop into a diseased seedling. Whether successful infection occurs depends partly on soil conditions (moisture content, temperature, nutrient status, pH) during germination; if these are favourable to the pathogen infection will probably occur, if not the seedling may escape infection. Soil and environmental conditions may also play a part in determining whether infected seeds develop into infected seedlings, but to a less extent as the pathogen is within, and partly protected by, the seed. They do, however, greatly influence the subsequent development, severity, and spread of the pathogen.

Pathogens which overwinter on or, especially, in planting material would seem to be in a very favourable position for infecting the seedling and thence the older plant, as they do not have the problem of bridging the gap between inoculum source and potential host plant. Under natural conditions, however, they must be able to remain dormant in or on seed in soil and to 'time' the germination of their propagules to coincide with that of the host seed; premature germination of spores would clearly be ineffective unless the pathogen were able to survive in soil. Pathogens which destroy the seed which they infect are likely to be less successful than those which permit germination of the seed and the resulting development of infected plants. Seed is likely to be dispersed by natural agencies or man, and this can thus bring about spread as well as survival of seed borne pathogens. Recent accounts of seed transmission of pathogens include those of Wallen (1964), and Baker and Smith (1966), and an annotated list of seed borne pathogens is given by Noble, de Tempe and Neergaard (1958) and Noble and Richardson (1968). Noble (1971) discusses seed pathology.

Soil borne inoculum

Overwintering of pathogens in plant tissue on or in soil has been discussed above. There are also pathogens which survive in soil as such, either as free-living mycelium or, more often, as resistant propagules of various types. Although many of these attack seeds, seedlings or roots, others are foliage pathogens which spread from resistant propagules in the soil to the foliage when conditions become favourable in spring, as with the teliospores of *Entyloma calendulae f.sp. dahliae* (dahlia leaf smut).

Root-attacking fungi which are able to survive as saprophytes in soil – the soil-inhabiting fungi of Garrett (1956) – are to be distinguished from the more specialized root-inhabiting fungi which tend to die out in soil unless present in infected plant tissue or as resistant propagules. Soil inhabiters probably include such fungi as *Rhizoctonia solani*, *Fusarium culmorum*, *Macrophomina phaseoli*, and some *Pythium* spp. Some can grow freely through the soil and so tend to be generally distributed in it, can colonize dead plant tissue as competitive saprophytes, and in Garrett's view are to be regarded as relatively primitive parasites, perhaps fundamentally saprophytic. Since they can survive as saprophytes in soil they can no doubt overwinter as such. In his review, however, Menzies (1963) concludes that there are not many plant pathogenic fungi that have been clearly shown to act as free-living soil saprophytes. The situation is complicated by the wide host range of many such soil-inhabiting fungi and by their ability to produce resistant propagules, and some possibly comprise a mixture of saprophytic and parasitic strains. Furthermore, some pathogens attacking the shoots of plants, including *Alternaria brassicicola* on brassicas, can colonize dead host tissue in soil but do not survive for any length of time as free-living saprophytes in soil.

Root-inhabiting fungi seem to be more highly specialized parasites of rather low competitive saprophytic ability. They tend to die out in the continued absence of a host plant unless resistant long lived propagules are formed, and are characterized by an expanding parasitic phase in the living plant and by a declining saprophytic phase after its death (Garrett, 1956). Their distribution in soil thus depends upon that of the host plant. *Ophiobolus graminis* (take-all of cereals) has little saprophytic ability and apparently persists as mycelium in previously infected plant tissue in soil. Conditions which hasten breakdown of the tissue reduce survival of the fungus which may be a few months or as long as 2 years. In nitrogen deficient soils, however, the fungus disappeared relatively quickly although the infected wheat straw remained intact. In nitrogen rich soil on the other hand the straw decomposed rapidly and the fungus survived longer, suggesting that ample nitrogen permitted its slow saprophytic development in the straw (Garrett, 1956).

Root-inhabiting fungi usually invade living roots rather than dead tissues although there are exceptions, and normally are able to grow through the soil only when receiving nutrients from a food base, often *via* rhizomorphs as in *Armillaria mellea*. Overwintering of root-inhabiting fungi which attack annual plants is thus likely to be in dead roots or as resting propagules. The former perhaps provides a high inoculum potential over fairly short periods (for example the winter months) and the latter a lower potential over longer periods. Some such fungi overwinter in both ways, producing sclerotia or other structures which survive in a dormant condition for several years. The few root-attacking fungi which are obligate parasites, of which the best known is *Plasmodiophora brassicae*, survive chiefly as resting propagules.

Few of the pathogens which attack the aerial parts of plants survive for long as free-living saprophytes in soil although they may do so in infected plant tissue or as resting structures therein. In specialized root-inhabiting fungi the inability to produce such structures may be a serious drawback, particularly with wide crop rotations in which a susceptible plant may not be present for several years. However, the fungistatic principle apparently present in most soils might permit ordinary propagative spores to remain ungerminated but viable until susceptible roots appeared, and possibly the latter are able to overcome this as yet unidentified principle, perhaps by root exudates in the rhizosphere. To be effective the resting structure should be able to remain dormant until susceptible roots become available, and there would be a further advantage if only the latter could stimulate germination. There are several reports of plant material or organic manures stimulating germination of resting structures but the effect is often generalized, non-hosts as well as hosts of the pathogen being effective in this respect. Progressive maturation in which the propagules attain maturity – and sometimes germinability – over a longer period of time might also increase the chances of successful encounters between germinating propagules and susceptible roots.

Resistant overwintering structures in fungi may be sexually produced (zygospores, oospores, some ascospores and teliospores), asexual spores (chlamydospores), or vegetative organs (sclerotia). Fruiting bodies such as perithecia, cleistothecia and pycnidia may also be involved in overwintering and may show a gradual maturation of the spores within them. Oospores often undergo prolonged dormancy, can be difficult to germinate experimentally, but are probably important in seasonal carry-over of many pathogens belonging to the Peronosporales. Oospores of *Peronospora destructor* (downy mildew of onion) may not germinate for 4 years and can survive for twice that time, depending on soil conditions, while those of certain other downy mildews have not been observed to germinate. Teliospores of some smuts may germinate almost immediately whereas those of others – especially if soil borne – may remain dormant for several years, showing irregular germination. Overwintering of bunt (*Tilletia caries*) teliospores is greatest with smutted heads buried in soil, less with bunt balls and least with separated spores.

Several fungi overwinter in soil as chlamydospores. One of these is *Fusarium solani f.sp. phaseoli* (bean root rot) in which bean roots and other plant material induce germination. The mycelium and thin walled conidia lyse rapidly in soil, and some soils apparently reduce formation of chlamydospores and hence seasonal carry-over of the pathogen. These observations suggest the possibility of control by measures which inhibit production of overwintering propagules or which bring about premature germination of such structures in the absence of susceptible plants. Soil fungistasis might enable some conidia to remain dormant in soil sufficiently long to enable overwintering to occur and this possibility merits further investigation. The recent report by Kuhlman (1969) that the relatively thin walled conidia of *Fomes annosus* (butt rot of conifers) can survive for 10 months in forest soils in North Carolina, U.S.A., is interesting in this connexion. Also of interest is the report by Chesters and Blakeman (1966) that *Mycosphaerella ligulicola* (ray blight of chrysanthemum) survives as epiphytic mycelium on the root surface of chrysanthemum cuttings, the latter thus functioning as symptomless carriers of the fungus. The distribution of such contaminated rooted cuttings by nurserymen no doubt facilitates spread of the pathogen. Whether this occurs with other pathogens is not known but if it does it could be of considerable significance in their seasonal carry-over and spread.

The seeds of some parasitic angiosperms can remain dormant in soil for several years, may undergo progressive maturation, and may require the presence of plant roots for appreciable germination to occur. The factor which stimulates germination has been extensively studied in *Striga asiatica* (witchweed) which attacks the roots of grasses and cereals in warmer areas, and which was identified in the U.S.A. about 16 years ago. There was some evidence that *Striga* seed might itself produce the factor and that the latter might be involved in after-ripening of the seed. Although the chemical nature of the stimulator is not known it seems to be similar to those involved in germination of *Orobanche* seed and in eel-worm hatching factors. Several organic substances, including *D*-xyloketose, are reported to stimulate germination of witchweed seed to varying extents (see Tarr, 1962).

Many fungi produce sclerotia of different shapes and sizes, ranging from less than 1 mm in *Sclerotium cepivorum* (white rot of onions) to 0·3 metres across in *Polyporus mylittae* ('black fellows' bread' of Australia); they tend to be small in root-infecting fungi. Sclerotia originate from localized branching, septation, thickening and usually darkening of hyphae and may be rather loosely constructed or differentiated into a protective rind and looser inner tissue. In some parasitic fungi the sclerotia contain host tissue. On germination they may produce mycelium, conidia or fruiting bodies (for example apothecia in *Sclerotinia*, stromata containing perithecia in *Claviceps*) (figure 17.3). Sclerotia are resistant structures which serve for overwintering, very often in soil; they can remain dormant for long periods of time and their germination may be stimulated by roots –

(a)

microsclerotia of *Verticillium dahliae* are said to survive for 14 years in field soil (Wilhelm, 1955).

Longevity depends greatly on environmental conditions, and the sclerotia of *Phymatotrichum omnivorum*, which have been investigated in the U.S.A., are apparently rather sensitive to desiccation since they did not

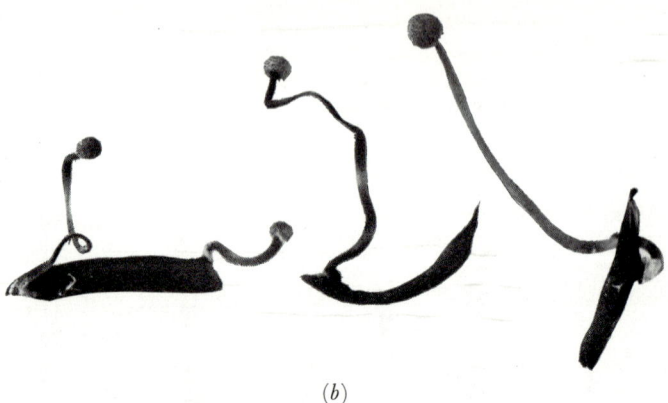

(b)

Figure 17.3 Sclerotia (ergots) of *Claviceps purpurea* on *Lolium perenne*. The sclerotia fall to the ground in the autumn and germinate in the spring to produce stalked stromata in whose spherical heads the perithecia-containing asci are borne. The ascospores are liberated and initiate infection of grass inflorescences. The ergots contain poisonous alkaloids which caused outbreaks of ergotism (St Anthony's Fire) in the Middle Ages when rye bread (rye is very susceptible) was extensively eaten. *C. purpurea* also attacks grasses and can cause injury to cattle feeding on infected grasses. Infected heads (*a*) and germinating ergots (*b*) are shown.

survive air drying for more than an hour although survival after 5 years in soil of intermediate moisture content ranged from 10 to 16% (King, Loomis and Hope, 1931; Taubenhaus and Ezekiel, 1936). These sclerotia also failed to survive −13°C for more than a day in the laboratory (Ezekiel, 1945) and this may in part determine the northern limit of cotton root rot, one of the diseases caused by the fungus. This limit corresponds fairly well with the line at which the lowest observed air temperature was −23°C. Spontaneous germination in the absence of susceptible roots may also occur. Little is known about the possible role of rhizomorphs in seasonal persistence of pathogens but these structures may be homologous with sclerotia (Garrett, 1956). The latter have been most intensively studied in root-infecting fungi but some of the fungi attacking the aerial parts of plants also produce sclerotia, for example *Botrytis cinerea* and *Claviceps*.

   Effective overwintering structures may be essential for prolonged survival of root-inhabiting pathogens unable to survive as saprophytes in soil. Many shoot pathogens also produce overwintering structures in the infected tissues of the host plant in or on soil although survival of some appears to be as persistent mycelium rather than as resistant propagules as such. The factors affecting the survival of overwintering structures in soil are considered above. The soil would seem to be a medium for saprophytes rather than plant parasites, especially as regards the more specialized ones and those not producing overwintering structures. For stem and leaf pathogens it tends to become 'a burial ground rather than a base of operations' (Menzies, 1963).

Inoculum from other sources

There are many other ways in which pathogens can be introduced into the crop area, of which only a few examples need be given. Diseased vegetables and fruit may be on sale in shops and markets and be unwittingly disseminated by the purchasers; seasonal carry-over and dispersal may thus be combined. Vegetables and fruit kept in store over

(a)

Figure 17.4 Mummified apple (a) and pears (b) bearing conidial pustules of *Sclerotinia fructigena* (brown rot). Such fruits are not only worthless but also serve for seasonal carry-over of the fungus in orchards and stores.

M

the winter may be discarded by householders in the spring when fresh ones become available (figure 17.4). Infected potato parings may be thrown on the garden where potatoes are to be planted. Old soil liable to contain pathogenic fungi and nematodes may be removed from the glass-house to the garden, and similarly plant material which has overwintered in the glasshouse. Old field clamps may be a source of infection. The tracing of such obscure sources of inoculum is sometimes a severe test of the pathologist's powers of imagination and deduction.

Inoculum from more distant sources sometimes causes outbreaks of disease, as with air borne uredospores of *Puccinia graminis tritici* brought in by south-westerly winds from Morocco *via* the Atlantic coast to Great Britain, as described by Zadoks (1965) (figure 17.5). Such sources may be within the same land mass or overseas, and are generally infected fields which, because of milder climatic conditions, are sown earlier. As well as air borne inoculum there is that imported by man on or in diseased plant products of commerce – fruit, vegetables, seeds and other planting material, vegetable fibres, and miscellaneous plant material such as leaves used

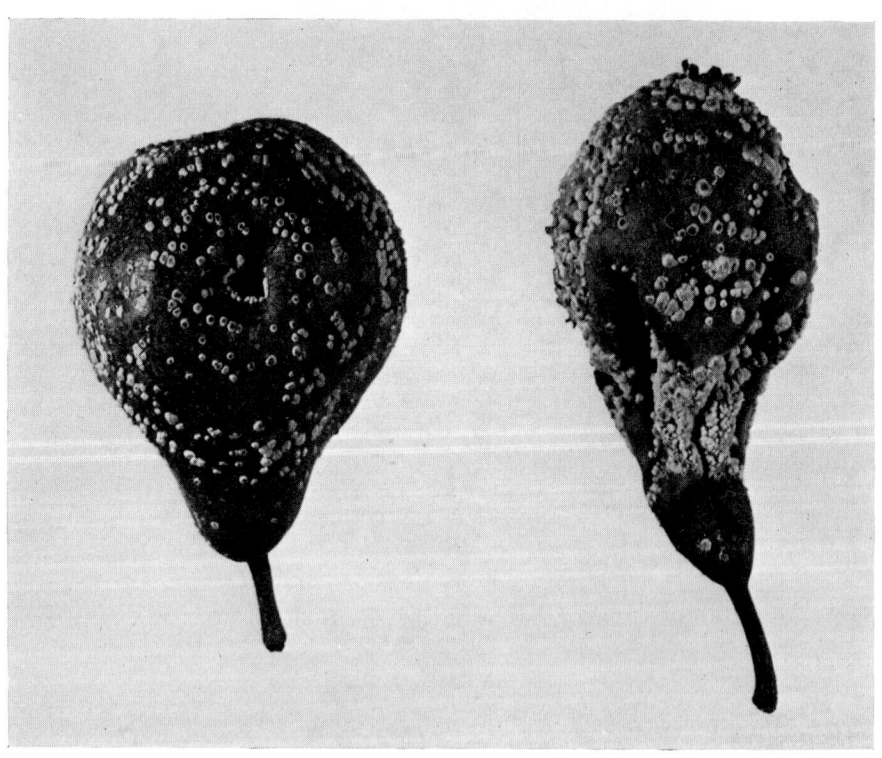

(*b*)

as packing or incidentally present, straw around bottles, and so on. There are the spores or fruiting bodies – especially the more resistant ones – brought in on the clothes of long distance travellers, especially those concerned with agriculture or horticulture and the great expansion of rapid air travel in recent years has increased the possible dangers of this. 'Luxury' plant products such as orchids may be transported from country to country, or even from continent to continent, in a few days under conditions designed to keep them fresh and no doubt having a similar effect

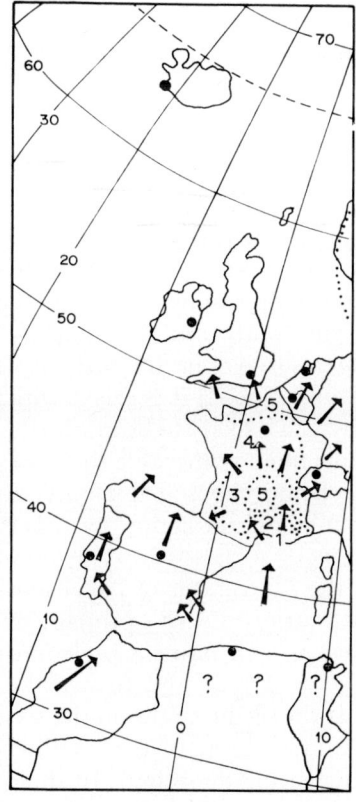

Figure 17.5 Migration tracts of *Puccinia graminis* on wheat in western Europe. The arrows denote the probable direction of uredospore dispersal by air currents. The numbers 1–5 indicate the usual date of appearance of the disease in France: 1, before 5 June; 2, before 15 June; 3, before 30 June; 4, before 10 July; 5, after 10 July.

on any pathogens present. Interchange of seed or other planting material may also introduce pathogens and should be rigorously controlled.

The significance of inoculum from distant areas as sources of infection is uncertain. Many countries have systems of legislation designed to minimize the introduction and internal dissemination of pathogens and pests, but there is little defence against air borne spores and it is not easy to control movement of plant materials within countries, although this may be possible on a selective basis. Long distance dissemination is considered elsewhere (p. 362). There may be different races of pathogens in different parts of a large land mass, and introduction of a race from one area into another may have disastrous consequences. The bringing together of different races might result in two compatible strains of a heterothallic pathogen meeting, and the sexual state of a hitherto asexual fungus could thus develop. This would increase the genetical variability of the pathogen (through hybridization) and give rise to new and more virulent races, and might also provide it with another method of overwintering.

Transfer of pathogens from inoculum source to crop

This occurs in various ways, depending on the type of pathogen and its method of transmission. Finding a susceptible plant may be a considerable problem where pathogen and potential host are far apart, and in such cases much of the inoculum is likely to be wasted. Hence it is a sound general principle to have this season's fields as far away as possible from inoculum sources, and crop rotation is important in this respect.

The mycelium of pathogens within perennial plants which have died back or lost their leaves during the winter normally begins to grow with the host in the spring, such plants being permanently and systemically infected to varying extents. Where the pathogen survives on the surface of the plant or planting material, as in contaminated seed, it is faced with the problem of invading the tissues, a process which is likely to be markedly affected by environmental conditions. It is thus more vulnerable than the pathogen already within the seed or plant, being exposed not only to changing environment but also to possible antagonistic action by other microorganisms, in the seed or in the soil.

Spread of pathogens from seed to plant – the SP transfer of Baker and Smith (1966) – can be by spores on the seed coat or infective propagules produced on germination of seed borne spores, as with smuts. Cotyledons often become infected from inoculum on the seed coat and thence the pathogens spread to other parts of the plant. If the seed remains in the soil the pathogen may attack the young roots and/or stem of the seedling before or after emergence, the latter sometimes being depressed. In these cases the old germinated seed becomes profusely colonized by the pathogen and acts as a source of inoculum and a food base for the pathogen. Infected seeds may fail to emerge and then form an inoculum source for adjacent uninfected seedlings. Overwintering structures such as pycnidia on seeds may liberate spores which infect nearby seedlings, and some sclerotia produce apothecia (*Sclerotinia*) or stromata containing perithecia (*Claviceps*) which actively discharge air borne infective ascospores. Sclerotia in the soil frequently produce infective conidia or hyphae.

In most of these cases the pathogen is in, on, or near the plant and contact between the two is thus present from the start or fairly easily made. In other cases, however, pathogen propagule and potential host plant may be some distance apart, a condition which handicaps the pathogen. This handicap can be reduced in various ways, for example, by host tissue being necessary for germination of the dormant propagule, or by the infecting structure showing tropic or tactic responses which enable it to 'seek out' potential hosts. Several cases of zoospores moving towards plant tissue – presumably as a response to substances secreted by the latter – have been reported in roots and leaves, and rhizomorphs, mycelial strands and hyphae may show chemotropic responses of this sort. Zoospores, however, can swim only fairly short distances and chemotactic responses may help them in making their way to suitable sites for infection once they have reached the plant, for example in finding stomata. Progressive maturation of propagules and their germination over a period of time, rather than all simultaneously, might also ensure that at least some of the propagules are infective when and if susceptible roots grow into their vicinity. It is likely that nematodes not only disseminate the spores of root-attacking fungi but also inoculate them into the root while feeding. Although the distance to which nematodes move through the soil is probably fairly small they may be carried long distances by streams or irrigation water.

Rain splash enables spores at the soil surface to reach the leaves, and forcible discharge mechanisms might have a similar effect. Spores produced on plant residues buried in the soil, especially if deeply buried, are likely to remain there unless they can produce a mycelium able to grow to the soil surface and there liberate infective spores. This probably happens in some soil borne smuts such as *Entyloma calendulae* in which the secondary dikaryotic mycelium, formed after germination of the soil borne teliospores, produces sporidia at the soil surface. These sporidia are rain splashed on to the lower leaves of plants in the spring. The presence of a weed cover may also hamper the effective dissemination of spores produced by soil borne pathogens.

Transportation of propagules from inoculum source to distant potential host plants is by air currents – a random and wasteful process – or by vectors, particularly insects, or man. Insects are of importance in carrying some viruses and this is, of course, not a random process, the insect feeding on the plant involved. In the absence of the appropriate insect the virus may be unable to pass from inoculum source to plant, and the insect is often necessary for successful inoculation of the virus. This probably applies also to some insect transmitted fungi and bacteria, although these usually have other methods of transmission. Man can transfer inoculum from one field to another on his boots, clothing or machines and this is probably of some importance with pathogens carried in soil, for example

Plasmodiophora brassicae. Spores which rely entirely on random distribution by air for their transportation to the newly sown fields are very dependent on weather conditions, direction and speed of air currents, and other factors. A large initial spore production may be necessary for success, especially if the inoculum source and the potential host plants are distant. Burial in the soil may render the inoculum source ineffective and this, especially if combined with crop rotation, can be very useful in control of some diseases.

18 The dispersal of plant pathogens

Dispersal is what happens between take-off of a spore and its deposition – it does not include its germination or infection of the plant – whereas spread implies that the pathogen reaches and infects plants (Van der Plank, 1967). These and other terms, (dissemination, transmission) are, however, rather loosely used. Spread can be used to denote progressive colonization of the infected organ or plant, passage of the pathogen from infected plants to others in the same field or crop area, or long distance spread of pathogens between plants which are widely separated, as in intercontinental spread. Many pathogens spread from plant to plant by means of infective propagules, which may be spores, bacteria or viruses, but there are other pathogens which do not spread in this way or which do so only to a very limited extent. Most of the pathogens restricted to roots have little power of independent movement through the soil (except sometimes by rhizomorphs or similar structures) and their spread is likely to be by water borne or insect borne propagules or by redistribution of contaminated soil or diseased roots. *Plasmodiophora brassicae*, generally tends to occur in patches indicating areas of contaminated soil although this pattern is commonly upset by ploughing or other measures which scatter the spores or diseased root tissue. Such patches, if undisturbed, enlarge slowly from year to year provided susceptible plants are sown.

Although dispersal of fungi is mostly by means of spores, dissemination of hyphal fragments occurs in some fungi as described by Pady and Kramer (1960), Pady and Gregory (1963), Kramer *et al.* (1964) and Harvey (1970). In the United States, Pady and Kramer (1960) found that the numbers of hyphal fragments (mainly of *Cladosporium, Alternaria* and *Penicillium*) were greatest during the growing season ($175–1750/m^3$ in summer) and least in winter ($35–212/m^3$) and showed a viability of 29–82%. A detailed investigation by Pady and Gregory (1963) in England in July–August gave figures of 10–599 (average 126) fragments/m^3, mostly of *Cladosporium*. The hyphal pieces ranged from less than 10μm to more than 100μm but were mainly $20–40\mu$m long. Dematiaceous fragments were more numerous than hyaline ones, and conidiophores, especially the terminal portion, were abundant. On growth the hyphal fragments produced a germ tube from one or both ends, the germ tube frequently developing into a short conidiophore bearing a spore. Germination of the fragments ranged from 1–43% (average 16·2%) as compared with 16–90% (average 62%) for *Cladosporium* spores. In Kansas, U.S.A., Kramer *et al.* (1964) found that hyphal fragments tended to reach their maximum after a long period of dry weather during which they dried out and became more easily detached. Harvey (1970) observed that the number of hyphal fragments mainly of *Cladosporium*, was generally low ($< 10/m^3$) except during July–September when daily averages rose above $30/m^3$ and reached $176/m^3$ in August. Viability was also relatively low with maxima of 9·5–34·5%. There seem to be few reports of plant pathogenic fungi being disseminated in the form of hyphal fragments, and spores would seem to be better adapted for dispersal. The generally low viability of hyphal fragments would also be a disadvantage. Since, except in powdery mildews (Erysiphaceae) and certain other Ascomycetes, the hyphae of most of the fungi which attack the aerial parts of plants are within the host tissue rather than on the surface, there would seem to be little scope for their spread by hyphal fragments.

The most frequent agents involved in dispersal of plant pathogens are: air, water, insects and other animals, and man.

Dispersal by air

Many of the fungi which attack the aerial parts of plants spread by means of small spores of extremely varied morphology and origin. These propagative spores include conidia, uredospores, basidiospores, ascospores, and others. Many of the dry ones are dispersed by air currents, others (often slimy spores) may be dispersed by insects or water. A combination of air and water may be involved in dispersal, as in air disseminated splash droplets containing spores, or a combination of air and insects as in viruliferous insects blown about by the wind. For effective spread – bearing in mind the high wastage rate inevitable in random dissemination by air currents – the pathogen must produce numerous spores which are successfully liberated, dispersed, and deposited in a viable condition on susceptible plants under conditions conducive to infection; in other words production, liberation, dispersal and deposition of spores are involved.

Spore production

Propagative spores are produced in many different ways – in sporangia, on simple or complex conidiophores, in or on ascocarps and basidiocarps, by budding or fission, within pycnidia, perithecia or sori of various types, and in other ways as described in books on mycology (see Stakman and Harrar, 1957; Hughes, 1953; Hawker, 1960). Fungi show a great diversity in their methods of producing propagules and many different paths towards more efficient production and liberation of spores seem to have been explored. Spore output per unit area of infected tissue may be increased by close aggregation of sporophores, branched or whorled sporophores, production of spores in chains or clusters, by a more or less continuous production of spores within the sorus, or by successive crops of spores. The numbers of spores produced can be astronomical. Powdery mildews may produce several thousand conidia per square centimetre of infected leaf surface, a fairly modest output compared with 100,000 or more in some downy mildews. A single smut sorus may contain millions of spores, a heavily infected barberry bush is said to produce up to about 70,000 million aeciospores of *Puccinia graminis* at one time (and there may be several crops of spores in the spring), and a relatively small apothecium of *Sclerotinia* can produce about 30 million ascospores. The spores produced by large polypores such as *Fomes* are even more numerous. Heavily rusted wheat fields produce so many uredospores that 'spore-clouds' may be seen rising during harvesting, and implements may be coated with a fine reddish deposit of spores.

Equally important as numbers of spores are the duration and periodicity of sporulation. Some pathogens produce a more or less simultaneous 'crop' of propagules followed by other crops, as occurs with the sporangiophores of *Peronospora*. The sporophores of others may bear several successive propagules, for example those of *Phytophthora* and *Cercospora* to mention but two. In some rusts a uredium produces uredospores over a period of time and may eventually produce teliospores. The capacity to produce a steady stream of infective propagules over a prolonged period of time is likely to be advantageous to the pathogen.

Some fungi show a diurnal periodicity in sporulation, as in nocturnal production of sporangia by some species of *Sclerospora*. These are probably chiefly temperature–moisture effects but might in some cases be related to periodicity in susceptibility of the host plant. Similar periodicity in spore discharge (Hirst, 1953), and in germination and formation of appressoria (Yarwood, 1936*a*) has been reported.

Spore liberation

This may be passive, the spores being released by moving air or water, rain splash, humidity changes, contact or shock, or active in which the spores are forcibly discharged by a sudden release of energy in the sporophore.

Active spore discharge is accomplished in different ways in different fungi. The sporangium itself (as occurs in *Pilobolus*) or individual spores (for example basidiospores) may be discharged. The 'squirting out' of ascospores from some asci is apparently due to controlled apical bursting of the turgid stretched ascus within which a considerable hydrostatic pressure develops. The ascospores in one ascus may be discharged singly in succession, particularly acicular ones, but more often all the spores are liberated in one squirt. There may be a simultaneous discharge of many asci – 'puffing' – from apothecia. In most cases the spores are projected only a centimetre or so and this type of discharge seems to depend on fairly damp conditions, being triggered off by changes in temperature, light, humidity and possibly other factors. In some perithecia the ascospores are forcibly discharged through the apical ostiole, and the ascus itself is ejected from the cleistothecium in some powdery mildews, subsequently bursting to scatter the spores.

Many Basidiomycetes and 'mirror'- or 'shadow-yeasts' (Sporobolomycetaceae) produce ballistospores which are forcibly discharged by the well known drop (or possibly bubble: Olive, 1964; Ingold and Dann, 1968) excretion mechanism whose nature has yet to be elucidated, despite considerable investigation. Discharge occurs only under damp conditions when the cells involved are turgid, and the spores are usually discharged much less than a millimetre. Other types of spore are also forcibly discharged from the sporophore in various ways. The sudden rounding-off of turgid structures is involved in the discharge of aeciospores of some rusts (which may be to a distance of more than a centimetre), in the discharge of the sporangia of *Sclerospora philippinensis* (Weston, 1923), and possibly in that of the conidia of certain powdery mildews; whether the latter occurs is, however, doubtful.

Some sort of squirting mechanism has been suggested for the forcible discharge of conidia in *Nigrospora sphaerica* (Webster, 1952) and *Pyricularia oryzae* (Ingold, 1964), as well as in *Entomophthora muscae*. In some downy mildews the sporangia are flicked off their fine attachments by violent hygroscopic twisting movements of the branched sporangiophores, due apparently to drying of the latter (as occurs in *Peronospora tabacina*, blue mould of tobacco; Pinckard, 1942), and a somewhat similar mechanism may perhaps operate in *Botrytis cinerea* (Jarvis, 1962).

An interesting discharge mechanism has been described by Meredith

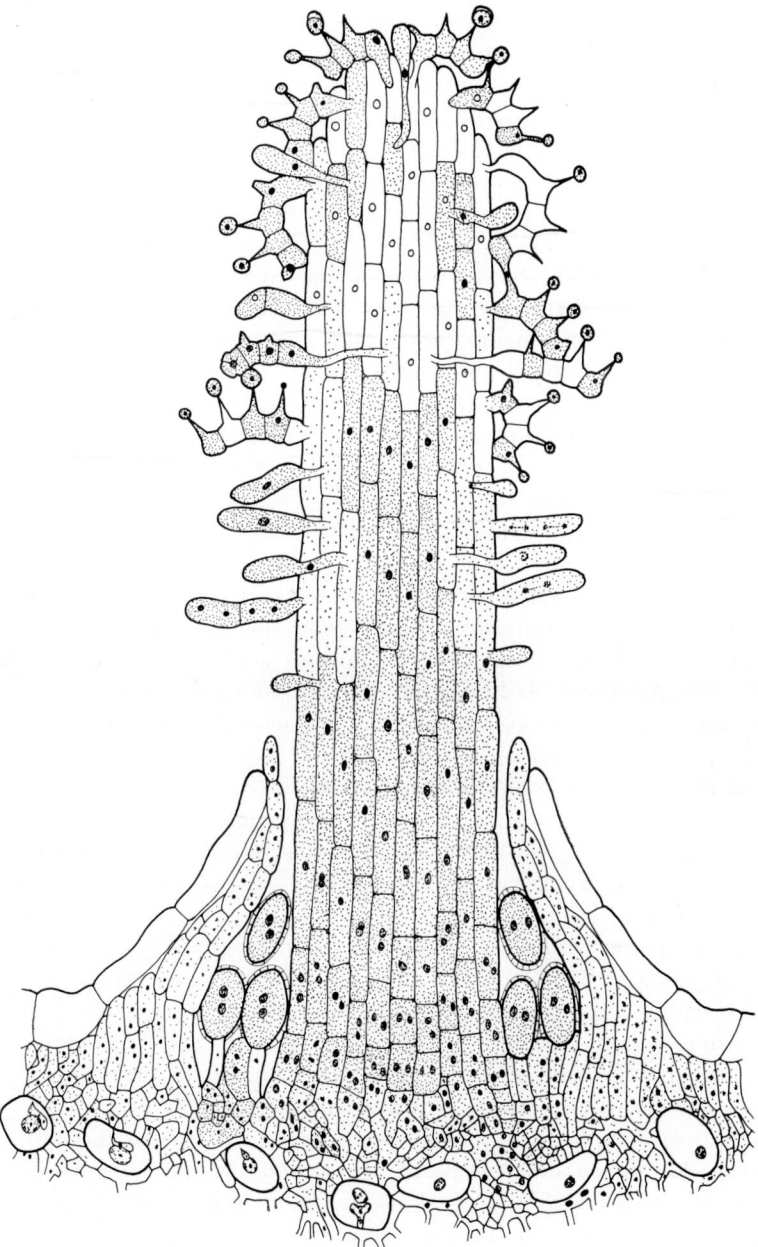

Figure 18.1 Teliospore column of *Cronartium flaccidum* growing up through a uredium. The teliospores are germinating *in situ* to produce basidiospores which are forcibly discharged × *c* 40.

(1961) for *Deightoniella torulosa* (black tip of banana) in which drying results in retraction of the conidiophore apex and eventual discharge of the conidium. This is associated with the appearance of a gas phase (presumably water vapour) in the conidiophore as it resumes its normal shape. This is reported to occur in other Fungi Imperfecti, and other mechanisms involved in the detachment of conidia from conidiophores will no doubt be found. Not all these methods project the propagule to any great distance but they detach it and so facilitate its further dispersal by other means.

Many fungi appear to have no particular mechanism for spore release, the spores falling off the sporophores when mature or being dislodged by external agents. Spores formed within the tissues of the infected plant may be liberated only on dissolution of the tissues (especially resting spores) or may be pushed by underlying growth pressure through the overlying tissues and to the exterior, as in acervuli. Slimy spores (Gloiosporae of Mason, 1937) are often detached by insects or water splash although in some cases they may dry up and be blown off the sporophore. Dry spores (Xerosporae) tend to be liberated by wind or by the mechanisms noted above. The presence of sterile disjunctor cells between spores in a chain probably facilitates their dispersal, as in *Albugo*. Conidia may be extruded to the exterior in a gelatinous thread (spore tendril, cirrhus) through the terminal ostiole of pycnidia, and swelling of gelatinous substances is apparently involved in spore liberation from the sporangia of some Mucorales and in the formation of gelatinous horn-like columns of teliospores in, for example, *Cronartium ribicola*. These columns raise the teliospores above the plant surface and so facilitate dispersal of the basidiospores formed and forcibly discharged on germination of the teliospores while still in the column (figure 18·1) Similar considerations perhaps apply to the raised telia of *Puccinia malvacearum* and some other rusts in which the teliospores germinate *in situ* (figure 18·2).

Splash mechanisms may also liberate spores, including slimy ones, from the plant surface. Raindrops or dripping water falling on spores on the wet leaf splash up numerous spore-containing droplets, of which the larger ones (over 50–100μm in diameter) carry most of the spores (Gregory, 1961) and may be scattered to a distance of 0·3 m or more horizontally. The smaller droplets, perhaps below about 20μ m, may become air borne (Ingold, 1967). Splash dispersal is considered further on p. 366. Large raindrops falling on infected plant organs may liberate dry spores by a shaking effect or possibly by percussion waves resulting from the impact ('rain-tap' and 'puff' of Hirst and Stedman, 1963). It is possible that rust uredospores and smut teliospores, which are not generally raised above the plant surface, are released by vibration of the infected organ in the wind and this may also apply to other spores which are loose and powdery

Figure 18.2 Raised coherent telia of *Puccinia malvacearum* on a hollyhock leaf and petiole The teliospores are thin walled and germinate *in situ* to produce a grey film of basidiospores which are forcibly discharged and spread the fungus. Their dispersal is no doubt facilitated by the elevated telia.

at maturity – indeed Ingold (1960) suggests that long sporophores are of value only to fungi very close to ground level or growing on rigid substances.

Vibration or shock due to wind, falling water, and insects and other animals is probably of importance in liberating propagules which are easily detached from weak points at maturity and which have no special release mechanism. Convection currents and 'blow-off' ('deflation') may also remove spores, particularly those raised above the substrate, and it seems that the stronger the wind the more spores are liberated, as shown by Smith (1966) for uredospores of *Puccinia graminis*. Turbulent rather than constant wind may be more effective in removing spores. According to Stephanov (1935, quoted by Gregory, 1961) the minimum wind speed required to remove spores of some fungi was only a few kilometres per hour, but Gregory and Stedman (1953) found that spores of *Lycopodium clavatum* were rarely removed from clean glass slides by the low wind velocities likely to occur within crops, although wind speeds above about 16 km/hour removed more than half the spores from horizontal surfaces within the first minute. The formation of smut spores on the apical parts of plants, or in spore balls whose sterile enveloping cells increase wind resistance without adding much to weight, possibly increases the efficiency of blow-off (Hirst, 1959). Air currents flowing over cup-shaped structures tend to produce a double eddy system which can effectively remove loose spores therein (Brodie and Gregory, 1953) and this might be significant in cup-shaped rust sori.

Dry wind does not detach the spores of some fungi but it has been shown that air carrying minute water droplets – as in mist – can in some cases do so, presumably due to collisions between droplets and spores (Davies, 1959, in *Verticillium albo-atrum*). In other fungi, including *Phytophthora infestans*, spore release seems to be associated with rapid changes in humidity rather than moving air. Although conidia of *Venturia inaequalis* are thought to be removed from their conidiophores chiefly by water they occur in air during dry as well as wet weather. Much remains to be learned about spore liberation, and new ways in which this occurs no doubt await discovery. Without an efficient means of liberation the disseminating spores of many pathogens which attack the shoots of plants are likely to be wasted. Conversely, artificial methods of preventing spore release could be of value in the control of such pathogens.

Surfaces, including those of plants and the ground, are normally covered by a thin layer of still air of varying thickness. In calm air within the crop, and particularly at night, this boundary layer may be a few millimetres thick whereas in turbulent weather it may be only a fraction of a millimetre. Spores on, and perhaps slightly adhering to, a plant surface may not be able to escape from this layer except in turbulent weather. This probably applies to bacteria which are liberated by rain splash or insects rather than by air currents as such. The significance of the active spore discharge mechanisms briefly discussed above may lie in enabling the propagule to pass through the still boundary layer into the turbulent air outside, thus facilitating its dispersal. Structures such as long projecting sporophores, chains of spores, synnemata, and protruding perithecia probably perform a similar function and it may be significant that spores formed close to plant surfaces (including uredospores, and conidia of *Alternaria*) tend to be present in the air by day when the boundary layer is generally thin. Propagules released at night when the layer is usually thicker are often projected at liberation, as with some ascospores (Hirst, 1953, 1959).

Many fungi show a periodic rhythm (circadian periodicity) in spore liberation. This may be related to a corresponding rhythm in one or more of the factors affecting liberation – chiefly temperature, light and wind, which are generally greatest by day, and humidity which is usually highest at night. It may also be conditioned by periodicity in spore production. Some powdery mildews tend to liberate their conidia during the day, especially around noon, and according to Yarwood (1936*a*) each conidiophore of *Erysiphe polygoni* produces and abstricts a single conidium daily, this depending on the natural alternation of light and darkness. *Taphrina deformans* liberates its spores in the evening, mirror-yeasts (Sporobolomycetaceae) and some downy mildews in the early hours of morning, and *Phytophthora infestans* during the morning. These effects are perhaps associated with humidity and/or temperature changes although light may also be involved (Hirst, 1953).

Spore dispersal

As pointed out by Schrodter (1960) in his review, transportation of air borne spores is governed exclusively by external forces of a physical nature, and the problem thus assumes a physical rather than a biological character; reference should be made to this paper and to Gregory (1961) for theoretical treatment of the principles involved. Fungal spores in air behave as inert particles, perhaps similar to those in smoke, with terminal velocities ranging from about 0·05 to about 2·5 cm per second, larger spores falling more rapidly than small ones. Although atmospheric turbulence blows spores in all directions much more quickly than their gravitational rate of fall, the latter can be important in calm conditions or in sheltered places, as in the crop canopy, and the gravitational pull, albeit comparatively weak, is constantly exerted.

Wind, in the sense of horizontal air movement, is one of the most important factors in spore dissemination, but it does not normally lift spores except when forced upwards by obstacles in its path. Spores do, however, rise high in the air. This promotes more extensive dissemination and is due chiefly to atmospheric turbulence, including the development of rising eddies. In considering the effects of winds localized variations as well as general wind directions and speeds have to be taken into account. Turbulence can arise from shearing between moving air layers of different horizontal velocity (dynamic turbulence), from the upward movement of warm air and its replacement by colder air (thermic turbulence), and by winds flowing over obstacles such as buildings, hills and trees. All these are important in spore dissemination and enable spores to rise above their place of origin.

Turbulence redistributes spores and affects the progressive dilution of spores with increasing distance from their source and it has been calculated that in calm weather only about 0·05% of the spores should travel more than about 100 m from a spore source close to the ground, as compared with about 10% in dull windy weather and many more in warm sunny weather with active convection occurring (Gregory, 1958). Nevertheless, there is ample evidence that with normal wind and turbulence conditions spores, especially small ones, can travel considerable distances. Those of *Phytophthora infestans* have been reported by various observers (cited by Schrodter, 1960) to travel distances of 200 m to more than 60 km depending on wind strength and degree of turbulence. Very small spores may travel such large distances than they can almost be regarded as suspended in the air. In moist air it is possible that spores become heavier due to absorption of water, and so fall more rapidly. This could be of importance in that such spores are likely to fall on the crop during wet weather, which is also conducive to infection, development and spread of the pathogen. Some idea as to the distances to which spores could theoretically be carried is provided by the estimate given by Stakman and Harrar (1957) that uredospores of *Puccinia graminis* falling from a height of 1·6 km at 12 mm per second could be carried over 1120 km by a wind of 32 km per hour; the viability of spores after such long journeys is discussed below.

The effects of air currents on spore dispersal are complex and varied. A steady wind blowing fairly strongly tends to carry spores along horizontally without allowing them to rise to any extent, except on encountering obstacles in its path. Slight breezes and irregular gusts blowing in different directions can cause confused and random air movements, especially if convection currents are rising, and this turbulence may carry spores to considerable heights, thus facilitating their dispersal. These irregular air movements are often more effective in bringing about multidirectional spread of pathogens than are stronger steady winds.

Spores have frequently been found at high altitudes, and spore-bearing air may reach the 'equilibrium level' at which it becomes insufficiently buoyant and convection ceases. Up-draughts in thunderstorms are said to rise as high as 10,640 m and living spores have been caught in the stratosphere above this height.

Balloon borne direct flow samplers have shown the presence of fungi and bacteria at heights of up to 27,360 m, the numbers in the highest sampling altitudes (18,240 m–27,360 m) being about 1 microbe per 56·6 m³, as compared with 1 per 9·3–14·1 at 9,000–18,240 m and 1 per 1·4–2·8 at 3,000–9,000 m. *Alternaria*, *Cladosporium* and micrococci predominated at very high altitudes but *Aspergillus*, yeasts and other bacteria also occurred (Bruch, 1967).

Uredospores of *Puccinia graminis* commonly occur several thousand metres above infected wheat growing areas, and convection currents are regarded as one of the main agents responsible for the lifting of spores. Various ways in which spores return to earth from high altitudes have been suggested. Sedimentation is a slow process, especially for small spores, and is unlikely to be of much significance except in calm or moist air from which the spores may take up water and so become heavier. Falling raindrops catch spores and carry them down to earth or partly so ('rain-scrubbing'). Possibly, spores can act as condensation centres for raindrops or electrostatic attraction might be involved. Raindrops may be up to about 0·5 cm in diameter and those of diameter about 2 mm are most effective in collecting spherical particles in their path, being about 25% effective with small spores (4 μm in diameter) and 80–90% effective with larger ones of 20–34 μm (Gregory, 1952). Since raindrops may fall quite rapidly (up to about 32 km per hour) they are likely to remove spores from the air fairly quickly, especially if they fall vertically through still air. Rain is probably the most important method of bringing spores down from high altitudes but other methods have been suggested, including down-draughts of convectional origin, although these probably redistribute rather than deposit spores. Once in the lower, more turbulent layers of air deposition may be by eddy diffusion.

Spore deposition

Deposition of spores on plant surfaces is not well understood. Spores suspended in raindrops may be deposited on plants but run the risk of run-off into the soil unless they can in some way attach themselves to the plant surface. Air borne spores have to penetrate the boundary layer before reaching the surface. Agents which disperse spores are also likely to deposit them and eddies of air may deposit spores on the lower as well as the upper sides of leaves and on vertical, sloping or horizontal surfaces. The orientation of the spore at landing may be of importance. In still air spores may fall by gravity on to the plant surface, and impaction plays an important role in deposition of some, particularly the larger ones. Impaction is relatively slight with small spores approaching large obstructions at low speed, but much greater with large spores especially when moving quickly towards small obstructions. It may be significant that many foliage pathogens whose propagules are dispersed by air often produce quite large spores, that is efficient impactors (*Helminthosporium, Alternaria,* downy mildews, powdery mildews, rusts) whereas many air borne soil fungi have small spores (*Penicillium, Aspergillus*). The former tend to be deposited on plants, the latter to miss them. The suspension of spores in splash droplets probably improves their impacting ability and may be important for small spores (Hirst, 1959). High impacting ability would thus seem to reduce the chances of spores being dispersed within a dense crop whereas low ability might render deposition difficult. The requirements for deposition and for dispersal within the crop are at variance and a compromise spore size of about 10 μm may have evolved, since many air disseminated spores are of about this size (Gregory, 1952).

The nature of the surface also affects impaction. Wet, sticky, rough or hairy vegetative surfaces are more efficient than dry, smooth ones in catching small spores, and fine hairs projecting through the boundary layer trap spores which could otherwise flow past. In a recent review Chamberlain (1967) considers deposition of particles in some detail and concludes that impaction is an important mechanism provided that the particles measure more than about 10 μm, that the obstacle is small (centimetres or less), that the approach velocity exceeds a metre per second, and that the surface is wet, sticky or otherwise retentive. The possible significance of the weak electrostatic charges carried by spores and plant surfaces in relation to deposition merits study.

Long distance dissemination of spores in air

Uredospores of *Puccinia graminis* have been caught at high altitudes and in air far distant from the nearest vegetation, suggesting dispersal over hundreds and possibly thousands of kilometres. On theoretical grounds it is estimated that flights of 10,000 km are quite conceivable (Schrodter, 1960) and there is considerable circumstantial evidence attributing outbreaks of disease to spores blown in from inoculum sources hundreds of kilometres away. One of the best examples of this is the northwards movement of *P. graminis* uredospores from the southern U.S.A. to the wheat belt as described by Stakman and Harrar (1957). Rust can spread northward from northern Mexico through the U.S.A. and into Canada – at least 3,200 km – in as little as 2 months. This may occur in relatively short successive jumps with intervening local multiplication of the fungus, or as

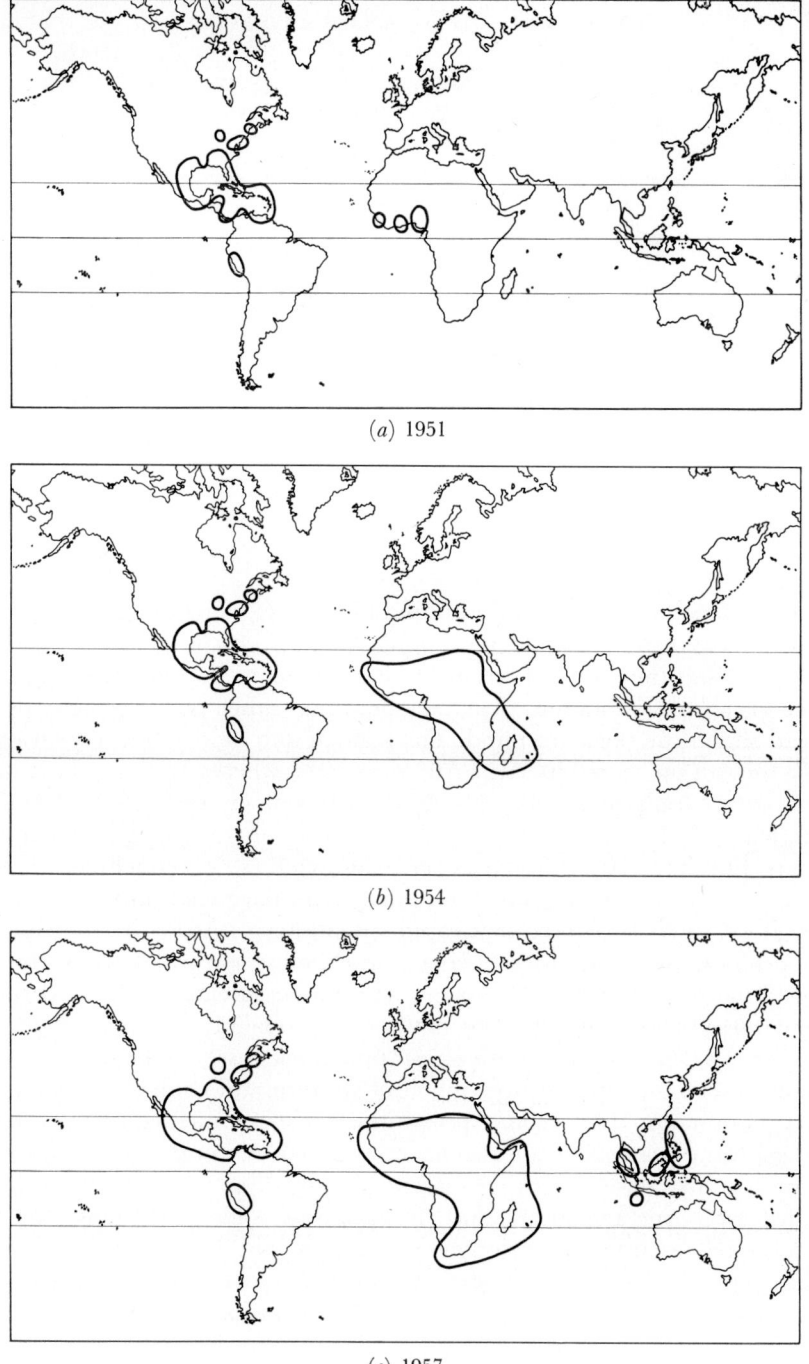

(a) 1951

(b) 1954

(c) 1957

Figure 18.3 (a–d)   The spread of *Puccinia polysora* (maize rust) across Africa to the Far East
and Australasia between 1951 and 1962.

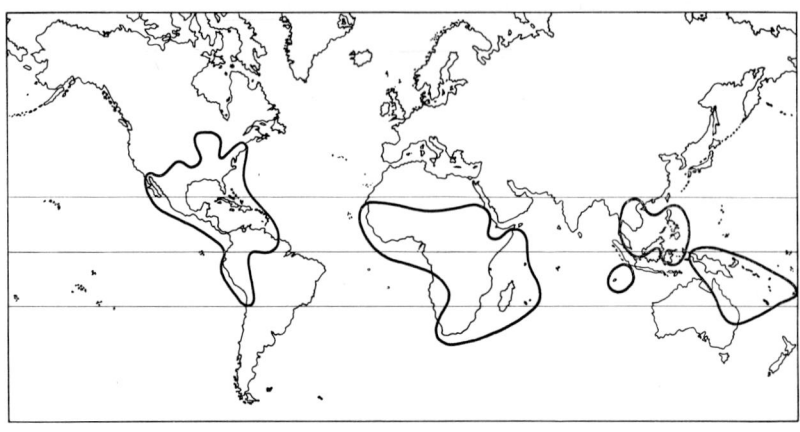

(d) 1962

waves of infection over several hundred kilometres, depending on weather conditions and the abundance of spores.*

In assessing the value of circumstantial evidence on effective long distance aerial dissemination of pathogenic fungi other possible methods of spread should be borne in mind. The sudden and destructive appearance of *P. polysora* on maize in West Africa in 1949 whereas previously it had been known only as a relatively mild pathogen in the U.S.A., Central America and the Caribbean Islands (also Peru in 1940) suggested aerial dispersal over the Atlantic. However, Cammack (1959) concluded that it was probably introduced into West Africa on maize seed imported by air from the U.S.A. Its subsequent rapid spread across Africa in a few years was perhaps by wind, there being few effective natural barriers to its spread (figure 18.3). Other pathogens which have spread rapidly after their initial introduction, possibly by air borne propagules, include *Phytophthora infestans* and *Puccinia malvacearum* (hollyhock rust), which appeared in Spain in 1869 and spread over much of western and central Europe in 5 years (Gaumann, 1950); some spread in the form of infected or contaminated planting material may also have occurred. Natural barriers such as mountains and deserts lacking susceptible plants may effectively protect against air borne inoculum, and the spores of some pathogens may be inadequately adapted to prolonged journeys by air. Thus air borne spores from external sources do not seem to play any part in rust outbreaks in the wheat growing areas of Australia and Argentina (Chester, 1946).

* The recent appearance of coffee rust in Brazil (Wellman, 1970) is attributed by Bowden *et al.* (1971) to uredospores of *Hemileia vastatrix* transported by wind from Angola (Africa) to Bahia (Brazil) where it had probably been present for 4–5 years.

Although there is a great deal of evidence that spores can be transported long distances they may not arrive in sufficient numbers to cause
outbreaks of disease, particularly if the inoculum source is weak or if
considerable dilution and/or deposition occurs *en route*. The viability of
air borne spores is of major importance in this respect, and it should be
remembered that in long distance dissemination the spores may be present
in the air for days or months, depending on the atmospheric conditions
and the size of the spores. Very small spores may remain air borne almost
indefinitely under certain conditions. Larger spores may also be transported quite rapidly – under certain conditions of turbulence and wind
speed the sporangia of *Phytophthora infestans* may travel about 72 km in
ony 2·5 hours and so are likely to arrive in good condition, particularly
if humidity is high (Schrodter, 1960).

Spores differ in their longevity and susceptibility to the hazards likely
to be encountered during a long flight. Uredospores of *Puccinia graminis*
seem to survive very well whereas aeciospores are less robust and the basidiospores of *Cronartium ribicola* (pine blister-rust) may have a viable range
of only a few hundred metres (Gregory, 1961). The latter have a half-life
(that is the time in which half the population dies) of only 5 hours as
compared with 70 hours for the uredospores of *Puccinia coronata* at 10°C,
15 hours for dried deposit of tobacco mosaic virus on leaves, and more
than a year for sclerotia of *Corticium rolfsii* in soil (Yarwood and Sylvester,
1959).

Longevity depends greatly on conditions of storage. The main factors
influencing survival of air borne spores are humidity, temperature, and
radiation. Desiccation is greatest during the day and near the ground but
at higher altitudes spores may lose water less rapidly and have even been
found germinating in clouds (premature germination in the absence of
the host would, of course, be disadvantageous to plant pathogens). The
combined effects of such meteorological factors as temperature and humidity on viability of spores are not well understood, but freeze-drying
indicates that damage is related to temperature and speed of drying. It
is a matter for speculation whether some sort of freeze-drying of spores
might occur in the upper atmosphere. Many of the spores found as regular
components of the air spora are able to withstand desiccation, and the lower
temperatures prevailing in the upper atmosphere may favour survival.

Radiation is perhaps a more serious hazard, particularly the increased
ultraviolet radiation at high altitudes on spores unsheltered by clouds.
Pigmented spores, such as those of *Alternaria* and *Cladosporium*, are probably protected to some extent and it is possible, although it has not
been demonstrated, that low temperature and desiccation are also protective. Photo-reactivation – the reversal with near-ultraviolet or visible
light of ultraviolet radiation damage to a biological structure (Jaggar,

1958) – occurs in many microorganisms and might minimize such damage to spores returning to earth from high altitudes. As Gregory (1961) points out, however, they might be expected to show an increased mutation rate (conceivably a source of new parasitic races). On present evidence it seems that the greatest hazard to air borne spores is the harmful radiation to which they are exposed at higher altitudes. This is not likely to be serious in lower layers, especially if cloudy, and those below about 3000–4000 m are perhaps a suitable medium for the transport of microorganisms (Gislen, 1948).

It is possible that spores of pathogens are transported on seeds disseminated by air or birds but there is little information on this.

Most aspects of aerobiology are covered by Gregory (1960, 1961), Stakman and Christensen (1946), Schrodter (1960) and Hirst (1959). Spore liberation is discussed by Ingold (1960, 1965, 1967), long distance transport by Hirst, Stedman and Hogg (1967), Hirst, Stedman and Hurst (1967) and by Hirst and Hurst (1967), and microbes at high altitudes by Bruch (1967). The recent symposium on air borne microbes (Gregory and Monteith, 1967) is an invaluable source of information. An excellent account of the liberation and dispersal of fungal spores has recently been written by Ingold (1971).

Dispersal by water

Water splash as a method of liberating and dispersing fungal spores has been studied by Gregory *et al.* (1959) who allowed drops of water to fall from known heights on to films of conidial suspension (macroconidia) of *Fusarium solani* on horizontal glass slides. The resulting droplets which were splashed up were caught, counted and their spore content recorded. It was found that the total number of droplets and the number of droplets carrying spores both increased as the thickness of the film decreased and as the size and velocity of the falling drop increased. Considerable numbers of droplets were splashed up; for example, a drop of 5 mm diameter falling 7·4 m on to a horizontal film 0·1 mm thick produced over 5200 droplets of which over 2000 carried one or more spores. The droplets consisted of water from both the incident drop and the film, and droplets containing spores were also splashed up when drops of spore suspension were allowed to fall on to a film of water on a horizontal slide. The diameter of splash droplets ranged from about 5 μm to some 2400 μm with a median diameter of about 70 μm (140 μm for droplets containing spores), and droplets of 164–655 μm tended to travel further than smaller or larger droplets. In still air droplets travelled a horizontal distance of about 10 cm (70 μm diameter) and 20 cm (droplets 140 μm in diameter) and small spores were more readily picked up from suspension than large ones.

Large drops of water (in the form of rain or overhead irrigation) falling at their terminal velocity are probably most active in splash dispersal, much more so than small drops. Large droplets containing spores are not likely to travel far but smaller droplets (perhaps below about 20 μm in diameter) may become air borne and dispersed by wind, probably behaving like dry spores after take-off. Indeed, in very small droplets the water no doubt evaporates, especially in dry air, leaving the spores it carried to be disseminated by air currents. Although large droplets are not likely to travel far, splash-dispersed spores deposited on a wet surface are presumably liable to be resplashed by subsequent raindrops falling on them, so that prolonged rain or overhead irrigation is likely to extend their spread.

In splash dispersal the spores are carried and often deposited on the plant surface in a droplet of water which could provide the moisture required for their germination, especially in humid weather. Apart from bringing about a variable amount of horizontal spread (depending on the size of the droplets) splash mechanisms enable spores to progress up a plant or group of plants from infected lower leaves bearing spores. Drops of water or of spore suspension dripping from upper leaves on to lower ones can be effective in this respect since a great deal of splash dispersal can result from large drops falling at only half their terminal velocity.

Splash dispersal, although usually thought of as a mechanism for liberating and dispersing slimy spores, may also play a part in the dispersal of roughened spores which adhere strongly to each other or to plant surfaces. An example of this is provided by *Hemileia vastatrix* (coffee rust) in which, according to Nutman *et al.* (1960), the roughened uredospores cling together and are broken up by water. They then float singly to the surface of the water drop from which they are splash dispersed by further raindrops. It would be interesting to find out whether the roughened spores of other fungi are dispersed in this way.

The cells of many plant pathogenic bacteria and the slimy spores of such important genera of fungal plant pathogens as *Septoria*, *Fusarium* and *Colletotrichum* are splash-dispersed, and it is a little surprising that relatively little information on splash dispersal is available. Many of the experiments on this method of dispersal have been carried out in the laboratory and less is known about splash dispersal under field conditions. However, Gregory *et al.* (1959) studied the dispersal of the conidia of *Nectria cinnabarina* by allowing five successive drops of water (5 mm in diameter) to fall from a height of 7·4 m on to wet sporodochia of the fungus on sycamore (*Acer*) twigs inclined at an angle of 45°. Fewer and smaller droplets were produced as compared with those splashed from horizontal glass slides, but all the droplets (estimated at about 2600 per drop) from the inclined twig contained conidia, mostly ten or more per droplet. Lateral spread was limited, most of the droplets falling within about 10 cm of the sporodochia from which they were liberated – possibly water splash effectively spreads pathogens over a limited area, such as a single leaf or several adjacent leaves.

Leaves are not rigid structures, neither are they usually horizontal. Hence information on the pattern of splash dispersal of spores from non-rigid inclined surfaces of plants is needed for a proper understanding of splash mechanisms as a method of liberating and dispersing fungal spores and bacteria.

Splash dispersal is dispersal by a combination of water and air, but water itself may be an agent of dispersal. Thus, the propagules of aquatic fungi are often disseminated by water, such spores sometimes showing adaptations which are thought to facilitate this, for example tetraradiate conidia and those with slimy appendages, as described by Ingold (1953). True water dispersal no doubt occurs with soil-inhabiting fungi in wet or irrigated areas, and it is said that ergots of *Claviceps* on aquatic grasses can float and so may be dispersed by water. Irrigation water and rain run-off may carry away propagules when flowing over diseased plants but dispersal in this way is probably of limited scope and many spores are likely to germinate with prolonged immersion. Some spores, especially slimy ones, are readily removed by water but some dry spores adhere rather firmly to the sporophore when submerged. Fragments of diseased plant tissue may also be carried along by flowing water. Examples of pathogens which can be water dispersed include *Xanthomonas malvacearum* (bacterial blight of cotton) and *Plasmodiophora brassicae* (clubroot of brassicas).

Water is much less important than air in dispersal of plant pathogens as most plants are terrestrial and pathogens would be handicapped were their propagules entirely dependent on water for dissemination. Water probably plays some part in the spread of pathogens which attack aquatic higher plants but many of these have leaves which are exposed to the air and so able to utilize air currents for spore dispersal. There is also the possibility of propagules germinating prematurely in the water which is transporting them, and dispersal by moving water is likely to be slow. Hence water dispersal of plant pathogens is of little significance in long distance dissemination although it can be important in localized spread of some pathogens.

Dispersal by insects, mites, nematodes and other animals

Insects

The diverse and interesting relationships between microorganisms, including plant pathogens, and insects are discussed in detail by Leach (1940) and Carter (1962). Shorter accounts are given by Broadbent (1960), Gaumann (1950), Austwick (1957: fungi), Bawden (1957: viruses), Madelin (1966, 1968a: entomogenous fungi) and others. This is a very large subject and only a brief outline can be given here.

In some associations the insect is partly or almost completely dependent on the fungus for its food or on the ability of the latter to soften or predigest the substrate while the insect may disseminate the spores of the fungus, leading to a kind of mutualism. In others the fungus is semiparasitic on the insect or may rely on it for entry into the host plant. In termite gardens the termites cultivate fungi for food and conversely there are fungi which are entomophagous. Although many small and large animals are occasional disseminators of plant pathogens it seems that only in insects has such transmission become specialized and of importance. This is particularly true of viruses spread by insects but the situation here is complicated by the fact that some of the leafhopper-transmitted agents multiply in their insect vectors and may have slight adverse effects on them – the insect is an alternate host of the pathogen as well as a disseminating and inoculating agent (Chapter 4). It is possible that some fungi also multiply within their vectors. Many insects colonize specific plants and in so doing spread pathogens so that insect dispersal is not a random process and is likely to be less wasteful of spores than is random wind dispersal. It has the serious disadvantage that spread will be curtailed if the appropriate insects are absent or in short supply, and many of the insects which spread plant pathogens have a rather limited flight range although this may be increased if they are blown along by wind.

Several systems of classifying the various types of insect transmission of pathogens have been proposed. Dissemination may be purely mechanical without damage to the plant, the pathogen being carried from plant to plant by the insect, as in spread of *Claviceps* by insects which feed on the honeydew in which the conidia are produced. In a few cases there may perhaps be biological transmission as in *Erwinia amylovora* (fireblight of apple and pear) in which the bacteria survive in the intestinal tract and possibly contaminate the eggs of the fly vectors. Dissemination may be accompanied by plant injury as in *Ceratostomella ulmi* (Dutch elm disease) spread by bark beetles, apparently a purely mechanical process. In others there seems to be some sort of relationship between vector and pathogen which may be obligatory (cucumber beetles and *Erwinia tracheiphila*, cucumber wilt) or otherwise.

Many insects (pests) cause injury to plants without direct involvement of pathogens, some injecting phytotoxic substances into the plant tissue thereby causing characteristic symptoms which may resemble those caused by pathogens, as with hopperburn of potato leaves caused by jassids. The affected tissue may subsequently be colonized by fungi and bacteria which tend to aggravate the damage. As well as transporting the pathogen the insect may also enable it to enter the plant tissues either by direct injection during feeding (stigmatomycosis), or by causing galls which the fungus invades (as in perennial canker of apple caused by *Neofabraea perennans*). Some insects have specialized structures such as pouches or bristles in or on which the pathogen is borne. Dissemination is occasionally accompanied by overwintering in the insects. Insect transmission reaches its zenith in viruses (Chapter 4) but insects are also important as a means of disseminating some bacterial and fungal plant pathogens. The two groups are briefly considered below.

Bacteria

Although some bacterial plant pathogens are disseminated by insects most of them also spread by other means, and there seems to be little biological relationship between bacterium and insect, the latter acting as a mechanical carrier and often as an inoculating agent as well. The bacteria may be carried externally or internally, and in a few cases the insect may be appropriately modified. *Erwinia amylovora* (fire blight of apple and pear) can be spread by flies, aphids, ants, beetles, wasps and bees as well as by rain splash and pruning. The bacteria are reported to occur in the intestines of flies and to contaminate the eggs. *E. carotovora* is spread by larvae of the cabbage root fly and also by seed corn maggots which thus spread black leg of potato. Bacterial wilt of maize, caused by *Xanthomonas stewarti*, is seed borne but is spread chiefly by flea beetles which feed on leaves, the bacteria then colonizing the xylem vessels and causing wilt. The bacteria also overwinter in the beetles which are thus in part responsible for seasonal persistence, dissemination and inoculation. *Erwinia tracheiphila* (cucumber wilt) appears to be completely dependent on cucumber beetles for these three operations and the relationship is thus obligatory for the bacterium. *Pseudomonas savastanoi* (olive knot) is spread by the olive fly, the females of which have special anal sacs containing the bacteria. The eggs become contaminated during laying and bacteria also enter the developing embryo. Infection of the twigs results from such eggs deposited in oviposition wounds, and when they emerge the adult flies carry the bacteria within them. There seems to be a close symbiotic relationship between bacterium and insect in this case but infection also occurs through fresh leaf scars.

Several other bacterial plant pathogens are reported to be insect spread although most of them are also disseminated in other ways. Indeed it is probable that many bacteria utilize insects which feed on plants for both dissemination and entry into the plant. Little is known about the survival of bacteria on or in insects which are wind disseminated over long distances and there seems to be no reason why some at least should not survive such journeys. Bacteria have been found at high altitudes but there is little information on their viability at such heights.

Fungi

Spread of fungal plant pathogens by insects is fairly widespread and is obligatory for a few. Some insects show modifications which apparently facilitate dissemination or, more rarely, overwintering of fungi and the insect may function as an inoculating agent as well as a disseminator.

Insects which feed on plants and move through the crop would seem to be favourably situated for picking up, transporting, and inoculating fungi. Large numbers of fungal spores are frequently to be found on insects, adhering to their bodies and harboured by the numerous bristles often present, and insect dispersed spores are generally slimy and sticky. Less often, fungal spores are present within the insect and it is suspected that some multiplication of the fungus may occur although this in no way approaches that of some viruses within their insect vectors. According to Austwick (1957) about sixty-six species of fungi causing plant diseases are transmitted by more than a hundred species of insects belonging to at least six orders. Transmission occurs in various ways, with or without wounding of the plant.

In transportation without wounding the insect acts simply as a carrier, transporting spores from infected to healthy plants. Spores of *Ustilago violacea* (anther smut of Caryophyllaceae) are thus carried from the infected anthers to uninfected flowers by pollinating insects, and similarly for *Botrytis anthophila* (anther mould of clover). The conidia of *Claviceps* are spread from infected ovaries to healthy ones by insects which feed on the sugary honeydew in which the conidia are produced. Other fungi infecting the shoots and roots of plants are likely to be fortuitously disseminated by insects which move or are carried from plant to plant. Richardson and Saunders (1968), for example, attribute the partial control of potato blight by aphicide sprays to the destruction of aphids which carry mycelial fragments and sporangia of *Phytophthora infestans* on their bodies and leg bristles, and so spread the pathogen over short distances.

More frequently, however, transportation is accompanied by wounding – the insect carries the fungus and also places it in wounds, thus facilitating infection. The wounds may be caused by mechanical breaking, other animals or by the insect itself. The spores of *Ceratocystis fagacearum* (oak wilt) are carried by various insects, chiefly nitidulid and scolytid beetles, to existing wounds caused by breaking, woodpeckers, squirrels and other causes. Mycelial mats of the fungus develop beneath the bark, crack it open and give off a characteristic odour which apparently attracts insects. These feed on the fungus and also carry small spores which fertilize the receptive hyphae and so lead to development of perithecia – the fungus is heterothallic. In some cases the insect or the fungus is adapted to insect transmission. Female siricid (*Sirex*) woodwasps carry hyphae and conidia of *Stereum sanguinolentum* (heart rot of conifers) within the inter-segmental sacs at the anterior end of the long ovipositor. The eggs are contaminated with the fungus during laying and are deposited well within the wood of the tree, and the fungus is reported to precede the larva as the latter bores through the wood. The fungus is contained in 'hypopleural organs', modifications of the larval integument. *Ceratostomella ulmi* (Dutch elm disease) grows within the egg galleries of bark beetles (*Scolytus*) and contaminates emerging adults which also ingest the slimy spores and so spread the fungus to adjacent healthy trees.

More specialized are the diseases (stigmatomycoses) in which the fungus is injected into plant tissue by the insect vector. Several parasitic yeasts, notably *Nematospora*, are transmitted in this way, the acicular ascospores being sucked up the feeding stylet of stainer-bugs (*Dysdercus*, *Nezara*) whence they lodge in the stylet pouches and are injected into young cotton bolls (*Nematospora gossypii*, internal boll disease: Frazer, 1944), bean pods (*N. phaseoli*, 'yeast spot') or coffee berries (*N. coryli*, *N. gossypii*). It is thought that *Nematospora* is almost entirely dependent on plant-bugs for dissemination and entry into the plant. Many other interesting associations between pathogens and insects could be mentioned, some of them of economic importance, for example *Endothia parasitica* (chestnut blight) in which the sticky pycnospores are disseminated by insects, birds and in other ways.

Many insects attack the fruits of plants, and fruit-rotting fungi often enter through wounds including those caused by insects. The spores of *Aspergillus niger*, which causes 'smut' of fig fruits, are reported to be introduced by certain beetles and fruit flies, and *Sclerotinia* spp. (brown rot of various fruits) can enter through feeding and oviposition wounds made by insects. Some fungi causing stem rot (for example *Physalospora tucumanensis*, red rot of sugarcane) also invade through insect wounds and it is suspected that some leaf-attacking fungi behave similarly. *Pycnostysanus azaleae* (bud blast of rhododendrons) is associated with the leaf hopper *Graphocephala coccinea* and the disease is very slight in the absence of the insect (Howell and Wood, 1962) (figure 18.4).

Less is known about the transmission of root pathogens by insects but it seems likely that this occurs in the soil and that insects feeding on roots also introduce fungi into them. The original insect damage may thus be

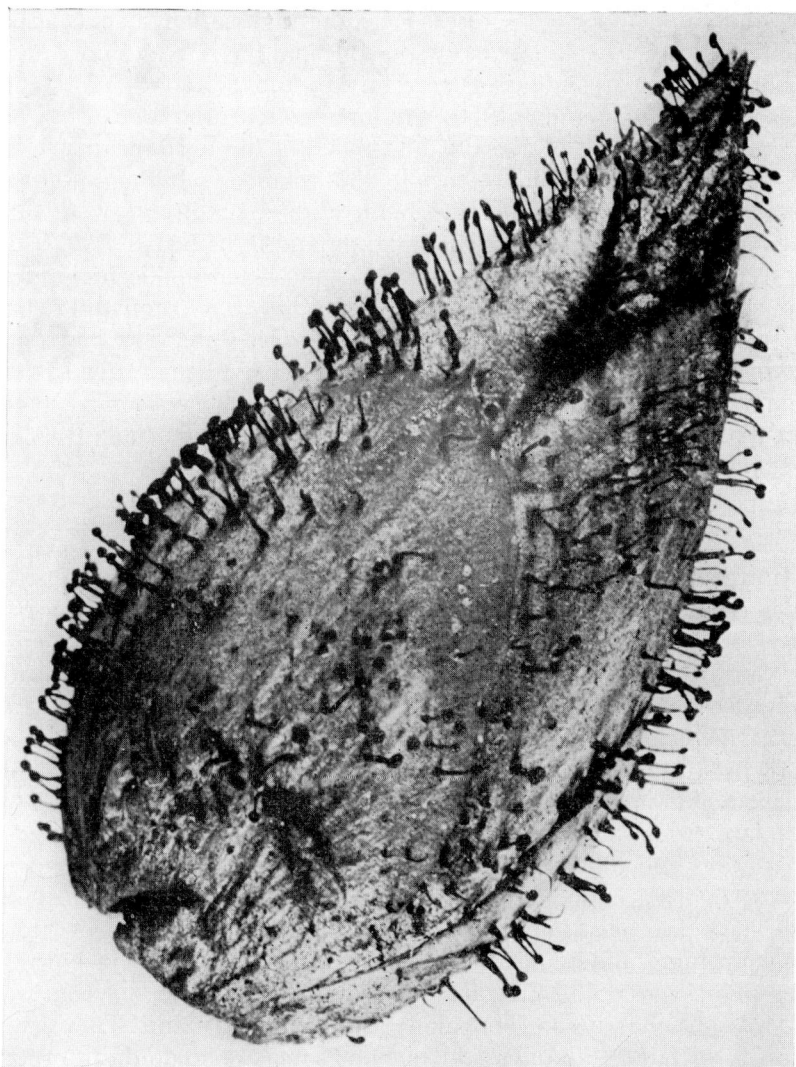

Figure 18.4 Synnemata of *Pycnostysanus azaleae* on a rhododendron bud (bud blast). This fungus is thought to be spread by leaf hoppers and, although the details are obscure, it seems that the fungus infects the developing flower buds in the summer, grows in them during the winter, and prevents the development of flowers in the spring.

greatly aggravated by subsequent fungal invasion. Insects which feed on cotton plants have been found to contain *Fusarium oxysporum f.sp. vasinfectum* (cotton wilt), the fungus being recovered in viable condition from faecal pellets of various grasshoppers. It seems possible that such insects disseminate this normally slowly spreading fungus and might explain the occasional appearance of the disease in hitherto disease-free fields or parts of fields, but other explanations are possible and the relationships between soil borne pathogens and insects need further study. According to Hanson, Milliron and Christensen (1950) the fungi (often fusaria) causing basal stem rot and root rot of cereals and grasses in the north-central U.S.A. enter through insect wounds, especially those caused by billbugs (*Calendra*). The insect may also weaken the plant and so predispose it to fungal attack in addition to carrying the fungi on and in its body.

Insects act as diploidizing agents for some heterothallic fungi, transferring fertilizing spores (spermatia, oidia) between compatible strains and so bring about the formation of the perfect state. The best known example of this is the diploidization of receptive hyphae of rusts by insect borne spermatia, but similar fertilization occurs in some Ascomycetes and other Basidiomycetes. This phenomenon has obvious similarities with insect pollination in higher plants.

Mites

Mites transmit some viruses (for example reversion disease of currant) as described in Chapter 4 and, although wingless, are perhaps transported by winged insects or wind. Transmission of fungal pathogens by mites has been little studied, although *Pediculopsis* mites are thought to be involved in a wheat disease apparently caused by *Nigrospora oryzae* in Spain. Incipient spikelets within the enclosing leaf were killed and overgrown by a mixture of fungus and mites, the latter transporting conidia in their abdominal sacs and apparently feeding on the fungus in the rotting plant tissue. Somewhat similar associations have been observed between mites and other fungi – with *Fusarium* on wheat in Italy and with *Sporotrichum* in carnation bud rot and silver top of *Poa pratensis* in the U.S.A. Mites have also been implicated in Dutch elm disease, and as vectors of blue stain fungi and of microorganisms which cause decay in bulbs and other plant material. Mites are commonly regarded as scavengers but they may disseminate and inoculate pathogens into plants. They are frequently associated with diseased tissue and some are no doubt transported by flies and other winged insects.

Nematodes

Some viruses are transmitted by nematodes (Chapter 4) as are some bacterial and fungal plant pathogens. *Corynebacterium fascians* – leafy gall of various herbaceous plants – is carried by ectoparasitic nematodes (*Aphelenchoides*) and typical 'cauliflower' symptoms developed only when both nematode and bacterium were inoculated into strawberry plants (Cross and Pitcher, 1952). Leaf spotting and 'twist' (deformation of the flowering shoots) of certain grasses and cereals (including wheat) are caused by *Dilophospora alopecuri*, a fungus which is thought to be transmitted by the ectoparasitic nematode *Anguina tritici* (see Leach, 1940). The pycnospores adhere to the nematodes by terminal bristle-like appendages and are thus carried to the young growing point where some germinate and infect the very young leaves which become spotted after unfolding. The nematode itself infects the young ovaries and causes characteristic galls (seed galls) so that in this case a pathogenic fungus is being transmitted by a pathogenic nematode. This does not appear to be an obligate association for either although the fungus is said to be more effective when the nematodes are present. The condition was investigated by Atanasoff (1925).

There is also evidence that some root infecting pathogens, particularly fungi, may enter roots through wounds made by nematodes and this may perhaps be of more frequent occurrence than is at present realized. Cotton wilt caused by *Fusarium oxysporum f.sp. vasinfectum* is an example of this, the pathogen being associated with root knot nematodes and probably others (Smith, 1953). The nematodes may also affect the physiology of the root, making it a more suitable medium for the fungus (Powell and Nusbaum, 1960; Powell, 1963). The reverse has also been reported; the fungus (? *Pyrenochaeta lycopersici*) causing tomato brown root rot reduced the invasion of tomato roots by the potato root eelworm *Heterodera rostochiensis* (James, 1968). Bacterial wilt of carnations, caused by *Pseudomonas caryophylli*, is reported to be more severe in the presence of root knot nematodes which probably facilitate entry of the bacteria (Stewart and Schindler, 1956). Nematodes in relation to plant pathogens are discussed by Leach (1940) and more recently by Pitcher (1965), Fielding (1959), Slack *et al.* (1963), Pitcher (1961: nematodes and root rot diseases), and Christie and Perry (1959).

Other animals

Many animals, small and large, disseminate plant pathogens, such dissemination being carried out by anything which moves through the crop area and touches the plants. With reference to conidia of *Mycosphaerella linorum* (Pasmo disease of flax) it has been stated that 'any creature that walks, runs, jumps, or crawls through infected fields when plants are wet is an agent in the spread of the fungus, because animals such as spiders, mice, frogs, birds, and dogs have been known to disseminate the spores (quoted in Stakman and Harrar, 1957). Fungal spores can become attached to the fur of animals or the feathers of birds, and the latter may feed on, or carry, insects which are in turn carrying pathogens. Woodpeckers are thought to spread the spores of tree pathogens and Heald and Studhalter (1914) estimated that a single downy woodpecker was carrying several hundred thousand spores of *Endothia parasitica* (chestnut blight) when shot. Indeed, it is thought that the rapid spread of this fungus in North America may have been partly by insectivorous birds.

Migrating birds may possibly be involved in relatively long distance and discontinuous spread of pathogens. Broadbent (1965) found that tomato mosaic virus could be spread by house sparrows and this perhaps applies to other easily transmitted viruses, as reported for spread of potato virus X by rabbits and dogs (Todd, 1958, cited by Broadbent, 1960). Some spores, especially resting spores, pass unharmed through the intestines of animals and so may be disseminated in dung, as are the spores of *Plasmodiophora brassicae*. Slugs frequently feed on plants and probably disseminate spores of plant pathogens externally in their slime and internally in faeces. Spores of some fungi are known to pass uninjured through slugs but the significance of this in nature, although not known, is probably not great since slugs are unlikely to travel long distances at any speed. The giant African snail, *Achatina fulica*, transmits *Phytophthora ? palmivora* the cause of foot rot of pepper in Sarawak (Turner, 1967).

Dispersal by man

Man can be responsible for the spread of pathogens within the crop area, within the land mass (intracontinental spread) or between land masses (intercontinental spread), and he has been particularly active in the latter two respects.

Short distance spread may result from transportation of propagules on clothes, implements and farm animals or in soil on boots, tractors or in other ways. Such operations as ploughing inevitably redistribute the soil to varying extents and with it pathogens, and may also provide the initial plant injury necessary for entry by some pathogens. Soil erosion can have similar effects and spread of pathogens from farm to farm may result from loaning of implements or machines. Diseased plant material on the soil may be distributed, and wilt (*Verticillium albo-atrum*) is reported to follow the paths of cultivation in hop gardens as well as being spread by pickers (Keyworth, 1942). Dissemination is likely to occur during transplanting or as a result of soil falling from root crops during removal from the fields after harvesting. Some pathogens can spread from infected to healthy plants during pruning or tying, as with tobacco mosaic virus and bacterial canker (*Corynebacterium michiganense*) in tomatoes. Some potato viruses can be passed from infected to healthy tubers during cutting before planting. Pathogens can be spread in diseased nursery stock and the prevalence of anthracnose (canker) of willow, a destructive disease caused by *Marssonina salicicola*, is probably due to distribution of cuttings taken from diseased trees. Pathogens can be disseminated in many other ways. Thus, the turbulence due to low-flying helicopters engaged in crop-spraying can bring about extensive scattering of plant material, some of which may be infected.

Man is adept at long distance dissemination of pathogens and pests and is undoubtedly the major agent in this, although such dissemination may sometimes be by birds or air borne spores. Long distance dissemination of pathogens by man occurs in various ways, including: (1) On or in planting material and edible parts of plants. Man when moving from one area to another has often taken these along with him and in so doing has un-wittingly introduced new pathogens, pests, and weeds, or new strains of these. Pathogens most likely to be spread in this way are those producing resistant propagules but others no doubt persisted during leisurely migra-tions with stops for cultivation *en route*. In modern times the exchange of infected plant material and cultures of pathogens between research workers and others engaged in agriculture is a dangerous practice unless licenced and carried out with the most rigorous safeguards against escape of the pathogen from the laboratory. Travellers may bring back seeds or other planting material. The remains of fruits purchased in one area may be discarded several thousand kilometres away after a journey of less than a day in an aeroplane with air-conditioning admirably suited to survival of pathogens. The remains of fruit and vegetables taken aboard an air-craft in one continent may be off-loaded in another. In these and other ways plant pathogens may rapidly travel long distances under conditions which favour their survival. (2) As propagules, especially long-lived ones, carried on the clothing of travellers. This has considerable relevance to persons engaged in agriculture or horticulture who may be walking through, for example, bean fields in the U.S.A. one day and through similar fields in the British Isles a day or two later. (3) In international plant trade, as discussed by Moore (1957). Seeds and other planting material, grain, fruits, vegetables, plant fibres and flowers are now being distributed around the world on an unprecedented scale and more rapidly than ever before. This creates a dangerous situation and complex systems of legislation, inspection and certification may be necessary to minimize the risk of importing new pathogens and pests – particularly so in pre-dominantly agricultural countries or in those whose economy may be based on a single 'cash' crop. The import of some plant material may have to be completely banned and a rigorous restriction placed on others.

It is fortunate that not every new pathogen or pest which is introduced manages to establish itself. The climatic conditions of its new home may be unsuitable, the native varieties of plants may be resistant, the inoculum may be insufficient and may never reach a susceptible plant and, if it

N

does, it may be possible to arrest its further spread and eventually to eradicate it. As Moore (1957) points out the real risk arises when the same pathogen is repeatedly imported in large enough quantities to establish itself.

Many plants have been introduced by man from the Eastern to the Western hemisphere and with them a number of pathogens. These include *Endothia parasitica* (chestnut canker) brought in from the Orient, and *Cronartium ribicola* (blister rust of pines) and *Ceratostomella ulmi* (Dutch elm disease) from Europe. More recently *Striga asiatica* (witchweed, a root parasite of maize, sorghum and other cereals) has appeared in North America, possibly imported on seed from Africa or Asia, and the rust *Hemileia vastatrix*, present in Africa and Asia, is now (1970) reported on coffee in Brazil. Such pathogens as *Phytophthora infestans* (potato blight), *Pseudoperonospora humuli* (hop downy mildew), *Uncinula necator* (grape powdery mildew), *Plasmopara viticola* (grape downy mildew), and more recently *Puccinia polysora* (maize rust) have spread from the New World to the Old as described by Stakman and Harrar (1957).

Similar long range dissemination of bacterial pathogens, nematodes, viruses and insects by man has no doubt occurred and will occur again. In some cases the pathogen is of little significance in its country of origin but becomes destructive when introduced to new and often more susceptible varieties of its host plant growing under different climatic conditions. Despite strict inspection and quarantine several destructive plant pathogens have appeared in Great Britain in recent years, for example *Erwinia amylovora* (fireblight of apple and pear), *Puccinia horiana* (chrysanthemum white rust, said to have been imported in stock from Japan in 1963: Baker, 1967) and *P. pelargonii-zonalis* (geranium rust). Older importations include *P. malvacearum* (hollyhock rust, 1873), *P. chrysanthemi* (chrysanthemum rust, 1897), *Sphaerotheca mors-uvae* (American gooseberry mildew, 1906), *Pseudoperonospora humuli* (hop downy mildew, 1922), *Puccinia antirrhini* (antirrhinum rust, 1933) and *Corynebacterium michiganense* (bacterial canker of tomato, during the Second World War: Moore, 1957).

These examples indicate a steady inflow of pathogens accidentally brought about by man. A more sinister possibility is the deliberate introduction of destructive plant pathogens into enemy areas during war, and there is little doubt that this form of biological warfare is being investigated and could, under the right conditions, be a very effective weapon. Pathogens could also be introduced in peacetime, a practice which would be very difficult to detect and prove.

19 The spread of pathogens within crop areas; epiphytotics

In this chapter are considered some of the ways in which pathogens multiply and spread through populations of susceptible plants, sometimes causing extensive outbreaks of disease if conditions for development of the pathogen are favourable. A comprehensive account of these aspects is given by Van der Plank (1963) in a book which, for the first time, puts the epidemiology of plant pathogens on a mathematical basis and '. . . is a landmark in the history of Plant Pathology, giving us for the first time a coherent and developed theory of plant epidemiology, a notable intellectual achievement' (Gregory, 1965). The factors which influence the spread of pathogens through crop areas are considered in the following chapter.

Tracing the course of a plant disease outbreak by ground observations over an extensive crop area is a laborious and expensive procedure involving numerous trained observers, and there would seem to be considerable scope here for the use of aerial photography – particularly so when studying the progress of pathogens which spread rapidly. An extensive area of crop can be photographed from the air in a relatively short period of time so that the development of the disease can be recorded at frequent short intervals, thus giving a far more detailed picture of the overall spread of the pathogen than could be obtained from ground observations. Aerial photographs taken in the early stages of a disease outbreak can also yield valuable indications as to the likely sources of inoculum and the method of spread of the pathogen. In many cases the early spread of pathogens whose spores are splash dispersed tends to be restricted and the areas of diseased plants are fairly well defined. This is in contrast to the more rapid spread of pathogens with air borne spores which results in larger and less well defined areas of diseased plants, often with separate smaller areas of secondary infection. The use of aerial photography in studying the origin and development of plant disease outbreaks is as yet in its early stages but it has given promising results, as described by Brenchley (1965).

There are many pathogens which spread from plant to plant during the growing season and others which do not and these cause what have been termed 'compound interest' and 'simple interest' diseases respectively.

Compound interest disease

This denotes a disease whose increase is mathematically analogous to compound interest in money. The pathogen in the infected plants produces spores or other propagules which are disseminated and infect other plants in which it in turn produces spores which are disseminated and infect further plants, and so on. There are several or many generations of the pathogen in the life of the crop. The amount of uninfected tissue continually decreases as the pathogen spreads, so that the measured rate of spread in terms of newly infected tissue also decreases. In plotting the amount of disease against time the transformation $\log [x/[1 - x)$ is used where x represents the proportion of infected susceptible tissue, or of infected plants if the pathogen is systemic. This transformation allows for the diminishing amount of tissue available for infection as the disease progresses. Pathogens spreading by means of air disseminated propagules show this type of spread which will, however, be continuous only if the environment remains continuously favourable to spread and if the plants remain susceptible. These conditions are not usually fulfilled and the spread is usually discontinuous, accelerating when conditions favour the pathogen and slowing down when conditions become unfavourable. Many destructive plant diseases, including potato blight and black stem rust of wheat, show this compound interest type of spread which can, under conditions which encourage the pathogen, be extremely rapid.

Simple interest disease

Here, the increase of the pathogen is mathematically analogous to simple interest in money. There is only one generation of the pathogen in the life of the crop; the plants become infected from inoculum in the soil or in or on the planting material, and the pathogen does not spread from plant to plant during the growing season. The number of infected plants may increase as the season progresses but these represent new infections from pre-existing inoculum rather than spread from one plant to another. In the increase of simple interest diseases the $\log [1/(1 - x)]$ is plotted against time, thus allowing for the fact that with increasing infection the number of plants remaining available for infection decreases.

Simple interest pathogens include soil borne fungi which attack roots, and seed, or soil borne smuts which infect seedlings and subsequently sporulate in the inflorescences of the mature plants, provided that the pathogen does not spread from the smutted heads. Pathogens of this type do not spread from plant to plant during the crop season and their dispersal occurs in the intercrop period – by air disseminated spores liberated during harvesting, by man distributing contaminated or infected planting material, or by contaminated soil or diseased plant trash which is blown about by the wind or carried by water. Under certain circumstances a simple interest pathogen may spread from plant to plant during the growing season and so behave as a compound interest pathogen. An example of this is a root infecting fungus whose propagules are carried by irrigation water to other plants which then become infected and liberate propagules, and so on.

Since simple interest pathogens do not spread during the season their incidence can be reduced by destroying infected plants, thereby diminishing the amount of inoculum available for infection of the fields of the following season. Sometimes, however, the percentage of diseased plants is so high that their destruction is not feasible, and heavy loss of crop results. This is likely to happen when heavily contaminated or heavily infected seed is sown, or where the soil is severely contaminated with a pathogen, provided that environmental conditions favour development of the disease.

Development of disease outbreaks

Outbreaks of disease in annual crops depend on the presence of susceptible plants, weather suitable for the pathogen, adequate amounts of effective inoculum and, in some cases, the presence of effective vectors. Development of the disease is related to the distribution of infected plants in the very early stages of the outbreak, in turn related to the position of the inoculum source. Seed borne pathogens usually produce a more or less random distribution of diseased seedlings provided the sowing seed is uniformly infected or contaminated and that all parts of the field are equally conducive to infection (which is sometimes not the case). A similar situation holds when the inoculum source is diseased plant material or self-sown seedlings scattered over the fields. It also holds for uniformly contaminated soil, although soil borne pathogens tend to occur in restricted patches in part denoting areas favourable to infection.

Plants infected from inoculum sources outside the field may be irregularly distributed or there may be a directional effect if the sources are concentrated near one particular part of the field, for example, near one corner. This will depend, however, on other factors such as the pattern of of air currents and the distance between source and field. 'Spot' infections – isolated infected plants – tend to result from spores blown in from distant sources. Careful study of the distribution of infected plants in the early stages of disease outbreaks can yield valuable clues as to the whereabouts of the inoculum sources.

These initial or primary foci of infection (that is, local areas of higher than average disease) may fail to develop further if the weather is unfavourable to the pathogen, or they may develop at different rates and in different ways depending on environmental conditions and on the characteristics of the pathogen and plant. As Van der Plank (1960) points out, there is no such thing as a typical epidemic, the variety of epidemics being infinite. From these primary foci the pathogen spreads to other parts of the field and to other fields, and such spread is generally uneven. Dispersal may be along a steep gradient, that is disease decreases sharply with distance from the focus so that the latter enlarges while remaining fairly sharply defined, or it may be along a shallow gradient in which disease decreases slowly with increasing distance from the focus, so that new 'daughter' or secondary foci develop at some distance from the primary focus of infection (Van der Plank, 1967). Disease-free areas may thus separate primary and secondary foci, particularly with pathogens whose propagules can travel considerable distances and remain viable.

Van der Plank (1967) deduces that establishment of new foci from dispersal along shallow gradients is comparatively rare but is nevertheless important in the spread of plant pathogens. Steep and shallow gradients are two extremes of a range of dispersal gradients, so that patterns of spread and distribution of foci are of an infinite variety. As the pathogen spreads more foci develop, existing ones enlarge and overlap, and the original pattern is lost as more and more of the plants in the crop area become infected. The original pattern of infection may, however, persist to some extent if the pathogen ceases to spread in the older crop. This reduced spread could be due to the development of a dense crop canopy which hinders spore dissemination, to the older plants being more resistant, to the weather becoming less favourable to the pathogen, or to a combination of these factors.

There are many variations on this theme, due sometimes to the pathogen being dispersed in more than one way. Spores dispersed by rain splash may not travel very far but may be carried much further by wind disseminated insects, the latter setting up secondary foci of infection. Localized spread of *Endothia parasitica* (chestnut blight) in the U.S.A. is probably by air borne ascospores whereas new foci far ahead of the infected trees have been attributed to the sticky pycnospores carried on the beaks of migratory birds (Leach, 1940).

As the susceptible tissue of a plant, or the plants in a focus, is increasingly attacked and colonized by a pathogen the latter encounters ever-increasing difficulty in finding uninfected tissue or plants to parasitize. Its future progress then depends on its capacity to travel longer distances and so set up secondary foci of infection in which the process is repeated as long as a favourable environment prevails. Hence dispersal along shallow as well as steep gradients will be advantageous, and both are involved in the overall spread of pathogens in crops.

The speed with which a pathogen spreads through a crop area is of importance in the development of epiphytotics. Spread is by a succession of infection cycles and, other things being equal, the shorter the period between infection and sporulation, the more numerous the infection cycles per season, and the more rapidly is the pathogen likely to spread. Van der Plank (1960) points out that the rate of increase of a pathogen is much greater up to the onset of an epidemic than thereafter, and that the date of onset is of considerable practical importance in, for example, the application of fungicidal sprays. Date of onset is arbitrarily taken as some convenient point before 5% of the susceptible tissue is infected (or 5% of the plants infected in the case of systemic pathogens). The onset point may be selected as the most useful in practice – for example, in assessing potato blight the starting point is 0·1% of the foliage infected (about one lesion per plant). Assuming 3–4 million potato plants and three–four primary blight foci per sq. km the disease will have increased about a millionfold up to the onset as compared with about a thousandfold increase (from 0·1 to 100%) thereafter, most of the plants being slightly infected at the onset (Van der Plank, 1960). In terms of the numbers of infected plants the epiphytotic is thus well advanced by the time that the disease becomes apparent in the field.

The rate of increase per cent per unit of time (r) up to the onset point is considered to be a fundamental concept in epidemiology; the unit of time may be a day or longer, depending on the speed with which the disease develops. The magnitude of r depends on many factors including environmental conditions as they affect the component events of the infection cycle, susceptibility of the plant, aggressiveness of the pathogen and, where appropriate, the number, activity and transmitting efficiency of any vectors involved. The estimation of r is described by Van der Plank (1960) who gives a few representative estimates – for example, 57% per day for spread of *Phytophthora infestans*, 9·2% per day for cauliflower mosaic virus, and 12·5% per day for *Puccinia triticina*. These estimates refer, of course, only to the conditions of the particular experiment whose data are being used.

Other factors which affect the early rate of spread of a pathogen include the amount of inoculum and its distance from the crop. Reduced inoculum delays the onset of disease by amounts related to the percentage reduction and to the rate of spread of the pathogen. Van der Plank (1960) has calculated that when $r = 9.2\%$ the onset of cauliflower mosaic would be delayed $17\frac{1}{2}$ days by reducing the percentage infection in the transplanted seedlings from 3% to 0.6%. With faster spreading pathogens such as *Phytophthora infestans* the delay would, however, be much less than this, and it follows that with such pathogens crop sanitation, to be effective, has to be more thorough than with slowly spreading pathogens. Reduction of inoculum sources by crop sanitation, seed treatment and other methods is thus likely to be most effective with pathogens which spread slowly (including many systemic ones) while other methods of control (chemical, plant breeding) may be more suitable for those which spread rapidly.

Production of inoculum from infected plants in the field declines as the fungus in old lesions, or in the older parts of lesions, loses its capacity to sporulate, so that these lesions cease to play an active part in spread of the fungus. Similarly the first infected plants in a field may, at a certain stage in their development, cease to be infectious because they die or stop liberating spores. If the infected area is large the diseased plants in the centre, although perhaps still liberating spores, may be ineffective as inoculum sources because they are too far away from uninfected plants. The distance between inoculum source and crop is of great importance in that progressive dilution of air borne spores occurs with increasing distance and the number of spores reaching the crop is less with a distant inoculum source than with a near one. The 'safe' distance separating inoculum source and crop depends on the size of the source and the distance to which its propagules can be transported in a viable condition. For disease below the onset point the number of lesions is thought to decrease inversely at least as the fourth power of the distance from the inoculum source.

Development and spread of pathogens in irrigated crops

Irrigated crops are widely grown in the drier parts of the world and irrigation is used to supplement rainfall during prolonged dry weather in areas where crops are normally rain grown. Hence a knowledge of how irrigation affects the development and spread of plant pathogens is desirable. Irrigation affects the plant, the microclimate (p. 409) around the plant, the pathogen and vectors of the pathogen, if any such are involved. Water may be applied to the soil in which the plants are growing (ground or surface irrigation) or to the plants themselves (sprinkler or overhead irrigation).

Ground irrigation

This has a direct effect on the soil and, generally speaking, heavy ground irrigation leading to high soil moisture for long periods of time is likely to favour Phycomycetes whose zoospores are disseminated by water, including *Plasmodiophora brassicae*, *Pythium* spp., *Phytophthora* spp. and *Aphanomyces eutiches* (pea root rot). Heavy irrigation also favours certain other fungi including some species of *Fusarium* and *Armillaria mellea* (Garrett, 1944). Excessive soil moisture, by promoting anaerobic conditions, is likely to damage roots and so render them more liable to attack by soil borne fungi. Other pathogens, including some of the seed – and soil borne smuts, are favoured by dry soil. There may be indirect effects of irrigation on disease incidence. Irrigation can hasten the breakdown of diseased plant material during the rainless months between crops or it may affect the soil microflora in such a way as to discourage pathogens. Thus, the control by irrigation of common scab (*Streptomyces scabies*) of potato has been ascribed by Lewis (1964) to increased development of certain bacteria antagonistic to *Streptomyces*.

Ground irrigation affects the incidence of air borne pathogens in several indirect ways. It may bring about a state of high turgor in the leaves which favours infection by many bacterial and some fungal leaf pathogens but which is said to discourage others (some powdery mildews). Optimum soil moisture, as obtained with careful ground irrigation, is likely to be reflected in vigorous plant growth and a dense crop canopy which is shaded, cool and humid, so that moisture tends to persist on the surface of the plants. Fungi such as *Alternaria dauci* (carrot leaf blight) and *Mycosphaerella berkeleyi* (peanut leaf spot) attack the lower leaves of their host plants and are thus favoured by a dense canopy which results from ground irrigation. Such irrigation of large areas of crop tends to increase the humidity and lower the temperature of the crop area, and these changes favour some pathogens. The effects of ground irrigation on disease incidence are clearly complex and in most cases can only be determined by field experiments.

Sprinkler irrigation

This has a more direct effect than ground irrigation on air borne pathogens. It can bring about quite considerable microclimate effects. In Israel the temperature of wet potato leaves irrigated by sprinkler dropped to 22° C as compared with 30–36° C for leaves of unirrigated plants on a hot summer day when air temperatures were 24–29° C (Rotem and Palti, 1969). Changes of this magnitude could well enable some pathogens to infect irrigated plants although they are unable to infect unirrigated ones.

Prolonged sprinkler irrigation encourages the sporulation of some plant pathogens but its effects in facilitating the dispersal of water splashed propagules are probably of greater importance. Sprinkling also redistributes spores over the infected plants and into the soil, and thus might increase the incidence of tuber infection by *Phytophthora infestans* arising from spores washed into the soil from infected potato plants, and it also washes off and redistributes fungicide from sprayed plants. Most of the bacteria and fungi which attack plants are favoured by sprinkling but powdery mildews are an exception – indeed Yarwood (1959*b*) obtained some control of several powdery mildews (especially *Erysiphe cichoracearum* on cucumber) by water applied with considerable force in such a way as to produce a washing effect. Sprinkler irrigation might have a similar effect and does in fact discourage powdery mildews, as does heavy rain.

Sprinkling can also prolong the viability of dispersed propagules, such as the sporangia of *Phytophthora infestans*, which are sensitive to dry conditions. Rotem and Palti (1969), in their interesting account of irrigation

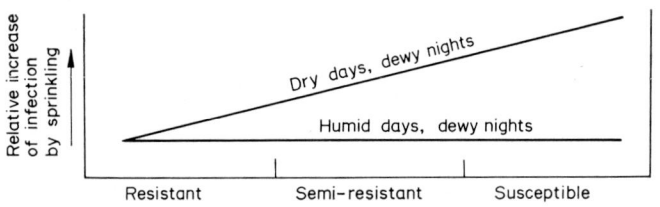

Figure 19.1   Resistance of dispersed spores to drought

and plant diseases, compare *P. infestans* and *Alternaria porri f.sp. solani*, both of which attack potato and tomato in Israel and produce their spores at night. The conidia of *A. porri* are dispersed at noon and are sufficiently drought resistant to survive for several days although they normally germinate when dew falls. Sprinkling has little effect on the incidence of this fungus since its conidia can survive the dryness of the day and dew is sufficient for their germination and infection of the plant. By contrast, the sporangia of *P. infestans* are dispersed earlier in the morning and, being drought susceptible, may not survive if the day is very dry. Sprinkler irrigation, especially if carried out near the time of sporangial dispersal, may provide the moisture needed for germination and infection of the plant, and so enable the fungus to spread. Sprinkling can be expected to have a marked effect on the spread of drought susceptible plant pathogens but less on the spread of drought resistant ones, and these effects will be greatest on dry days and least on humid days, as shown in the accompanying diagram (figure 19.1) taken from Rotem and Palti (1969).

The spread of pathogens by sprinkling can be minimized by sprinkling as infrequently as is possible without harming the plants and by sprinkling at the time of day which is least likely to spread the pathogen; this involves a knowledge of the times at which the spores are liberated and dispersed. Measures which reduce the density of the crop canopy – including wide spacing of the plants and judicious use of fertilizer – will also be helpful in minimizing the spread of plant pathogens by sprinkler irrigation. From the point of view of disease control, ground irrigation is preferable to sprinkling but the latter has many practical advantages and is less demanding of labour. On a garden scale, however, the householder watering his plants with hose or watering can would be well advised to apply the water to the soil rather than to the plants, since the latter practice tends to encourage some of the pathogens which may be present.

Epiphytotics

Epiphytotics are epidemics of plant disease and the term pandemic has been used to describe destructive epiphytotics which develop on a continental scale. 'Epidemic' refers to disease outbreak in man but is commonly applied to plant disease, and epidemiology is used rather than 'epiphytotiology'.

Some epiphytotics are caused by pathogens which are endemic (long established) in an area, their seasonal incidence being determined largely by climatic and agricultural conditions, and in a season which is abnormally conducive to its development, even a normally mild endemic pathogen may become destructive. Pathogens and their host plants tend to attain an equilibrium over long periods of time, especially under natural conditions in which the more susceptible genotypes of the plant, and possibly the more destructive genotypes of the pathogen, are gradually eliminated. This trend is, however, greatly reduced in many agricultural and horticultural plants which man endeavours to keep genetically uniform.

Under conditions conducive to its spread a pathogen could in theory infect all the susceptible plants within the crop area provided it spreads sufficiently rapidly. This can happen in perennial crops and in relatively small areas of annual crops but time may be insufficient for it to spread over very extensive areas of annual crops unless there are multiple initial infections throughout the area. The course of epiphytotics varies a great deal according to the pathogen, crop, and environmental conditions, and as noted above, there is a beginning (onset) and an end but the intervening course of events is very varied. Epiphytotics in annual plants are limited to the growing season whereas those affecting perennial plants may develop over a number of years until all or nearly all the plants are infected.

It is difficult to define the point at which an outbreak of disease becomes an epiphytotic or even to define the latter satisfactorily. Although the most spectacular epiphytotics are those which sweep destructively through large areas of crop in a short time, there are also those which develop relatively slowly and which are not immediately destructive. In other epiphytotics some of the plants are severely, and others only slightly, damaged and the disease may be more destructive in some parts of the crop area than in others due to localized differences in climate, soil, topography and other conditions. Thus severe damage does not necessarily occur in all epiphytotics but is likely to do so if the disease reaches its full potentialities, and weather conditions are of critical importance in this. Neither do all epiphytotics affect large areas of crop – there may be very destructive outbreaks over limited areas. The only factor which seems applicable to all epiphytotics is that a high percentage of the plants become infected although there is no numerical threshold at which an outbreak is deemed to become an epiphytotic.

The form which an epiphytotic takes depends on the characteristics of pathogen and plant and on the weather. At one extreme are those which develop slowly ('tardive': Gaumann, 1950), at the other those which develop rapidly ('explosive'), and there are many intermediate types.

Slow epiphytotics

Slow epiphytotics are often associated with perennial, long lived plants such as trees, and the causal pathogens tend to be systemic to varying extents. They sometimes take several or many years to reach their full potentialities and infected plants may survive for several years before dying, as occurs in Dutch elm disease (*Ceratostomella ulmi*) and chestnut blight (*Endothia parasitica*). Most systemic pathogens spread less rapidly than non-systemic ones although some systemic viruses with efficient insect vectors can spread fairly quickly. Slow development may be due partly to the relatively slow multiplication of some systemic pathogens which may in turn be related to a lengthy sporulation period, or to a lengthy incubation period in some viruses. Another possible reason is that systemic pathogens which infect large perennial plants (trees) have further to move from plant to plant and it is perhaps significant that those which attack small herbaceous plants spread more rapidly than those which attack trees. Systemic fungal pathogens usually produce fewer generations of propagules than non-systemic ones, sporulation being delayed as the fungus grows through the tissues of the plant. In extreme cases only one generation of spores is produced, as in systemic smuts which infect the seedling and sporulate in the flowers of the mature plants.

Systemic pathogens which inhabit perennial plants tend to be quite long lived and have been described as 'low death rate pathogens' as distinct from 'high birth rate pathogens' which produce numerous spores rapidly, although the distinction is not absolute. The latter are often controlled by fungicides or resistant varieties, the former by crop sanitation. The relatively slow spread of systemic pathogens of trees is well illustrated by swollen shoot of cacao, a destructive virus carried by slowly moving, flightless mealy-bugs. Under conditions of unrestricted natural spread the percentage of infected trees on a farm in West Africa rose only from 31 to 75% in 2·5 years, and spread from farm to farm was also slow – in 1947 the largest area of disease had reached a radius of only about 16 km after continuous spread since 1922 (Posnette, 1947). *Ceratocystis fagacearum* (oak wilt) is thought to spread chiefly by root grafting between adjacent trees and may be stopped by roads or other barriers (Riker, 1951), although there is some evidence that insects may also be implicated in its spread. Peach yellows and tristeza disease of citrus are examples of slowly spreading, systemic diseases of trees caused by viruses.

Systemic pathogens of small herbaceous plants spread rather more rapidly and one broccoli plant infected with cauliflower mosaic resulted in 131 infected plants (out of 400) by the end of the season (Jenkinson, 1955). Van der Plank (1959) suggests that maximum rates of multiplication for systemic pathogens of trees are about 10-fold a year as compared with perhaps 10,000-fold for those attacking herbaceous plants and very much higher rates for local lesion pathogens, for example as high as a billion-fold for *Phytophthora infestans*. These rates refer to transformed numbers (the multiple infection transformation of Gregory, 1948) instead of simple increase in percentage disease, which takes into account the fact that as a pathogen spreads progressively fewer uninfected plants – or less uninfected tissue – remain, so that the measured rate of spread inevitably decreases. Viruses which cause local lesion diseases are rarely responsible for epiphytotics but local lesion fungi can be very destructive. This epidemiological difference is perhaps related to the fact that many viruses are spread rather slowly by insects which feed on living systemically infected plant tissue, whereas the (usually) more rapid spread of local lesion fungi is by air borne propagules produced in enormous numbers in a short period of time. The epidemiological characteristics of systemic pathogens are discussed by Van der Plank (1959, 1960).

Rapid epiphytotics

Rapidly developing epiphytotics are chiefly caused by non-systemic pathogens with high rates of multiplication ('high birth rate pathogens') and fairly short generations. Annual crops, or perennial plants grown as annuals, are often attacked. These epiphytotics are characterized by a rapid increase of disease to a usually distinct peak followed by a sharp decline as environmental conditions become less favourable, as the plants perhaps become more resistant with approaching maturity, as the crop canopy develops and restricts spore dispersal, or as the pathogen itself begins to produce overwintering spores instead of disseminatory ones. The form of these epiphytotics is governed largely by environmental factors and they follow a broad seasonal rhythm related to development of the crop and the climatic conditions.

Some pathogens attack several organs of the plant and so develop in several waves. *Venturia inaequalis* attacks apple leaves in spring and under favourable conditions the leaf phase of the disease increases through the summer until nearly all the leaves may be infected in the autumn, with considerable leaf shedding. Conidia from the infected leaves attack the young fruits and fruit scabbing may increase until harvest. A third phase of infection occurs during storage when the pathogen spreads from diseased to healthy fruit. *Xanthomonas malvacearum* can cause cotyledon spotting, leaf necrosis (angular leaf spot), stem lesions (black arm), and boll (capsule) infection of cotton plants, each stage being initiated by inoculum from one or more of the previous stages. In these cases the several waves of infection on different parts of the plant differ in the pattern as well as in the time of development. *Alternaria brassicicola* (dark leaf spot and other diseases of brassica crops) can cause seedling disease when infected seed is sown but is of little significance on the foliage in Britain; nevertheless it is extremely destructive to the flowers, fruit and seeds. This pathogen remains at low ebb in the infected plant until flowering occurs and can then develop in epiphytotic form from the fairly small amount of inoculum produced by the (usually) small number of leaf lesions present. There are, no doubt, other pathogens showing this type of behaviour.

Conditions which favour epiphytotics

It has been said that the development of epiphytotics is basically the logistical problem of getting enough material (inoculum of the pathogen) to the right place at the right time. Broadly speaking, an epiphytotic is likely to break out when a susceptible crop variety in a susceptible condition is exposed to abundant viable inoculum of a virulent pathogen under environmental conditions favourable to infection and spread. These conditions must all obtain more or less simultaneously and the absence of any one of them may result in failure – hence comparatively few of the thousands of plant pathogens cause epiphytotics. Spread may, for example, be restricted by the amount of inoculum present. Despite weather conditions favourable to it a fungus may fail to spread to any great extent because of an insufficiency of inoculum due to sparse sporulation during a long previous spell of weather unfavourable to it. The environment, especially weather conditions, can hold the balance between plant and pathogen and so may critically affect the course of a disease outbreak. Thus, inoculum may build up during weather favourable to the pathogen but it will be wasted if it is not dispersed or if it is dispersed during weather which is unfavourable for infection. This triple interaction between plant, pathogen and environment may be further complicated by the presence of vectors of the pathogen and by the efforts of man to control disease. Development of epiphytotics is thus a complex process, as is the analysis of the numerous factors involved (see, for example, the interesting accounts by Van der Plank 1960, 1963, 1967). Some of the conditions which are conducive to epiphytotics are:

1. The pathogen must be virulent to the crop variety under cultivation, and a short sporulation (latent) period will be advantageous in that spread of the pathogen is thus likely to be accelerated. Spread will be enhanced if the pathogen in the infected tissue continues to produce propagules for a long time. Inoculum must be produced in adequate quantities at the right time and it must also be efficiently liberated, disseminated, and deposited on the plants in a viable and vigorous condition. The spores must be able to germinate and infect, and the more rapid these events the more successful the pathogen is likely to be. Van der Plank (1960) suggests that stem rust might be minimized by cultivating those wheat varieties on which *Puccinia graminis* develops only slowly (that is a low r value) due perhaps to their resistance to infection, although they are susceptible on the conventional scale used in assessing resistance. High aggressiveness in the sense that one spore, or a few spores, can infect is also likely to be advantageous to pathogens.

2. The plants must be susceptible to the pathogen and must be at a susceptible stage of growth when inoculum is deposited on them. Young plants are sometimes more susceptible but the opposite may be true. An epiphytotic may fail to develop because the plants become less susceptible as they mature. Predisposing factors, such as plant injury or application of fertilizers, are also relevant in this respect.

3. Intensive monoculture of susceptible plants over large areas is generally considered to favour the development of epiphytotics. Some diseases are likely to reach epiphytotic proportions only when the host plants are crowded together, and Van der Plank (1960) defines the epidemic point in crowding as that at which the birth rate of the pathogen exceeds its death rate; this is not a constant figure but depends on other factors and is likely to be lower in seasons favourable to the disease. In Van der Plank's view the development of epiphytotics is likely to be discouraged by having a small number of large homogeneous fields as compared with a larger number of smaller fields. Disease control measures such as sanitation and spraying can be more effectively applied over large continuous

areas of crop, and concentration of the plants in a single compact field reduces to a minimum infection from outside. In a crop area divided into several small fields, often under different management, some may practise inadequate disease control, thus providing a source of inoculum for adjacent better managed fields; this is less likely to happen with large, homogeneous crop areas. This view is questioned by Waggoner (1962) who concludes on theoretical grounds that the probability of an epiphytotic ravaging a crop within a season is likely to be reduced by subdividing the fields and scattering them.

The cultivation of early, mid-season and late varieties of a crop, all susceptible to the same races of the pathogen, within a restricted area may encourage disease as a more or less continuous supply of inoculum is thereby achieved. The planned distribution of crop areas can help to reduce outbreaks of plant disease and this aspect of disease control has so far received little attention. Crops are being grown in increasingly larger units, and many of the operations involved – sowing, weeding, harvesting and so on – are carried out mechanically or chemically. This offers scope for more effective disease control both in application of control measures themselves and in planning to reduce disease incidence and spread.

4. Environmental conditions must be favourable to the pathogen at all points in the infection cycle – sporulation and subsequent liberation, dissemination and deposition of the spores in a viable condition as well as germination, infection of the plant, and growth in its tissues. They must also be favourable to any vectors involved in spread or inoculation of the pathogen. Weather, especially temperature and moisture conditions, is of key significance in the development of epiphytotics, particularly with rapidly developing diseases of annual plants, and the weather conditions conducive to a number of destructive pathogens have been investigated. Weather during the intercrop period, as well as during the crop season, can be important in seasonal carry-over of pathogens and so may affect the initial outbreak and subsequent spread of pathogens. In considering the development of epiphytotics the date of appearance and the early development of the disease are of critical importance. A delay in appearance may make the difference between a mild and a destructive outbreak, it may enable the plants to pass through their most susceptible phase in the near-absence of the pathogen, and the crop may be harvested before the pathogen reaches its full potentialites. This is particularly true of pathogens with a moderate rather than an extremely rapid rate of spread. The former, once left behind, may be unable to 'catch up' with their potential host plants whereas the latter may manage to do so.

Secondary outbreaks; mixed varieties

Provided both are susceptible to the same races of the pathogen, a disease outbreak in one variety can be expected to give rise to a secondary outbreak in a following variety. The infected plants of the earlier sown susceptible variety provide a massive inoculum for the later sown variety which, even if more resistant, is likely to be more severely attacked under these conditions of abnormally high inoculum (this is assuming that the inoculum survives between the two crops and that environmental conditions are suitable for the pathogen). If, however, the earlier sown variety is highly resistant it will bequeath less inoculum to the following susceptible variety so that, in the absence of other inoculum, the latter variety will be less severely attacked. Successive planting of susceptible varieties is thus likely to result in severe outbreaks of disease and build-up of inoculum, and should be avoided wherever possible.

Growing a mixture of cultivars of different horizontal resistance, including highly susceptible ones, in the same field may result in high levels of inoculum which bring about more disease in the resistant varieties. Sprague (1953), for example, reported that the presence of a few trees of a susceptible variety of apple can cause considerable mildew (*Podosphaera leucotricha*) in more resistant varieties. On the other hand, the presence of highly resistant plants between susceptible ones will reduce the amount of inoculum as compared with what would have been produced had all the plants been susceptible, and so will tend to restrict the spread of the pathogen. Mixing of varieties is not very frequent but is sometimes practised in orchards and, in such cases, it is advisable to grow the most highly resistant varieties available.

Other epidemiological patterns

There are, of course, many other ways in which diseases develop. The sowing of heavily contaminated or heavily infected seed under conditions favourable for disease development can result in fields in which nearly every plant is infected, and similar widespread infection can occur in plants growing in soil heavily contaminated with pathogens. In these cases epiphytotics develop without spread of the pathogen from plant to plant in the field. Some seed–or soil borne fungi cause seed rot and pre-emergence or post-emergence blighting which may kill some of the infected seedlings, whilst those which survive are likely to be diseased and to act as inoculum sources for other plants, thus initiating epiphytotics.

Among the rusts (Uredinales) one finds interesting variations in life cycles, which affect their survival and spread. In autoecious rusts all the spore stages occur on the same plant and there is a cyclic development of the fungus, aecia and spermogonia usually appearing in the spring, followed by uredospores and teliospores in the summer and autumn. The aeciospores of heteroecious rusts do not infect the plant on which they are produced and the fungus alternates between two different – sometimes widely different – species of host plant. This alternation may be obligate or the rust may persist from year to year as uredia or mycelium in a perennial uredial host plant. In heteroecious rusts each type of spore has its own function; uredospores – rapid spread of the pathogen during the growing season; teliospores – overwintering and production of basidiospores; basidiospores – dispersal and transfer of the rust from plant species A to species B; spermatia – fertilizing spores; aeciospores – dispersal and transfer of the fungus from plant species B back to A.

There are several variations of the complete life cycle as described above. Some rusts (including *Puccinia malvacearum* on hollyhock) produce only teliospores which germinate more or less immediately and *in situ* to liberate basidiospores by means of which the rust spreads. Other rusts produce only aeciospores or only uredospores. Other variations are described by Cummins (1959) and Wilson and Henderson (1966).

Environmental conditions also affect the epidemiology of some pathogens. Under certain climatic conditions the teliospores of some rusts are not formed or, if formed, are apparently functionless in that the alternate host species is not present. This occurs with *P. graminis* in barberry-free areas where the rust may be present throughout the year on alternative host plants or where there may be an annual influx of uredospores from distant sources. Oospores of some downy mildews, cleistothecia of some powdery mildews, and the perfect stages of some Ascomycetes (for example, the perithecia of *Claviceps* or the apothecia of *Sclerotinia* or *Diplocarpon rosae*) do not form in some areas or under certain climatic conditions. This may be because only incompatible strains of the fungus are present. Thus, Smith (1970) found that *Erysiphe polygoni* on pea (*Pisum sativum*) and certain other plants is heterothallic so that lateness or irregularity in the formation of cleistothecia could be due to the absence of compatible mating types rather than to an unfavourable environment or the nutritive condition of the host plant. Some pathogens which normally spread by air borne propagules may fail to do so under certain conditions; although *Sclerospora sorghi* (downy mildew of sorghum) may produce numerous sporangia, in some areas these rarely seem to bring about spread of the disease, possibly because the climatic conditions needed for this type of infection may be exacting and rarely prevail for sufficiently long in the field. Only the oospores seem to be effective, these being liberated into the soil from where they infect the next crop and the pathogen thus spreads from plant to plant only slowly.

Viruses may be unable to spread because their vectors are absent and a curious situation is described by Hewitt (1953) in Pierce's disease of the grapevine (alfalfa dwarf disease virus) in California. Although this virus is transmitted by several species of leafhopper there was no evidence that it spread from diseased to other vines, or that the removal of diseased vines or control of the vectors by insecticidal sprays reduced the incidence of the disease. It seems that the virus, which has a wide host range, enters the vineyards from outside and possibly from infected plants other than vines, but the explanation of these effects is unknown. The virus is apparently restricted to the xylem tissue and is likely to be spread only by insects which are xylem feeders; it may be that the effects described above are in some way related to differences in the behaviour of the vectors of the virus on different species of plants.

From the examples given above it is clear that a thorough knowledge of the life cycle and epidemiology of the pathogen, and of the effects of environmental factors on these, is needed for the formulation of rational control measures. Three interesting and instructive examples of this are described by Ogawa, Hall and Koepsell (1967) in the semiarid climate of California where spread of pathogens by rain is minimal. *Monilinia laxa* (blossom blight of almond) overwinters on infected trees and produces spores after the rain and fogs of early winter. The blossom is most susceptible when the stigmas and anthers are exposed and the conidia of *M. laxa* are disseminated to only limited distances. Development of the disease depends largely on the inoculum level, and satisfactory control can be obtained by an eradicant fungicide (sodium pentachlorophenate) applied to the trees in winter. *Sphaerotheca pannosa* attacks plum fruits shortly after flowering and only limited sporulation occurs on the fruit; inoculum comes chiefly from infected roses and the liberated conidia do not remain viable for very long. Eradication of roses near plum orchards minimized the inoculum available at the time of fruit susceptibility and so gave adequate control. Inoculum of *Pseudoperonospora humuli* (downy mildew of hops) is derived from perennial mycelium in infected plants, less than 1% of the latter producing diseased shoots in the spring. Dispersed spores die within a few days and spread occurs largely during wet weather, much of the season being unfavourable in this respect. Hence the disease can be controlled by prompt destruction of the diseased plants which are the primary source of inoculum each season. These three examples illustrate how careful study of the epidemiology of pathogens sometimes enables effective control measures to be devised.

Long term relationships between pathogens and their host plants

When introduced into a new area a pathogen may develop in one of several ways. If unsuited to its new environment or new host plants it may die out or become only a minor nuisance. If well suited it may increase from year to year, spread rapidly, and break out in epiphytotic proportions. Under natural conditions less susceptible varieties of the plant then begin to predominate until they and the pathogen attain an equilibrium – the pathogen 'settles down' and becomes endemic. This severe initial outbreak followed by a gradual decline in destructiveness is said to be characteristic of what happens when some pathogens are introduced into areas suitable for their establishment and spread. The plant–pathogen equilibrium may, however, be upset if new races of the latter evolve, and some pathogens perhaps maintain themselves through rapid production of such races. *Plasmopara viticola* is considered by Gaumann (1950) to be as destructive to grapes in Europe now as when it was introduced nearly a century ago, perhaps because control by fungicides was practised as soon as the disease appeared, with the result that there may have been little if any natural elimination of the more susceptible vines. Present-day varieties may be as susceptible as those of a century ago although this would be difficult to demonstrate. Other pathogens such as *Uncinula necator* (grape powdery mildew) and *Phytophthora infestans* may be less destructive now than formerly, but it is equally likely that their apparent diminution is due to improved agricultural methods and man's efforts to control them. No direct comparison between modern races of pathogens and those present a hundred years ago is possible, and too much reliance cannot be placed on written records.

Maize in Africa is now less susceptible to *Puccinia polysora* than when the rust first appeared there about 20 years ago, probably due to the emergence of resistant maize varieties under selection pressure from the pathogen. This gradual predominance of resistant varieties is likely to occur whenever plants are exposed to selection pressure from pathogens, but such varieties are less likely to develop if only genetically uniform crop varieties – protected from selection pressure – are grown.

Pathogens vary greatly in their long term relationships with the plants they attack. In a very general way many can be grouped as mild endemic, sporadic, and major endemic pathogens.

Mild endemic (chronic) pathogens occur in most seasons to a varying but usually minor extent, rarely causing serious damage. They tend to reduce yields by small and undeterminable amounts each year but rarely sufficiently seriously to justify special control measures. The comparative mildness of attack is due to various causes. Some diseases develop comparatively late in the season when the infected plants are nearing maturity, or they may affect the older parts of shoot or root which have passed their productive peak. Fungi which colonize senescent tissue, for example *Cladosporium herbarum*, no doubt come into this latter category. Climatic conditions may be such that the disease rarely attains its full destructiveness, the pathogen not being completely 'in tune' with the environment and the temperature and/or moisture regime may permit only a limited development of the disease in most seasons. The plants may have developed resistance or tolerance to the pathogen over long periods of time and so are only slightly affected by it. Many of the leaf spot diseases fall into this group as do some root diseases which (as far as one knows) cause only minor root browning each year, some rusts which affect the older leaves or older plants, and some viruses which appear to have only a slight and inconspicuous effect on the plant. Most of these are probably pathogens which have been parasitizing their host plants for hundreds if not thousands of years and have in that time reached an equilibrium with them.

Occasionally, however, a hitherto mild endemic pathogen becomes more destructive and develops to epiphytotic proportions. This may be due to the appearance of races with new parasitic potentialities through such variation producing mechanisms as hybridization, gene mutation, and parasexuality. New races of pathogens may be introduced from elsewhere, and other conditions which may enhance the destructiveness of an existing pathogen include (*a*) widespread cultivation of more susceptible crop varieties which have not previously encountered the particular races present in the area, (*b*) the appearance of more effective vectors of pathogens – by mutation or introduction from elsewhere, and (*c*) adoption of new agricultural practices which encourage the pathogen; for example, a changed sowing date may result in earlier infection of the crop, closer crop rotations are likely to encourage root diseases, overhead as compared with furrow irrigation will probably favour many foliage pathogens, application of insecticides may control an insect pest but indirectly favour insect vectors of pathogens, and the use of a new fungicide may favour pathogens hitherto kept under control. All these changes in cultural practices – and others – may convert minor pathogens into major ones. Mild endemic pathogens may appear to be of little practical significance but in many cases the losses they cause are not accurately known, and they constitute a potential danger which should be borne in mind when changes in agricultural practices are being considered.

Sporadic (seasonal) pathogens are of irregular incidence, in some seasons affecting only scattered plants but in others becoming more widespread. They tend to be rather critically dependent on certain weather conditions for their full development, and become serious only in seasons with such weather. Many downy mildews (Peronosporaceae) need wet or prolonged humid weather for sporulation and infection, and fail to develop or spread in dry seasons. Although individual plants may be severely damaged, the percentage infection is small in an unfavourable year. In favourable years, however, sporadic diseases can be widespread and destructive.

Major endemic pathogens affect crops every year, often causing appreciable damage and becoming severe in seasons favourable to their development and spread. In most seasons, the weather is suitable, as occurs in development and they not infrequently cause epiphytotics, for example potato blight, black stem rust of wheat, and coffee rust. Under natural conditions some of these attain a balance with their host plants, but weather exceptionally favourable to the pathogen or the appearance of new races can result in serious outbreaks. These pathogens are liable to become destructive if introduced into new areas of susceptible crops under favourable weather conditions, often increasing to epiphytotic proportions before resistant or tolerant plants develop under selection pressure. Resistance or tolerance is not likely to develop if, as often happens, man attempts to keep the crop plant genetically uniform; in this case it may be a long time before the pathogen becomes 'mild'.

20 The factors which influence the spread of pathogens within crop areas

Numerous factors influence the extent and speed of spread of pathogens through crop areas. In this chapter they are considered under plant factors, pathogen factors, biotic factors, and environmental factors, affecting not only production, liberation and dispersal of propagules, and survival of inoculum between successive plantings of a susceptible crop, but also infection of the plant, as discussed in Chapter 16.

Plant factors

The susceptibility of a plant to a pathogen is obviously the most important plant factor influencing the spread of the pathogen. Very susceptible plants are likely to be invaded and colonized by pathogens more rapidly than resistant plants, and production of spores is more rapid and more profuse in the former, with the result that the pathogen spreads more rapidly. Even slight and almost undetectable differences between two varieties in, for example, the time elapsing between infection and sporulation may have an appreciable effect on disease spread during the life of the crop since during that time – which may be several months – many generations of spores will have been produced. With many pathogens such as rusts, the spore-bearing structures continue to produce spores over a period of time, rather than all simultaneously, so that the generations overlap.

The plant's resistance to a pathogen may change with age, older plants often becoming more resistant, so that the pathogen encounters increasing difficulty in finding susceptible tissue. In some diseases, however, plants become more susceptible with increasing age so that – provided there is adequate inoculum and a suitable environment for development and spread of the pathogen – the disease tends to increase in the older crop. Pathogens present in a latent condition in young plants may develop as the plants become older and more susceptible. Apart from production of spores there may be difficulties in the effective dissemination of spores produced within the denser crop canopy formed by older larger plants, particularly if the spores are splash dispersed and produced on the older, lower leaves. In this case, spread of the pathogen may be largely confined to the infected plant or within a group of adjacent plants rather than occurring freely through the field, as it previously did in the smaller young plants before the canopy formed. Even if plants become more susceptible as they age, spread of the pathogen may be reduced by this physical effect in crops which form a dense canopy. On the other hand, spore production and infection are likely to be enhanced by the higher humidity and possibly by the reduced light intensity obtaining within the crop canopy. Similar effects could presumably occur with pathogens which are spread by insect vectors. The spread of contagious viruses may, however, be expedited as plants grow larger and come into contact.

From these considerations it is clear that the spread of pathogens within and between plants which are becoming older and larger is complex and influenced by several factors, some of which favour the pathogen while others discourage it.

Pathogen factors

The infection cycle of a fungus spreading from plant to plant by air borne spores comprises a series of events which are influenced to different extents by environmental factors. The cycle begins with production, liberation, dissemination and deposition of the spores, and is followed by their germination and entry of the infection structures into the plant, with subsequent production of infected tissue on or in which the next generation of spores is produced. In many pathogens the successive events of the infection cycle are reasonably well related to the normal rhythm of the environment but occasionally the two may be out of step, as when a pathogen produces spores which are unable to infect the plant because of insufficient moisture or unsuitable temperature. Inadequacy in any of the events of the infection cycle is likely to result in reduced spread of the pathogen and, conversely, spread will be most rapid when all the processes in the infection cycle are functioning efficiently. The rate of spread of a pathogen is affected by the rapidity with which infection and subsequent sporulation occur, that is, by the duration of the infection period, the incubation period, and the sporulation period, and also by the duration of the infectious period (the time during which the fungus within the infected tissue continues to produce spores).

The **infection period** is the time elapsing between spore germination and established infection, and may range from several hours to several weeks in different parasites, being shorter in aggressive ones. It is a range rather than a well defined point; spores which germinate rapidly may infect in 3–4 hours, the majority may require 12 hours or so, and slow germinators may require longer if indeed they succeed in infecting at all. The infection period is critically dependent on environmental conditions and may be considerably extended if these are unfavourable, so much so that in extreme cases infection may fail. Rapid infection enables a parasite to take the fullest advantage of short spells of weather suitable for infection, and thus minimizes its most vulnerable period – that between spore germination and established infection. The infection period for many plant pathogens is about 12–24 hours, and rarely more than 2 days. There are, however, cases in which it may be considerably longer – as in the case when a number of events have to occur on the host's surface before infection can be accomplished. Thus in some smuts fusion between hyphae or spores of two primary (monokaryotic) mycelia derived from germinating basidiospores may be necessary before infection can occur, the resulting secondary (dikaryotic) mycelium or spores produced by it being the infective phase. The infection period is also lengthened if the fungus or bacterium grows on the surface of the plant before infecting it.

The **incubation period** is the period between inoculation and the appearance of visible symptoms or, more precisely perhaps, between spore germination and appearance of symptoms. It comprises the infection period plus the time needed for the physiological changes induced by the pathogen to be expressed as symptoms – normally the first indication that infection has occurred. It has also been used to describe the period between spore germination and subsequent production of spores by the established pathogen (the sporulation or latent period) which in some parasites can be surprisingly short (5–6 days) under optimum conditions. This usage denotes the full life cycle of the pathogen and is of importance in epidemiology in that it represents the time between successive generations of spores, and is hence a measure of the likely rate of spread of the pathogen. Usually, however, incubation is taken as the time between inoculation and appearance of symptoms. Its duration depends on parasite, host and environment, being shortest with aggressive parasites, highly susceptible hosts and environmental conditions conducive to infection. With many pathogens it is 1–2 weeks but is considerably longer with others (for example, 3–4 weeks for *Mycosphaerella musicola*: Goos and Tschirch, 1963), whereas with some it may be only a few days under very favourable conditions. It is a range rather than a definite point and is related to the rapidity of spore germination and infection. In certain smuts, including *Sphacelotheca sorghi* (covered smut of sorghum), the very young seedling is infected from seed borne or soil borne spores, but no noticeable symptoms appear until the infected plant produces smutted flowers – in such cases the incubation period is technically several months although 'physiological symptoms' such as increased respiration, may occur much sooner. Other smuts visibly affect the growth of their host plants.

The **sporulation period** (reproduction period of Gaumann, 1950; latent period of Van der Plank, 1963) is the period between inoculation and sporulation. This period – during which the pathogen colonizes the host plant to varying extents before finally producing its propagules – represents a generation. The spores are often discharged but in some diseases they may not be liberated until the host tissue decays, as with those of *Plasmodiophora brassicae*, in which case they often function as resting propagules. The sporulation period has a considerable bearing on the rate at which pathogens spread and is thus an important factor in epidemiology. It varies greatly in different pathogens. Sporulation of some fungi occurs a few days after symptoms have appeared but under very favourable conditions for the pathogen it may occur before symptoms appear, as in *Peronospora parasitica* where sporangiophores can develop on green leaf tissue. Other fungal pathogens, including some systemic ones, may take weeks or even months to produce their spores and these often cause slowly spreading diseases, as occurs in smuts which infect the seedling and sporulate in the mature plant. Some of the Hymenomycetes which attack the trunks and branches of trees may take several years to produce their basidiocarps, and similarly the aecial stages of some rusts on conifers.

The **infectious period** is the period during which the fungus within the infected tissue can produce infective propagules. It may extend to several weeks in obligate or non-obligate parasites in which the infected tissue remains alive and functional for some time.

Assuming susceptible plants and environmental conditions favourable for spore dissemination and infection, a pathogen is likely to spread rapidly if it has a short sporulation period, thus allowing a large number of infection cycles to occur during the season, and if the infectious period – during which the pathogen in the infected tissue retains the capacity to produce spores – is long. The spore producing structures of some fungi, including the uredia of rusts, may produce spores over several weeks, so that a continuous supply of inoculum is available for spread during that time. Conversely, pathogens which produce small numbers of spores and/or take a long time to do so, or in which the spore bearing structures produce only one 'crop' of spores, are likely to have fewer generations during the life of the crop and so to spread relatively slowly. However, some pathogens – including many downy mildews – compensate for their sporophores bearing only one crop of spores by producing large numbers of sporophores more or less simultaneously at regular intervals, and the sporangiophores of some Peronosporaceae, although bearing only one

crop of sporangia, are produced in such large numbers that these pathogens can, under suitable conditions, spread very rapidly.

The development and subsequent spread of many pathogens is closely
related to the amount of inoculum present at the beginning of the season,
and this will be partly related to the amount of disease in the fields of
the same crop plant in the previous season. Weather conditions and soil
conditions during the intercrop months also affect the amount of inoculum
which survives. Hence a pathogen may be more severe in one area because
generally, the winters are mild and permit survival of its inoculum to a
greater extent than in areas with more severe winters. A wet intercrop
period may reduce inoculum by accelerating the breakdown of diseased
plant material left on the field after harvest. Ineffective ploughing or
other crop sanitation measures permit inoculum to survive and so bring
about heavy and early infection of the following crop. These considerations apply chiefly to inoculum in the form of diseased plant residues, infected self-sown seedlings or plants growing from infected tubers or roots
remaining in the soil after harvest. As the growing season progresses,
the amount of inoculum in the soil diminishes as more plants become
infected and as the inoculum itself dies out, but this does not apply to
those pathogens which are able to increase saprophytically in the soil.
The distance separating the newly sown fields from the inoculum source is
also important and more disease is normally to be expected when this
distance is small and especially when the same crop plant is sown in the
same fields in 2 successive years.

In some cases inoculum sources include infected weeds which are so
widespread and abundant that it is not feasible to eliminate them, but
the races of a pathogen which attack weeds may not be able to infect
cultivated plants and in this case the weeds are irrelevant as inoculum
sources. There is also the depressing fact that some pathogens seem to be
able to multiply very quickly from inoculum present in such small amounts
that it is not possible to detect and destroy it. Consequently the inoculum
is always present in sufficient quantities to start the disease in the following
season.

Biotic factors

Biotic factors which influence the spread of pathogens include the
numbers, activity and efficiency of transmission of vectors, these being
particularly important for some viruses but also relevant for vector
transmitted fungi and bacteria. They also include the activities of hyperparasites or antagonists. Under suitable conditions, hyperparasitic fungi
can, to some extent, reduce the spore output of rusts, powdery mildews

and other pathogens, and so tend to diminish the speed with which these pathogens spread, but in many cases the relatively small diminution in spore numbers does not sensibly check the progress of the pathogen. Spore-bearing structures are often eaten by insects and slugs but the significance of this in reducing spread of pathogens is doubtful since these animals might, in fact, disseminate the spores. Of greater significance, perhaps, is the reduction in overwintering structures, such as sclerotia, of pathogens which can result from the activity of antagonistic and hyper-parasitic fungi during the intercrop months.

Antagonism or synergism can also occur between different pathogens attacking the same plant so that the development of one pathogen may be reduced or increased in the presence of another (interactions p. 279). Fewer or more plants are thus attacked, or the plants are attacked less or more severely, by the first pathogen and its spread is correspondingly slower or greater. Man's efforts to minimize the spread of pathogens – for example by fungicidal spraying – might also be considered a biotic factor.

Environmental factors

The environment of a plant pathogen is the infected plant, but most pathogens spend part of their life outside their host, and during this time they are exposed to the environment including the weather. Some pathogens survive as resistant overwintering structures outside the plant and many produce numerous disseminatory propagules. Hence weather is likely to exert chiefly a twofold effect on pathogens – on their spread and on their survival between crops. There are other ways in which weather affects plant pathogens, very often indirectly by its effect on the resistance of the host plant, on soil conditions, on the numbers and activity of vectors of pathogens, and on the survival of diseased crop residues and self-sown seedlings, infected plants and infected alternative or alternate host plants. Hence the effects of environment on the incidence and spread of plant pathogens are likely to be complex.

Moisture (humidity and free water), temperature and light are the more important meteorological factors influencing the development and spread of plant pathogens. Atmospheric pressure within the limits normally prevailing is not known to be of any significance in this respect although Bortels (1947), cited by Yarwood (1959), reported that the change from low to high barometric pressure increased the resistance of beans to *Pseudomonas medicaginis*, of tobacco to *P. tabaci*, and of potato to *Erwinia carotovora*.

Generally speaking, fungi and bacteria which attack the shoots of plants are favoured by wet conditions but the reverse holds for powdery mildews. Moisture can affect the spread of plant pathogens in several ways. First, it can affect sporulation, as with downy mildews which require high humidity for production of their sporangia. Second, it can affect liberation and dissemination of spores since the spores of some pathogens are splash dispersed and so require raindrops for successful dissemination. Whether dew can accomplish this is doubtful but it is conceivable that heavy dew might cause water to drip from leaves on to diseased leaves below, thus bringing about splash dispersal. There may also be adverse indirect effects such as heavy rain destroying spore-bearing structures, washing spores from leaves, or encouraging the development of hyperparasites which reduce sporulation. Third, infection of the plant may be affected by moisture: many fungi and bacteria require a film of moisture on the plant surface for spore germination and invasion of the tissue. This is less applicable to pathogens which are introduced into the plant by vectors or which enter through wounds, and free water seems adversely to affect spore germination in many powdery mildews and so reduces infection.

The persistence of moisture on the plant surface is probably more significant in plant infection than is the actual amount of water present, and factors which prolong persistence of moisture are thus likely to bring about increased infection and so enhance the spread of many pathogens. Under favourable conditions some pathogens can infect in a few hours, but others take 12 hours or more and require moisture for that period of time. Persistence of moisture on plant surfaces is favoured by high humidity, still air, wet soil and shade, many of which conditions obtain in the crop canopy. Mist, fog and dew are other conditions which can provide the moisture necessary for infection. Mists are likely to occur near the sea and large expanses of water, while fog often develops inland. The effects of smog on the development and spread of plant pathogens are interesting. Smog can be expected to discourage the growth of pathogens as well as plants, and sulphur dioxide is injurious to some of the fungi which attack plants – notably *Diplocarpon rosae* (black spot of rose).

The frequency of rain may be more significant than its quantity in bringing about the spread of some pathogens, especially those whose spores are dispersed by rain splash, and in such cases spread may be related to the number of days on which rain falls rather than to the amount of rain.

Soil moisture may influence the development of root-attacking pathogens through its effect on the roots, the soil microflora, and the pathogen in the soil, and these effects are complex and little understood. As is well known, *Plasmodiophora brassicae* is severe in wet soil whereas *Streptomyces scabies* (potato scab) is worst in dry soil, and infection of seedlings by many seed or soil borne smuts is usually greatest at moderate soil moisture.

Temperature is often important – although generally less so than moisture conditions – in the development and spread of pathogens. It is also important in their geographical distribution, discussed later in this chapter. Many pathogens are fairly tolerant of temperature in that, within limits, their spread is retarded rather than prevented by an unsuitable temperature, infection and sporulation taking longer. Maximum development and spread of such pathogens tend to occur over a range of temperature (often of several degrees centigrade), rather than at one specific temperature. Outside this range spread falls off and eventually ceases at fairly well defined lower and upper limiting temperatures.

Such pathogens as *Taphrina deformans* (peach leaf curl), *Spongospora subterranea* (potato powdery scab) and *Puccinia striiformis* (yellow rust of wheat and barley) are favoured by fairly cool weather, whereas the opposite is true of *Corticium rolfsii* (southern sclerotial wilt of many plants), *Pseudomonas solanacearum* (brown rot) and other pathogens commonly found in warm areas. Temperature may also indirectly affect the spread of pathogens by its effects on survival of inoculum, incidence of vectors and hyperparasites, resistance of the plant, and soil conditions: the last named is particularly relevant with pathogens which attack roots and seedlings.

Comparatively little seems to have been reported on the effects of light on the spread of plant pathogens, although intensity and quality of light are known to influence sporulation and probably affect spore germination and infection. Light intensity is reduced within the crop canopy and it is possible that its quality is also changed, so that infection and sporulation are likely to be modified and in turn to affect the spread of pathogens from plant to plant. Leaves fully exposed to bright sunlight in still air become warmer and this may affect infection and sporulation. Light may indirectly influence the spread of plant pathogens through its effects on their vectors, on the natural epiflora of the plant, or on the behaviour of stomata in the case of pathogens which enter plants through stomata.

Wind is another meteorological factor which affects the spread of pathogens, being important in the dispersal of spores and air borne vectors of pathogens; irregular air movements are generally more effective in bringing about multidirectional spread of pathogens than are stronger, steady winds blowing in one direction, as discussed in Chapter 18.

From what has been written above it will be clear that the effects of weather on the incidence of plant pathogens are complex. The weather requirements of many plant pathogens are only imperfectly understood or are appreciated in only a very general and empirical way, but some have been investigated as is evident from the following few representative examples. Potato blight caused by *Phytophthora infestans* is thought to originate from occasional infected plants growing from infected tubers.

It is favoured by wet weather with cool nights and warm days – the sporangia germinate best at 10–13° C while maximum sporulation is at about 18–24° C. Under suitable climatic conditions there may be an interval of only about 4 days between inoculation and sporulation, the sporangia developing on the newly invaded tissue rather than on that killed by the fungus; the latter can then spread very rapidly. Ascospores of *Venturia inaequalis* (apple scab) released from perithecia overwintering in dead leaves seem to be the principal source of inoculum. A cool, moist spring favours the disease with subsequent wet, windy weather facilitating spread of the conidia – the latter are not easily detached from their conidiophores when dry. Ascospores germinate well at 11–22° C and the leaf surface must remain wet for at least 9 hours for successful infection to occur. Moisture deposited at a time when it is likely to persist will thus be more effective than transient moisture in promoting infection.

Black stem rust of wheat caused by *Puccinia graminis f.sp. tritici* may originate from infected barberry bushes or from air borne uredospores from distant sources. A film of moisture in the form of dew, fog, or light rain for 4–8 hours enables infection to occur if the temperature is suitable (22–27° C). The pathogen is favoured by long periods of warm, moist weather and can then spread rapidly, the incubation period being only a week or less. The conditions for development and spread of *Plasmopara viticola* (downy mildew of grape) are discussed by Gaumann (1950). Maximum sporulation occurs at 22–24° C and high humidity (100%, dew) at night between 1 and 3 a.m. Under these conditions the sporulation period may be as little as 4 days whereas it is correspondingly longer if temperature and/or humidity are lower, few sporangia being produced below 60% relative humidity. Spore germination and infection are also favoured by high humidity and temperature (18–24°C) and the processes of sporulation and infection may be completed before dawn. The disease can be very destructive when the nights are warm and humid with heavy dew or other moisture deposition, particularly if the days are cloudy so that the foliage tends to remain wet longer. Powdery mildew of rose caused by *Sphaerotheca pannosa* differs from the preceding examples in that it appears to be favoured by dry weather. In Britain it is often widespread in September when the dry, warm days encourage dissemination of conidia, and the colder nights with dew formation enable spore production, germination and infection to occur; these two opposing ecological requirements are to some extent met by the natural alternation of day and night. This is certainly not the whole story since mildew can be severe in warm, humid weather in the spring, and the effects of environmental conditions are not well understood.

An interesting example of the effects of weather, chiefly temperature and atmospheric moisture, on the distribution and incidence of *Bremia lactucae* (downy mildew) and *Erysiphe cichoracearum* (powdery mildew) on lettuce in the Salinas Valley, California, is described by Schnathorst (1962). *Bremia* occurred in areas of low average temperature (13°C) and high average humidity (88%), and depended on both of these factors, as compared with 17–19°C and 77% for *Erysiphe* in which temperature was the more important. In some areas both pathogens were present to varying extents, in others only one or the other occurred.

Although the weather conditions which favour some plant pathogens are known in a very general sort of way, as in the association of a disease with a certain type of weather, a precise analysis of this in terms of temperature, moisture and light, has been attempted in only a few cases. Synthetic weather regimes produced in the laboratory and glasshouse should be useful in this respect.

In addition to the overall effects of weather on plant diseases over extensive areas there are local variations in weather conditions which may be sufficient to cause localized outbreaks of a disease or to prevent its development. This is likely to occur under borderline conditions in which even a rather slight change in one weather component can have a decisive effect, particularly if plant and pathogen are finely balanced. Development of *Pyricularia oryzae* (rice blast) in Florida is said to require night temperatures above 22°C whereas they are usually 20–21°C so that the pathogen spreads only on exceptionally warm nights. If, however, short rice is grown under flood conditions the night temperature of the air just above the water surface may be several degrees higher, due to low albedo (heat reflection) of still water combined with reduction of outgoing radiation by the rice leaves. This temperature increase is sometimes sufficient to permit destructive outbreaks of the disease, whereas the latter did not occur with unflooded rice at normal temperatures (Arsdel, 1965).

Fungal attack of coniferous seedlings growing under deep but not under shallow snow is apparently due to enhanced fungal growth in the warmer conditions of deep snow where the temperature remains just below freezing point (Gaumann, 1950). *Cronartium ribicola* (blister rust) can be destructive to pines in localized cooler, wetter areas such as the base of slopes, in small narrow valleys, and in small clearings in the woods. There are other cases in which some localized deviation from the overall surrounding weather pattern results in enhanced development of a pathogen. *Cladosporium fulvum* (tomato leaf mould) is favoured by warm, humid conditions and can be extremely destructive in glasshouses although rarely so on outdoor plants in Britain. *Bremia lactucae* (downy mildew) is favoured by comparatively low temperature and high humidity and is thus more frequent on lettuce in winter and early spring than in the warmer summer months.

Localized meteorological events can also upset the rhythm of the infection cycle and so affect disease incidence. In Ceylon the basidiospores of *Exobasidium vexans* (tea blister blight) are normally most numerous in the air between midnight and 4 a.m. but heavy thunderstorms in the early afternoon resulted in a second peak of spore concentration during or immediately after the rain (Shanmuganathan and Arulpragasam, 1966).

Among the accounts of weather in relation to plant diseases are the early ones of Foister (1935, 1946) and more recently Miller (1953), Bourke *et al.* (1965) and Hepting (1963: climate and forest diseases).

Microclimate

In considering the effects of weather on disease incidence it should be remembered that except for wind, it is conditions within the crop and in the immediate vicinity of the plants that are relevant. Growing plants modify the environment close to them, producing what has been called a microclimate or ecoclimate, and these changes may be considerable within a dense crop canopy with its reduced circulation of air and reduced light intensity. Man creates an artificial microclimate when he grows plants in glasshouses, under cloches, or by overhead or ground irrigation (see p. 384). Disease incidence may thus be increased or reduced and it is sometimes possible to control disease by appropriate modification of the microclimate. Meteorological data as customarily recorded on a Stevenson screen in the open air several metres above ground afford a useful guide, but clearly do not necessarily give an accurate picture of the microclimate. Neither do they usually record the temperature of the plant surface exposed to sunlight or the length of time during which the surface remains wet – and the latter is a critical factor in infection, since many fungal spores require water for germination. A surface wetness recorder based on continuous weighing of a smooth block of expanded polystyrene, thought to be comparable in this respect to the leaf surface, has been described (Hirst, 1957) and is likely to prove very useful. Other methods of measuring the temperature, humidity and surface wetness of the microclimate are listed by Yarwood (1959a). According to Waggoner (1965) the differences between microclimate and air conditions can be predicted from rough estimates of meteorological factors and resistance of the leaf to diffusion of water, an imperfectly understood subject.

The differences between microclimate and surrounding atmospheric conditions are likely to be greatest when the air around the plants is still. A greater range of temperature occurs at and near the soil surface than in the air several metres above, and may damage plants directly as well as affecting disease incidence. Thus unshaded leaves near the soil tend to be warmer than those further up the plant in sunny weather, and the absence of powdery mildew (*Uncinula necator*) on the lowest unshaded

o

leaves of grapevines as compared with severe infection on the upper leaves has been attributed to this. Other explanations are possible, however; thus, older leaves might be more resistant. The failure of rust (*Puccinia chrysanthemi*) to develop on chrysanthemum leaves in the sun, despite favourable air temperature, was attributed to the considerably higher temperature (up to 9°C above that of the air) of the unshaded leaves (Campbell and Dimock, 1955). Conversely, leaves may be cooled by water present on them. Some observers have reported quite marked differences in the temperature of leaves as compared with that of the air. Unventilated leaves exposed to bright sunlight may be as much as 10°C warmer than the air whereas at night they tend to be cooler. These effects vary in magnitude in different parts of the plant. Fruits and stems in sunlight tend to become warmer than leaves because the cooling effect of transpiration is greater in the latter, and similarly for the upper as compared with the lower sides of hypostomatous leaves. The temperature increase is generally less near the tip of a large leaf than near the petiole, and less on a single leaf than on a cluster of leaves, these differences being related to differences in resistance to convectional exchange (Waggoner, 1965).

Microclimate also affects the water humidity pattern at the plant surface and within the crop, and this can have a critical influence on spore germination, infection and sporulation. Leaves and fungi can perhaps absorb moisture from humid air and the spores of some fungi germinate in the apparent absence of free water, but in many others water is necessary for germination and is provided by rain, fog, dew or water exuded from the plant itself. Dew condenses on leaves and other surfaces when the temperature of the surface falls to the dew point of the surrounding air, and the lower the air humidity the lower the dew point; the dew point is about 16·5°C for air which has a 90% relative humidity at 18°C whereas it is 7°C for air of 50% humidity at 18°C (Yarwood, 1959a). Cooling of leaves at night is thought to be due chiefly to emission of infrared radiation, this being favoured by a clear sky, low incoming radiation and a dark surface.

The amount of moisture and its duration on the plant are both important in infection and some pathogens require a minimum of several hours, others 12 hours or more of continuous moisture. Shade, high humidity, still air, wet soil and other factors which prolong the persistence of moisture on the plant encourage infection and hence the spread of pathogens. Dew formation often occurs at night and in the early morning and may persist for 6–8 hours or probably longer within the shaded crop canopy. It is clearly adequate for infection of plants in rainless areas by pathogens such as *Pseudoperonospora cubensis* on cucumber (Duvdevani, Reichart and Palti, 1946), and several rusts (*Puccinia carthami, Uromyces fabae, U. striatus*) have been collected in the extreme north of the Sudan where rain rarely falls (Tarr, 1955). Dew formation is a gentler process than rainfall which, if heavy, can damage delicate spore-bearing structures and wash spores from the plant. However, rainy weather can persist for longer than dew and so is more likely to provide prolonged wetness, especially if the showers are light and frequent, and splash dispersal of spores occurs with rain but probably not with dew unless it is exceptionally heavy.

Different events in the infection cycle may have somewhat different moisture requirements. Sporulation of *Phytophthora infestans* is favoured by high humidity, spore dispersal requires rather drier conditions while water is necessary for germination and infection. Yarwood (1956c) suggests that foliage pathogens can be classified into four main groups based on their requirement for high humidity. (1) In the anthracnose group – acervular fungi with slimy spores – it is required for sporulation, spore dispersal and invasion of the host plant; (2) in the downy mildew group it is required for sporulation and invasion; (3) in the rust group it is required for invasion; and (4) in the powdery mildew and virus group, high humidity is required for none of these processes. These groups are not completely distinct and, as Yarwood (1959a) points out, they could be further divided on the basis of requiring free water in the form of rain, dew, or high humidity.

There is much uncertainty as to humidity conditions at plant surfaces. Some investigators have recorded appreciably higher humidity at such surfaces as compared with the air humidity, but others have found only slight differences. In still air the humidity at the surface of a transpiring upper leaf could be above ambient, whereas that of a sunlit well ventilated lower leaf which is not transpiring could be reduced because of the warming of the leaf, particularly if it is near the soil where the temperature is probably higher than at the top of the plant. Humidity within a shaded, fairly unventilated bushy crop such as potato may be high enough to permit germination of spores which would not germinate at the lower humidity of the atmosphere. At high humidity there might, under certain conditions, be sufficient condensation of water on the plant surface to bring about germination of fungal spores. Light intensity is reduced considerably within the crop and its quality is perhaps altered. Germination of some spores is reduced by bright light and sporulation may also be affected. Air currents are likely to be more sluggish within the crop canopy and this may affect liberation, movement and deposition of propagules.

From this brief outline it is clear that the microclimate in the immediate vicinity of plants and within crops can be markedly different from the surrounding macroclimate and this should be taken into account in epidemiological studies. Microclimate also affects the breeding and behaviour of insect and other vectors of plant pathogens, and is discussed in relation to plant disease by Yarwood (1959*a*) and Waggoner (1965); agrometeorology is discussed by Weille (1965).

Methods of investigating the effects of weather on the development and spread of plant pathogens

Although meteorological conditions may remain fairly constant over several hours, as in warm, still, cloudless weather, they normally change due to wind, rain, clouds obscuring the sun, and other causes. These irregularities may be localized and there is an overall diurnal rhythm in which temperature drops at night and humidity tends to rise. Over a period of time rain may fall more often at night but there may be so many exceptions that such generalizations are of little value to the epidemiologist. Changes in one meteorological factor are likely to bring about changes in others and the microclimate varies on different leaves and even on different parts of the same leaf. As Waggoner (1965) says – 'measuring the temperature and humidity upon the diverse leaves that spores alight upon is a hopeless and entangling task'. He suggests a theoretical analysis of these factors based on a knowledge of the environment and the plant, rather than an attempt to record meteorological conditions at the plant surface. This synthetic approach has given promising results, predicted disease development being similar to its observed development in the field.

Another promising technique is the experimental production in the laboratory or glasshouse of weather conditions which are likely to obtain in the field; disease development under these different climatic regimes can then be observed and the results extrapolated to the field. Comparable theoretical and experimental approaches can be used with other aspects of epidemiology, for example in investigating spore dispersal, and such methods will become increasingly important as our knowledge of meteorology and epidemiology increases. Observational methods in which development and spread of diseases are correlated with climatic conditions, and such factors as spore liberation and dispersal are also yielding valuable results which are useful in devising more effective ways of applying fungicides (see Hirst, 1958).

There would appear to be considerable scope for the use of computers in the study of epiphytotics and in the assessment of the relative importance of the numerous factors which influence the development and spread of plant pathogens. An example of this kind is the simulator described by Waggoner and Horsfall (1969) for *Alternaria solani*, the cause of early blight of potato and tomato; the following account is taken largely from their summary (Waggoner and Horsfall, 1969*a*).

This simulator ('Epidem') uses the temperature, relative humidity, wind speed, sunniness and wetness for each 3 hours of each day. Each

3 hours it modulates the course of a number of fungal stages according to the different effect of the weather factors upon them. These stages were formation of conidiophores, formation of spores, departure of spores on wind or rain, finding a host, germination of the spores, penetration of the host, incubation of the infection and expansion of the lesion. Much of the information required was already available but additional information on other phenomena (for example the fertility of conidiophores that had liberated their conidia) was needed for the simulator and was obtained by appropriate experiments.

Selecting 5 years of diverse weather and disease severity, the observed epidemics were satisfactorily mimicked by furnishing the appropriate weather data to the simulator. Having been verified in this way the simulator could be used to assess the relative importance of the various characteristics of plant, pathogen and weather in incidence of the disease. It could also be used to predict changes in the pattern of disease development likely to result from changing weather conditions. Computer analysis of epiphytotics is still in its early stages but it is likely to prove very useful as a means of ascertaining which are the critical factors governing the development and spread of plant pathogens. Its limitations, at least at the present time, should however be appreciated, and it may well be that relatively simple models can be as useful in determining the weather requirements of plant pathogens as are the more complex models which use computer techniques.

Climate and geographical distribution of plant pathogens

Climate is a major factor influencing the geographical distribution of living organisms, plant pathogens included. Temperature and moisture are probably the two main components involved and different climatic zones tend to be characterized by different plant pathogens. In general, certain species of Erysiphaceae predominate in dry regions whereas in the wet tropics dark mildews (Meliolaceae) become more prominent, although powdery mildews still occur. Peronosporaceae generally occur in wet areas but some rusts can develop under fairly dry conditions, presumably using moisture in the form of dew rather than rain. More species of *Cercospora*, a leaf spot pathogen, occur in warm areas than in temperate areas of similar rainfall whereas *Ramularia*, in many ways a similar pathogen, is widespread in both, although perhaps less so in the tropics. Many other examples could be given. Assuming the presence of susceptible plants, the main factors governing geographical distribution of plant pathogens are moisture, temperature and, of course, effective methods of dissemination.

Climatic factors can also influence overwintering – the intercrop period may be too severe for survival of the pathogen or of the plant in which it normally overwinters. The alternate hosts of a heteroecious rust may be absent, part of the life cycle being omitted, as with *Puccinia graminis* in barberry-free regions and other methods of overwintering or annual re-infection may then occur. In the tropics and subtropics the cleistothecia of some powdery mildews, the oospores of some downy mildews, and the teliospores of some rusts may not be produced, seasonal carry-over being by asexual spores, perennial mycelium or infected plants present throughout the year. Hyperparasitic or epiphytic fungi may reduce the development of plant pathogens in some areas, sometimes preventing completion of their full life cycle, for example *Cerebella* (*Epicoccum*) on *Claviceps*. Pathogens may thus behave differently under different climatic conditions, a possibility that should always be borne in mind. Climate also affects vectors and a pathogen may be absent because its vectors are lacking or present in insufficient numbers.

Some fungal pathogens may be unable to attack the roots of potential host plants because of the absence of nematodes through whose feeding lesions they normally invade and unfavourable soil conditions, including *p*H, may prevent the establishment of some soil borne pathogens. In their interesting paper on the prediction of plant disease occurrence Reichert and Palti (1967) point out that temperature is likely to be the major factor governing the occurrence of plant pathogens in areas of moderate to high rainfall. In arid and semiarid conditions, however, the length of the period during which moisture is available is mostly the limiting factor, this being dependent on dew, irrigation and other practices (for example density of stand) which influence moisture conditions within the crop. Thus, *Synchytrium endobioticum* (potato wart disease) is inhibited by temperatures exceeding 21–23°C so that, even if introduced, this pathogen is unlikely to develop in areas where soil temperatures rise to about 30°C, as happens in many countries in the tropics and warm arid zones. *Corticium* (*Sclerotium*) *rolfsii*, a root and seedling pathogen of many plants in the warmer areas of the world, is likely to occur in climates where mean temperatures of 20–30°C coincide with considerable rainfall, and will be restricted to irrigated summer crops in arid and semiarid regions. *Xanthomonas citri* (citrus canker) thrives at temperatures above about 20°C in areas with rain throughout the year but is not likely to develop in regions with dry summers, such as in many Mediterranean countries.

Reliable predictions as to the plant pathogens which are likely to flourish in the climatic and agricultural conditions of a particular region would be very useful in deciding which crops or varieties of crops can safely be grown. Such predictions depend on having a fairly detailed knowledge of the relationships between plant pathogens and their environment but such information is available for only relatively few pathogens.

Slow climatic changes occurring in a region over long periods of time will eventually influence the pathogens which attack the crop plants therein. Thus, the recent marked increase in *Colletotrichum coffeanum* (coffee berry disease) in East Africa may be due mainly to a climatic change towards wetter, cooler conditions which favour infection by the fungus (Bent, 1969).* Moore (1940) has attributed the increase of *Puccinia antirrhini* (snapdragon rust) in north-west Europe in the middle 1930's to a succession of hot summers which began in 1933. In this situation any reliable information on long-range climatic trends would be useful in fore-casting the likely incidence of plant pathogens on a long term basis.

On a smaller scale the increasing pollution of the environment brought about by man might result in weakened plants more liable to attack by some pathogens, or chemical pollutants might control certain pathogens – as in the case of sulphur dioxide controlling *Diplocarpon rosae* (black spot) on roses (Saunders, 1966).

* This view is questioned by Griffiths and Waller (1971) who, after a critical analysis of climatic data, were unable to find any significant climatic differences between the 1960's and the 1950's.

21 The forecasting of plant diseases

Plant diseases vary in incidence from season to season owing to differences in the amount of inoculum, environmental conditions, numbers and activity of vectors, and other factors which affect the development and spread of pathogens. Effective control measures are worthwhile in a year of severe disease but unnecessary in others, and reliable forecasting of the likely incidence of plant diseases can thus save the farmer a great deal of money provided it can be done sufficiently early for him to organize effective control measures. Equally important, it will enable him to avoid wasting time and money on unnecessary control measures.

Empirical forecasting of the likely incidence of various plant diseases has been carried out for many years. It has often been based on practical experience and field observations on disease outbreaks in relation to weather conditions, certain types of weather being favourable to certain diseases. For example, warm, damp weather with overcast skies is 'potato blight weather', whereas warm, dry weather encourages some powdery mildews. Temperature and moisture are usually the guiding factors as these are easily observed and are of critical importance in the development of many diseases. More systematic forecasting based on measurable data has developed since the Second World War although warning services against potato blight and apple scab have been in operation for much longer than this in some countries.

From an agricultural point of view the prime importance of plant disease forecasting lies in the possibility of thereby developing effective warning systems. Forecasts based on weather conditions during the crop season may be useless in this respect as the pathogen may already be incubating in the plants by the time that an accurate warning can be made. Such 'late warnings' are likely to be unsatisfactory, and to be effective a warning should predict the infection date in good time. Ideally the aim should be to give the cultivator as much time as possible to organize control measures before the pathogen is likely to attack the crop. Reliable forecasting is sometimes possible only a few days before the infection date and it is essential to get the warning to cultivators as quickly as possible using such communication media as radio, television, telephone, newspapers, local agricultural officers and so on.

It is equally important that forecasts should be correct. Complete reliability is rarely possible but to be effective a disease warning system must have the confidence of cultivators, and this involves being right most of the time. The forecaster naturally tends to cover himself by predicting epiphytotics whenever there is a chance of their occurrence, thus occasionally forecasting outbreaks which fail to develop. On the other hand he can save growers the expense of costly control measures by accurately forecasting low disease incidence. There are, however, borderline cases in which it is impossible to be sure whether a disease is likely to be severe or otherwise.

Forecasting and warning systems involve considerable expense and are only likely to be economically justifiable (1) for destructive diseases of important cash or food crops, (2) for diseases which can be reliably predicted early enough for effective control measures to be applied, and (3) for diseases against which control measures are available and economical to use. If a disease can be reliably predicted before the crop is sown it may be advisable to plant a resistant instead of a susceptible variety, or even a different crop altogether, or to delay or advance the sowing date, in years when severe outbreaks are forecast. When presowing forecasting is not possible the farmer will probably have to resort to chemical methods of control – application of fungicides, or insecticides against insect vectors. If a disease can only be reliably forecast after its appearance it may sometimes be worthwhile to rogue out infected plants provided that they are not too numerous, that the operation can be done as soon as the disease appears, and that the pathogen involved is one which spreads fairly slowly.

Reliable forecasting of diseases which are controlled by fungicidal spraying of the crop can be useful to the farmer in several ways. Not only will it help him to decide whether or not to spray his fields but, equally important, it will enable him to apply the fungicide at a time when it will give maximum protection. Accurate prediction of an infection date is important in this, bearing in mind that most fungicidal sprays are preventive rather than curative. The effectiveness of spraying depends not only on using an effective fungicide properly applied in the right quantity but also on applying it at the right time. If applied at the wrong time it is likely to be rather ineffective and may necessitate a further application. Hence the timing of the first and of subsequent applications of a fungicide is of critical importance, and prediction of infection dates can be helpful in this respect.

Predictions of the likely incidence of pathogens in areas with different climates can also be useful in, for example, growing plants for seed. Such plants can be grown in places climatically or otherwise unfavourable to individual seed borne pathogens. Seed from cotton plants grown under irrigation in arid regions is unlikely to carry *Xanthomonas malvacearum*, a bacterial pathogen which is favoured by wet conditions. Seed potatoes are grown in areas unfavourable to the insect vectors of virus diseases; the incidence of potato leaf roll in certain hilly parts of the British Isles, for example Northern Scotland, is much reduced because the aphid vectors are discouraged by the fairly low temperatures, high humidity and high wind velocities. Predictions based on the known climatic requirements of pathogens and the climate of the region concerned can indicate whether a particular pathogen is likely to become serious if introduced into that region. The potentialities of this method of producing pathogen-free seed are now being explored.

Methods used in forecasting

A rational system of prediction should be based on those factors which influence the initial appearance and subsequent spread of the pathogen. These factors are numerous and, in practice, attention is concentrated on a few of the more important ones. Thorough knowledge of the life cycle of the pathogen, the ways in which it overwinters and spreads, and the method of infection is also necessary, as is knowledge of the susceptibility of the plant at different stages of growth.

A general procedure for devising forecasting systems for fungal parasites of plants has been outlined by Weille (1965). The environmental conditions necessary for the overwintering, development and spread of the fungus are first investigated under controlled conditions in the laboratory. A 'tentative climatological model' is thus formulated which indicates the sequence of climatic conditions that obtain at specified times of the day in relation to the events of the infection cycle (sporulation, spore dispersal, infection). This tentative model is then tested in the field, with observations on disease development in relation to meteorological conditions. In the light of these results a more precise definitive model is constructed; some of the factors involved in this will be in terms of microclimate and these have to be related to meteorological data as conventionally measured (macroclimate). This is done empirically and several synoptic model situations are thus determined which cover all weather conditions likely to encourage epiphytotics. Disease incidence can then be forecast by reference to these synoptic weather maps. This may sound relatively straightforward but '. . . the relationship of weather to plant disease is the net result of the action, reaction and interaction of an extremely complex set of operations' (Bourke, 1970) and, in practice, it is necessary to select the key weather factors for inclusion in the model and to discard those of minor importance and this selection is likely to be a problem.

The methods used in forecasting mostly fall into four main groups based on: (1) weather conditions during the intercrop months, particularly as affects survival of inoculum, (2) weather conditions during the crop season, (3) the amount of disease in the young crop, and (4) the numbers of propagules of the pathogen in the air, soil, or planting material.

Weather conditions during the intercrop period

These are usually related to survival of the pathogen or its vectors between crops. Intercrop weather which reduces overwintering of the pathogen or its vector is likely to minimize inoculum sources for the following crop. The kind of intercrop weather which permits overwintering can be determined by observation and experiment, and can be used in forecasting. The severity of blue mould (*Peronospora tabacina*) of tobacco in the southern U.S.A. appears to be closely related to winter temperatures, especially those in January. The disease appeared early and tended to become severe – depending on the weather during the crop season – when January temperatures were above normal and approached the optimum for mildew infection ($16 \cdot 5°C$). Low temperatures in January led to late appearance of blue mould and relatively little damage even when conditions during the growing season were favourable for its spread. The basis of this relationship is not understood, but it may be that cold winters destroy the overwintering phase of the fungus, possible oospores or subsidiary hosts. Outbreaks of the disease further north in Ontario, Canada, are thought to originate from spores blown in from tobacco areas of the U.S.A., and the severity of blue mould in the latter areas could thus be used to forecast its likely incidence in Ontario. The 2–3 weeks which separate the appearance of the disease in the two areas would give ample warning, but weather conditions in relation to spore dissemination and disease development would also need to be considered.

A somewhat different case is that of bacterial wilt of maize caused by *Xanthomonas stewarti*. In the U.S.A. the bacteria overwinter in adult flea beetles which tend to die during a cold winter – hence a mild winter is likely to be followed by severe wilt, and *vice versa*. In Illinois it is said that if the sum of the monthly mean temperatures for December to February exceeds $32°C$ wilt will occur and if it exceeds $37 \cdot 8°C$ it will probably be severe. In New York, however, wilt was severe at temperature indexes above $32°C$ and light to moderate below $32°C$. Other factors are no doubt involved in the survival of the beetles during the winter, and this case indicates that a forecasting system which is reliable in one area is not necessarily so in another. The incidence of curly top of sugarbeet in parts of the U.S.A. is related to the numbers of the leafhopper vectors which successfully overwinter on weeds and to the earliness of their movement into the beet fields. A very hot, dry summer kills many of the weeds involved and a cold winter reduces the number of hibernating insects. Hence a study of the weather and the behaviour of the leafhoppers on their weed hosts enables forecasts of curly top incidence to be made before the new beet crop is planted.

Forecasts based on weather conditions during the intercrop period are fairly simple to carry out and in some diseases are surprisingly reliable. They can be made before the new crop is sown, but under very favourable conditions a rapidly multiplying pathogen may be able to develop epiphytotically from even the small amount of inoculum surviving a winter unfavourable to it. In such cases forecasts based on overwintering of inoculum should be treated with caution.

Weather conditions during the crop season

Weather is critically important in the development and spread of many pathogens and is thus used in forecasting some diseases. The meteorological factors which form the basis of such predictions are usually temperature and moisture (humidity, rain), outbreaks being likely to occur when certain combinations of these obtain for a certain period of time. These combinations will, of course, be different for different diseases and may vary for the same disease in areas with different climatic and agricultural conditions. The effects of weather on plant diseases are complex, influencing not only the events of the infection cycle but also the resistance of the plant, its ability to throw off or survive attacks, and the numbers and activity of any vectors of the pathogen. Hence the results of laboratory experiments on the effects of meteorological factors on pathogens, although valuable, are not always a completely reliable indication as to what happens under the more varied conditions of the field. Detailed observations over a number of years may be necessary before forecasting systems based on weather conditions can be formulated with confidence.

Forecasting of late blight of potato, caused by *Phytophthora infestans*, has been intensively investigated in Europe, the British Isles, the U.S.A. and elsewhere, and there is an extensive literature on the subject (see Miller and O'Brien, 1957 for a useful summary; also Bourke, 1955). The first successful warning system was in Holland where the four 'Dutch rules' were formulated about 40 years ago. The appearance of blight depended on (1) a night temperature below dew point for at least 4 hours (that is dew for at least this time); (2) a minimum temperature of 10°C or above; (3) a mean cloudiness on the next day of at least 0·8; and (4) at least 0·1 mm of rain during the next 24 hours. This method of forecasting has given good results in Holland but in south-west England it was found that the four rules could be reduced to two, *viz.* a minimum temperature of 10°C and a relative humidity not falling below 75% for at least 2 days. When applied in south-west England the Dutch rules tended to forecast blight appearance earlier than actually happened (Beaumont, 1947).

Blight can be expected 2–3 weeks after such a Beaumont period, provided inoculum is present and the plants are susceptible. Allowance has to be made for seasonal and regional differences in the growth of the crop and Beaumont periods are usually taken as relevant for main crop potatoes from about the last week in June onwards, somewhat earlier in south-west England. Successful regional forecasts of outbreak dates can be made for all parts of England and Wales based upon the occurrence of Beaumont periods as recorded at a network of synoptic meteorological stations (the operations chart method). Various modifications of this method of forecasting potato blight have been suggested from time to time and Grainger (1955) has designed a self-calculating blight forecast recorder (the Auchincruive Recorder) which simultaneously records temperature and humidity. The humidity pen is calibrated to give a line coinciding with the temperature line at 75% relative humidity and Beaumont periods can thus be easily recognized. This instrument has given promising results and similar ones could no doubt be designed for other diseases.

Some idea of the complex relationship between weather and blight is given by the results of laboratory experiments in the U.S.A. reported by Crosier (1934, cited in Bourke, 1953). Sporangia were formed at a relative humidity of nearly 100% plus a temperature of 18–25°C for at least 6 hours, or at a humidity of 100% at 12–15°C for at least 12 hours. Sporangia lose their viability in 1–2 hours at 20–40% air humidity or in 3–6 hours at 50–80% humidity, so favourable conditions for their germination must obtain soon after their formation. These conditions are the presence of moisture and a fairly low temperature (10–15°C) for 0·5–2 hours – at lower or higher temperatures germination is slower and less. Infection of the plant by the zoospores liberated from the sporangia requires at least 2–2·5 hours at 10–25°C and the fungus thereafter develops most rapidly at 18–21°C. The incubation period is 3–5 days under favourable conditions but may be much longer at high temperatures.

A preliminary model for identifying blight weather in Ireland has been prepared by Bourke (1953) for use with standard hourly meteorological reports. It requires minimal conditions of (1) at least 12 hours of high humidity (90% or more) and a temperature of 10°C or above: conditions favourable for production of sporangia, and (2) free moisture on the leaves for a subsequent period of at least 4 hours (for germination and infection) or, if there is no rain, conditions which ensure a film of condensed water for that time (that is, relative humidity at least 90%). Working models of this sort can be very useful in disease forecasting although, as Bourke (1953) points out, to be workable they inevitably suffer the defects of over-simplification and over-rigidity. In a general way dry and/or sunny anticyclonic weather is unfavourable to blight while muggy overcast weather favours it. There are, however, variations in different areas. In Lima (Peru), for example, the humidity at night rather than during the day seems to be important in blight development, the disease being favoured by nocturnal humidity above 95%, only slight variation in daily tempera-ture, and minimum temperatures of 10–13°C. Danger of blight infection is slight when night humidity is less than 95% (Miller and O'Brien, 1957). A multiple regression equation between blight infection and weather has been developed in Germany by Schrodter and Ullrich (1965). This is thought to hold good with field measurements of macroclimate and might form a basis for predicting epiphytotics. The same workers also describe a method of 'negative prognosis' based on weather conditions during the interval between emergence of early potatoes and the onset of an epiphy-totic, the period during which severe outbreaks are unlikely as determined from measurements of temperature, humidity and rainfall (Ullrich and Schrodter, 1966).

Since 1958, observations on blight incidence have been statistically correlated with weather conditions at fifteen trial sites in representative potato-growing areas of the German Federal Republic to provide the basis of a forecasting system, as described by Bourke (1970). This system takes account of four different stages in the life cycle of *Phytophthora infestans* which laboratory work has shown to be related to different kinds of weather. These stages are: (1) sporulation, which requires 10 hours or more of moist conditions (i.e. hours during which there is measurable precipitation or at least 90% relative humidity); (2) germination of the sporangia and infection of the plant, requiring moist conditions for over 4 hours; (3) mycelial growth, depending on temperature but not on moisture; and, (4) suppression of spread of the pathogen in dry periods when the relative humidity is less than 70%. The different weather sequences are weighted by multiplying them by empirically derived para-meters in accordance with the air temperature, that for dry periods being of course negative.

Data on temperature, relative humidity and rainfall are recorded at some fifty weather reporting stations, codified on a weekly basis, and fed into a computer which weights the observations with the appropriate parameters and calculates a weekly weather rating. A current total weather rating is obtained each week by adding together the weekly ratings starting from a known average date of emergence of early potato crops. A total rating less than 150 warrants a negative forecast and the date on which 150 is reached (the first critical date) is an alert at which growers are advised to be on the look-out for blight, which is likely to appear 10–40 days later. Immediate control measures are implemented when the total weather rating reaches 270, the disease normally appearing between 15 days before and 15 days after this second critical date. This system has been in practical operation since 1967 and has given promising results which are likely to improve when the weather ratings from a group of stations, rather than that from the nearest station, are taken into account by growers and when adjustments are made for the varying dates of emergence of the plants.

Forecasting and warning systems for other downy mildew diseases have been devised. That for grape mildew (*Plasmopara viticola*) was one of the earliest and has been in operation in parts of Europe for more than 40 years. Warnings are issued as soon as the weather favours germination of the oospores and infection of the plants. In the Perugia (Italy) area outbreaks are likely if the dew point is higher than 12°C, the minimum temperature for germination. In France the first outbreaks are predicted from the presence of active oospores, temperatures above 11°C and precipitation keeping the soil surface wet for several days. Secondary spread depends on active sporangia, rain and a temperature over 8°C, particularly on persistent moisture on the leaves for 6 hours or more at 11–20°C. Generally speaking, epiphytotics of this disease are likely if the nights are warm, humid and with heavy dew or mists, or in rainy weather, particularly if lack of sunshine prolongs the persistence of moisture. Fungicidal spraying is based on the forecasts and some systems also take into account the rate of growth and production of new unprotected foliage. According to Miller and O'Brien (1952) in some years forecasting has reduced the number of spray applications from five or six to one or two. In 1938 it is said to have saved spray materials in south-west France valued at 200 million francs, and on the average two applications a year are saved, equivalent to 20 kg of copper sulphate per ha or about 30,000 tonnes for the whole of France. The German 'incubation calendar', based on temperature and moisture conditions, appears to be a highly reliable guide to spraying and its use is thought to have resulted in great increases in yield during the period 1913–1938.

Forecasting other downy mildews including *Pseudoperonospora cubensis* on cucurbits and *Phytophthora phaseoli* on Lima bean has been investigated. The latter is predicted on a rainfall-temperature basis. A day is considered favourable for the disease when the 5 day mean moving temperature (as recorded graphically) is less than 26°C with the minimum 7°C or above, and the 10 day total rainfall 3·05 cm or more. The disease is likely to appear after about 8 consecutive favourable days (Hyre, 1957). Similar systems could no doubt be devised for other downy mildews, for example *Pseudo-*

peronospora humuli on hops, but the expense involved can only be justified in the case of destructive disease of important crops.

Although attention has been concentrated on downy mildew diseases, the forecasting of others has been investigated in recent years. The spread of leaf spot of groundnut caused by *Mycosphaerella berkeleyii* (*Cercospora personata*) and *M. arachidicola* (*C. arachidicola*) in Georgia, U.S.A., is favoured by diurnal periods of 10 hours or longer with relative humidity at or above 95% and with temperatures above about 21°C during these periods; this might be used in predicting outbreaks (Jensen and Boyle, 1965, 1966). In Ceylon a simple calculating device has been designed by Kerr and Rodrigo (1967a) to enable tea growers to forecast the incidence of blister blight (*Exobasidium vexans*) 2–3 weeks later. This is based on percentage infection on the youngest two leaves and a bud, picked and brought to the factory, and duration of sunshine. The latter is negatively correlated with duration of surface wetness (Kerr and Rodrigo, 1967), which influences spore germination and infection.

Amount of disease in the young crop

This has given successful results in forecasting wheat leaf rust (*Puccinia rubigo-vera f.sp. tritici* = *P. recondita*) in Oklahoma, U.S.A. (Chester, 1942). The wheat fields become infected by inoculum chiefly from overwintered local infections, and the weather during December–March, especially that in March, is critical in determining infection. The amount of infection at the beginning of April largely determines the subsequent development of the disease until harvesting in June since the weather during April–June is almost always favourable to it. Overwintering and early development of the disease are periodically assessed by counting the number of rust sori on a thousand tillers of a susceptible variety of wheat (Cheyenne), and the extent to which these findings apply over the whole area is estimated by a statewide survey at the end of March. Two–three thousand sori per 1000 tillers on 1st April indicates about 5% loss of crop, which is about average in most years. If rust is likely to be severe the farmer has still time in which to abandon the crop in favour of others. Although there may be some rust multiplication during occasional mild moist spells in winter the rust concentration is usually low (often less than one sorus per 3000 leaves) by late winter. The fungus does not increase to any extent below about 10°C since uredospore germination, infection and incubation are slow and uncertain below this temperature. In Oklahoma March is the first month in which temperatures approximate to 10°C and this month is therefore a critical one. Thereafter, conditions are generally favourable to rust development but to reach epiphytotic proportions the pathogen has to reproduce itself some thirty million-fold (to about 100 pustules per leaf) and this requires several consecutive generations, each of about 10 days. The vital early stages of multiplication take place at a time (March) when conditions for the fungus tend to be rather borderline and can thus be decisive in the overall development of the disease. Winter temperatures are also involved to some extent but are less important. The general conclusion is that the development of leaf rust on winter wheat in the spring is determined largely by the weather conditions (especially temperature and precipitation) during the spring month in which the mean temperature is near 10°C. This is March in Oklahoma, April in Illinois, and mid-April to mid-May in New York (see Chester, 1946). Elsewhere the critical month may be earlier or later – for example, January in India, May in Canada, and forecasting systems might be devised accordingly.

The epidemiology of leaf rust of wheat in Oklahoma is interesting in that there seem to be three phases involved: (1) a winter period which allows the pathogen to survive, but only at a rather low level, (2) a critical month or so in which the conditions permit its increase to varying extents and so largely determine its subsequent severity, and (3) a period favourable to spread of the pathogen from the inoculum produced in (2). It is possible that a similar situation holds for other pathogens, but no others seem to have been described.

Amount of inoculum in air, soil or planting material

Perhaps the best example of this is apple and pear scab (*Venturia inaequalis, V. pirina*). In some areas seasonal inoculum originates from conidia produced on infected shoots but more often from ascospores liberated from perithecia in leaves on the ground. In the latter case scab outbreaks are likely to be associated with discharge of ascospores in relation to development of the foliage, and forecasting can be based on this. The perithecia mature through the winter and in Germany the temperature after March 1st is said to be critical as regards ascospore discharge. Holz (1939, cited by Miller and O'Brien, 1957) concluded that the sooner a mean day temperature aggregate of 105°C (over 15 days) is reached after March 1st the sooner the perithecia will ripen. Moisture also plays a part in this and ripening may be delayed by drought in early spring. Ascospore discharge usually occurs a week or so earlier on scabbed leaves incubated under warm, moist conditions in the laboratory than on those in the orchard, and this gives time for warnings to be sent out. The number of ascospores in the air can be determined by spore traps set up in orchards or, more usually, by observing emission of ascospores from perithecia in scabbed leaves brought into the laboratory. In France the warning threshold for *V. pirina* on pears was about 1000–1500 ascospores per hour when the tree was between full bloom and fruit swell. In New York State fungicidal spraying is based on temperature and moisture, since perithecia discharge only when thoroughly wetted and infection is likely after 30 hours of leaf wetness at 5°C, 14 hours at 10°C, or 9·5 hours at 15°C, the temperatures being the mean over the period (Mills, 1944; Mills and La Plante, 1954). In England it was found that 'Smith Periods' were as satisfactory as 'Mills Periods'. The former are similar to the latter except that hours of 90% relative humidity or more, following rain, are substituted for leaf wetness (Preece and Smith, 1961). This enables meteorological data to be used for forecasting instead of a surface wetness recorder. From a study of spring rainfall as related to scab incidence Preece (1961) concluded that the total April rainfall usually determines the severity of the disease in England, and that many years which have a wet April also have a wet May. Spraying against scab has been carried out according to a calendar based on the stage of development of the flowers, for example at green bud, pink bud, petal fall and a further spray 2 weeks later.

Some diseases originate from inoculum blown in from distant sources and information on the incidence of the disease in such source areas, if known, can be of value in predicting the date and severity of outbreak in the receiving area. This may be supplemented by spore trapping to determine when inoculum begins to arrive in dangerously large quantities. Knowledge of the circulation of the air currents which transport the inoculum is also likely to be useful, as discussed by Zadoks (1965) in an interesting account of the epidemiology of three rusts which attack wheat in Europe.

The distribution and concentration of plant pathogens in the soil can be used to predict the likely distribution and intensity of the disease in a susceptible crop planted in that soil. Numerous ergot sclerotia in a field could bring about severe outbreaks of the disease under suitable weather conditions. The amount of soil borne inoculum can be determined very approximately from the severity of the disease in the preceding crop, or samples of the soil can be assayed in the laboratory. Such soil testing is reported by Melville and Hawken (1967) to provide a reliable means of forecasting the incidence of club root in susceptible brassica crops in south-west England. Healthy rape seedlings, about 10 days old, are planted in pots containing the soil to be assayed. The water content is kept at about 70% maximum water holding capacity under standardized conditions in the glasshouse, together with adequate controls, and the plants are washed out and examined for club root after 5–6 weeks. In severe cases there is usually one large club on the tap root while in less severe infections only the lateral roots are affected.

Similar methods have been devised for other soil borne pathogens, for example *Aphanomyces cochlioides* (root rot of beet: Fink, 1948) and by laboratory assay of the microsclerotia of *Verticillium albo-atrum* using tomato plants (Wilhelm, 1950) or growth on culture media (Easton, 1967).

Methods have been described for assaying the sclerotia of *Sclerotium cepivorum* (onion white rot) by wet sieving (McCain, 1967), and the micro-sclerotia of *Macrophomina phaseoli* (stem blight of beans) by flotation (Watanabe, Smith and Snyder, 1967), to mention but two, and these could no doubt be used to predict disease incidence in susceptible plants subsequently planted in the soil. Similar methods could probably be used for soil borne nematodes and insect pests. Assay of plant pathogen popula-tions in soil is reviewed by Menzies (1963*a*).

Some pathogens are partly or exclusively seed borne and the degree of contamination or infection of planting material can be a useful indication of likely disease incidence. The amount of seed borne pathogen can be estimated in the laboratory, by germinating the seed under conditions suitable for development of the disease, or even from observations of disease incidence in the plants which produced the seed. Infected or con-taminated planting material can then be rejected or treated to render it safe for sowing, so that forecasting and control are here combined. This has particular relevance to seed borne smuts and bacteria and to virus infected planting material but its use could be extended to many pathogens which are borne on or in the planting material.

In recent years forecasting of potato skin spot (*Oospora pustulans*) has been suggested in Scotland (Boyd and Lennard, 1962). Infection of the tubers occurs at or about lifting time and is encouraged by damp conditions as well as by low temperature during storage. Over the period 1927–60 above average rainfall during September 21st–October 31st (taken as the lifting period) and below average temperature during October–December were closely related to the incidence of skin spot in the following season. A similar but less well marked correlation was obtained when October rain-fall figures were used.

Several other methods of forecasting plant diseases have been used with varying degrees of success. It has been observed that *Gnomonia veneta* (anthracnose of sycamore) regularly appears a few days before vine downy mildew in France and this could be used in forecasting. Similar correla-tions might be found with other pathogens although the scope of this method seems limited. The forecasting of rice blast (*Pyricularia oryzae*) has been studied in Japan for about 40 years. It is based largely on over-wintering of the fungus, conidial production and the appearance of conidia in the rice fields, and weather as related to the development of rice plants. 'Prediction fields' are established and examined for appearance of the disease, and are sown with susceptible early varieties which tend to become severely infected before the disease appears on other varieties (see Salmon, 1951). Somewhat similar prediction fields, sown 10 days earlier than normal and with extra nitrogen added, are used to predict several rusts attacking barley and wheat in Japan, these being used in conjunction with weather conditions and spore counts in relation to plant development.

Forecasting of vector borne pathogens, notably viruses, may be based on numbers and activity of the vectors, as with sugarbeet yellows in England. Hurst (1965) has shown that disease incidence is positively correlated with air temperature in winter and spring, and that it can be fairly accurately forecast from the average temperature in February. Winter conditions affect the survival of the green aphid vector, *Myzus persicae*, and if active insects survive the winter the sugarbeet crop is likely to be infected early. Spraying with systemic insecticides is generally carried out when the aphid population reaches an average of one green aphid per four plants: details are given by Hull (1968).

Another case in which forecasting is proving to be very useful is that of timber decay, as described by Chester (1950). Knowledge of the amount of decay in timber enables felling to be carried out at the most suitable time with regard to yield and quality. Decay can be assessed by such criteria as the presence and number of fructifications of the fungi involved, the presence of injuries, rotten branch stubs or of fire damage.

Many methods of forecasting are based on a survey of the viable inoculum available at the beginning of the crop season. These methods provide an early warning but have the disadvantage that many other factors may subsequently modify the course of the expected outbreak – unsuitable weather may prevent disease development despite the presence of ample inoculum. Other systems are based on weather conditions during the crop season, but these assume the presence of sufficient inoculum and will be irrelevant if this is not available. Forecasting systems should therefore take account of inoculum sources as well as the many factors, including weather, which affect the development and spread of the pathogen. Forecasting may be **empirical**, in which correlation is sought between the results of disease surveys and the corresponding weather factors in a particular area, or **fundamental**, in which the effects of different weather factors (moisture, temperature and so on) on plant and parasite, singly and together, are investigated in the laboratory and the conclusions extrapolated to the field, as described by Bourke (1955). In practice the two methods tend to merge. The results obtained in laboratory studies have in the final analysis to be tested under field conditions, and empirical forecasting has to be related to the biology of plant and pathogen.

Reliable forecasting can enable a farmer to apply control measures at the optimum time and, as in downy mildew of grapevine, it may enable the number of fungicidal sprays to be reduced. Early forecasts give the farmer sufficient time to rearrange his crop schedules and so avoid growing a susceptible crop in a season when disease is likely to be severe. Increasing interest is being taken in disease forecasting and this is an aspect of epidemiology which is of great practical value to all engaged in intensive cultivation of plants. Reviews are given by Miller (1959), Miller and O'Brien (1952, 1957), Waggoner (1960) and Wallin (1967: ground level climate and disease forecasting).

22 The assessment of disease incidence and crop loss

One of the most difficult problems of plant pathology is that of accurately assessing the incidence of disease in crops and relating this to subsequent loss in terms of yield and money. This is a complex subject whose numerous ramifications have been explored in detail by Chester (1950). It is important to the farmer who has to decide whether the monetary losses due to a disease warrant the trouble and expense of applying control measures. The monetary losses caused by diseases or the expense of controlling them are likely to be passed on to the consumer in the form of higher retail prices or government subsidies to the farmer, so that all users of agricultural produce will be adversely affected. Those responsible for the organization of research on plant diseases must have reasonably accurate knowledge of the economic importance of individual diseases if they are to apply their limited resources to the best advantage. This applies to all forms of plant damage whether due to pathogens, insect pests, nematodes, weeds, or other causes.

As Chester (1955) observes, the accuracy of disease appraisal in the field cannot approach that achieved in carefully controlled laboratory experiments, and he suggests that an error not greater than ±10% would be a reasonable target. Underestimates of losses can convey the false impression that a disease is of no economic importance, whereas overestimates may result in limited resources being concentrated on a particular disease to the neglect of other more destructive ones. Hence a reasonable degree of accuracy is essential and if this is not forthcoming there seems to be little point in making the assessment. Some of the published figures on disease losses are probably educated guesses rather than reasonably accurate estimates and, indeed, it is often difficult to assess the accuracy of the methods used in making the estimate.

Painstaking field measurements supplemented by detailed experiments in laboratory and glasshouse, carried out over several years, may be necessary before reliable methods of assessment can be devised for some diseases. With others, as where the plant is killed by the pathogen, the problem may be less difficult. In considering the losses caused by diseases, pests and weeds one should logically include the cost of control measures and also the expenditure involved in developing them. In some cases it may be necessary to grow a disease resistant but commercially less valuable variety of crop plant rather than a more valuable but susceptible variety, and this loss must also be attributed to the disease. Severe outbreaks of disease may lead to the abandonment of valuable crops, as with coffee rust in Ceylon, or centres of cultivation may have to be moved together with processing machinery, factories, administrative buildings, and other equipment; this is likely to involve considerable expenditure debitable to the disease.

Losses caused by diseases and pests are significant from another point of view, that is, that more hectares of the crop have to be grown to satisfy current demand, so that a proportion of the cultivated area is un-productive and the cost of cultivation thereof is wasted – the 'untaken harvest' discussed by Ordish (1952). In the absence of disease and in comparable conditions the same yield will be obtained from fewer hectares and the fields thus saved can be used for other crops or animals.

Diseases can be rather arbitrarily classified in various ways with respect to the crop losses they cause. Stakman and Harrar (1957) classify those of growing plants as disfiguring, debilitating, devastating, limiting, or annihilating. Others have attempted to classify diseases on a percentage loss basis (see Chester, 1950), suggesting five categories: (1) diseases which are thought to cause negligible losses, perhaps less than 1% – but some included here probably cause greater losses; (2) widespread diseases which apparently cause only minor losses, perhaps about 1% in many seasons; (3) those which cause about 1–5% loss and occasionally become severe in some areas or seasons; (4) those causing about 5–10% loss in most seasons and becoming very destructive in some; and (5) highly destructive diseases which cause more than 20% loss in most seasons and which, if uncontrolled, can result in the crop becoming uneconomic. These categories are of course very approximate and a pathogen may fall into different categories in different areas. Precise data on crop losses due to pathogens are usually not available and individual pathologists often have somewhat different ideas as to the losses caused by a particular pathogen. It is especially difficult to distinguish between the first three categories with any degree of confidence.

On a qualitative basis Chester (1950) suggests eight ways in which dis-eases reduce the value of a crop: (1) those which severely disable and frequently kill the plant, as damping-off and some root diseases; (2) those which destroy the commercially valuable parts of the plant, for example, fruit rots, boll rot of cotton, grain smuts of cereals, and flower blights; (3) those which destroy or sterilize the reproductive structures of the plant, thus causing complete or partial sterility – some viruses, ergot, inflores-cence smuts (some of these also come into the previous category); (4)

those which weaken and retard growth without killing the plant – some root diseases, some viruses, severe attack by foliage pathogens; (5) those which indirectly reduce yield or quality of the crop by reducing the efficiency of the plant, as in foliage diseases which adversely affect photosynthesis, or root diseases which reduce translocation; (6) those which render the product poisonous or unpalatable, as in ergot of rye; (7) those which cause deterioration of the harvested product during transport or storage; and (8) those which disfigure the product – petal spotting, blemishes on fruits and vegetables. These categories are not completely distinct and several are involved in such diseases as potato blight.

Three main categories of disease damage have been suggested by Grainger (1959). In the first category the whole plant is killed, damaged or debilitated, as in systemic virus and root diseases; in the second only localized parts of the plant or crop are affected, for example leaf spots and seedling diseases which thin the stand; in the third category the effects of a disease outbreak persist over several seasons, as with soil borne pathogens.

Some pathogens, often obligate parasites, generally attack vigorously growing plants and so affect the crop most in seasons of potentially high yield. They thus tend to reduce fluctuations in crop yields. Others, often relatively unspecialized parasites such as root-rotting fungi, attack chiefly weakened plants with the result that they cause greatest damage in seasons unfavourable to growth and thus exaggerate seasonal fluctuations in yield. In the first case it is possible for a diseased crop in a 'good' season to outyield a less severely diseased crop in a 'poor' season although in the former the pathogen is in fact causing greater loss of crop. The favourable effect of the environment may thus outweigh the harmful effects of the disease except in seasons when the latter develops in epiphytotic form. These considerations sometimes lead to false conclusions regarding the relative crop losses due to the two types of pathogen. Neither is the conspicuousness of symptoms always a reliable indication as to the effect of the pathogen on the plant and its yield as in chocolate spot (*Botrytis fabae*) of beans, which, although conspicuous, was found to have a negligible effect on yield (Grainger, 1959). Conversely, even a few leaf lesions may result in extensive defoliation and plant damage, as in *Diplocarpon rosae* (black spot) on some varieties of rose.

Disease, although injuring or killing individual plants, may occasionally result in increased yields. If a field is sown too thickly, thinning out of the seedlings by disease may be beneficial in promoting optimum plant populations per hectare – this, however, is not a practice to be recommended, and less risky methods of obtaining optimum plant populations are preferable. Some disease products such as ergots are articles of commerce, and the colour breaking of flowers due to certain viruses has long been of horticultural value. Leaf diseases which come in at the end of the season may hasten the drying-up and so expedite harvesting of the crop. Chester (1946) makes the interesting observation that hay made from wheat infected by leaf rust contains much more protein than that made from healthy plants, and this might be beneficial when the crop is used for forage. It is sometimes suggested that crop losses due to disease, pests and other causes reduce crop surpluses and so might be regarded as 'beneficial', but it is difficult to see how this can be true in a world in which under-nourishment and malnutrition are the rule rather than the exception. More effective methods of sending agricultural surpluses to areas where they are most needed would seem to be the solution.

Unappreciated damage caused by pathogens and pests

The severity of a disease is usually assessed on the differences between diseased plants and those which appear healthy but which are probably more accurately regarded as slightly diseased, since it is very doubtful whether completely healthy plants ever occur in the field. Apart from mechanical injury such plants are colonized and probably parasitized to varying extents by fungi, bacteria, insects, mites, nematodes and viruses although the damage may be so slight as to escape notice except on detailed examination. This is particularly true of damage to roots which are not normally visible but which frequently show varying amounts of discoloura-tion and pest injury when examined carefully. The effects of this appar-ently minor damage on yield are difficult to estimate since our methods of measuring them are far too crude to be of very much use. There is, how-ever, some indirect evidence that apparently minor pests and diseases, or those usually regarded as virtually harmless to the plant, may be respon-sible for damage and crop loss which is far from negligible. Potato virus X ('healthy potato virus') is estimated to have caused some 13% crop loss in the U.S.A. before its seriousness was realized and over the 20 years before control measures – certification and resistant varieties – were applied it probably caused an avoidable loss of at least 100 million bushels of pota-toes (Chester, 1955).

There are doubtless other diseases which cause considerable but unappreciated losses. Insecticidal spraying of lucerne in the apparent absence of any known important pest has resulted in considerable yield increases, and apparently minor soil nematodes and fungi probably cause appreciable losses in many crops. Partial sterilization of soil often results in greatly improved growth and increased yields in the apparent absence of major pathogens or pests. Some of this is undoubtedly due to beneficial microbiological effects, notably on nitrogen bacteria, but control of harmful soil borne pathogens, pests and nematodes may also be involved. These are aspects which merit detailed investigation.

Some plants which have been vegetatively propagated for many years probably contain viruses which cause ill defined or inconspicuous symptoms likely to be overlooked except on careful examination. Since most of the plants contain the virus the diseased crop is regarded as normal and 'healthy' although the virus may be causing appreciable crop loss. In some cases virus symptoms have been attributed to other causes. Such viruses are now being found and are probably present in many vegetatively propagated plants, ornamentals as well as agricultural ones. Several have been recorded on, for example, apple and cherry in recent years – Smith (1957) lists eight virus diseases of apple as compared with only one 20 years previously (Smith, 1937).

It seems, then, that what is commonly regarded as a disease-free crop is in fact rarely so. Present day yields, even in the apparent absence of diseases and pests, are probably well below what completely healthy plants can give, as suggested by results of field experiments in which plants are kept free from diseases and pests by repeated application of pesticides. Such elaborate and expensive control measures would rarely be economical to apply but there is probably a wide gap between present day yields and economically attainable ones. 'Normal' yield is sometimes taken to be that over large areas in good seasons, but may be used in the sense of an average, namely, that obtained in most years with average incidence of diseases and pests, and in practice corresponding to a long term average.

Pathogens and pests may adversely affect the quality as well as the yield of crops. Quality in this sense includes such aspects as the size, colour, taste and appearance (including presence of blemishes) of fruit and vegetables, the strength and length of fibres, and the durability and freedom from decay of timber. The nutritional value of the crop may be reduced, an aspect often disregarded, and this applies to products for human consumption as well as to forage crops. For example, anthracnose (*Colletotrichum graminicola*) attack on Sudan grass destroyed about 9% of the protein and fat in the herbage and increased its lignin content by about 20%, thus reducing its digestibility; the disease probably caused substantial reduction in quality without noticeably affecting the yield of dry matter (Burton, 1954). In some horticultural plants even a slight reduction in quality may render the product commercially unacceptable, as in flower blemishes on orchids, although the effect on yield in a quantitative sense is negligible.

Measuring disease intensity and crop loss

The objectives of disease appraisal are: (1) to measure the amount of disease present in terms of its prevalence (percentage diseased plants or organs) and severity on the individual plants, (2) to relate this to loss of crop, and (3) to evaluate this crop loss in financial terms and to assess its effects on the economy of the farm or plantation: this is largely a problem for agricultural economists and is not discussed here. The methods used in measuring plant disease are described in detail by Chester (1950) and more recently by Large (1966). They should be such that they hold good for different observers in different areas and different seasons – they must be comparable. They should be objective rather than subjective so that errors due to individual prejudice and misjudgement are eliminated as far as possible, and they should also be reasonably quick and simple to apply. Reduction in quality as well as quantity of crop may have to be taken into consideration. It is difficult to devise appraisal methods which comply with all these conditions and in practice the methods used are often compromises. The problem is further complicated in that the accuracy of the methods used is rarely known with confidence. Intensive techniques of assessment can be used in small experimental plots, together with statistically sound lay-out and sampling methods and these probably yield more accurate results than observational methods over large areas of crop but are feasible only for small areas.

Large (1966) has pointed out that devising methods of disease assessment involves a detailed knowledge of the disease and the way in which it affects the plant. He suggests a 'strategy of investigation' applicable to many diseases along the following lines. Studies are made of the morphology and development of the healthy plant from sowing to harvest and the course of the disease on plants in the field, over the whole range of attack. From these a standard diagram or key for disease assessment in the field is drawn up, which may later be modified for use by relatively untrained observers, being simplified if necessary. Field trials are carried out in which development of the disease is observed in detail and crop yields are recorded. Yields of plots kept free from disease by spraying or other means are also recorded for comparison, and the trials are run over a number of years. These are adequately replicated trials with a sound statistical foundation, and they permit a more detailed analysis of disease development and crop yields than would be possible over large areas. From these trials the methods of disease assessment which are likely to be most useful for disease survey work in the field are devised, and the calibration of disease severity with likely crop loss is attempted; graphical representation of the latter may be possible.

Methods of measuring plant disease

These should take into account the percentage of plants infected as well as the severity of infection – a fairly mild disease which affects most of the plants may cause greater overall damage than a severer one which affects only a few plants, or *vice versa*. The varied and sometimes ingenious methods which can be used are described by Chester (1950, 1959), and some of the more important are briefly discussed below.

1. Recording the percentage of diseased plants, organs, or tissues

This is particularly applicable to diseases which kill plants rather quickly or which cause about the same amount of damage to all the infected plants. These include: (*a*) damping-off diseases and root rots, (*b*) many virus diseases originating from infected planting material, such as tuber borne viruses of potato, but not those arising from postsowing infection, (*c*) diseases which cause total destruction of the infected organs, such as ergot and some inflorescence smuts. Smuts which destroy only some of the grains in the ear can be assessed by multiplying the average number of smutted grains per ear by the percentage infected ears – this is also a direct measure of the crop loss involved. The amount of disease in the harvested product is sometimes a useful indication of its prevalence in the crop, and the number of surviving plants in relation to the number of seeds sown gives a measure of fatal seedling disease, the germination capacity of the seed being taken into account. If a disease is very prevalent it may be quicker to record the percentage of uninfected plants whereas if it is sparse various special methods of assessment can be used, including counting the number of infected plants observed on walking for a known time or distance through the field – approximate percentage infection can then be calculated from the density of the plants.

Where applicable, direct counts of this sort are reasonably accurate and objective, but they cannot be applied to diseases in which different plants show markedly different amounts of infection. In some leaf diseases there may be only a few lesions on some plants and many on others, and the percentage of infected plants is unlikely to give an accurate disease assessment in such cases unless combined with severity estimates. The latter can be useful but are laborious and time consuming to carry out adequately. It may be necessary to record the percentage of infected plants, the percentage of infected leaves, and the percentage of leaf tissue destroyed. From these figures an overall figure of disease intensity can be calculated, but this method is likely to be possible only in small plot experiments unless satisfactory methods of sampling large crop areas can be devised. Several time saving modifications can sometimes be used, for example, the area of leaves or lesions of consistently regular shape can often be derived from simple formulae based on length and breadth or diameter.

If the incidence of a disease varies greatly on different plants it may be useful to record the number of plants or organs falling into known percentage disease groups, the latter preferably being categories which can most easily be distinguished by the human eye, for example, the series 0–3,

3–6, 6–12, 12–25, 25–50, 50–75, 75–87, 87–94, and 97–100% (Horsfall and Barratt, 1945); this is a logarithmical scale in which diseased tissue is assessed below 50% and healthy tissue above 50%. Where there are numerous small lesions or rust sori, which may coalesce, counting and measuring are impractical unless a satisfactory sampling technique can be devised. In such cases a diagrammatic comparison scale may be used, the grades of which should be convertible into percentages of diseased tissue.

Various other methods can be used including the amount of defolia-tion in diseases which cause leaf shedding, but the validity of such methods should be established before they are used in the field. In light infections with a random distribution of lesions the percentage of uninfected leaves can be a measure of the average number of lesions per leaf. 37% uninfected leaves, for example, indicates an average of one lesion per leaf (Large, 1966).

2. Descriptive scales and diagrams of disease intensity

These are widely used and are of many different types, ranging from disease ratings on a numerical scale (often 0–7) to subjective estimates such as 'moderate', 'severe' and so on. Although no doubt meaningful to the observer using them, they are of little use to other workers unless they can be more precisely defined, and efforts are being made to produce scales which give consistent results when used by different observers in different areas and different seasons. In such scales the various grades of disease are described in detail and may take into account the stage of development of the plants. An example of this is the scale for assessment of potato blight developed by the British Mycological Society (Anon., 1947), and given below.

0   Not seen in field.
0·1%   Only a few plants affected here and there. Up to one or two spots in 10·8 m radius.
1%   Up to ten spots per plant, or general light spotting.
5%   About fifty spots per plant, or up to one leaflet in ten attacked.
25%   Nearly every plant with lesions; plants still retaining normal form: fields may smell of blight but look green although every plant affected.
50%   Every plant affected and about half of the leaf area destroyed by blight: field looks green flecked with brown.
75%   About three-quarters of the leaf area destroyed by blight; field looks neither predominantly brown or green. In some varieties the youngest leaves escape infection so that the green is more con-spicuous than in varieties like King Edward, which commonly shows severe shoot infection.

95% Only a few leaves left green, but stems green.
100% All leaves dead, stems dead or dying.

Grades of disease incidence can also be assessed by comparison with standardized diagrams, photographs or even preserved specimens. These are often used for leaf spotting, blights, rusts, fruit spotting, mosaics, and other diseases. They must be simple to use, with the different grades of disease clearly distinct. Descriptive scales and diagrams can sometimes be advantageously combined. One of the earliest assessment diagrams was that of Cobb for leaf rust (*Puccinia triticina*) of wheat in Australia. This divided rust intensity into five grades, 1–50%, based on the percentage of leaf coverage by the pustules, and was subsequently extended to six grades in the U.S.A., the maximum grade corresponding to 37% of the actual coverage of the leaf area. The original Cobb scale has been modified in various ways – for example, in Russia nine grades of rust intensity have been used. This is a logarithmical scale with each grade having about twice the number of rust sori as the previous one, thus making the differences more easily detectable by the human eye, and it also covers the lower ranges of infection more adequately. Somewhat similar disease scales have been devised for other pathogens, including cereal mildew (*Erysiphe graminis*), cereal yellow rust of wheat (*Puccinia striiformis*), barley leaf blotch (*Rhynchosporium secalis*), common scab of potato (*Streptomyces scabies*), apple scab (*Venturia inaequalis*: Croxall *et al.*, 1952), tomato leaf mould (*Cladosporium fulvum*: Beaumont, 1954) and others (figure 22·1).

Logarithmical scales are generally preferable to arithmetical ones for several reasons. Pathogens and pests tend to multiply geometrically whereas time progresses arithmetically, and as Chester (1955) points out the increase from one to ten lesions or rust sori per leaf takes as much time and is at least as important epidemiologically as the increase from ten to a hundred. A logarithmical scale attaches equal importance to both increases, but not so an arithmetical one. The human eye is such that it can more easily detect differences of equal spread on a logarithmical than on an arithmetical scale.

It is often desirable to summarize the disease severity estimates carried out on a population of plants in the form of a single figure, variously termed an infection index, severity index, coefficient of infection, average infection, disease intensity, and others. There are several ways of doing this, varying in their mathematical basis, of which that devised by McKinney (1923) is widely used. This is:

$$\frac{\text{Sum of all the disease ratings} \times 100}{\text{Total number of ratings} \times \text{maximum disease grade}}$$

The maximum disease grade is the highest rating on the severity scale, for example, 7 in the case of a 0–7 scale. This method gives infection indexes

POTATO COMMON SCAB

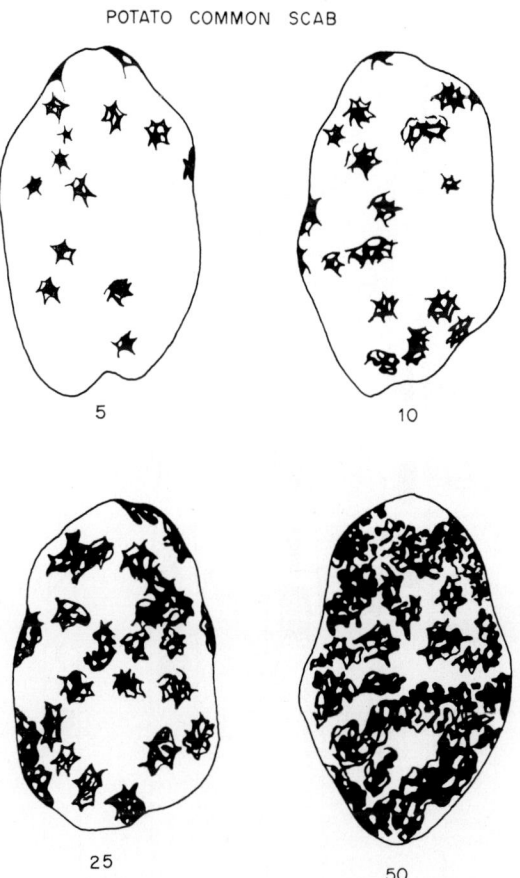

Percentage of surface area affected

(a)

Figure 22.1 (a–e) Provisional disease assessment diagrams designed to provide standard methods of assessing the percentage area of leaves or other plant organs affected by pathogens. The diagrams given here are (a) common scab (*Streptomyces scabies*) on potato tubers, (b) leaf blotch (*Rhynchosporium secalis*) on barley leaves, (c) powdery mildew (*Erysiphe graminis f. sp. hordei*) on barley leaves, (d) brown rust (*Puccinia hordei*) on barley leaves, and (e) yellow rust (*Puccinia striiformis*) on wheat leaves. In assessing the cereal leaf diseases the growth stage of the plant and the number of the leaf being assessed are recorded. It should be emphasized that these are provisional keys which may be amended before being issued in their final form.

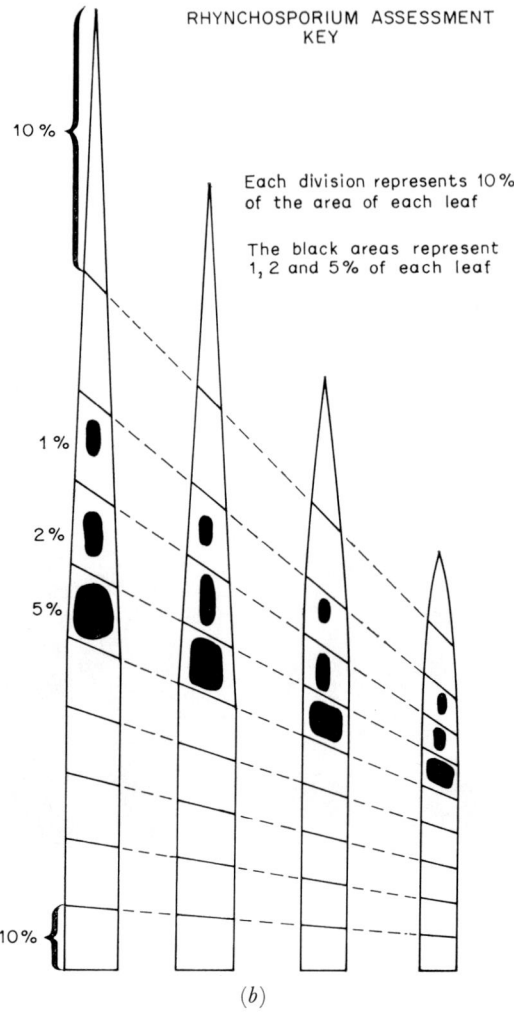

RHYNCHOSPORIUM ASSESSMENT
KEY

Each division represents 10%
of the area of each leaf

The black areas represent
1, 2 and 5% of each leaf

(b)

ranging from 0 (no disease) to 100 (maximum disease possible). Attempts are sometimes made to combine disease intensity with reaction type, the latter being an expression of the resistance of the plant and in the U.S.A. a 'coefficient of infection' for some rust diseases is obtained by multiplying disease intensity by reaction type. Since the two measures reflect different aspects of disease their combination into a single value can be misleading. A low coefficient could, for example, result from slight infection on a susceptible crop variety or from high infection on a very resistant one. This concept has, however, some practical use. Other methods of summarizing disease intensity are described by Chester (1955).

BARLEY MILDEW KEY

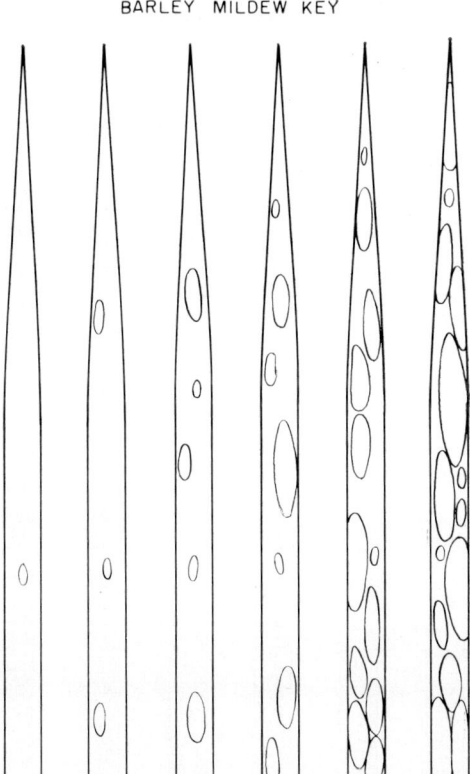

1   5   10   25   50   75

Percentage of leaf area affected

(c)

Severity estimates from fairly small areas can be combined to embrace larger areas – counties, provinces and countries – and maps of disease incidence over large areas can be constructed. Such an overall index can, for example, be obtained by using the following formula:

$$\frac{(\text{Field rating class} \times \text{no. hectares in class})}{\text{Total no. hectares}}$$

This makes allowance for the fact that the individual field ratings may be based on different numbers of hectares.

In some diseases there is a correlation between the percentage of infected plants, the percentage of organs attacked, and the severity of attack, so that the first named is an approximate indication of the last. Such

P

BROWN RUST KEY

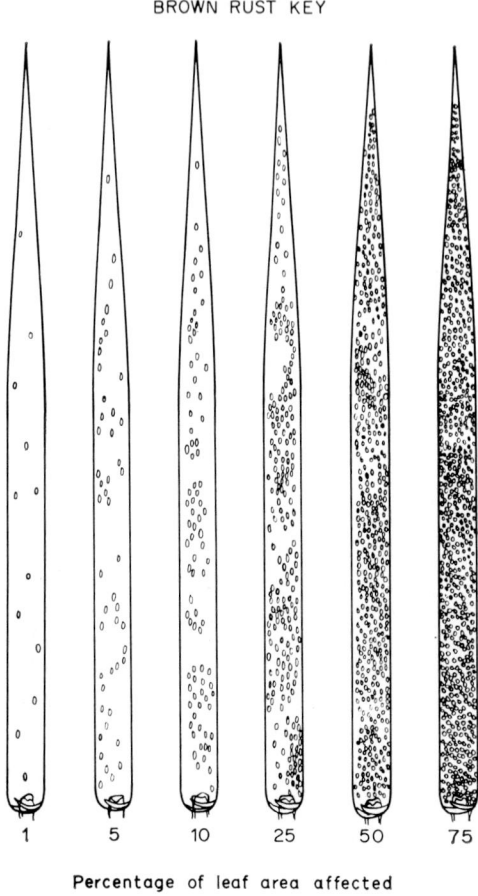

1   5   10   25   50   75

Percentage of leaf area affected

(d)

relationships can be especially useful in root diseases where a consistent correlation between root infection and some above-ground symptom – such as the degree of stunting or wilting of the plants – might permit root disease assessment to be made without digging up the plants. In forestry it is often important to assess the amount of decay in standing trees. This can be done by direct sampling using an increment borer which removes a small radial core of wood, but this is time consuming and laborious. Older trees are more likely to be decayed so that the diameter of the trunk tends to be correlated with decay, but this is often too vague to be of much use. There is sometimes a more reliable correlation between amount of decay and number of decayed branch stubs or surface injuries or fire injury, and these can be used in decay assessment.

WHEAT YELLOW RUST KEY

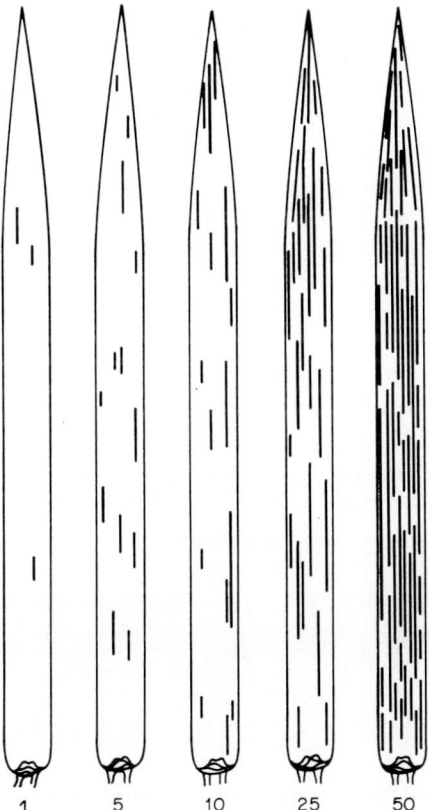

Percentage of leaf area affected

(*e*)

Methods of measuring crop losses

If a pathogen kills the plant before harvest a direct measure of crop loss is given by the percentage of diseased (dead) plants, and similarly for pathogens which cause complete sterility of plants grown for their fruits. In other cases a yield loss factor (Grainger, 1959), expressing the degree of debility caused by the pathogen, can be estimated and an approximate measure of crop loss can then be obtained by multiplying the percentage of diseased plants by this factor. This does not take into account any reduction in quality of the produce due to the disease and a further factor may have to be applied to cover this.

It is often difficult to estimate what the yield would have been in the absence of disease, and a further complicating factor can be the presence of other diseases and pests which cause crop loss. Different diseases tend to attack the crop at different times and the losses they cause are not additive. If, for example, one leaf pathogen causes 10% crop loss and a second one 5% the total loss will not be 15% but somewhere between 10% and 15%. The individual loss due to each of the several pathogens and pests attacking a crop can rarely be determined with any great confidence, and complex patterns of loss result from successive or simultaneous attacks of this sort. A pathogen which causes extensive necrosis or shedding of leaves reduces the opportunities for an accompanying or following obligate para- site which parasitizes only living leaves, quite apart from possible antagon- istic or synergistic effects. Further complications arise when a pathogen attacks several parts of the plant. For example, *Xanthomonas malvacearum* (bacterial blight) can cause seedling disease, blighting and shedding of leaves, stem lesions leading to breaking, and lesions on the bolls (fruits) of cotton plants. In such cases assessment of the damage caused by each phase of the disease may be necessary. There are also cases in which even a light in- fection renders the product worthless from a commercial point of view, as in flowers disfigured by petals potting pathogens, or diseased nursery stock.

Having determined the intensity of attack, the next step – and usually a more difficult one – is to relate it to crop loss. It is this latter aspect which is of greatest concern to the grower. Many of the methods used in relating crop loss to disease intensity are of two main types – statistical and experi- mental.

Statistical methods

These often involve the assembly and analysis of numerous reports of disease incidence, estimated crop losses, and yield figures. They are perhaps sometimes valid when extensive data are available, the assumption being that errors will thus tend to cancel each other out, but this assumption is often not justified and results obtained by statistical methods should be interpreted with care. The accuracy of such methods rarely approaches that obtainable in specially designed field trials with control plots kept as free as possible from disease. Among the more important statistical methods are:

1. Crop yields in years of different disease incidence. Over many seasons the analysis of yields in relation to estimated disease incidence may pro- vide quite useful information, but many factors other than disease affect yields and must be taken into account (weather, pests, farming practices, and the introduction of new varieties are some of them). This method is useful when one major disease is largely responsible for seasonal fluctua- tions in yield, or in a season when the disease is particularly severe as compared with one in which it is negligible. The direct effect of weather

on yield tends to even itself out over numerous seasons, so that relating crop loss to disease incidence in this way is often a long term project. Other aspects which should be considered are whether the disease is encouraged or otherwise by the climatic conditions which lead to good growth and high yield of the plant, and whether the pathogen is favoured or not by vigorous growth of the plant. 'Potato blight weather' also tends to encourage vigorous growth of the potato plant and so has a stabilizing effect on seasonal yields except when the disease is severe.

2. Comparisons of expected and actual yields. Growers and agricultural officers with long experience of a crop can often make reasonably accurate forecasts of yield quite early in the season. The difference between estimated and actual yields can be an indication of crop loss caused by a pathogen if the latter is the main cause of the reduction in yield, but many other factors are likely to be involved and this method has obvious limitations.

3. Analysis of yields before and after the application of control measures. Comparison of such yields can give interesting information about the overall damage caused by a disease over several years and over large areas. In Bavaria (Germany) downy mildew (*Pseudoperonospora humuli*) reduced hop yields from 720 kg per ha to 320 kg in 1926 and spraying increased yields to 1440 kg in 1927–1935. Similarly the introduction of curly top resistant varieties of sugarbeet in the north-west of the U.S.A. raised yields from about 12·5 to 35·0 tonnes per ha and averted crop failure over large areas (Chester, 1950). These and other examples give an indication of the magnitude of losses due to disease over large areas, but here again the possible effects of other factors such as improved agricultural practices, improved crop varieties, and the control of other diseases and pests, must be considered.

4. The use of questionnaires. In some countries extensive use is made of questionnaires on disease and pest incidence, growers and agricultural officers being asked to supply information on particular diseases and pests – their prevalence, severity, date of appearance, weather conditions, varietal susceptibility, estimated crop loss and so on. When properly organized such data from numerous growers can be valuable, but only if most of the growers can be relied upon to give reasonably accurate information. This implies a certain training and ability to carry out the necessary observations, which some growers will probably not have. This can be remedied to some extent by devising effective scales of disease incidence and severity, or by having trained recorders to make the observations. Some growers will fail to cooperate and it may be these who, through neglect or lack of interest, will tend to have the most severely diseased crops. This method has the advantage of enabling numerous data to be collected at fairly slight expense as copies of a printed questionnaire can be sent out to thousands of growers. The answers must, however, be carefully

checked and if possible supplemented by observations carried out by trained observers. In composing the questionnaire care must be taken to ensure that the questions asked are such that they can be answered reasonably accurately by relatively untrained observers – they must be clear and as few as possible.

Many other statistical methods of measuring crop loss have been proposed and are discussed by Chester (1950). If the agricultural or horticultural produce is subject to commercial or governmental inspection, as in grading for quality or certification for export, the records of this may sometimes provide information on disease incidence. Warehouse inspection of tobacco gives an indication of quality and this may be related to disease; this also holds for the rejection figures at canneries and the reports of grain inspectors. These marketing records are useful in a general sort of way but they rarely provide precise information on losses due to a specific disease. Crop prices, disease incidence on herbarium specimens, and the amount of money spent on disease control measures have all been proposed as possible methods of assessing crop losses, but all have obvious shortcomings.

It has been suggested that the volume of published pages concerning a pathogen may be a guide to its economic importance but there are notable anomalies in this. For example, the extensive literature on *Agrobacterium tumefaciens* (crown gall) is out of all proportion to its importance as a plant pathogen. Nevertheless in other cases, as with potato blight, there is an approximate correlation. In this connexion McCallan's 'index of disease importance' is of interest. This is obtained by multiplying the logarithm of the farm value of the crop by the logarithm of the estimated crop loss due to the disease as estimated in the *Plant Disease Reporter* (McCallan, 1946). This index, and other similar ones, can be useful in indicating where more effective control methods are needed and in apportioning funds for research on crop diseases. Such indexes are, however, only as accurate as the estimates on which they are based and so are often of uncertain value.

Experimental methods

Most of these methods are based on yield comparisons, (1) between artificially or naturally infected plants and uninfected ones, or between different grades of infection; (2) between disease resistant and susceptible varieties; (3) between infected plants and plants kept free from disease by protective chemicals or in other ways – this is probably the best way of relating yield reductions to disease incidence; or (4) between uninfected plants and plants mutilated to simulate disease damage. In all these methods it is essential that the experiments be properly designed so that the results can be analysed statistically and, if possible, they should be repeated over a number of seasons and in different areas.

Comparisons between infected and uninfected plants

There are many ways of doing this. Infected plants can be obtained by artificial inoculation, by interplanting diseased plants or scattering disease inoculum, by using contaminated or infected planting material, or by planting in contaminated soil. The experiments can be carried out in the glasshouse or field. Glasshouse experiments can be more precisely controlled, spread of the pathogen from infected to control (uninfected) plants can be minimized, and the plants can often be kept free from other pathogens, pests and other hazards which are liable to interfere with field experiments. A further advantage is that known races of a pathogen can be used whereas several races may be present in the field. It should, however, be remembered that glasshouse conditions are very different from those obtaining in the field and this is a serious drawback. Field experiments are preferable wherever possible, especially with pathogens, such as many seed borne and soil borne smuts, which do not spread from plant to plant during the growing season or which spread only slowly. Some pathogens tend to spread from the infected plants to the control plots which ideally should be free from disease. This can confuse the issue, and attack by other pathogens and pests is also likely to render the results difficult to interpret. Possible soil differences may also affect the results although these can, to some extent, be minimized by effective randomization of the plots. These disadvantages can sometimes be reduced by having barrier rows of immune plants between the plots, in an attempt to prevent unwanted spread of the pathogen and another method is to keep the control plots uninfected by chemical means, as described later.

Comparison of yields of naturally infected fields sometimes gives useful information on crop losses due to disease. In this method an attempt is made to select fields which are similar in all respects except that one contains diseased plants and the other healthy ones. In practice this is seldom possible and the comparison is usually between lightly infected and severely infected fields. Corrections may have to be made to allow for differences in soil and other factors in the fields being compared and this is often a complex and uncertain procedure. As many comparable fields as possible should be carefully selected over several seasons in order to even out these differences.

A modification of this method is to select pairs of similar plants, one of the pair being diseased and the other healthy. Detailed observations on the general growth and yield of the plants are then made and the results statistically analysed. Large numbers of pairs are required for this method to be worthwhile. Plants originally selected as healthy may become infected and some pairs may thus have to be discarded, but this can be avoided to some extent by selecting pairs at harvest time.

Comparable diseased and disease-free plots can sometimes be obtained by removing diseased plants from the latter and a similar number of healthy plants from the former. This can be useful in natural infections by pathogens which spread relatively slowly, as with some viruses, particularly if a heavy sowing rate has been used so that about optimal plant populations are present after removal of the plants.

Comparisons between resistant and susceptible varieties

Comparison of yields given by a disease susceptible crop variety and a closely related but resistant (preferably immune) variety in the presence of the disease can produce useful information. Since the two varieties may differ in innate yielding capacity it is advisable to apply a correction factor based on yields in the absence of the disease, and differential susceptibility to other diseases and pests may also have to be allowed for. Immune or resistant plants may occasionally occur in fields of otherwise susceptible plants, and resistant lines can sometimes be selected in this way. Such lines are likely to be very similar genetically to the parent variety except in their disease resistance, and the more similar they are, the better.

Experiments for comparing disease incidence and yields of resistant and susceptible varieties should be laid out in adequately replicated and randomized trials, either in experimental plots or as larger scale field trials. Detailed observations on the incidence of diseases and pests and accurate yield measurements should be made. Such experiments can yield valuable information if properly designed and carried out over several seasons and in several different areas. It may be necessary to provide inoculum of the pathogen in some years, and statistical analysis of the results should of course be carried out.

Similar observations can be made on farm plantings of resistant and susceptible varieties. Thus with irrigated cotton in the Sudan several thousand hectares of a susceptible variety attacked by bacterial blight (*Xanthomonas malvacearum*) gave an average yield about 18% less than that of a related resistant variety in an adjacent area. Since yield records showed that the latter area normally yields somewhat less than the former, and since bacterial blight was clearly the major factor affecting yields, the loss due to the disease could with some confidence be assessed as at least 18% in yield of seed cotton (Tarr, 1957). Details of the incidence of diseases and pests and of the yield of individual fields are recorded as a matter of routine in some agricultural undertakings, particularly the larger plantation-type ones, and analysis of these records over several years can produce interesting information on the general overall damage due to pests and diseases.

Comparisons between infected plants and those kept free from infection by chemical methods.

In these experiments one endeavours to obtain disease-free plants in various ways, often by applying protective chemicals to the plants or planting material or soil. The yield of such plants is then compared with that of diseased plants. The experiments can be carried out in fairly small replicated plots or over comparable fields, a properly designed lay-out being used so that statistical analysis can be applied. This method is widely used and is generally considered to be one of the most accurate methods of relating disease incidence and crop loss. Repeated applications of fungicide may be necessary to keep the plants uninfected, such treatment being a tool rather than an economic way of controlling the disease. 'Blanket' application of fungicides tends to control several diseases rather than one only, and this can be a drawback, the comparison then being between healthy plants and those attacked by several pathogens. This is a useful way of assessing the loss due, for example, to a complex of several leaf pathogens, or where one pathogen is the major cause of loss, but it should be remembered that some fungicides seem to affect the growth and yield of plants quite apart from controlling disease. There may be phytotoxic effects as when sulphur is applied to melons and tomatoes growing at high temperature. Bordeaux mixture is said to be beneficial to some plants in the apparent absence of disease, possibly through correction of partial copper deficiency. Dithane (unspecified) is claimed to produce yield increases greater than would be expected from the disease control obtained (Chester, 1950), and it is possible that some fungicides have growth promoting properties.

Little is known about these aspects but their possible occurrence should be investigated in experiments comparing fungicide treated and untreated plants in the absence of disease, and it may be necessary to apply an appropriate correction factor. Fungicides are likely to affect the epiphytic fungi and bacteria on the plant and thus may have indirect effects on pathogens. This is particularly true of soil disinfection which radically alters the composition of the soil microflora both quantitatively and qualitatively for a time. Elimination of one soil borne pathogen may enable another to take its place, or beneficial microorganisms may be encouraged. These possible effects often complicate the interpretation of the results of experiments with soil fungicides and should be allowed for in investigating crop losses due to pathogens.

In all experiments in which the yield of healthy and of diseased plants is compared adequate observations on disease intensity should also be made in order to correlate the two aspects. In due course a reliable correlation may emerge. Thus Large and Doling (1962) found that the mean percentage reduction in grain yield of spring barley and oats due to powdery mildew was approximately $2 \cdot 5 M^{0 \cdot 5}$ where M is the percentage mildew assessment at the growth stage between completion of heading and outset of ripening. This relationship is a purely empirical one derived from the results of experiments in which spraying with lime-sulphur was used to keep the appropriate plots free from mildew. Similarly, yield loss due to blight attack on the aerial parts of main crop potatoes in England and Wales was about 4% when the 75% blight stage (p. 437) was reached in mid-September, 13% when reached at the end of August, 28% in mid-August, and 50% at the end of July (Large, 1966).

Artificial simulation of disease by mutilation

Plant damage due to pathogens and pests can be imitated in various ways – by removing discs of leaf tissue of the appropriate size (leaf spot diseases), by removing leaves (leaf shedding diseases), and in general by removing or damaging other organs as appropriate to the disease being imitated. Defoliation or destruction of leaf tissue generally reduces yield except perhaps at harvest time, but the relationship between defoliation and subsequent yield reduction is complex and no doubt varies with the amount, time and method of defoliation, the plant involved, the environment, and other factors. Percentage loss is rarely, if ever, directly proportional to percentage defoliation and it is generally thought that under normal conditions most plants can withstand the loss of a few leaves without undue hardship, the remaining leaves tending to function more efficiently. If these remaining leaves are lost or destroyed, however, the plant suffers progressively greater loss, although the presence of active chlorophyll in stems, leaf sheaths, glumes and other parts may be a partial compensation.

The time at which defoliation occurs is also important. It is generally harmful in midseason rather than very early or very late in crop development, but heavy leaf shedding or destruction in the seedling stage can be very destructive and may be fatal. The reasons for the injuriousness of midseason defoliation are not understood but it may be that at this stage the plant is losing its ability to replace the lost leaves. Different plants show differences in this respect and defoliation is said to be injurious to barley and oats in the grass stage before the growing point has emerged from the crown, to flax plants in the bud stage, to soya plants when the beans are beginning to develop in the pod, and to onions when bulbing begins (Chester, 1950).

Most of the dry matter in cereal grains is apparently due to photosynthesis in the flag leaf and ear after the latter has emerged (Thorne, 1966) and disease attack on these is thus likely to have a special significance in relation to yield reduction. As might be expected, defoliation is least detrimental under very dry conditions. It generally lowers the quality of the produce, particularly when extensive. For example, it reduces the sugar content of fruits, the oil content of some seeds, and the amount of sugar and protein in wheat. The produce tends to be small, seeds to be shrivelled and the quality to be markedly reduced. All these effects lower the commercial value of the crop and should be considered in assessing crop losses due to pathogens and pests.

Experimental mutilation should imitate as fully as possible the natural course of the disease in the field. Under these conditions it seems that it gives a useful if slightly conservative estimate of yield reduction due to pathogens. No doubt the latter in addition to destroying or incapacitating plant tissue induces other harmful effects, for example, by production of toxins which diffuse to some extent in the tissues.

The methods outlined above are the more important ones used to relate yield loss to disease intensity. Such intensity–loss relationships can be summarized in the form of tables, regressions or formulae. There are other methods, as in obtaining correlations between stands and yields in the case of seed or seedling diseases in which the plants are killed and the stand thus reduced. The choice of methods to use will depend on the plant and on the epidemiological characteristics of the pathogen and wherever possible a combination of several suitable methods should be used. Methods of assessing crop loss due to diseases in cereals are described by Sackston *et al.* (1968). A recent account of disease assessment is that of Preece (1971).

Plant disease surveys

The foregoing is concerned chiefly with the assessment of plant diseases over fairly small areas. For many purposes, however, information on the prevalence and severity of a disease, or of several diseases, over much larger areas – regions, countries or even continents – is needed, for example, in estimating the relative economic importance of several diseases in order to allocate money and staff for research, or in the organization of cooperative control or eradication of a disease over large areas. Surveys may also be carried out (1) to ascertain the geographical distribution of races of a pathogen, (2) to record the occurrence of alternate hosts of rusts or of subsidiary hosts of pathogens, (3) to determine the geographical limits and incidence of established pathogens, and (4) to detect newly introduced pathogens and pests and to plot their subsequent spread and severity, with a view to eradication campaigns. Information of this sort is obtained by carefully planned disease recording throughout the area involved. Such surveys are of several types, depending on the objectives and the money and observers available. Since the latter two factors are normally limited and often inadequate many surveys are a compromise between what is desirable and what is practicable. In all disease survey work it is essential to devise assessment systems which give consistent results when used by different recorders and, ideally, there should be sufficient trained recorders to enable all sample areas to be examined at the same stage of growth. Alternatively, all the samples can be collected in a uniform way and sent to a central laboratory for disease assessment by a smaller number of experienced recorders. Whatever method is used the data are collated and statistically analysed by computer.

Useful information can occasionally be obtained by so-called 'opinion sampling' in which the opinions of random samples of growers are recorded, but for more reliable data it is often advisable to have the fields sampled by trained observers. The number of samples taken will depend on the nature of the disease and the resources available. Pathogens with air borne spores, such as the cereal rusts, tend to affect large areas comparatively uniformly and so require less sampling than those which are more irregularly distributed, such as soil borne pathogens. The more prevalent and evenly distributed the disease the fewer the number of samples likely to be required for a given degree of reliability. Sound methods of sampling are essential in disease survey work and Chester (1959) makes the following recommendations: (1) avoidance of border effects by sampling away from the edges of the field; (2) the use of mechanical devices to select the sampling area, thus obtaining random samples free from selective error due to prejudice on the part of the observer; (3) the sampling points should be widely distributed over the area being sampled; and (4) the sample should be taken at random from within the sampling area, for example, by using a quadrat or other suitable device thrown at random.

In some cases it may be preferable to take a number of small samples from different places and to bulk them into one composite sample. Whatever method of sampling is used it should be statistically sound, fairly simple and make the best possible use of the trained observers and funds available. Once the acceptable degree of error in sampling has been decided the minimum size and number of samples which will yield results within this limit can be calculated. Thus in sampling potato tubers a sample of 400 tubers should indicate the disease content within 1% error if the disease content is 3%; this is based on odds of 10:1. In practice a sample of 400 tubers would often be impractical and a sample of 100 tubers, giving a 2% error, would have to be used. The size of the sample has to be decided along these lines in each individual case as discussed in detail by Chester (1950).

If the survey is to be repeated over several years it may be advisable to have several standard observation plots on which detailed observations are made each year. The date of sampling will vary with different diseases but often it is at the height of the attack. Sometimes, as in fruit diseases, it is possible to remove the sample from the field and subsequently examine it at leisure in the laboratory. Sampling of harvested produce is another procedure which can be used, also post harvest inspection of stubble for the telia of black stem rust.

Surveying of plant diseases on the ground is inevitably a slow and therefore costly operation, much of the recorders' time being spent in travelling between the sampling areas. Attempts are being made to conduct surveys from moving vehicles on roads or from the air. Aerial methods are applicable only to those diseases whose effects are sufficiently conspicuous and characteristic to enable reliable identification to be made from a considerable distance. Diseases which cause striking colour changes in the fields (some virus diseases, rusts, powdery mildews), poor stands (seed and seedling diseases), or extensive browning of the foliage (as occurs in severe potato blight) are examples of these. In such cases aerial assessment is quicker, often cheaper, and can cover larger areas than ground assessment. The survey may be by fixed-wing aircraft or, better, by helicopters which are slower, more manoeuvrable and safer at low altitudes. Recording may be by observers in the aircraft or by aerial photography, especially in colour, giving a permanent record which can be studied and analysed in the laboratory.

Aerial surveying of diseases and pests is in its infancy but its scope is likely to increase as the techniques are improved. A possible complicating factor is that similar effects may be caused by different pathogens or pests; for example, wilting may be due to root attack by several fungi or insects, and supplementary observations by field observers may be necessary in such cases. Aerial assessment is clearly likely to be of greatest value where the symptoms recorded are due chiefly to one pathogen which causes conspicuous changes in the appearance of the crop. Panchromatic, infrared, normal colour or colour infrared film may be used in aerial photography of plant diseases, and such photography is likely to be very useful as a supplement to, or extension of, ground observations and measurements. Brenchley (1968) in his review suggests that a network of ground-assessed crops could be used to calibrate the tones shown on aerial photographs of the whole region being surveyed. Although not widely used, colour infrared photography is used in the U.S.A. to assess potato late blight, southern leaf blight of maize, virus diseases of citrus and smog injury to evergreen trees. Changes in the appearance of crops due to pathogens, pests, or other causes can apparently be detected by space vehicles orbiting the earth and this could be useful in assessing the distribution and severity of diseases over extensive crop areas.

A somewhat different type of survey is that in which the numbers of fungal spores or insects in the air are sampled by means of spore traps, insect traps, aircraft or in other ways. This can give useful information on the number of air borne propagules present, in turn related to the amount of disease in the fields.

23 The control of plant diseases: general considerations

This chapter considers the general principles of disease control and is followed by chapters on the more important control measures in use. Information on the control of plant diseases caused by viruses, bacteria and parasitic flowering plants will be found in the chapters on these pathogens.

Control of diseases of non-parasitic origin

The formulation of measures to control diseases of non-parasitic origin depends upon accurate diagnosis of the cause of the disorder. This is often more difficult than the diagnosis of diseases caused by parasites as the latter can often be detected and identified in the infected plant. Fungi and bacteria are frequently present as secondary invaders of plant tissue damaged by non-parasitic agents, and this can confuse the situation. *Cladosporium herbarum, Alternaria tenuis, Botrytis cinerea, Epicoccum nigrum* and other fungi commonly grow on damaged or moribund plant tissue but their significance may be difficult to assess since many such fungi seem to be able to act as saprophytes or parasites according to circumstances.

Once the nature of the disorder has been established the remedial measures are generally a matter of common sense and are often fairly simple and effective. They include the removal or correction of the harmful factor – for example, by washing phytotoxic substances from the soil, by correcting high soil acidity by liming, by improving the drainage of waterlogged soil, by regulation of the temperature in glasshouse crops or of soil moisture in irrigated crops, curing trace element deficiencies by supplying the plants with appropriate amounts of the deficient element, and so on. It may be possible to protect the plants from the adverse factor by covering them with straw or paper to minimize frost injury in gardens, by growing them in naturally or artificially shaded places to shield them against excessive heat, or by growing or constructing windbreaks to protect plants against damage from high winds. Cold-tolerant varieties of some vegetables, such as lettuce and peas, which are able to survive the winter in parts of the British Isles, have become available, and drought-tolerant varieties of crop plants have been developed for dry areas.

Except for the breeding of tolerant varieties the measures used to control diseases of non-parasitic origin are essentially corrective or protective and are based on the nature of the causal agent. In a sense their control lies in providing the best possible environment for growth of the plants and this in turn helps them to withstand or tolerate those pathogens which attack damaged or weakened plants.

Control of diseases caused by parasites

Although curative measures such as heat treatment can occasionally be used, control of plant diseases caused by parasites is based largely on prevention rather than cure – prevention of infection in the first instance or of spread of the pathogen if this fails, as it often does. It is important to reduce and delay the initial infection as much as possible since this may have a considerable bearing on subsequent development of the disease, particularly so with pathogens which do not spread very rapidly. Slight and/or late development of a disease may be acceptable to the farmer whereas severe early attack is likely to cause considerable crop loss or to necessitate the application of expensive control measures such as fungicidal spraying. Disease forecasting and the assessment of the amount of crop loss (and monetary loss) caused by a given amount of disease are clearly important in this respect, as is some knowledge of the rate of increase of the pathogen from a known amount of initial inoculum under the environmental conditions which obtain in the field. Rate of spread will depend on the spore output of a pathogenic fungus, the duration of the incubation and sporulation periods, the susceptibility of the plants, the efficiency of spore dissemination, and other factors as discussed in Chapter 20.

Except sometimes for valuable trees and bushes it is rarely feasible to treat individual plants or to attempt to cure them, and control measures are usually applied to populations of plants which may range from a dozen cabbages in a garden to many thousands of plants in large fields of cereals. With the advent of fungicides in handy household packs the treatment of individual perennial plants – whether gooseberry bushes, rose bushes or indoor cacti – is becoming increasingly popular, and this trend is likely to continue as long as the present interest in gardening persists. Natural populations of plants tend to attain an approximate balance with the pathogens and pests which attack them, but in modern agriculture and horticulture the intensive cultivation of (often) susceptible varieties of plants over large areas and under artificial conditions tends to provide conditions highly conducive to development of diseases. Effective control measures may then become essential if cultivation is to continue on an economic basis. Panama disease of banana and coffee rust have resulted in virtual abandonment of these crops in some areas and there would be other similar examples had not effective control measures been devised and successfully applied. Control of plant diseases can be a matter of vital national importance as well as of concern to the farmer, horticulturalist, forester and gardener.

All plants are attacked by pathogens and pests, some destructive and others of apparently minor importance, and a disease which is of little significance in one area may become a major problem in another where climatic and agricultural conditions are more favourable to it, or where the local varieties of crops are more susceptible. An example of this is *Puccinia polysora* (maize rust), a fairly minor pathogen of long standing in the New World, which proved very destructive when introduced into Africa about 20 years ago. Such outbreaks underline the need for preventing the dissemination of even apparently minor pathogens and the vital importance of such measures as plant quarantine, legislation concerning diseases and pests, international cooperation, and certification of plant material for export. Eradication of a pathogen is sometimes possible over a limited area but it is likely to be expensive, and prevention of entry is preferable wherever possible.

Intelligent control of a plant disease depends on a thorough knowledge of the pathogen and the host plant and their interaction, and these aspects need to be investigated in detail. This also applies to any vectors of the pathogen. The precise identity of the causal agent is of importance as experience with it or similar pathogens elsewhere can be of great help in devising control measures. Occasionally, however, an apparently new disease appears in a crop and quickly becomes destructive, so that immediate control measures have to be adopted before the disease can be adequately studied and sometimes before its cause has been established. In such eventualities empirical control measures have to be applied. These are based partly on whether a fungus, virus, bacterium or other agent is suspected to be involved and partly on intelligent application of general principles, including the application of such measures as crop sanitation (the destruction of all diseased plant material), crop rotation, selection of seed or other planting material from unaffected fields or areas, experimental application of fungicides, and so on. The observed effects of these measures may in turn give some indication as to the nature of the disease. Rational control measures can be devised and tested as more information becomes available but it may be years before the cause of the disease is established beyond doubt.

Disease control measures should of course be economic, that is, the

value of the crop saved should exceed the cost of control. It is often difficult to decide whether this is so, and the assessment of disease incidence
and crop loss is a key factor in problems involving the economic aspects of
disease control. Practical experience is often useful but there are borderline cases in which no reliable conclusions can be reached. Control of
highly destructive diseases and pests attacking valuable crops can be essential for worthwhile yields, and in such cases routine application of control
measures each season may be advisable. The doubtful cases include apparently minor diseases of valuable crops and major diseases of fairly low
price crops. It is doubtful whether fungicidal spraying for control of ring
spot (*Mycosphaerella brassicicola*) of cabbage would be an economic proposition, whereas similar spraying for control of leaf mould (*Cladosporium
fulvum*) attacking glasshouse tomatoes, a much more valuable crop, is
often worthwhile.

As well as being economically sound, control measures should ideally
fulfil certain other conditions. They should be sufficiently effective to
reduce the disease to an acceptable level, and simple, safe and inexpensive
to apply. Needless to say, few disease control measures fall into this
category but there are some which do so, for example, control of seed borne
smuts by seed treatment with fungicides of low mammalian toxicity.
Measures which control one pathogen may have little effect on, or may
encourage, other pathogens and pests or may have undesirable effects in
other directions. Late sowing, for example, may discourage some pathogens,
encourage others, and involve the risk of frost damage or drought before
harvest. Such cases have to be considered individually, often with the
help of pilot experiments in the field, and taking into consideration the
relative crop losses caused by the various pathogens, pests and agronomic
factors involved.

As Van der Plank (1963) pointed out, most control measures reduce
either the initial inoculum or the rate of spread of the pathogen, or both.
Crop sanitation, the growing of vertically resistant crop varieties, the sowing of disease-free planting material, the destruction of pathogens on or in
the planting material by chemical or heat treatment, and soil fumigation
all reduce the initial inoculum. Measures which reduce the rate at which
pathogens spread include the growing of horizontally resistant crop varieties and the application of protective fungicides; these measures reduce the
number of diseased plants and the severity of infection so that the amount
of inoculum at the end of the season is also reduced.

The methods of disease control are grouped by Sharvelle (1961) into
two major categories: (1) immunization – rendering the plant immune to
the pathogen by the development of immune or (more often) resistant
varieties of plants or, more recently, by the application of chemicals which
make the plant resistant to pathogens, and (2) prophylaxis – the preven-

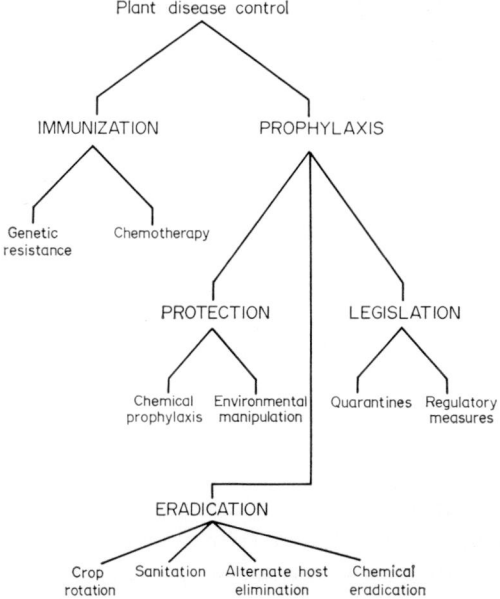

Figure 23.1 A diagrammatic representation of the various methods for disease control.

tion of disease development by chemical means, by manipulating the environment, or by eradicating the pathogen (figure 23.1).

The more important measures used to control diseases caused by pathogens fall into five main groups:

1. Measures which destroy the pathogen or prevent it from reaching the plants, including elimination of the sources of infection (inoculum) by various methods collectively described as crop sanitation. If the pathogen is not present in the area attempts can be made to prevent its introduction by plant quarantine or legislation. If it is present it can sometimes be eradicated or confined to a limited area.

2. Measures which reduce attack by the pathogen to varying extents. These include methods of growing plants which discourage their pathogens, which enhance their resistance, or which enable them to withstand attack more successfully. This is sometimes termed alleviation or disease control by cultural practices.

3. Measures in which chemicals are applied to the plant, thus forming a protective layer which kills the pathogen or inhibits its development. Systemic fungicides enter the tissues of the plant and render the latter toxic to the pathogen whereas other systemic compounds somehow make the plant more resistant to the pathogen, presumably so altering the

physiology of the plant that it becomes unsuitable for development of the pathogen.

4. Measures in which varieties of plants immune, resistant or tolerant to pathogens are selected and/or bred.

5. Legislative measures which seek to prevent the introduction of pathogens not already present (plant quarantine) or which forbid practices likely to encourage disease incidence. Many of these disease control measures involve, or should involve, international cooperation.

Disease complexes and disease-pest complexes

The grower is concerned with control of the complex of diseases – and pests – which attack his crops rather than with individual ones, although a single disease or pest may be the major cause of crop loss. It would seem logical to approach the problem of disease control with this in mind; that is, attention should be directed to the complex of diseases and pests which affect a crop. This will involve investigating possible interactions of the several or many pathogens which affect a crop in the field. As described above (p. 279) there may be antagonistic or synergistic associations between different pathogens caused, for example, by infection by one pathogen bringing about changes in the infected tissue which are unfavourable to a second pathogen. Weather conditions or cultural practices which discourage one pathogen may encourage another and, similarly, resistant varieties are unlikely to have adequate resistance against all the pathogens and pests which may attack the crop. The problem of controlling the complex of diseases which attack a crop is thus likely to be difficult if many major diseases are involved. It may, however, be simpler if there are only two or three major pathogens, especially if these are epidemiologically similar so that they are all likely to be controlled by similar measures.

If there is an antagonistic reaction between two crop pathogens, one of which causes considerably greater crop loss than the other, it may be worthwhile to accept infection by the milder pathogen as the price of protection against the more destructive one. The cost of doing this may in fact be less than that involved in control by fungicidal spraying, but an accurate knowledge of the monetary losses due to the two pathogens is necessary before this can be decided on.

Various factors have to be borne in mind when considering the control of a complex of diseases which affect a crop grown extensively over a wide area. A moderately destructive pathogen which attacks the crop in all areas may well cause greater overall crop loss than a more destructive pathogen which is severe in limited areas but of little significance in others.

In such a case it may be advisable to give priority to control of the more widespread disease in most areas except where the more destructive disease is locally severe.

In recent years there has been considerable interest in the control of disease-pest complexes, this being a logical development towards the control of all agents which damage plants and so reduce their yield. Seed dressings containing fungicide and insecticide have been available since the advent of the persistent chlorinated hydrocarbon insecticides such as gammexane (gamma benzene hexachloride) and dieldrin. These have proved useful for control of soil pests and soil borne or seed borne pathogens but the objectionable nature of some of these insecticides tends to restrict their use.

Systemic fungicides are now being produced and in combination with systemic insecticides will no doubt prove useful in simultaneous control of fungi and insects. Recent developments in the control of disease-pest complexes are discussed by Thomason *et al.* (1970) who suggest that 'tailored' mixtures of compatible nematicides, herbicides, insecticides, fungicides and possibly other protective chemicals might be used, perhaps in the form of granules or some other convenient formulation which could be added to the soil. The past preoccupation with individual diseases and pests, considered more or less in isolation, is likely to give way to the concept of control of all, or at least the major, agents which are harmful to the crop.

Choice of control methods

The type of control measures used depends to a considerable extent on the epidemiology of the pathogen – how it overwinters, how it spreads, and its host range. Chemical or plant breeding methods may be necessary for pathogens which spread rapidly whereas sanitation may be satisfactory for those which spread more slowly, and the standard of sanitation required for adequate control of the former will be higher than that for the latter and may not be possible. Fungicidal spraying of standing crops can be successfully undertaken in agriculturally advanced countries but is less likely to be a practical proposition in those less advanced. Control measures should be such that they are within the capacity – and the pockets – of those who have to apply them; in this respect some form of cooperative application of disease and pest control measures can sometimes be devised.

Chemical methods of controlling plant diseases and pests are now widely used. Chemicals protect against fungi, bacteria, insects, mites, nematodes and other organisms which attack plants, while herbicides are helpful in eliminating competing weeds. Nevertheless, chemical control of diseases, pests and weeds has several inherent weaknesses and dangers. One is that the prolonged and extensive use of protective chemicals, and especially the more persistent ones, leads to increasing pollution of the environment with attendant harmful effects on other organisms. In recent years it has become apparent that the large scale application of crop protection chemicals can have harmful side effects including the tainting of food crops and the poisoning of birds, insects and other animals, some of which are beneficial. Some insecticides, notably the systemic organo-phosphorus compounds, are of very high mammalian toxicity and extremely hazardous to use; special precautions must be taken and although less dangerous ones are being developed there is still considerable risk. The chlorinated hydrocarbon insecticides (gammexane, DDT, dieldrin, aldrin and others) are highly insecticidal and some are very persistent and liable to be accumulated in animals. They are stable substances and likely to persist almost indefinitely in food chains under natural conditions. It is to be expected that their continued and probably intensified use will lead to their slow build up in plants, soil, water, fish, animals, and man. This could have disastrous effects and strict control with, where necessary, prohibition of the use of these highly toxic and persistent chemicals is essential before the damage becomes irreparable. Some of the unpleasant effects of these chemicals are described by Carson (1963), Rudd (1965), Coleman–Cooke (1965), Mellanby (1967), and others.

Few fungicides are as potentially dangerous as the organo-phosphorus and chlorinated hydrocarbon insecticides but the regular application of fungicides, particularly those which kill a wide range of fungi, might change the natural microflora of fungicide treated plants and thereby enable other pathogens to become more destructive. There are few published reports of investigations along these lines but Hislop and Cox (1969) found that, although the application of captan markedly reduced the fungal flora of apple buds and leaves, the numbers and types of non-bacterial microorganisms returned to normal within a few months after spraying was discontinued. In this case there was apparently no carry-over of the effects of the fungicide on the microflora from one year to the next.

Change-over from one fungicide to another can, however, have undesirable effects. The increase of currant powdery mildew (*Sphaerotheca mors-uvae*) in parts of England in recent years has been attributed to the fact that lime-sulphur, which is effective against powdery mildew, is largely being replaced for control of big-bud mites by acaricides which do not control mildew. Similarly, the replacement of sulphur fungicides, effective against apple powdery mildew (*Podosphaera leucotricha*), by other fungicides (for example captan) for control of scab (*Venturia inaequalis*) could encourage mildew if such replacement fungicides are not effective against mildew. Repeated fumigation of soil affects pathogens and non-pathogens therein and so changes its microbiological status, but little is known about the permanence of such changes or about the time taken by fumigated soil to revert to its prefumigation condition when fumigation is discontinued.

A second danger is that edible produce harvested from plants which have been treated with a protective chemical may contain traces of it, and the long term effects on the human body of many of the chemicals used in crop protection are unknown. There may be chemical spray residues on fruit at harvest time or – even more dangerous – residues from chemicals applied to produce to prevent spoilage during transportation and storage. Maximum permitted concentrations of chemicals in edible produce are stipulated in some countries, but even assuming that these are followed by all growers the long term effects of these permitted amounts of chemicals on the human body are unknown.

A third disadvantage of crop protection by chemicals is that the organisms against which the chemical is used will almost inevitably develop resistance to it in time (p. 536). A fourth danger is that some crop protection chemicals are highly toxic to man and must be applied with extreme care. Even so, accidents are liable to happen in the manufacture, packaging and application of such chemicals and in the disposal of the supposedly empty containers after use: the used containers may be left in a corner of the field or thrown into a nearby stream. Unopened containers may be kept in an unlocked store. In these and other ways the extensive use of highly toxic crop protection chemicals can be dangerous to animal life and to man himself. These dangers can be minimized by stringent legislation on the use of the more toxic chemicals but, unfortunately, not all users follow the regulations.

Sometimes, however, the application of crop protection chemicals can have beneficial effects, apart from those expected, on disease incidence. An interesting case of this is described by Brooks and Dawson (1968) who found that take-all (*Ophiobolus graminis*) and eyespot (*Cercosporella herpotrichoides*) were less severe on winter wheat which had been drilled directly into stubble or pasture previously treated with paraquat herbicide than on wheat drilled into land which had been ploughed. The decrease of take-all was attributed to reduced spread of *O. graminis* in the relatively undisturbed soil which had been direct-drilled rather than to any direct effect of the herbicide. The application of herbicides may destroy weeds which are undetected or symptomless hosts of pathogens which attack crops. Chickweed (*Stellaria media*) has, for example, been found by Tomlinson *et al.* (1970) to be a symptomless carrier of cucumber mosaic virus and a likely source of inoculum for lettuce and other vegetables (see p. 66).

In view of the dangers and disadvantages of disease control by chemical means it is preferable, whenever possible, to use alternative methods – biological methods, cultural methods, crop sanitation, and the growing of resistant varieties, especially those with effective horizontal resistance. It should, however, be remembered that the use of crop protection chemicals has enabled the yield level of many crops to be increased, as discussed by Holmes (1960), and that there are some pathogens and pests which cannot be controlled in any other way.

Biological control has been successfully used to control pests but little attempt has been made to use it to control plant pathogens. The use of hyperparasitic and antagonistic fungi in disease control has been investigated to only a limited extent. It has not yet yielded very promising results but more work on the potentialities of this method of disease control is needed. One of the difficulties is that climatic conditions are often the critical factor in determining the activity of the hyperparasite, but there would seem to be some scope in introducing new or more efficient strains of hyperparasites for disease control. The hyperparasite may be dependent on the host pathogen for its continued existence, in which case a permanent but limited population of the pathogen will be needed to obviate the necessity of introducing the hyperparasite each year.

Biological control is likely to be inexpensive as compared with, for example, the production and application of crop protection chemicals. Furthermore, hyperparasites have a capacity for genetical variation and so are likely to produce new strains which are able to attack resistant strains of the host if such strains arise. The hyperparasite is, in a sense, a living fungicide able to adapt itself to changes in its host, whereas pesticides are unable to do this, although man can sometimes alter their pesticidal properties by modifying their molecular structure.

Another problem with biological control is that the hyperparasite and its host pathogen tend to reach an equilibrium which permits both to survive. The possibility of shifting this equilibrium in favour of the hyperparasite would seem to be worth investigating.

Control measures should be used to supplement one another. It may be possible, for example, to control a disease in a resistant crop variety with less fungicide than is needed for its control in a susceptible variety. The chances of newly evolved races of a pathogen becoming established are likely to be reduced if the infected resistant plants are destroyed after harvesting, thereby eliminating the new races. Rational planning of the regional planting of varieties of crop plants in relation to the distribution and severity of the pathogens and pests which attack them can sometimes be used in the overall strategy of crop protection and the importance of this aspect of disease control is now being appreciated.

Some diseases can be satisfactorily controlled by applying a single control measure such as seed treatment for a pathogen which is exclusively seed borne, but a combination of measures is necessary for the control of others. Thus, crop sanitation, crop rotation and seed treatment can all be used to control a pathogen which survives in crop residues and on seed. Some control measures are particularly relevant to certain types of disease or pathogen, as with crop rotation in control of fungi which attack roots and which are frequently soil borne. Many smuts are seed transmitted and can be controlled by some form of seed treatment. Fungicidal spraying or resistant varieties may be necessary to control pathogens which multiply rapidly so that even a small quantity of inoculum can, under the right conditions, lead to severe outbreaks of disease.

Whatever control measures are used it is always advisable to grow the most resistant varieties of the crop plant available – particularly those with high horizontal resistance – provided that these varieties are satisfactory in other respects. The cultivation of such varieties reduces the spread of the pathogen in the current season and so minimizes the inoculum available for infection of the crop in the following season.

From the purely financial point of view, it may occasionally be more profitable for the grower not to attempt to control certain diseases in some seasons. An example of this is given by Ordish (1964) who points out that, although high rainfall encourages blight, it has an even greater effect in promoting vigorous growth and high yield of the potato plant, so that controlling blight in wet seasons is likely to result in very high yields leading to a crop surplus with correspondingly low prices for potatoes – in addition to involving the grower in the expense of applying the control measures. Hence it may be more important to the grower to control blight in rather dry seasons, when any measures likely to increase yield are worthwhile, than in wet seasons, despite the prospect of more severe blight in the latter.

Disease control in developing countries

Many countries in the tropics and subtropics are less advanced agriculturally than some in temperate regions. Different and often less sophisticated measures are likely to be required for disease control in such developing areas. In some countries elaborate disease control is practised on 'cash' crops grown on an intensive plantation scale for export whereas relatively little attempt is made to control the diseases and pests which attack peasant food crops. A major problem is that of protecting plants against a complex of harmful agents which cause crop loss, and a wider approach to plant protection becomes necessary if such loss is to be minimized. Generally speaking, plant protection chemicals of high mammalian toxicity are not to be recommended for developing areas where their use might prove hazardous. There is a need for safe, inexpensive protective chemicals for use in such areas, and of robust, simple, inexpensive equipment for applying the chemicals, rather than costly, elaborate machines which, although more efficient, are more difficult and more expensive to operate, maintain and repair, as discussed by Jepson (1956).

An inclined drum with a hinged lid, rotated by a cranked handle and fitted internally with wooden baffle plates can be mounted on trestles to make a satisfactory machine for applying fungicides to small quantities of seed. Such simple mixers can be made cheaply by the local carpenter or blacksmith from a suitably modified clean oil drum, a length of metal pipe, and wood. Application of fungicides by a watering can with a fine rose was quite effective in control of potato blight (Martin, 1940). In the Sudan application of 2, 4-dichlorophenoxyacetic acid by watering can to irrigated sorghum gave as effective control of witchweed (*Striga hermonthica*) as application by knapsack sprayer; this should reduce the cost and increase the simplicity of witchweed control as well as minimizing the danger of spray drift (Tarr, 1957*a*).

Dusting of pesticides, although often less efficient, may be preferable to application by spraying as dusting is simpler and requires less water, which may be in short supply in dry areas. Simple hand operated dusters working on the bellows principle are inexpensive and often quite adequate for their purpose.

Disease control by cultural methods or resistant varieties is very useful in developing countries but chemical methods may be feasible if effective, safe, inexpensive, and easy to apply – as in seed treatment carried out either by the cultivators themselves or on a cooperative basis. Covered smut (*Sphacelotheca sorghi*) of sorghum (figure 23.2), for example, can be effectively, economically and safely controlled by treating the sowing seed with fungicidal powders. Such treatment, if applied to all the sowing seed, would greatly increase yields of this crop in many countries. Padwick (1950) has estimated that this smut causes about 6.6% crop loss to sorghum in the former British colonies of Africa, an amount of grain which, according to the calculations of Vallega & Chiarappa (1964), would feed four million people for a year.

As agricultural development proceeds more complex and more effective control methods can be applied, but meantime there is considerable scope for devising measures to control diseases and pests which are inexpensive, safe, easily applied, and reasonably effective: needless to say this is much more difficult than it sounds! Nevertheless, the damage caused by pathogens can sometimes be reduced by growing resistant or tolerant varieties of crop plants, by modifying the sowing date, by fertilizer treatment, by crop sanitation, by sowing only seed collected from uninfected plants, by pulling out infected plants as they appear, and by crop rotation, although the last named may not be possible if land suitable for cultivation is limited. The plant pathologist working in agriculturally underdeveloped

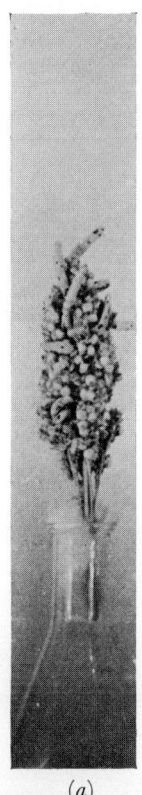 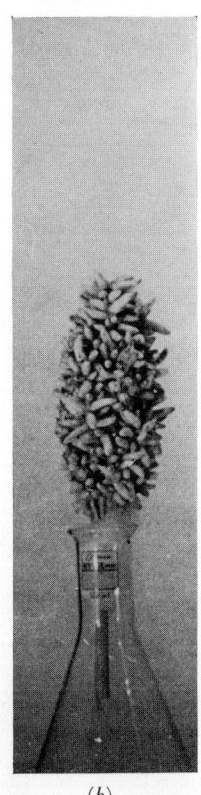 

(a) (b) (c)

areas has constantly to remember that the disease control measures needed
may well be different from those commonly used in more advanced
countries.

The measures used to control plant disease are here considered under
the following headings:

1. Sanitation: the elimination of sources of infection (inoculum).
2. Cultural practices which minimize attack: alleviation.
3. Plant protection by chemical and physical means.
4. Plant breeding methods: immune, resistant and tolerant varieties of
   plants.
5. International and legislative aspects of disease control.

These measures are discussed chiefly with reference to fungal and
bacterial pathogens of plants but they are also applicable in varying degree
to diseases caused by viruses, except that there are no practicable chemical
methods for control of viruses although chemical control of their vectors
may be feasible. They apply, with appropriate modification, to plant
injury caused by nematodes, insects and mites, but these pests are likely

(d)   (e)

Figure 23.2 The four smuts of sorghum.

(a) Long smut, *Tolyposporium ehrenbergii*; several or many grains are replaced by smut sori up to 3 cm in length.

(b) Covered smut, *Sphacelotheca sorghi*; individual grains are replaced by oval-conical smut sori up to about 1 cm in length and with a fairly permanent surrounding membrane.

(c) Loose smut, *Sphacelotheca cruenta*; infected heads are looser, bushier and darker green, and the glumes proliferate up to about 2 cm in length. The soral membrane ruptures before emergence of the head and is thus rarely seen in the field.

(d) Head smut, *Sphacelotheca reiliana*; the infected head is partially or completely replaced by a large whitish gall (up to about 5 x 15 cm) which soon ruptures to expose a mass of dark spores mixed with a network of long thin filaments, the vascular strands of the infected head.

(e) Unsmutted head.

to show special features which have to be considered when devising control measures. Much information is given in the series of books on the control of diseases, nematodes, insect pests, vertebrate pests and weeds being published by the National Academy of Sciences, Washington, D.C., from 1968 onwards.

24 Disease control by plant sanitation

This is the simplest and no doubt one of the earliest of disease control measures to be used. Destruction of diseased plant material, whether in the form of plants in the fields or crop residues after harvest, is an obvious way of reducing inoculum. Sources of seasonal carry-over are considered elsewhere (p. 329) but briefly they comprise infected plant material remaining in the fields after harvest, infected plants which survive the intercrop period, infected self-sown seedlings, infected weeds or cultivated plants in gardens, infected plant products of commerce, soil borne infection, seed borne infection, diseased plant material brought in from other areas, and air borne inoculum from distant areas where diseased crops are growing. All these sources of inoculum may have to be destroyed or avoided but the first step is to find out which are involved, and to concentrate on these. Hence sanitation is selective: the presence of inoculum does not in itself prove that it plays a major part in carry-over of the pathogen although it is wise to assume that it does so unless demonstrated to the contrary. Not all infected weeds are necessarily able to pass on their pathogens to cultivated crop plants. Different physiological races are sometimes involved and this can only be determined by cross-inoculation experiments and sometimes from observations on the distribution of the disease in the field.

If efficiently carried out, plant sanitation can be a very effective control measure but inoculum sources of some pathogens are so widespread, varied and abundant that their total destruction is almost impossible. It is particularly useful in gardens where diseased plant material can be completely destroyed. Over larger areas, however, effective sanitation becomes much more difficult and laborious unless mechanized or chemical methods can be used. These include ploughing to bury the crop residues, or treatment with chemicals which destroy the pathogen or the residues, which hasten the microbiological breakdown of the residues, or which encourage antagonistic microorganisms. The effect of these chemicals on the soil and its inhabitants must of course be carefully investigated, and pilot experiments should be carried out before large scale application is attempted. It has been suggested that 'burning machines', rather similar to those used on roads, could be pulled slowly across the fields to destroy crop residues but the effects of such a drastic procedure – in effect surface sterilization – on the soil would need consideration. The time honoured methods of collecting and burning are likely to be effective but extremely laborious over large areas, and some indication of the standard of sanitation required for an acceptable degree of control would often be useful. This standard will normally be higher for a pathogen which spreads rapidly from a small amount of inoculum than for one which spreads more slowly.

In the case of potato blight (*Phytophthora infestans*) Van der Plank (1963) has calculated that there is little point in trying to eliminate more than about 99% of the inoculum – in itself a formidable task – because only relatively slight benefit is likely to accrue from increasing the standard of sanitation at this high level. This is particularly true if there are other sources of inoculum which are not controlled by sanitation. Under weather conditions which favour it *P. infestans* can spread rapidly from a small amount of inoculum as in the case described by Van der Zaag (1956), and cited by Van der Plank (1963), in which one blighted shoot per km² of a very susceptible potato cultivar was sufficient to cause an epiphytotic in the Netherlands. Sanitation is more likely to be effective against plant pathogens in which development of an epiphytotic is dependent upon a relatively large amount of inoculum, than against those in which severe outbreaks can develop from small amounts of inoculum.

Plant sanitation is particularly applicable to pathogens which do not spread from plant to plant in the field and to slowly spreading pathogens of narrow host range attacking annual crops in regions where there is a well defined intercrop period of several months during which susceptible plants are absent. During this intercrop period possible sources of inoculum can be systematically searched for and destroyed before the next season's plants are sown. It is of less value with crop plants which are grown more or less continuously throughout the year in that inoculum of their pathogens is always present.

Sanitation is frequently a compromise between what is desirable and what is humanly possible, and legislation and inspection may be necessary to enforce it in cases where a high standard of sanitation is essential for the well being of an important crop. Enforcement can be expensive and unpopular and should be resorted to only when unavoidable. On the other hand, there are some sanitation measures, such as the burning of cereal stubble after harvest, which are fairly easily applied. Sanitation becomes of great importance where a crop is grown in the same field for several or many consecutive years, as is often the case in intensive farming. In the absence of sanitation the pathogens and pests of that crop tend to build up year by year unless effectively controlled. Sanitation should thus be combined with crop rotation, the length of which depends partly on the viability of the pathogen in soil.

Sanitation is also applied to individual plants especially bushes and trees. The diseased branches or shoots are removed ('tree surgery') and burned, and the cut surface is treated with a fungicide such as Bordeaux paste or lead paint. The cut should be made at some distance below the observed lower limit of the diseased area, since the pathogen may extend beyond the latter, and healthy cambium is necessary for production of the callus which will eventually seal the cut surface. Some of the fungi which cause canker diseases can be treated in this way, for example *Nectria galligena* on apple.

In some diseases it may be possible to remove the diseased parts and treat the exposed tissue with an effective fungicide. Painting the galls caused by *Agrobacterium tumefaciens* (crown gall) with sodium dinitrocresol in methanol was effective on almond trees (Ark, 1941), and some success has been reported with antibiotics although these do not appear to have been taken up to any great extent. One of the control measures against *Sclerotinia* spp. (brown rot of apple and stone fruits) is to destroy diseased twigs and the typically mummified fruits which may remain on the trees for some time after harvesting. The spread of silver leaf (*Stereum purpureum*) in Britain is reduced if the diseased wood of plum trees is removed and burnt by mid-July, thus reducing the formation of fruiting bodies of the fungus. If carefully carried out, these and other similar measures can reduce the incidence of pathogens, notably those localized on twigs or the smaller branches. They are less suitable for leaf diseases, although removal of diseased leaves, if carried out sufficiently early and thoroughly, can delay the spread of pathogens, particularly in glasshouses. Removal of all the diseased tissue could be fatal to trees in which most of the branches are infected, but it is sometimes possible to cut away much of the upper part of the tree and to allow regrowth from the remaining basal part. In all cases, the wounds should be treated immediately with a fungicidal paste, since many of the pathogens which attack tree branches are wound parasites.

Roguing – the removal and destruction of plants as they become diseased – may be worthwhile in a valuable crop attacked by a slowly-spreading pathogen whose effect on the plant is conspicuous, so that infected plants can easily be recognized. It should be carried out as early as possible and becomes impracticable if many of the plants are infected. Roguing has been used to minimize virus attack in potato plants being grown to produce certified disease-free tubers. Provided there is no infection from outside sources, Waller (1969) considers that the removal of the easily observed sugar cane plants attacked by *Ustilago scitaminea* (whip smut) during the first 8 months of the crop in Kenya would considerably reduce the amount of inoculum produced. To be effective, roguing may have to be carried out at regular short intervals and so it is likely to be too costly for most crops. Its practical scope as a method of disease control is thus limited.

The main methods of destroying inoculum of plant pathogens are mechanical, chemical and by flooding.

Mechanical and chemical methods

Manual methods of destroying or neutralizing diseased plant residues are laborious and expensive and are being replaced by various mechanical and chemical methods. These include ploughing after harvest, care being taken to ensure that the residues are buried rather than redistributed.

The mechanical methods used to bring about the destruction of the propagules – often resistant sclerotia and chlamydospores – of soil borne pathogens include tillage, ploughing, and soil inversion as described by Sewell (1965). The first two methods expose some of the propagules to desiccation and other harmful agents, and may also bring about their premature germination so that, in the absence of susceptible plants, the incidence of the pathogen is reduced. Ploughing has been used successfully to control groundnut blight (*Corticium rolfsii*) in Georgia, U.S.A. (Boyle, 1956) and Tanzania, ploughing to a depth of 20 cm giving complete control in the latter country (Clinton, 1957). *C. rolfsii* attacks groundnut plants near soil level and to do so requires supplementary food materials from organic matter in the soil; burying crop residues by ploughing renders them unavailable to the fungus and so reduces incidence of the disease. The disease is also reduced by measures which prevent the accumulation of plant litter on the soil surface during the growing season.

Ploughing which buries sclerotia, such as those of *Claviceps* and *Sclerotinia*, which germinate to produce perithecial stromata or apothecia, physically prevents successful discharge and dispersal of the ascospores. Such sclerotia often form on the aerial parts of the plant and eventually fall to the soil surface from where more or less unimpeded ascospore discharge and dispersal can take place, thus facilitating infection of the above ground parts of the plant. In such cases ploughing would seem to be a promising method of control but it is difficult to ensure complete burial of all sclerotia or to prevent some of them returning to the soil surface during subsequent cultivation. Ploughing to a depth of about 75 cm together with inversion of the contaminated soil was reported by Green (1958) to be effective in reducing mint (*Mentha*) wilt caused by a species of *Verticillium* whose microsclerotia are largely confined to the upper 45 cm of soil. As well as burying inoculum to what one hopes to be a safe depth, ploughing is likely to redistribute propagules of pathogens and so facilitate their dispersal. It is a control measure which should be carefully carried out and thoroughly tested in the field before being practised on a large scale.

Ploughing or, more often, herbicides are also used to destroy self-sown seedlings growing in the autumn or spring from seeds scattered during harvesting. Thorough examination is often necessary to find such seedlings since they are often partially hidden by weeds. Surviving infected plants from the previous season may have to be destroyed in similar ways, also alternate and alternative hosts of pathogens. Regrowth from plant roots remaining in the soil is likely to occur when essentially perennial plants such as cotton are grown as annuals. It may be necessary to pull out such plants and their roots, using special implements or to destroy them by ploughing (often not very effective) or chemical means. Special techniques such as treatment of the cut stems with herbicides can sometimes be devised (Tarr, 1957b).

Several examples of the use of chemicals in crop sanitation can be mentioned. Chemical defoliation is reported to reduce the incidence of some diseases, and the destruction of blighted potato haulms before lifting the tubers reduces the liability of the tubers to blight and viruses. The herbicides used have included arsenites, chlorates, and dilute sulphuric acid but these are being replaced by safer ones such as diquat (a bipyridyl herbicide) and dinitrophenol (DNOC). Mechanical haulm cutters and pulverizers have also been devised.

Flooding

Flooding has been used against pests and for control of a few plant diseases, notably Panama disease of banana caused by *Fusarium oxysporum f.sp. cubense*. Under laboratory conditions, Stover (1953) found that the fungus grew best and survived longest in soil of 25% saturation, and that at higher moisture levels growth decreased. In baiting experiments, the fungus colonized small sterile squares of banana leaf from moist soil after 12 weeks, but colonization of squares in flooded soil was very slight after this time (Newcombe, 1960). Under field conditions in Honduras, flooding with 0·6–1·5 m of water for 4–6 months materially reduced soil inoculum of the fungus, but the water used for flooding occasionally contained *F. oxysporum cubense* spores. Field observations suggested that soil that had been flooded and subsequently drained might be more favourable for growth of the fungus than is unflooded soil, and this was supported by the results of laboratory tests (Stover, 1953, 1959). Ploughing to 20–25 cm between flooding periods resulted in redistribution and a greatly reduced incidence of the fungus (Stover, 1959).

Q

Flooding for 5 weeks is also reported to destroy the sclerotia of *Sclerotinia sclerotiorum* (pink rot of celery) in the Everglades area of Florida. Circulating water was more effective in this respect, the sclerotia being destroyed in about 20 days by the circulating water used for growing rice in a 3 or 4 year rotation (Moore, 1949; Stover and Moore, 1953). Another example of inoculum destruction by flooding is the eradication of *Phytophthora parasitica* var. *nicotianae* (tobacco black shank) by the 3–4 months' flooding used to grow swamp rice in a 2 year tobacco–rice rotation in Java (Van Schreven, 1948, cited by Sewell, 1965).

A somewhat different case is the great reduction in the amount of bacterial blight (*Xanthomonas malvacearum*) carried by diseased cotton trash following several days' flooding with irrigation water in the Gezira area of the Sudan (Andrews, 1937); in one experiment, cotton sown in a trash contaminated field which had been flooded for 4 days showed 2·1% infected seedlings as compared with 69·5% in an unflooded, contaminated field. The destruction of the bacteria following flooding has been attributed to the action of bacteriophage present in Gezira soil and irrigation water (Massey, 1931). In Israel, *Pyrenophora teres* on barley, *Alternaria porri f.sp. solani* on tomatoes and potatoes, and *A. dauci* on carrots, all survive on crop residues throughout the rainless summer months, and the persistence of these pathogens in the residues is inversely correlated with the amount of irrigation water applied to the soil, persistence being longest in un-irrigated soil (Rotem and Palti, 1969). The way in which irrigation water hastens the disappearance of these fungi is not known – it might be due to the growth and sporulation brought about by the water in the absence of susceptible plants leading to premature exhaustion of the food reserves in the residues, to microbial effects such as antagonism, to anaerobic conditions during irrigation, or to other factors.

Several explanations of the harmful effects of prolonged flooding on soil borne plant pathogens have been put forward. Lack of oxygen may be involved in some cases or, more often perhaps, accumulation of carbon dioxide in the soil. The survival of *Fusarium oxysporum f.sp. cubense* in soil after 2 weeks depends on the formation of chlamydospores, since the conidia are not apparently very long-lived in soil, and Newcombe (1960) found that carbon dioxide and flooded soil both largely inhibit chlamydospore formation, whereas they at first stimulate the production of conidia. Consequently the fungus, although able to survive in banana plantation soil containing organic matter, is likely to die out in a fallow, flooded field where organic matter is in short supply. From her laboratory experiments, Newcombe (1960) concluded that the main factor in the elimination of *F. oxysporum* by flood fallowing is a high carbon dioxide content in the flooded soil combined with a decreased availability of colonizable substrates. In flooded soil, carbon dioxide stimulates germination of the conidia, presumably by overcoming the fungistatic factor present in soil, but prevents the formation of chlamydospores so that the fungus dies out when the organic matter is exhausted. A similar situation perhaps holds for other soil borne fungi, but few cases have been investigated.

Considerable microbiological changes occur in soil which has undergone prolonged flooding, and the observation that circulating (aerated) water is more effective than static water in ridding soil of the sclerotia of *Sclerotinia sclerotiorum*, as discussed above, suggests that microbial action rather than anaerobic conditions may be the major factor involved here. The fact that cracked or abraded sclerotia, more liable to be affected by soil microorganisms, were destroyed more rapidly than intact ones would seem to support the microbial explanation.

Whatever the mechanisms involved, it remains true that flooding on a large scale is an expensive operation, even supposing the large quantities of water required to be available. During flooding the land is out of cultivation, and this is likely to be a serious disadvantage if land suitable for cultivation is limited. There is also the potential danger of introducing new pathogens with the water used for flooding. For these and other reasons, flooding is only rarely used as a disease control measure. The literature is reviewed by Newhall (1955) and Sewell (1965).

Eradication of pathogens

The logical end point of sanitation is eradication, in which the pathogen is eliminated from a region by systematic destruction of all diseased plants and plant material combined with measures to prevent its reintroduction. This is likely to be possible only if the pathogen involved has a narrow host range. One of the best known examples is citrus canker (*Xanthomonas citri*) which was eradicated in Florida, Alabama, Georgia, Louisiana, Mississippi, South Carolina and Texas, as described by Dopson (1964). The pathogen was probably introduced from Japan in about 1910. Eradication campaigns involving the destruction by burning of about twenty million citrus trees had virtually eliminated the disease about 25 years later, and a further destruction of scattered diseased trees resulted in apparently complete elimination by 1952. Similar eradication campaigns have been mounted against two virus diseases of peach (mosaic and phony peach) and Dutch elm disease (*Ceratostomella ulmi*) in the U.S.A. with varying degrees of success.

Eradication may be possible over a limited area, such as a state, provided reintroduction of the pathogen can be prevented. It is likely to be a costly and lengthy procedure if the pathogen attacks a valuable crop and is widely distributed, but on a long term basis may be worthwhile.

The decision whether to attempt to eradicate a pathogen over an extensive area involves consideration of such factors as the host range of the pathogen and its possible occurrence on wild plants, the feasibility of preventing reintroduction of the pathogen after it has been eradicated, and the cost of the campaign in relation to estimated long term benefits. Apart from the considerable cost of destroying the plants, it may be necessary to pay compensation to the cultivators whose crops are affected, and the value of the produce inevitably lost when numerous plants are destroyed has to be taken into account. Eradication can often be profitably undertaken against pathogens of recent introduction and/or limited distribution, and should be carried out as early as possible, before the pathogen has time to spread.

The eradication of alternate hosts of destructive rusts can be beneficial in two ways. Not only does it reduce inoculum, but elimination of the aecial host tends to reduce the probability of new races of the rust arising. Elimination of barberry bushes infected by *Puccinia graminis tritici* is a case in point. Barberry eradication has been practised for many years in some parts of the U.S.A., and in the early years was effective, reducing the annual losses due to rust from 1,820 million litres in 1915–1919 to about 550 million litres in 1925–1929, by which time (1929) about 18 million barberry bushes had been destroyed (Van der Plank, 1963). Nowadays its value in reducing stem rust is rather uncertain, since the disease can still be destructive in some years, infection originating from uredospores carried by air currents from rusted wheat in the southern U.S.A. and Mexico. According to Wilson and Henderson (1966), *P. graminis tritici* has never been isolated from aecia on barberry in Britain, so that barberry bushes are presumably of no importance as a source of rust inoculum for wheat. Black stem rust occurs on wheat in England, especially in the south-west, and is thought to originate each year from uredospores blown in from western Europe. In this case barberry eradication would presumably be of little use in controlling stem rust, and eradication is also unlikely to be highly effective – except in reducing the production of new races of the pathogen – in areas where there are other and possibly more important sources of inoculum.

Eradication can also be aimed at plants, especially perennial ones, which are alternative hosts of pathogens attacking crop plants. Such alternative hosts may be wild plants which are sometimes difficult to find and destroy because the symptoms are inconspicuous or absent (symptomless carriers of viruses). Ornamental plants or vegetables grown in gardens may harbour pathogens of crop plants. In the irrigated Gezira area of the Sudan *Malvaviscus arboreus*, a perennial ornamental Malvaceous shrub, developed typical albeit mild symptoms of leaf curl a few years after its introduction from India in 1936. Inoculation experiments showed that it was infected with cotton leaf curl virus and that it was a source of virus for the valuable

Gezira cotton crop. No doubt it had become infected with the virus from cotton. Cuttings were thereafter distributed throughout the Gezira without it being realized that they were infected, since leaf curl symptoms are not conspicuous on *Malvaviscus*. A campaign to eradicate this shrub was organized and its further cultivation in the Gezira was prohibited, thus eliminating a permanent reservoir of the virus.

25 Disease control by cultural practices

Agricultural and horticultural practices should be such as to reduce attack by pathogens and pests as well as encouraging optimum growth and yield of the plants. This can be difficult to achieve since a practice which discourages one pathogen may favour a second or may be undesirable or impossible from other aspects. Weather conditions, the availability of labour or land, and pressure of other work may make modification of such cultural practices as sowing date and crop rotation difficult to carry out. Cultural measures which discourage pathogens are essentially good crop husbandry and are perhaps the most satisfactory methods of control, but the practices involved may not be acceptable to the cultivator. It is unfortunately true that few diseases can be completely controlled by such methods alone, although they are often valuable as subsidiary aids.

The numerous cultural practices which can be manipulated to alleviate or control plant diseases are discussed exhaustively by Stevens (1960) who uses the term to include cropping methods, harvesting and storage methods, tillage, crop rotation, soil management, resistant varieties of plants and land-use planning. The more important cultural methods used in disease control are described below.

Planting material

Only pathogen-free, mature, undamaged planting material of high germination capacity should be sown. It may be necessary to obtain certified healthy material or to use an effective seed treatment to destroy possible seed borne contamination or infection. It is most important that planting material of vegetatively propagated plants such as potato and sugarcane be virus-free, and the production of pathogen-free seed, tubers and other propagating organs is an expanding industry. The planting material should also be mature and intact otherwise it is liable to be attacked by soil fungi when sown. Even minute breaks in the seed coat may enable fungi to enter, with resulting decreased emergence and poor stands. This is particularly true of seed with a fragile seed coat (some varieties of groundnut) and soft seed. Seed injury may occur on the standing plants before harvest, during harvesting, during storage or during sowing, especially in mechanical sowing with imperfectly adjusted seed drills. Bulbs, tubers and other propagative structures are liable to similar damage, which is likely to bring about extensive rotting in store. Storage conditions are critically important in this respect and should be such that seed rotting and pest infestation are reduced to a minimum. These aspects are discussed by Dykstra (1961: production of pathogen-free seed) and Christensen (1957: fungal deterioration of stored grain).

Method and depth of sowing

Faulty mechanical sowing can damage the seed and so predispose it to attack by soil fungi. It may also result in uneven distribution of seed with consequent overcrowding and damping-off in some places and isolated seeds, unable to push up through the overlying soil, in others. Sowing should be as uniform as possible, with minimal damage to the seed, and giving approximately the optimum population of plants per hectare for that particular crop. Overcrowding may result in abnormally high humidity and other effects on the microclimate within the canopy of the adult plants, and so may encourage some pathogens and pests; a dense canopy can, however, reduce the spread of some pathogens by physically hindering the dissemination of their propagules.

Depth of sowing has an important effect on some pathogens, notably those which attack seedlings. By delaying emergence, deep sowing prolongs the susceptible phase between germination and emergence and so favours many pathogens. This has been shown in several seedling diseases caused by *Fusarium* and *Rhizoctonia* and in some smuts which attack seedlings (see Tapke, 1948). Fairly shallow sowing is preferable whenever possible, but much depends on the nature of the soil – in dry soil fairly deep sowing may be necessary to ensure adequate moisture for the germinating seed.

An interesting example of disease control by adjusting the sowing depth is given by Hardison (1948) who found that good control of blind seed disease of perennial ryegrass, caused by *Gloeotinia temulenta*, can be obtained by planting infected seed at least 1·25 cm deep and with complete soil coverage. In this disease infected seeds are the only source of inoculum and burying such infected seeds prevents the emergence above soil level of the apothecia formed on them, thus preventing effective dissemination of the ascospores.

Conditions for germination, emergence and growth

These should be made as favourable as possible in order to encourage rapid germination and vigorous early growth, at which stages plants tend to be susceptible to pathogens. The longer the period between sowing and emergence, the poorer the latter is likely to be, because of damage by soil inhabiting microorganisms, insects and nematodes. Factors which retard germination and early growth thus tend to encourage attack by soil borne pathogens and so to increase seed bed losses. Planting should be in properly cultivated soil of suitable texture, pH, moisture content, fertility and temperature. If emergence is likely to be slow it may be advisable to apply a fungicidal or fungicidal-insecticidal seed dressing to provide some protection for the seed and young seedling, or judicious use of fertilizers may be beneficial. These aspects are of particular importance in seed and seedling diseases where, for example, cold waterlogged soil can result in slow germination and extensive rotting of sown seed.

Moisture and temperature cannot normally be regulated in the field except in irrigated crops with which an approximately optimal soil moisture content can sometimes be achieved by frequent light waterings rather than periodic drowning. Thus, a stand of sorghum was about 84% when furrow irrigated, 55% when flat irrigated and 48% when rain grown (Tarr, 1954), the relatively poor stands of the latter two treatments being due to pre-emergence pathogen and pest attack encouraged by unfavourable soil moisture conditions. Soil moisture can also be controlled in glasshouses and sometimes in seed beds. Soil conditions affect not only germination and early growth of the plant but also pathogens present in the soil or on the seed; thus, to take an over-simplified example, growing a crop at a temperature appreciably higher (or lower) than that optimal for the pathogen tends to discourage the latter. Many pathogens, however, have temperature requirements similar to those of their host plants, as would be expected, and this principle is in practice of limited application. It can, however, sometimes be used with winter and summer sowings of some crops in tropical and subtropical areas, in which different varieties with different temperature requirements are grown.

Apart from seedling diseases these soil and environmental factors also influence the infection of established plants by pathogens, and some of them can be manipulated to reduce disease. As is well known, *Plasmodiophora brassicae* (club root of crucifers) is less severe in alkaline soils and heavy liming can be beneficial. Some factors such as temperature, moisture and light can be regulated to reduce the incidence of diseases and pests in glasshouses – for example, control of *Verticillium* wilt of tomato by raising the temperature. The water supply to irrigated crops can to some extent be regulated and the method of irrigation is likely to affect pathogens;

overhead sprinkler irrigation encourages the spread of many pathogens attacking the aerial parts of plants to a much greater extent than furrow irrigation, whereas the latter may distribute propagules of soil borne pathogens. In Israel, the diseases of tomato caused by *Stemphylium botryosum* (*Pleospora herbarum*) and *Xanthomonas vesicatoria* were increased by overhead sprinkling whereas *Leveillula taurica*, a powdery mildew favoured by dry conditions, was reduced. Sprinkling resulted in a higher humidity and a lower air temperature but furrow irrigation had little effect (Rotem and Cohen, 1966). Such alterations of microclimate could also affect the incidence of pests, including the vectors of viruses. Humidity in some crops, particularly fruit trees and bushes, can sometimes be reduced by wider spacing, clean cultivation and suitable pruning.

Sowing date

Pathogens are able to infect susceptible plants only under certain environmental conditions, and their requirements in this respect are sometimes exacting: some downy mildews, for example, require prolonged high moisture for infection. Plants tend to reach maximum susceptibility at a certain stage in their development and to be resistant at others. It may, therefore, be possible to so manipulate the sowing date that the crop passes through its susceptible phase at a time when the pathogen is either absent or unable to infect because of unsuitable environmental conditions. Long association between plant and pathogen leads to some degree of synchronization between the two under natural conditions, but it may be possible to break this synchronization when growing plants artificially, or to breed varieties which can be grown under conditions unfavourable to the pathogen. With rain-spread pathogens the crop can be grown in such a way that it is likely to pass through its most susceptible phase in fairly dry weather, provided of course that there is sufficient moisture for good growth of the plants. Similarly it may be possible to grow plants at a time when climatic conditions discourage the vectors of a pathogen.

Any considerable alteration of sowing date is likely to expose the crop to hazards of various sorts – other pathogens and pests, the danger of failing to mature before the end of the season, and the possibility of frost early in the season are some of these – so this method is of limited application and should be carefully investigated before being applied on a large scale. With irrigated crops grown in areas with fairly uniform climatic conditions throughout much of the year – especially where frost does not occur – it can nevertheless be useful in the control of some pathogens. It may be possible to select or breed early maturing varieties of crops able to produce satisfactory yields when sown early in order to avoid pathogens and pests, and similarly late maturing varieties. In temperate areas adjustment of sowing date tends to be less useful in that there is usually a fairly well defined growing season during which moisture and temperature are suitable for growth. Early sowing of broad beans, particularly if planted in the previous November, often enables the plants to produce their pods before heavy aphid infestation occurs, and similarly for early sown potatoes in respect of blight (*Phytophthora infestans*) in south-west England and there are other cases in which early or late sowing enables plants to escape attack by certain pathogens or pests.

Fertilizers

It has been known for many years that fertilizer treatments can affect the severity of plant diseases. High concentrations of nitrogen, particularly if in readily assimilated form as in nitrates, often predispose towards disease susceptibility, the plants becoming 'soft' and tending to remain in a vegetative condition. There are exceptions to this generalization – some smuts, for example, are reported to be discouraged by application of nitrogenous fertilizers, possibly because the more rapid growth of the plants enables them to pass through their susceptible phase more quickly. Many obligate parasites tend to be most severe on vigorous plants and heavy manuring, especially with nitrogen compounds, encourages some rusts and powdery mildews. By contrast it seems generally accepted that increased available potash and phosphate discourage some pathogens at least, and deficiency of these elements may result in reduced resistance of the plant. Deficiency of some trace elements also predisposes plants to attack by some pathogens and pests. Predisposition of this sort is apparently associated with the effects of the nutrients on the plant, the resulting physiological changes bringing about increased or decreased susceptibility as the case may be. Modifying the concentrations of available nutrients in the soil by appropriate fertilizer treatments can sometimes be used to reduce disease. This usually involves a series of field trials to determine which fertilizer treatments result in least disease, but observations on disease and pest incidence in routine fertilizer trials can yield useful information. Laboratory tests are less useful in that their results are not always borne out in the field.

As well as affecting the inherent susceptibility of the plant, fertilizers are also likely to influence the pathogen, especially if soil borne, and the interaction of plant and pathogen; the overall effects of fertilizers on disease incidence are complex and can only be determined by trial. They also affect the growth of the plant and can to some extent compensate for the damage caused by pathogens and pests. By skilful use of fertilizers it is sometimes possible to stimulate plant growth to such an extent that the crop, although diseased, gives a worthwhile yield. The pathogen may still be causing considerable damage which is, however, partially counteracted by the more vigorous growth resulting from application of fertilizers. A plant in vigorous growth is more likely to be able to replace tissue destroyed by pathogens than is one growing poorly, and fertilizers are important in this respect. This is not control of the pathogen, it simply increases the plant's capacity to tolerate attack.

Crop rotation

Continuous cultivation of land with one crop (monoculture), although agronomically undesirable, is sometimes unavoidable or considered to be worthwhile, in which case it may be necessary to take special precautions against build-up of pathogens and pests. Often, however, some kind of crop rotation can be practised and this should be planned with control of pathogens and pests in mind; indeed crop rotation can be used as a disease control measure, particularly so with root diseases in which it is, or should be, a basic procedure.

The survival of plant pathogens in soil is discussed elsewhere (p. 340). It is generally thought that some fungi, particularly fairly unspecialized parasites which infect roots, can survive as free-living saprophytes in soil for limited periods. Fungi with high cellulolytic ability are thought to disappear from soil more rapidly. Many more, probably, survive in soil as resistant propagules or in plant material, and this is true also – but to a less extent – of the pathogens which attack the aerial parts of plants. The length of time during which a pathogen persists in soil depends on the longevity of its survival propagules as well as on the microbiological and chemical conditions of the soil, and other factors. This is of critical importance in crop rotation since for successful control the interval between successive susceptible crops must be longer than the effective survival period of the pathogen. Crop rotation rarely if ever leads to eradication of the pathogen since the latter may survive in susceptible weeds or in a dormant condition in the lower reaches of the soil where microbiological activity is greatly reduced. Most crop rotations aim to reduce the pathogen content of the soil to a fairly low level at which it causes only minor damage or is insufficient for infection. This 'safe' interval between successive susceptible crops can only be determined in field trials, and the rotation experiments frequently carried out by agronomists can yield useful information on this. A compromise is often necessary with pathogens which survive inordinately long in soil, and not surprisingly an interval of 7 or 10 years between successive sowings of a profitable cash crop would rarely be acceptable to the farmer.

The host range of the pathogen is also of great importance when using crop rotation as a control measure. If the pathogen can infect numerous species of plants, wild and cultivated, it may persist on weeds or in other crops comprising the rotation. *Phymatotrichum omnivorum*, the cause of Texas root rot of cotton and other plants in the south-west U.S.A., attacks over 2000 different species of plants, many of which are common weeds. It also produces numerous sclerotia which may be several metres deep in the soil and persist for as long as 12 years under non-susceptible crops. Crop rotation alone is unlikely to give effective or practicable control in this case and has to be combined with other measures – deep ploughing to dry and aerate the soil and so destroy the sclerotia, and application of organic matter to encourage microbial activity in the soil.

It might be expected that crop rotation would be most successful for the control of specialized parasites unable to survive for long as free-living saprophytes in the soil. Unfortunately many such parasites produce resistant propagules – sclerotia, chlamydospores, oospores – which may survive in a dormant condition for many years, show progressive maturation, and be activated by plant roots. Ideally the plants in the rotation should stimulate the germination of these propagules and yet be resistant to the pathogen, so that the latter perishes through premature germination of its propagules in the absence of susceptible roots. This is difficult to achieve with fungi which attack roots although some success has been obtained in the use of trap crops or catch crops for control of some angiospermic root parasites, as described below.

The crops comprising a rotation are usually botanically unrelated so that they will have different nutritional requirements and tend to be attacked by different pathogens and pests. Stevens (1949) has suggested that in those cereal diseases which are not soil borne it might be advantageous to combine rotation with resistant varieties, a rotation of different varieties of a cereal rather than different crops being practised. It is argued that 5–10 years of a new resistant variety will lead to the virtual disappearance of those races of the pathogen able to attack the previously grown varieties, so that the latter can then profitably be grown again. As is subsequently remarked (Stevens, 1960) this has not been proved, and neither has it been shown to be invalid in actual practice.

Crop rotation is a generally useful method of disease control which, although especially applicable to those which are soil borne, can profitably be used against many of the pathogens, nematodes and insects which attack plants. It ensures some degree of spatial separation between inoculum surviving in fields cropped in the previous season and the newly planted fields. The control of plant diseases by crop rotation is reviewed by Curl

(1963), and the survival of plant pathogens in soil is discussed by Menzies (1963).

Avoidance of plant injury

The entry of some pathogens is facilitated if the plant is injured and this is particularly true for those pathogens which cause decay in vegetables, fruits and other organs which contain stored food material. Injury can occur while the organs are still attached to the plant, during harvesting, transit, storage and marketing. Increased mechanization of almost all agricultural and crop handling procedures together with the tendency to send produce long distances to market and to store it for considerable periods all combine to result in increased damage. In the U.S.A., peaches and apricots harvested by an inertia tree shaker (the method used when the fruit is shaken off the tree into a catching frame) developed more decay, caused by various fungi, than fruit which had been harvested by hand (Ogawa *et al.*, 1963).

There are also numerous natural agents which injure plants and provide entry points for pathogens – insects, birds, slugs and climatic visitations such as hail, high wind and frost. Deterioration may be due to pathogens present before harvesting (as occurs in brown rot, *Sclerotinia*) or which enter after harvesting (for example some fruit rots caused by *Penicillium* spp.), and ranges from minor blemishes to extensive soft or dry rotting of produce. The losses can be great and it is clearly important to minimize injury before, during and after harvesting, although some damage during harvesting is inevitable. Apples, for example, should never be picked without their stalks since *Sclerotinia fructigena* (brown rot) can enter the fruit through the wound resulting from removal of the stalk.

Postharvest operations such as transportation, handling and grading of produce also entail some mechanical damage. Potato tubers which had been graded by mechanical reciprocating riddles, fitted with bare wire screens, were more seriously attacked by *Fusarium caeruleum* (dry rot) than were those graded by hand (Foister *et al.*, 1952) and Boyd (1952) suggests that the tubers of certain potato varieties (for example, Golden Wonder) are less liable to infection partly because their thick skin provides some protection against injury during mechanical riddling. Some sort of pre-storage treatment may be advisable to facilitate natural healing of wounded tissue and potato tubers are sometimes kept at about 21°C for 2 weeks since this encourages rapid suberization and reduces the entry of wound parasites. 'Market pathology' is discussed by Stevens and Stevens (1952), and Bratley and Wiant (1950).

Some pathogens also enter the leaves, stem and roots of plants through injuries of various kinds. Prominent among these are many of the wood rotting Basidiomycetes and Ascomycetes, and some opportunist pathogens (*Botrytis cinerea*), root-infecting fungi and bacterial pathogens. The primary injury may be due to insects, nematodes, agricultural machines and implements, adverse weather conditions, chemicals (especially herbicides and smog), fire (in forests) and other causes. All such injury should be kept to a minimum, not only because of its directly harmful effect, but also because damaged plants become more liable to attack by pathogens.

Trap crops

These can sometimes be planted to induce germination of soil borne propagules of pathogens, after which the trap crop is ploughed in or otherwise destroyed before the crop itself is sown. Several such trap crops may be required for worthwhile reduction of the pathogen and these must of course be destroyed before the pathogen produces its propagules. This method is said to reduce populations of the pineapple root knot nematode in Hawaii, one or several plantings of tomato being used as a trap crop (Godfrey and Hoskins, 1934). Witchweed (*Striga*), a phanerogamic root parasite of maize and other cereals, can be alleviated by several trap crops of Sudan grass ploughed in after 6–8 weeks, but before the parasite flowers. A further development is to sow a non-susceptible crop which nevertheless brings about germination of the propagules of the pathogen which then dies out in the absence of susceptible plants. Trap cropping may find some use in controlling pathogens of narrow host range which survive chiefly as soil borne propagules whose germination is stimulated by plant roots, but as yet it finds little application in the control of plant pathogens.

Biological control

Promising results have been obtained in biological control of certain pests, and similar efforts are being made to control plant pathogens but except perhaps in some root diseases the results have been disappointing. Biological control of root pathogens consists basically of encouraging the growth and activity of *Trichoderma*, some Actinomycetes, and other soil microorganisms which are antagonistic to the pathogen, generally by virtue of the antibiotics which they produce. This can sometimes be achieved by partial sterilization of the soil, by the use of selective fungicides or by addition of organic material. The mechanisms of disease control obtained in these ways are complex and little understood. Many antagonistic microorganisms which have been isolated from soil, prove effective against some pathogens in sterile soil or on culture media in the laboratory, but are less effective in natural soil in the field. Nevertheless, control of plant diseases by encouraging antagonistic soil microorganisms has been reported, for example, in *Phymatotrichum omnivorum* (root rot of cotton) by adding organic matter or green manure, and in damping-off of alfalfa caused by *Pythium ultimum* and *P. debaryanum* by adding oat straw and antagonists (Gregory *et al.*, 1952).

The hyphal lysis often brought about by antagonistic microorganisms is generally ascribed to antibiotics or cell wall degrading enzymes which they produce. Recently, however, Ko and Lockwood (1970), working with *Cochliobolus victoriae*, *Glomerella cingulata* and *Fusarium solani*, have concluded that mycelial lysis of these fungi in soil is caused by the activation of β-D-glucosidase and chitinase within the mycelium, rather than by antibiotics or enzymes produced by mycolytic microorganisms in the soil. This activation is thought to follow deficiency of nutrients brought about by soil microorganisms, since lysis characteristically occurs under conditions of deficient nutrients or declining nutrient levels. Some mycolytic microorganisms are known to produce enzymes (chitinase, glucanase) which can degrade fungal hyphae but, on the other hand, Ko and Lockwood (1970) point out that some mycolytic bacteria are not known to produce chitinase and, conversely, some non-lytic microorganisms produce chitinase and glucanase.

Although antagonism has been studied chiefly in relation to soil fungi and root diseases it no doubt also affects the activities of pathogens attacking seedlings, the aerial parts of plants, and fruits. Bacteria and fungi antagonistic to some plant pathogens in the laboratory have been recovered from the surface of seeds, leaves, petals and other organs, and their significance under natural conditions needs investigation. Encouragement of the epiflora of seeds has sometimes resulted in less subsequent infection (Simmonds, 1947) and, conversely, increased infection may follow its removal (Sallans *et al.*, 1949). Somewhat similar results have been reported with *Botrytis cinerea* on lettuce leaves and tomato fruits (Wood, 1951; Newhook, 1951, 1957).

The potentialities of using antagonism to control plant diseases merit exploration. There would appear to be several approaches: (1) to so alter the environment, in particular nutritional conditions, that antagonists are encouraged; (2) to introduce new and more effective species or strains of antagonists; and (3) to isolate and identify the antibiotics, if any, involved in the antagonism; these could then perhaps be produced commercially for disease control. Antagonists occur among fungi, bacteria, Actinomycetes and possibly other groups of microorganisms, and fungal pathogens may be antagonized by other fungi, bacteria or Actinomycetes. Other possible associations which may in time become useful in plant disease and pest control include viruses *versus* fungi, bacteria, insects and (possibly) nematodes; bacteria *versus* insects and fungi; fungi *versus* fungi, insects and nematodes. The control of plant diseases by antagonistic organisms is reviewed by Wood and Tveit (1955).

The use of hyperparasitic fungi in disease control has occasionally been investigated with no very striking results. Hyperparasites are found in most groups of fungi and many of those which attack the fungal pathogens of plants are Ascomycetes and Fungi Imperfecti. They are mainly non-obligate parasites in that many can be grown on culture media, and there appears to be no record of hyperparasitic species among such obligate parasites as rusts, smuts, powdery mildews and downy mildews.

Mycoparasites can be classified into several groups on a nutritional basis: (a) obligate mycoparasites which apparently grow only on the living host fungus and cannot as yet be cultured, for example *Piptocephalis* on other Mucorales; (b) near-obligate mycoparasites which grow only on the living host or on culture media containing extracts of the host fungus, for example *Calcarisporium parasiticum*; (c) ecologically obligate mycoparasites which can be grown in axenic culture but occur naturally only as mycoparasites, for example *Eudarluca* (*Darluca*) on rusts; (d) facultative mycoparasites: many of these are soil saprophytes or weak parasites and some including *Trichoderma*, produce antibiotics and can be antagonists – in fact the distinction between hyperparasitism and antagonism is sometimes a shadowy one. Other fungi in this group include *Corticium* (*Rhizoctonia*) *solani*, and several species of *Pythium and Penicillium*. Many of these appear to be versatile, fairly unspecialized fungi with fairly simple nutritional requirements. Accounts of mycoparasitism are given by Boosalis (1964), and Barnett (1963).

Laboratory experiments on the control of pathogens by hyperparasitic fungi not infrequently give promising results which are not borne out in field trials in which different conditions obtain. Several workers have attempted to use *Eudarluca australis*, better known as its pyncidial state *Darluca filum*, for control of rusts. This fungus sometimes appears to reduce rust incidence under natural conditions, the output of uredospores and/or teliospores being appreciably reduced in severe infections. *Eudarluca* is encouraged by warm, wet weather and so is likely to be severe only in wet areas or wet seasons; its effectiveness in reducing rust attack is largely determined by climatic factors over which man has little control. The provision of extra inoculum of the hyperparasite is thus unlikely to give any marked control unless the weather is very favourable to it, as discussed by Chester (1946). There are several other pathogens which attack rusts – *Xanthomonas uredovorus*, *Tuberculina* spp. usually on aecia and spermogonia, *Cladosporium aecidiicola* and *Verticillium hemileiae* on *Hemileia vastatrix* (coffee rust). Other hyperparasites of plant pathogenic fungi include *Cicinnobolus* spp. on powdery mildews, particularly in warm wet areas; *Trichothecium* spp. on *Plasmopara*, *Pythium*, *Helminthosporium* and various other fungi; *Coniothyrium minitans* on the sclerotia of *Sclerotinia*; *Dactylella* spp. on *Pythium*, *Phytophthora* and other species of Peronosporales, sometimes attacking the oogonia and oospores. Many hyperparasitic fungi have been reported but convincing evidence of their parasitism is not always forthcoming. Further investigation of the potential use of mycoparasites in disease control is clearly needed: among the possible approaches are the introduction of new species or more aggressive strains of hyperparasites, the provision of conditions which favour their development, and methods of enhancing their aggressiveness and spread.

Further information on biological control of plant diseases and an extensive bibliography will be found in Darpoux (1960).

26 Physical and chemical methods of disease control (1)

This chapter describes physical methods of destroying pathogens carried by planting material and the ways in which fungicides are applied to plants and plant material. The next chapter outlines the development and testing of fungicides, the more important groups of fungicides including antibiotics and systemics, the use of oils in disease control, chemotherapy, the ways in which fungicides inhibit fungi, and the development of fungicide resistant strains of fungi.

The literature on disease control by chemical methods is extensive, and no attempt is made here to cover all aspects in detail. Further information can be obtained from Martin (1964) who gives an account of the principles of crop protection, and from Evans (1968), Sharvelle (1961), Martin (1963) and Torgeson (1967, 1969).

Physical methods

Of these, heat treatment is the most important and is used chiefly to eliminate pathogens and pests from planting material. It is particularly useful when the pathogen is within the tissues of the material and so largely out of the reach of fungicides except perhaps systemic ones or certain fungicides in solution or suspension (p. 499). *Puccinia menthae* can be treated by immersing the rhizomes of mint in water at 44°C for 10 minutes, followed by application of cold water before planting, and treatment at 48°C for 35 minutes gave promising control of *Verticillium albo-atrum* on this plant in the glasshouse (Porter and Himelick, 1952). Hot water treatment has also been used against nematodes in narcissus bulbs (43–44°C for 3 hours), mites and other pests in strawberry runners (43–44°C for 20 minutes) (Anon., 1955), and against some pathogens which survive as dormant mycelium within the seed. Wheat seed infected by *Ustilago nuda* (loose smut) (figure 26.1) is often immersed in water at 54°C for 10 minutes after 4–6 hours' soaking in cold water to ensure complete wetting;

Figure 26.1 Loose smut (*Ustilago nuda*) of wheat. Smutted heads often emerge slightly before unsmutted ones and the spores are blown about and infect the ovaries of other heads at the time of flowering. The mycelium of the fungus remains dormant within the seeds so infected until the latter germinate to develop into plants with smutted heads. The remains of the thin membrane which at first encloses the mass of smut spores can be seen. Infected seed can be disinfected by heat treatment.

there are several variations of this process and the way in which the pathogen is destroyed is open to some doubt. This is a somewhat cumbersome and complex method of seed treatment and the temperature has to be precisely controlled, hence it is best carried out on a cooperative basis. Heat treatment can also be applied against bacteria carried within seeds and its use in freeing peach trees from peach yellows virus is well known.

Heat is a useful method of disinfecting planting material but there are practical difficulties in its application. The margin of safety between effective destruction of the pathogen and the risk of damaging the seeds or other material being heated is often small, and rather precise temperature control is needed. This is likely to involve the use of expensive equipment which may, however, be worthwhile on a cooperative basis. Planting material which has been disinfected in hot water has to be dried before storage, and can become recontaminated. Germination tests on the heated seed are advisable to ascertain whether it has been damaged. For these reasons hot water treatment is usually time consuming and tends to be used only when satisfactory alternatives are lacking. The pathogen within the seed is probably killed by the heat as such, but it may be that fungitoxic substances produced during anaerobic respiration of the steeped seed also play a part. In this respect the cold water method of controlling *U.nuda* as described by Sharvelle (1961) is of interest. In this the seed is soaked for 4 hours at 15–21°C, drained, and then stored in air tight containers for 70 hours at 21°C or 30 hours at 32°C, after which it is drained and quickly dried before applying a seed dressing. In this case it seems possible that the fungus is killed by substances produced during anaerobic respiration of the wet seed. Soaking sorghum seed carrying spores of *Sphacelotheca sorghi* in water for 4 hours followed by thorough drying reduced subsequent smut infection; premature germination of the smut spores may have occurred or fungitoxic substances developing during anaerobic respiration may have been involved.

Physical separation of the propagules of pathogens from seed is sometimes possible. It is claimed that *Ustilago hordei* can be separated from barley seed by flotation in water, the smut spores floating to the surface (Krasnopoyasovskii, 1966) and ergots (sclerotia) of *Claviceps purpurea* can be removed from grass seed by floating them off in brine. Differential sieving may separate dodder seeds from crop seeds if there is a sufficient difference in size. An ingenious method is to mix the contaminated crop seed with iron filings. These adhere to the rough dodder seeds and the latter are then removed with magnets (Chester, 1947).

Chemical methods

The application of chemicals to plants for control of insects and fungi has been practised for many years. The first such chemicals were probably used against insects. Sulphur may have been used as a fungicide in biblical times, followed by copper, arsenic, zinc and mercury compounds within the last 150 years or so; an interesting chronology of fungicides is given by Horsfall (1956) and reference may also be made to Horsfall (1945) McNew (1959) and McCallan (1967). The production of plant protection chemicals has made great strides since the mid-1930's when organic fungicides were developed, and particularly so since the Second World War. It is now a considerable industry and the search for new chemicals goes on apace. Substances used in plant protection are sometimes termed 'pesticides' and include fungicides, bactericides, nematicides, insecticides, acaricides, rodenticides, herbicides and others; of these we shall be concerned chiefly with fungicides.

Fungicides are applied to plants in various ways, as discussed below, and can be classified as protective – those which kill the pathogen before it attacks the plant – and therapeutic fungicides which inactivate the pathogen after it has entered the plant. Fungicides kill fungi whereas fungistatic substances (fungistats) prevent their growth, and spore suppressants prevent sporulation. The last named include dichlofluanid and tetrachloro-o-cresol as investigated by Corke (1967) for possible control of *Gloeosporium perennans* (apple canker). Spore suppressants and fungistatic substances are useful in disease control but fungicidal action is to be preferred in that the pathogen is thereby destroyed rather than temporarily inactivated. Contact fungicides are those which are aimed at the fungus itself either before or after it has found the host plant, as compared with residual fungicides which are applied to the plant before the fungus reaches it so that it forms a protective layer over the plant surface. These terms are suggested by Horsfall (1956) who points out that 'eradicant', as applied to fungicides, has been used in a different sense by different authors although often connoting the destruction of a pathogen within an infected organ – therapy or cure. Fungicides which kill fungi on plant surfaces including powdery mildews on leaves and fungi on the seed coat, have been termed 'direct' as distinct from 'protective' fungicides which are applied before infection occurs (Martin, 1964). There are also systemic fungicides, as described in the next chapter.

Application of fungicides

Fungicides can be applied to the standing crop, to seed and other planting material, to soil, to plant products, and in other ways.

Application to standing crops

Spraying or, less often, dusting crop plants with fungicides is widely practised, especially in countries where disease control has become almost a routine procedure or where crops are intensively grown on a plantation scale. Dusting is generally less effective but can be useful on a fairly small scale in gardens and glasshouses; it should be carried out during still weather and when the plants are damp with dew or rain. It has some advantages over spraying – no water is needed, a dust is easier to handle and dusting appliances are usually less cumbersome than those used in spraying. In dusts the fungicide is appropriately diluted with a finely divided filler and under some conditions such dusts may be harmful to the operators if inhaled. Dusting as a method of applying fungicides to crops has been less intensively investigated than spraying, and rather little is known about the physical and chemical factors which affect the performance of dust fungicides in the field. They can be applied by hand or power operated machines, or by aircraft.

In fungicidal sprays the carrier is usually water although organic carriers such as kerosene may be used in low volume spraying and have been used for applying insecticides, Various substances are sometimes added to water based sprays in order to improve their efficiency – dispersing agents, emulsifying agents, spreaders and stickers. Dispersing agents keep the fine particles of the fungicide in a uniform suspension, reducing their sedimentation. These protective colloids include water dispersible cellulose derivatives and are extensively used in the preparation of wettable powders; these contain surface active substances which cause the powder to disperse evenly when added to water.

Emulsifying agents, such as soap, retard the settling out of droplets of water-immiscible liquids (for example oils) from the spraying liquid and are commonly added to the fungicide during its preparation at the factory. Many surface active substances function as emulsifiers and are used as such. Spreaders facilitate contact between the spray and the plant surface so that the former spreads over the latter instead of forming drops which eventually run off. Surface active detergents can be used for this purpose and spreaders are usually incorporated in spraying materials during their manufacture. Stickers are used to improve the retention of spray or dust deposits by plant surfaces. Many factors affect this; fine particles are generally more tenacious than coarse ones, and spreaders, especially those not easily removed by water, may enhance retention in that they improve coverage. Thus, some of the older spreaders such as lime-casein and gelatin can function as stickers. Oils, including cottonseed oil, and adhesives such as polyvinyl acetate and polybutenes also show promise in this respect. 'Safeners' are sometimes used to reduce the phytotoxicity of some fungicides, for example, lime with arsenates.

Fungicidal deposits are removed from leaves chiefly by rain and dew, but it should be remembered that rain and dew are also responsible for some redistribution of fungicide over the sprayed leaves or over new leaves which have since developed. Such redistribution may protect leaf areas not covered by the initial spraying and so could be beneficial, as suggested by Horsfall (1956) and Hislop (1966). This might well be true during periods of light rain but heavy rain would probably wash away much of the spray deposit. It is probable that leaf exudates solubilize fungicidal deposits and so bring about redistribution, although there is evidence that some detoxification of the fungicide may also occur (Hislop, 1966). Localized systemic action in which the fungicide moves within the leaf tissue might also be responsible for limited redistribution, but little is known about this.

That the vapour given off by fungicides, particularly the more volatile ones, can act at some distance has been known for many years. The painting of hot water pipes in greenhouses with sulphur is an example of this, and the practical importance of vapour action during storage of mercury treated seed has been reported by Arny and Leben (1954). Similar vapour effects in which the growth of powdery mildews on leaves was inhibited at distances of several millimetres beyond the edge of the fungicidal deposit have recently been described by Bent (1967) and Hislop (1967). This effect is likely to be of importance with pathogens whose spores germinate best at high humidity rather than in water, as in many powdery mildews. Indeed, as Hislop (1967) has pointed out, it is difficult to see how residual protectant fungicides could otherwise be effective against such spores, and he postulates that fungicides which control powdery mildews are likely to act in this way. Conidia of powdery mildews can presumably take up molecules of fungicide from vapour whereas those of many other fungi do so chiefly from solution.

Fungicidal sprays are applied in various ways and by a wide variety of spraying equipment. The application rate may be up to and sometimes over 1125 litres/ha (high volume spraying) or down to a few litres per hectare (low volume spraying) or, in extreme cases, less. High volume spraying in which the spray liquid is applied under pressure through special nozzles normally gives good coverage of the plants but has several serious drawbacks. These include heavy expensive machinery and the trouble and expense of transporting large quantities of water through the fields. In recent years, and especially when applying fungicides over large areas, medium and low volume spraying has been developed. As the volume of spray liquid per hectare is reduced the concentration of fungicide must be correspondingly increased if the same amount of fungicide per hectare is required. Droplet size is reduced to give a more or less complete film of spray or numerous small, discrete droplets. This can be achieved by directing a current of air against a jet of the fungicide, rather on the principle used in scent sprays, and various types of atomizers are available. Land based spraying equipment ranges from the small hand operated sprayers used by the gardener to spray his rose bushes, through knapsack sprayers which may be manually operated or motorized, to large tractor drawn machines with a horizontal spraying boom spanning up to 6·6 m or so; these are adjustable for height and nozzle pressure and are operated from the tractor. Larger machines with booms up to about 16·50 m may be used where large numbers of hectares have to be sprayed.

Aerial spraying from fixed wing aircraft or helicopters may be feasible where there are extensive areas of uninterrupted crop and no hazards such as overhead cables, trees or buildings. It is of little use where crops are grown in fairly small individual fields. The slip stream of the aircraft or the downdraught from the helicopter can be used to disperse the fungicide.

As mentioned above, high volume spraying necessitates heavy equipment and large amounts of water. Low volume spraying also has its problems. The droplets are small – often less than about 100 μm – and may have become particles through evaporation before reaching the plant surface. Such small droplets or particles are liable to be carried away by air currents and tend to be diverted from solid objects in their path, so that their deposition presents problems. The larger droplets – above 100 μm or so – produced in high volume spraying are less subject to these tendencies and so usually give a better coverage. The problem of droplet evaporation in low volume spraying can, to some extent, be alleviated by using a less volatile carrier (for example oil) than water for the fungicidal spray: these aspects are discussed by Martin (1964) and Fulton (1965).

In his detailed discussion on spraying Courshee (1967) points out that, despite the supposed necessity for uniform and complete coverage of the plant surface with the fungicide, adequate disease control is often obtained with poor coverage. Application of Bordeaux mixture by watering can give satisfactory control of potato blight (Martin, 1940) and according to Large et al. (1946) a deposit of about 2μg of copper per sq. cm of leaf surface controls the same disease no matter very much how the deposit is distributed. At present fungicides are usually applied in fairly large amounts and are liable to redistribution to varying extents after deposition. Under these conditions complete coverage and high tenacity of the deposit are not necessary – indeed high tenacity would reduce redistribution and so could be disadvantageous. Better coverage – as complete as possible – and strong retention of the deposit (which would reduce redistribution) are necessary if smaller amounts of fungicide are to be used effectively in disease control. Courshee (1967) considers that in much commercial spraying a lot of fungicide is applied by poor machines, and that equally good results might be obtained by applying smaller amounts of fungicide more efficiently. This would involve the design and production of spraying machines 'more closely matched to the properties of slightly soluble fungicides which adhere to leaves strongly'.

The choice of fungicide and its rate of application should be based on the results of plot experiments and preliminary field trials carried out under as near natural conditions as possible. Several applications may be necessary during the season and these should be appropriately timed to give optimum control. The spraying programme may be based on experience or on forecasts of the likely outbreak of disease or both and it is clearly desirable to apply a protective spray just before the inoculum arrives or before conditions become favourable for infection, but this is not always possible.

The spraying of trees, as in orchards, can present problems. Conventional machines fitted with vertical booms can be used to spray small trees and bushes, or manually operated spray lances can be used. For larger trees there are machines capable of producing a spray under high pressure but more often the spray is blown into the trees by compressed air.

Several other methods of applying fungicides and other protective chemicals to plants have been devised. Suitable fungicides may be volatilized from electrically operated devices, or in the form of 'smokes' in which the fungicide is volatilized at a fairly low temperature by combustion of suitable chemicals such as a mixture of sucrose and potassium chlorate. Care must be taken to avoid phytotoxic combustion products. In aerosols the pesticide is dissolved under pressure in a liquid which rapidly volatilizes at atmospheric pressure; on pressing the button the liquid is discharged from the container as a fine spray in which the solvent evaporates leaving the pesticide in a very finely divided state. Although best known in relation to insecticides and other household sprays aerosols are now being developed for application of fungicides. Smokes and aerosols are convenient methods for use in small enclosed spaces such as glasshouses, where they can be used as a form of fumigation or for treatment of individual plants. Attempts have been made to apply protective chemicals in spray and dust form simultaneously, as in 'vapodust' or fog-spray, and this might be useful when several chemicals are being applied at the same time.

Spraying or dusting against pathogens and pests involves the use of rather complex and expensive machines and considerable 'know how'. Hence it is a method of disease control which is commonplace in agriculturally developed countries but may be difficult to implement successfully in less developed areas unless expert advice and assistance are available. There is considerable scope for devising simple, inexpensive machines for use in such areas, and for producing effective crop protection chemicals which are inexpensive, harmless to man and animals, and easy to apply. Agricultural cooperatives may help in this, and the application of pesticides rarely presents any insuperable difficulties in crops grown intensively on a plantation scale. Chemical control of airborne pathogens is discussed by Evans (1971).

Application to seed

Some pathogens are seed borne and, if on the surface of the seed, can be reduced or eliminated by applying a suitable chemical. If the seed is infected – containing the pathogen internally – rather than contaminated it is unlikely that conventional dry chemical treatment will be effective although some form of heat treatment (p. 490) or wet treatment (p. 499) may be possible. Treatment may be directed against specific fungal or bacterial pathogens carried by the seed, as in treatment against seed borne smuts, or it may be used to protect against soil borne pathogens and so to improve germination and emergence. This latter aspect is of some importance and it may be worthwhile to treat the sowing seed with a suitable fungicide even in the absence of seed borne pathogens, especially when conditions are unfavourable for germination and early growth. In such cases the protective film of fungicide around the germinating seed tends to give protection during the vulnerable period between germination and emergence.

Early methods of disinfection included sprinkling the seed with such fungicides as formaldehyde or copper sulphate solution followed by mixing with a shovel on the barn floor, and drying. Satisfactory mixing is difficult to obtain in this way and phytotoxicity has to be guarded against. Present day seed treatment is chiefly by dry powders and, to a lesser extent, by wet methods such as slurries. The testa or seed coat which covers the seed is often a fairly tough layer, and renders the seed less susceptible to chemicals than, for example, are the leaves so that certain fungicides which are phytotoxic when applied to foliage can safely be used as seed dressings, notably mercury compounds.

Fungicidal treatment of seed can be by dry or by wet methods.

Dry methods. In these a predetermined amount of the powder fungicide is applied to the seed and thoroughly mixed before being bagged and stored. The powder contains a known percentage of the active fungicide – often up to about 10% for mercurials but 50% or more for some organic fungicides – mixed with an inert powder. Substances to reduce the dustiness of the powder, to improve its adhesion to the seed, or to colour the seed dressing and hence the treated seed may be added, but it must previously be ascertained that such additives do not reduce the effectiveness of the seed dressing. Thus the addition of small quantities of certain dyes to a mercuric chloride-iodide seed dressing significantly reduced its effectiveness against *Xanthomonas malvacearum* (bacterial blight of cotton: Tarr, 1953). The rate of application of the seed dressing to seed may be as high as 1:150 with hairy seed but is often about 1:300 to 1:500 depending on the plant and pathogen involved. Heavy application can be obtained by the 'excess method' in which a large quantity of the dressing is mixed with the seed to ensure maximum uptake. Stickers such as Methocel, a soluble cellulose acetate, can be used for the same purpose ('pelleting').

Wet methods. Among these are steeps, slurries and short-wet treatments. In steeping, the seed is soaked for varying lengths of time in a solution of the fungicide or bactericide and then removed, allowed to drain, and dried. Although very effective in destroying pathogens on the seed it is a cumbersome and time-consuming procedure and there are likely to be phytotoxic effects unless very carefully carried out. There are also the practical difficulties of drying large quantities of soaking wet seed without damaging it. Steeping is essentially a batch rather than a continuous process and selective absorption of the fungicide by the seed may occur. After treatment the fungicide remains as an adherent film over the seed.

Maude (1966a) has shown that soaking infected pea seed in a 1% aqueous suspension of captan, dichlone, chloranil, spergon and thiram (80% commercial wettable powder) for 24 hours at 30°C virtually eliminated *Mycosphaerella pinodes* (figure 26.2) and *Ascochyta pisi* although only thiram had no adverse effect on emergence under field conditions. Shortening the soaking period resulted in less effective disinfection and a 0·2% suspension of thiram was subsequently found to give the best control. The steeped seeds had imbibed water but were dried without detriment by a current of warm air. Although thiram is normally considered to be insoluble in water it seems that it does dissolve to the extent of about 30 p.p.m. after 24 hours (Maude and Shuring, 1969) and that the dissolved thiram is removed from solution by the seed. Maude and co-workers (Maude, 1966; Maude et al., 1969; Maude and Shuring, 1969) found that the thiram soak method described above disinfected seed infected with a number of other fungal pathogens including *Leptosphaeria nodorum* (wheat), *Pyrenophora graminea* (barley) and *Phoma betae* (beet). It was less effective against some other seed borne pathogens, notably *Ascochyta fabae* on tick bean (*Vicia faba*) and severely depressed the germination of some flower seeds.

Soaking seed for a day is a slow process, especially when the seed has thereafter to be dried, and although suitable for disinfection of small quantities of seed it is unlikely to be feasible for the commercial treatment of large quantities. In this respect the report by Maude and Shuring (1969) that soaking in a 0·2% Vitavax (2,3-dihydrocarboxanilido-6-methyl-1,4-oxathiin) suspension for 6 hours completely eliminated *Ustilago nuda* from wheat seed is of interest and promising results have been obtained with other systemic fungicides applied as seed dressings (p. 524).

A method which attempts to combine the advantages of dry and wet

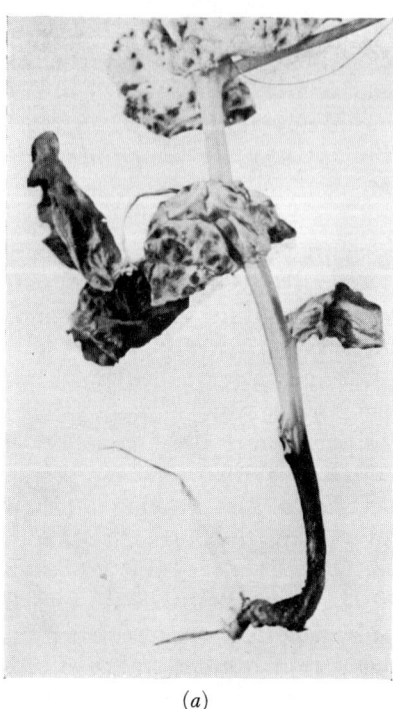

(a)

treatment is the slurry process in which a small volume of a fairly concentrated suspension of the fungicide in a wettable formulation is thoroughly mixed with the seed in specially designed machines. The treated seed dries quickly and can be stored immediately. This is a very accurate method of applying fungicides to seed and obviates the hazard of flying fungicidal dust which occurs in powder treatment. In a refinement of the slurry method widely used in the U.S.A., Europe and Britain, a small volume of concentrated fungicidal liquid is sprayed as a fine mist over the seed as it falls through the mixing chamber. Some of the machines used for treating seed are described by Sharvelle (1961).

Chemical treatment is a fairly simple and inexpensive disease control measure for pathogens carried on the seed, but several commonsense precautions are necessary. Care must be taken in handling the chemicals used, particularly the concentrated suspensions or solutions of fungicides used in slurry treatments. Irritating and possibly toxic dust is almost always present in the air when powder dressings are applied, and operators should wear effective masks to avoid inhaling it. This is particularly so when hand operated seed treaters, such as rotating inclined drums, are used although flying dust is greatly reduced in well designed continuous flow machines; even here, however, masks are advisable. Whenever

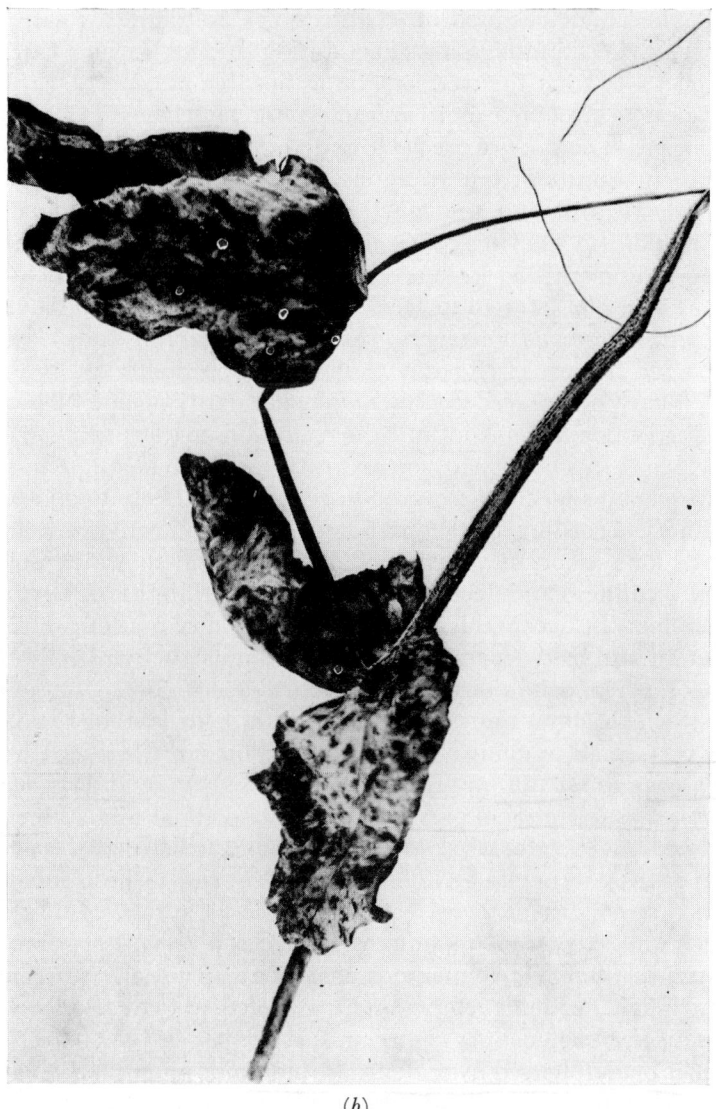

(b)

Figure 26.2 *Mycosphaerella pinodes* on pea (*Pisum sativum*). (*a*) This destructive pathogen causes root rot, foot rot, stem rot, leaf spot and pod spot. Pycnidia and perithecia of the fungus can be seen in the infected stem. (*b*) Infected seed can be disinfected by soaking in fungicidal suspensions.

possible, powder treatment could be carried out in the open and treated seed should be handled with caution, especially if a mercurial seed dressing has been used. It should be unnecessary to add that treated seed must not be eaten by human beings or stock, but this has occasionally happened.

Some of the fungicides used in seed dressings are slightly volatile and to some extent exert a fumigating effect during storage. In such cases it may be beneficial to treat the seed as soon as possible in order to prolong the storage period, provided there are no phytotoxic effects.

Field trials should be carried out to determine the most effective fungicide and the optimum rate of application. Too little fungicide will give inadequate control and too much is likely to prove phytotoxic. Such trials should use heavily contaminated seed, artificially inoculated if necessary, although that from severely infected plants in the field should, wherever possible, be used in seed treatment trials. Trials should be run at different places and for several years in order to test the seed dressings over as wide a range of climatic conditions as possible.

The effectiveness of seed treatment depends partly on how contaminated the seed is and on how favourable the conditions are for infection; a treatment which is satisfactory in one area may prove inadequate in another. The degree of disinfection required to reduce the disease to an acceptable level differs according to the pathogen. Highly effective disinfection is necessary for pathogens which spread rapidly and in which only a few diseased seedlings can infect most of the plants in the field. Less effective treatment may be acceptable for pathogens which do not spread from plant to plant in the field (many inflorescence smuts) or which spread only slowly, or when conditions are unfavourable for spread, or with crop varieties which show some resistance. With some pathogens, however, even a very small amount of residual infection surviving seed treatment can be responsible for appreciable crop loss. A residual infection of *Xanthomonas malvacearum* of only 0·017%, giving about forty-three infected cotton seedlings per ha was estimated to have reduced the yield of seed cotton per hectare by about 17% (Tarr, 1961) and this was attributed to the fact that conditions were very favourable for spread of this bacterial pathogen and the variety of cotton involved is a very susceptible one. In such cases highly effective methods of seed treatment are called for.

Many fungicides and bactericides have been used to treat seed. Elemental sulphur and such copper compounds as copper carbonate were among the earlier ones, followed by mercurials (inorganic and organic, as bactericides as well as fungicides), and organo-sulphur compounds such as thiram, captan and others. Quinones – chloranil and dichlone – are also used. Seed treatment chemicals are described by Sharvelle (1961), and some are listed in the next chapter.

Provided they are compatible, insecticides can be incorporated into fungicidal or bactericidal seed dressings as a protection against insects – wireworms, termites, cockchafer grubs and possibly others. The potentialities of such dual purpose seed dressings are likely to increase as more effective and safer crop protection chemicals become available. Their uses in protecting cotton and other crops in the Sudan are discussed by Tarr (1959,1959a, 1960). Some of the insecticides likely to be used are dangerous to man and animal life generally, and their use should be strictly controlled or prohibited. There is a great need for safer but equally effective ones. The scope of seed treatment as a disease control measure will be considerably increased as satisfactory systemic fungicides become available, thus enabling protection of seedlings and young plants to be intensified and extended.

Several other methods of treating seed have been devised. Fumigation with gases such as chlorine is an elaborate procedure in which application rates have to be carefully controlled, otherwise phytotoxicity is likely to occur. These methods do not appear to have been taken up on a commercial scale.

Other types of planting material – tubers, bulbs, cuttings and others – can also be treated with fungicides and bactericides. The material can be soaked in a solution of a suitable fungicide for a predetermined time, care being taken to avoid phytotoxicity, or it can be dipped or dusted in a suitable fungicidal preparation. An organo-mercurial dip helps to control potato dry rot (*Fusarium caeruleum*), dipping sugarcane cuttings in Bordeaux mixture or a mercurial fungicide reduces black rot (*Ceratostomella paradoxa*), and brassica seedlings can be protected for some time against *Plasmodiophora brassicae* (club root) by dipping their roots in a 4% suspension of colomel dust (mercurous chloride) before transplanting. Seed treatment is discussed by Purdy (1967).

Application to soil

Many pathogens and pests are present in soil, especially those which attack the roots of plants. Some pathogens survive between crops as free-living saprophytes in the soil but more, probably, survive in the form of resistant propagules. It is the aim of soil treatment, whether by physical or chemical methods, to destroy soil borne pathogens, insects or nematodes as the case may be. It is usually a case of partial rather than complete sterilization, and ideally one hopes to preserve and indeed encourage beneficial soil microorganisms while destroying the injurious ones.

The more drastic methods used to treat soil have a considerable effect on its physical, chemical and biological characteristics, and it is sometimes difficult to decide whether the improved plant growth following treatment is due to control of pathogens or pests or to other beneficial changes in the treated soil. Even when it appears that control of a soil borne pathogen is the major factor the precise way in which this is brought about is often far from clear. Destruction of the pathogen may be by direct action of the fungicide, or the latter may selectively encourage antagonistic fungi which inactivate the pathogen, or there may be other interactions which reduce its incidence or ability to attack the plant. Vectors of pathogens may be destroyed, or nematodes which make the wounds through which the pathogen normally enters the roots may be killed by the chemical applied to the soil.

Physical and chemical methods are used to destroy pathogens, pests and weed seeds in soil. Heat is the most important physical agent and it is possible that some degree of partial sterilization of the surface layer of the soil occurs when bare soil is exposed to continuous bright sunlight in tropical areas. Heat treatment is best carried out by means of steam, but ovens for baking small quantities of soil can be satisfactory, provided the temperature can be adequately controlled – the soil should be maintained at about 97°C for one hour (Martin, 1964). Precautions must, of course, be taken to prevent recontamination of treated soil by pathogens.

In steam heating a temperature of about 80°C for 30 minutes is usually aimed at. This can be obtained in various types of steam heaters but these involve considerable labour in moving the soil. A more convenient procedure is to lead the steam into the soil through pipes buried therein, and a permanent system of built-in pipes may be used in glasshouses where it is desired to treat the soil as a regular routine. The ease with which steam penetrates through the soil depends considerably on its physical structure, and movement may be slow in compacted soil. Superheated steam or steam under pressure may be necessary in some cases and as far as possible the soil should be loosened and large lumps broken up before the steam is applied (see Sharvelle, 1961 for details of steam treatment). Phytotoxic substances such as ammonia may develop during steaming and it is advisable to allow several days to elapse before planting in the steamed soil. Steaming of soil is possible in glasshouses, frames and seed beds, but is generally impracticable on a field scale, except with very valuable crops.

Various chemicals have been applied to soil to destroy pathogens, pests, nematodes and weed seeds. Some are volatile (fumigants), others relatively non-volatile. Ideally, such substances should freely permeate the soil, should be effective against the pathogen at low concentrations, should not damage the soil, should not be phytotoxic, and should be safe, easy and inexpensive to apply. No such compound is known and many soil fumigants – substances such as chloropicrin, methyl bromide and formaldehyde – are caustic, volatile liquids which are unpleasant and dangerous to handle. They show varying degrees of effectiveness against pathogens and pests, and some find considerable application in fumigating nematode-infested soil.

One of the earliest soil fumigants was formaldehyde applied as a drench using 0·4 litres of formalin (40% formaldehyde) with 2 litres of water per 100 m² of soil area, the treated soil being watered and thereafter covered for a day or so to minimize escape of the fumes. Planting can be carried out 1 or 2 weeks later depending on weather and soil conditions. Present-day volatile fumigants are usually injected into the soil by hand-operated injector guns or by tractor mounted equipment for large areas (see Sharvelle, 1961). Depth of injection is adjustable but is often about 9 cm, and a few millilitres of fumigant are applied in each injection at spaced intervals. The depth of injection will depend on the type of soil and other considerations, as will the spacing of injections and the amount applied. The latter varies considerably in different fumigants and with chloropicrin is about 56–394 litres/ha. Extreme care must be taken when using these volatile fumigants and it is advisable to wear protective clothing including rubber gloves, rubber boots and respirator. The fumigated soil should be watered and covered with plastic sheeting for 1 or 2 days after which it should be left for several weeks before planting in it. Fumigation is usually more effective in warm sandy soils through which the fumes can spread rapidly than in cold, heavy clay soils or those containing much organic matter.

Other fumigants produced in recent years include metham-sodium (Vapam: sodium N-methyldithiocarbamate) a colourless liquid which decomposes rapidly in moist soil to release a fumigating gas. It can be mixed with water and sprinkled over the soil with a watering can, or large areas of soil can be sprayed. After treatment the soil is watered thoroughly to wash the fumigant down to a depth of 9 cm or so, and treated soil should not be planted for 2–3 weeks. Dazomet (tetrahydro-3, 5-dimethyl-2H-1,3,5-thiadiazine-2-thione) is a wettable powder used at about 440 kg/ha and applied with a fertilizer spreader or by spraying a suspension in water, followed by thorough mixing and 'sealing in' with water. In soil dazomet releases methyl isothiocyanate and it is effective for control of nematodes, wireworms, some weeds, and some soil borne fungi such as *Pythium, Rhizoctonia, Fusarium, Verticillium* and *Colletotrichum* (Martin, 1968).

Some relatively non-volatile fungicides have been applied as suspensions or dry powders to soil; for example, zineb (zinc ethylene-1,2-bisdithiocarbamate) as a drench in lettuce seed beds reduces *Bremia lactucae* (downy mildew), and quintozene (PCNB, pentachloronitrobenzene) which is applied to soil against soil borne pathogens especially those which produce sclerotia (*Corticium solani, Sclerotium cepivorum* and others). After treatment the soil should be thoroughly disced to ensure maximum mixing of the fungicide.

Soil treatment is expensive and is mostly used in glasshouses, frames and seed beds although its use with crops of high commercial value may be economic. Great care has to be taken in handling and applying the conventional fumigants, such as chloropicrin, and protective clothing is usually advisable. Phytotoxicity must also be guarded against, which may involve sowing test plants in the fumigated soil. For these and other

R

reasons soil fumigation is a laborious and time consuming procedure, but the advent of effective fungicides which can be applied as a powder or spray to soil is a promising development which is likely to increase the scope of this method of disease control. Soil fungicides are discussed by Domsch (1964) and soil treatment is discussed by Purdy (1967).

Application to plant products

Postharvest diseases caused chiefly by fungi and, to a lesser extent, bacteria cause heavy losses to fruit, vegetables and other plant products during transit and storage. Indeed it seems illogical to strive for high yields by controlling diseases and pests in the fields only to lose much of the valuable end product after it has been harvested. Deterioration and rotting of plant products can be reduced by refrigeration but this is expensive and not always satisfactory as some fruit-rotting fungi (*Penicillium*, *Botrytis*) can develop at quite low temperatures. It is not surprising that chemical methods of controlling postharvest diseases are being increasingly used, sometimes to supplement refrigeration.

Decay of fruits and vegetables is caused by numerous species of fungi and bacteria (especially *Erwinia carotovora*), many of which are wound parasites, with *Penicillium* spp. and *Rhizopus* spp. perhaps the worst offenders, but species of *Botrytis*, *Sclerotinia*, *Trichoderma*, *Fusarium*, *Alternaria*, *Phytophthora*, *Aspergillus* and *Diplodia* are often involved. Many of these fungi are ubiquitous, produce enormous numbers of spores and spread rapidly when conditions favour them.

In some fruit rots the initial infection occurs in the field before harvesting, as with grey mould of strawberries caused by *Botrytis cinerea*, in which case a preharvest application of a suitable fungicide may give some degree of control. Other fungi, including the penicillia which rot citrus fruits, enter the fruit during or after harvesting, often through wounds and bruises, and some form of postharvest treatment is needed. In some cases protection is required for only a few days, after which time superficial wounds cease to permit the entry of pathogens. This is true of superficial injuries in the peel of oranges and apples in respect of *Penicillium* spp., and protection by an unfavourable environment or by fungistatic chemicals during this short vulnerable period can give some degree of control. Disfigurement of fruit by superficial saprophytic fungi reduces its market value so that treatment to eliminate disfigurement may be worthwhile even when the actual amount of fruit-rotting is small.

The methods used to combat storage diseases include fumigation, exposure of the produce to fungicides in solution or suspension, and the physical separation of individual fruits by wrapping them in paper often impregnated with fungicides or fungistats. Hydrocooling and prompt refrigeration are also widely used to control storage and transit diseases.

It is advisable to fumigate produce as soon as possible after harvesting but fumigation is not widely practised because of the lack of suitable fumigants which should be reasonably volatile, effective against the micro-organisms causing the deterioration, of low phytotoxicity, and non-tainting. Sulphur dioxide and, to a lesser extent, nitrogen trichloride, ammonia, tetrachloroethylene and dichloromethane are used commercially as in the fumigation of grapes against *Botrytis* using an initial application by volume of 1% sulphur dioxide for 20 minutes followed, if necessary, by repeat fumigations at 7–10 day intervals with 0·25% sulphur dioxide for 30–60 minutes. Fumigation of grapes by sulphur dioxide is effective, fairly inexpensive and does not leave toxic residues, but it causes bleaching of red grapes and under humid conditions corrodes metal.

Wet treatment of produce is best carried out with fungicidal solutions rather than suspensions as the latter tend to settle out and so are less easy to apply. This is undoubtedly one of the most effective methods of applying postharvest fungicides and a high degree of disinfection can be obtained by immersing the produce in the fungicidal solution contained in tanks for several minutes. Other methods of application include flooding the produce on the moving conveyor belt with a fungicidal solution, spraying or foam application. The tank immersion method requires a fairly large volume of fungicidal solution which must periodically be topped up, hence it is suitable for application of stable, inexpensive fungicides.

Numerous substances have been used as postharvest fungicides. Borates, including borax (sodium tetraborate), at one time extensively used to treat oranges, are now less popular. One problem is that at the 6–8% concentration needed for effective control borax crystallizes out on the equipment and treated fruit, from which it is difficult to remove completely. More soluble borates have been tested and also a mixture of 4% borax and 2% boric acid for 2–6 minutes at about 43°C with thorough rinsing after treatment. Further difficulties include the tendency for boron to accumulate in the peel of the treated fruits and the problem of safely disposing of the borate – containing water remaining after washing the fruit.

In view of these disadvantages, borates have largely been superseded by other fungicides, notably sodium o-phenylphenate for control of *Penicillium* rots of citrus and many other fruit and vegetable rots. Sodium o-phenylphenate can be phytotoxic unless a sufficiently high alkalinity (pH 11·5–12) to minimize the formation of phytotoxic o-phenylphenol is maintained. Alkalinity can also be maintained by the addition of about 1% hexamine (hexamethylenetetramine) which precipitates free o-phenylphenol as the insoluble hexamine phenate and also stabilizes the pH at about 11·8. A residue tolerance of not more than 25 p.p.m. o-phenylphenol and its sodium salt in apples and 10 p.p.m. in citrus fruits is stipulated in the U.S.A.

Other fungicides which have been used to control postharvest diseases include dichloran (Botran, DCNA; 2,6-dichloro-4-nitroaniline) as an aqueous suspension containing 0·1–0·2% active ingredient applied for 1 or 2 minutes to control *Rhizopus* rot of peach. Several antibiotics have been tested as fruit fungicides and bactericides – the antifungal polyenes nystatin and pimaricin show promise in this respect when used at about 100 p.p.m. – but aqueous solutions of these antibiotics rapidly lose activity when exposed to light and, in view of their use in medicine, no significant residues in treated fruit would be permissible.

Other methods of applying postharvest fungicides have been devised. Thus, a copper sulphate paste applied to the cut stems of water-melons has been recommended to prevent infection by *Diplodia* spp. Wrapping individual citrus fruits in tissue wrappers impregnated with biphenyl (diphenyl, phenylbenzene) or lining the containers with papers so impregnated, is used to control fruit rots due to *Penicillium* spp. in several citrus growing countries. Biphenyl vapour strongly inhibits mycelial growth of several fruit-rotting fungi but it is fungistatic rather than fungicidal. Biphenyl largely prevents the sporulation of penicillia on decaying fruit but sporulation is likely to occur when the wrappers are removed. Wrapped fruits develop a slight taint which disappears on exposure to air for a few days but which may, in current jargon, create consumer resistance. Treated citrus fruits become liable to rotting by *Alternaria citri* since treatment accelerates ageing of the remains of the calyx and receptacle (the 'button') and so facilitates the entry of the fungus. Another disadvantage is that biphenyl-tolerant strains of *Penicillium* not infrequently arise, especially in packing houses. Biphenyl treatment has nevertheless proved of great value in control of the fruit rots caused by penicillia. It is said to be of fairly low mammalian toxicity and residue concentrations up to 110 p.p.m. on a whole fruit basis are permitted in citrus fruits in the U.S.A. as compared with 70 p.p.m. in most European countries.

Many new fungicides, including systemic ones (p. 523) are being tested for postharvest treatment of fruit and vegetables and detailed accounts are given by Eckert (1967,1969), Eckert and Sommer (1967), Turner (1959) and Smith (1962). Storage decays cause heavy losses and, as Eckert (1967) points out, more sophisticated methods of postharvest treatment are needed to keep abreast of the new methods of packing fruits and vegetables which are now being developed. This will involve looking for fungicides suitable for postharvest treatment rather than attempting to modify existing ones developed for other purposes. In particular, bactericides to control bacterial soft rots of vegetables are needed.

The treatment of fruit and vegetables with fungicidal and fungistatic chemicals carries with it dangers in that the long term effects of these chemicals on human beings are not known. Some form of postharvest treatment is, however, necessary to control storage deterioration and every effort should be made to develop the safest possible fungicides or, better, to develop control methods based on modifying the storage environment or perhaps by irradiation of produce. In many countries there are government departments, such as the U.S. Food and Drug Administration, Pesticide Regulation Division of the Environmental Protection Agency, which stipulate the maximum permitted limits for residues of chemicals used in postharvest treatment of produce. This is a useful safeguard but too little is at present known about the long term effects of such chemicals on human beings for these limits to be accepted with confidence.

Other uses of fungicides

It is advisable to treat fence posts and timber used in building likely to come into contact with soil or water with a fungicide to reduce decay – creosote, pentachlorophenol, or copper naphthenate are frequently applied – and exposed surfaces of pruned or broken branches of trees should be treated with a suitable fungicidal paint which may contain copper, zinc or phenolic fungicides. Application should be as soon as possible after the wood is exposed, and lead paint can be quite effective for this purpose.

Most fungicides are protective but there are some which can be used as eradicants, that is they destroy the pathogen on the plant surface, as with powdery mildews, without injuring the plant. Pathogens of deciduous perennial plants often overwinter on the bark or between the bud scales and a suitable fungicidal spray applied in the spring can be effective as in control of peach leaf curl (*Taphrina deformans*). Phenyl mercuric chloride is sometimes used as an eradicant foliage spray against *Venturia inaequalis* although some varieties of apple may be damaged. Spraying apple trees with this fungicide in the autumn before leaf fall and in the spring just before bud burst considerably reduced scab (Hutton and Burchill, 1965; Burchill and Hutton, 1965) by suppressing the development of perithecia and ascospores. Similar suppression can be achieved by applying benomyl, a systemic fungicide (p. 525) just before leaf fall. Chemical destruction of overwintering structures might prove useful in the control of other pathogens.

27 Physical and chemical methods of disease control (2)

Sulphur was probably one of the first substances to be used as a fungicide as well as an insecticide, acaricide and general fumigant, and other early fungicides include copper sulphate, zinc chloride and mercuric chloride, the last named being used as a wood preservative in the early eighteenth century. These were followed by Bordeaux mixture and lime-sulphur in the late nineteenth century, and formalin, copper carbonate dusts and organo-mercurials (1913) as seed treatment chemicals. Organic fungicides – thiram, chloranil, dichlone and others – were developed from the mid-1930's onwards, and captan, one of the most successful of them, was produced nearly 20 years ago. The many new crop protection chemicals which have been tested in recent years include guanidines, heterocyclic nitrogen compounds, quinones, phenols and antibiotics. It is sometimes said that new conventional fungicides superior to those already known are unlikely to be discovered, and that future research should be concentrated on systemic fungicides. The latter have given very promising results, but there would appear to be scope for systemic and non-systemic fungicides, or perhaps mixtures of the two. Interesting accounts of the development of fungicides are given by Horsfall (1956: a chronology of fungicides), McNew (1959) and McCallan (1967).

There are so many chemicals marketed for disease control (280 chemicals in about 590 formulations, according to McGrath, 1964) that it is not surprising that growers often need information about them. In Britain, there is a voluntary scheme for the official approval of such chemicals, and lists of approved products are issued periodically, together with recommendations on their use and warnings on any precautions to be taken. Much confusion arises when the same chemical is marketed in similar or slightly different formulations under different trade names by different manufacturers. Most fungicides have several names – the manufacturer's code number, the chemical name which is often too cumbersome for everyday usage (for example tetrachloro-p-benzoquinone), a coined name (chloranil) and several trade names (Spergon). The coined names are recommended by a committee of the American Standards Association but are not necessarily universally accepted, and there are comparable bodies which recommend coined names for fungicides in other countries.

Any fungicide should ideally fulfil the following conditions: (1) It should be effective at concentrations which do not damage the plant to which it is applied. Plants vary in their sensitivity to different chemicals, as do different organs of the plant or organs at different stages of development. Seeds with resistant seed coats are, for example, less likely to be damaged by fungicides than are leaves, and similarly dormant plants as compared with actively growing ones. These aspects must be investigated before fungicides or other crop protection chemicals are used on a field scale, otherwise there may be considerable damage to the crop. (2) It should not be poisonous to man or animals, neither should it cause skin irritation or allergies. If it is poisonous it must be capable of being used without danger to the operator or to others who may come into contact with the treated plants. (3) It should be sufficiently stable and tenacious to remain effective for the maximum time consistent with harvesting considerations. Crop protection chemicals applied to vegetables and fruit should have disappeared before harvesting begins and should not in any way taint the produce or reduce its palatability or nutritive value. (4) The application of the fungicide over a large crop area should not adversely affect the biological equilibrium of that area. This can happen with large scale spraying of insecticides which may destroy the natural parasites and predators which have hitherto kept other insect pests at a low level; one pest is thus replaced by another. In the same way, intensive application of fungicides might result in a rather similar situation, and the possible long range, harmful effects of fungicides on the natural microflora of the plant and of the soil must be taken into account. (5) The fungicide should be one against which pathogens do not develop resistance, as discussed below. Rather little is known about this aspect of fungicides. (6) The properties of the fungicide should be such that it can be applied accurately and effectively to the crop or to the plant material being treated. If, for example, it is used as a protectant it should remain as a uniform, persistent deposit over the plant surface. (7) In cases where two pesticides are mixed and applied simultaneously, as in fungicidal-insecticidal seed dressings, there should be no interaction leading to reduced effectiveness of either, that is, they should be compatible. (8) The fungicide must be stable under normal climatic conditions so that it can be stored without losing its potency. (9) Crop protection must, of course, be an economic proposition so that the substances used should be as inexpensive as possible, especially when used on low value crops.

The ideal fungicide, as judged on these criteria, has yet to be found, but fungicides have improved greatly in recent years, as have methods of formulation and application. Most fungicides show some degree of selectivity; dinocap for example is especially effective against powdery mildews whereas captan controls a fairly wide range of fungal pathogens but is relatively ineffective against powdery mildews.

Commercial development and testing of fungicides

The production of crop protection chemicals has become a major industry in the U.S.A. and other countries. In 1956, pesticide sales in the U.S.A. were estimated to be about 260 million dollars, of which about 82 million were spent on fungicides, including nearly 20 million on copper sulphate and 10 million on elemental sulphur and it is estimated that pesticides worth nearly 1,000 million dollars will be used in the U.S.A. in 1975 (Sharvelle, 1961). A detailed breakdown of world fungicide usage is given by Ordish and Mitchell (1967), who point out that the world's supply of fungicides is largely based on copper, sulphur, mercury and dithiocarbamates, and that most of these fungicides are used to control about a dozen major crop diseases. In addition, large amounts of mineral oil are used to spray bananas against Sigatoka disease caused by *Mycosphaerella musicola*.

The commercial development of fungicides from the initial screening to the final marketing is a complex and costly procedure, graphically described by Wellman (1967). Numerous chemicals have to be screened in the glasshouse or laboratory against a range of fungi. This wholesale screening would seem to be a very wasteful procedure, but many fungicides which would otherwise have gone undetected have been found in this way. Although our knowledge of what makes chemicals fungicidal is increasing, it has not yet reached the stage at which fungicides can be designed rather than discovered. The preliminary screening is likely to eliminate most of the candidate chemicals, and only about one in 3,600 compounds becomes a successful agricultural chemical. Taking into account the expense of further developmental work and testing, Wellman (1967) estimates that the cost of putting a crop protection chemical on the market is about 3 million dollars. At the present time (1972) about 1 in 10,000 candidate chemicals is successful and the cost of development etc. is estimated to have doubled to about 6 million dollars.

Preliminary screening is carried out in various ways. It can be done by investigating the effects of the trial chemical on spore germination or vegetative growth of a range of test fungi and bacteria on glass slides. Such tests should be standardized, and subsidiary tests on tenacity and weathering can also be performed. A more satisfactory method is to apply known amounts of the chemical to potted plants susceptible to the test pathogens being used. The treated plants are then inoculated with known amounts of the pathogens and kept under conditions conducive to disease development; in all these tests, conditions must be standardized as much as possible in order to yield comparable results. The test pathogens used may be a representative selection – perhaps a bacterium, a downy mildew, a powdery mildew, a leaf spotting fungus, a rust and possibly a virus – or they may be chosen on a selective basis to comprise pathogens such as *Phytophthora infestans* (potato blight), *Venturia inaequalis* (apple scab), *Exobasidium vexans* (blister blight of tea), *Hemileia vastatrix* (coffee rust), *Plasmopara viticola* (grape downy mildew), *Pyricularia oryzae* (rice blast) and others which cause serious diseases of important crop plants. The latter approach is attractive in that there is likely to be a worthwhile market for any chemical found to be effective.

Laboratory and glasshouse screening yields useful information and enables useless chemicals to be detected and discarded, but the final evaluation needs to be carried out in the field in the conditions under which the crop is normally grown. This involves carefully designed trials in which the rates and times of application of the fungicide are investigated and in which the fungicide is compared with the standard fungicides currently used to control the disease. Such trials should be run over a number of years, in several areas, and against the pathogens which the preliminary evaluation has indicated as likely to be controlled by the fungicide.

During this testing period other aspects of the fungicide have to be investigated and the plant required for its large scale manufacture has to be designed. Aspects needing investigation include the toxicity of the fungicide to plants and animals (including man), its persistence in sprayed plants (especially if it is to be used on food crops or edible produce), its tenacity and weathering on sprayed plants, its stability in storage, formulations, and compatibility with other crop protection chemicals. This last consideration is important as protective and other chemicals are increasingly being mixed and applied simultaneously. Two fungicides may so interact that their total effect equals their sum, exceeds it (synergism) or is less than their sum (antagonism). Synergism might be because the two fungicides have different mechanisms of toxicity or due to reciprocal activation perhaps resulting in the formation of a more highly fungitoxic reaction product (Scardavi, 1966, discusses synergism among fungicides). Incompatibility results in reduced effectiveness of one or both chemicals, presumably due to chemical or physical reaction between them, and it is clearly important that the compatibility of all protectants which are likely to be mixed should be investigated and that any incompatibilities found should be notified on the containers.

Testing of fungicides showing promise for the control of specific pathogens is carried out at some research stations, the new fungicides being compared with the ones in current use. These trials may be carried out on potted plants in glasshouses under controlled conditions, as with the use of apple seedlings by Moore (1964) and Rich and Richards (1959) in assaying fungicides for control of scab (*Venturia inaequalis*), and subsequently in experimental plots and in commercial plantings.

The procedures briefly outlined above apply primarily to testing of foliage fungicides, but similar principles are involved in testing fungicides for use on seed or soil. Soil fungicides are, however, best tested in the field rather than in laboratory or glasshouse, since their performance depends considerably on soil conditions which are difficult to simulate. Laboratory test methods are useful if the results they give are an accurate indication of field performance – 'nevertheless, the final evaluations must be made in the field under a variety of environments before the true potential of a fungicide can be determined' (Torgeson, 1967). The methods used in evaluating fungicides are described by McCallan, Hamilton and Mills (1959), Horsfall (1956), Martin (1964), Torgeson (1967), and by the American Phytopathological Society (Anon., 1943, 1947*a*).

Main groups of fungicides

Brief notes on some of the more important fungicides are given below. No attempt is made to provide a comprehensive account and further information can be obtained from Martin (1963, 1964), Spencer (1968), Sharvelle (1961), Hassall (1969) and Torgeson (1969). There are several ways of classifying fungicides, that of Torgeson (1969) being used here.

Inorganic compounds, excluding sulphur

These comprise chiefly copper and mercury compounds.

Copper

Bordeaux mixture is prepared by adding a suspension of lime to a solution of copper sulphate. It was originally applied to grape vines in France to discourage thieves but its efficacy against mildew (*Plasmopara viticola*) was observed by Millardet in 1882, and Bordeaux mixture is still widely used. The original mixture was a bluish paste made by adding 15 kg of quicklime in 50 litres of water to 8 kg of copper sulphate crystals in 100 litres of water and was flicked over the vine bushes with a small switch of heather as described by Large (1940). Nowadays a spray suspension containing 5 kg of copper sulphate, 7·5 kg of hydrated lime and 450 litres of water is often used although this can be varied as required. The chemistry of Bordeaux mixture and its fungicidal action remains obscure despite much investigation (Martin, 1964). A gelatinous precipitate of cupric hydroxide stabilized by absorbed calcium sulphate is perhaps formed, from which soluble copper compounds are slowly liberated by the action of host secretions, fungus secretions, or rain water containing carbon dioxide and ammonium salts. Bordeaux mixture is used against a wide variety of Ascomycetes, Fungi Imperfecti, downy mildews and bacteria which attack the aerial parts of plants but less frequently against powdery mildews: methods of preparation are described by Sharvelle (1961). Burgundy mixture is a mixture of copper sulphate and sodium carbonate but tends to be phytotoxic. Cheshunt compound, a cuprammonium compound made by mixing copper sulphate (two parts by weight) with ammonium carbonate (eleven), is used as a soil drench to control damping-off diseases in seed beds and boxes.

These mixtures are tedious to prepare, and numerous 'ready-made' copper fungicides including dispersible cuprous oxide (Perenox) and copper oxychloride have been produced. These are often less phytotoxic, less corrosive to equipment and easier to use than Bordeaux mixture. Others, such as copper naphthenates, are highly fungitoxic but also phytotoxic. Copper carbonate formerly used as a seed dressing against smuts is now less frequently used. As Martin (1964) points out there are numerous fungitoxic copper compounds but their practical application is limited by phytotoxicity or difficulties in obtaining a satisfactory spray deposit. The fungicidal action of copper is reviewed by McCallan (1949).

Mercury

Many mercury compounds are highly effective fungicides and bactericides but their use in agriculture is restricted because of their toxicity to plants, man and animals. Mercuric chloride is used in wood preservation and also in the treatment of seeds and other planting material contaminated by pathogens but care must be exercised in its application. Mercurous chloride (calomel) is fairly insoluble in water and can be used in the treatment of turf diseases and as a root dip for brassica seedlings against club-root. Inorganic mercurials have generally been superseded by organo-mercurials for control of plant diseases. Inorganic fungicides are discussed by Martin (1969).

Organic mercury compounds

Numerous organo-mercurials have been tested as fungicides and bactericides, chiefly for treatment of seed or other planting material. One of the first was probably hydroxyphenylmercury chloride (Uspulun) and others include such compounds as methylmercuric dicyandiamide (Panogen), methoxyethylmercuriacetate (MEMA), phenylmercury acetate

(PMA) (figure 27·1) and tolylmercuric acetate (Agrosan G). Organo-mercury fungicides have the general formula R-Hg-X where R is an organic radical (alkyl, alkozyalkyl or aryl) and X represents an acidic radical. Although effective as fungicides and bactericides, organic mercury compounds are also highly toxic to man and animal life generally and this has mostly restricted their use to seed treatment; even this can be a danger to birds which consume treated seed when it is sown. Some organo-mercurials including phenyl mercury compounds are used as eradicant sprays, as in destroying *Venturia inaequalis* infection in overwintering apple leaves, but care has to be exercised in their application. Organo-mercurials are described by Martin (1964) and Ulfvarson (1969).

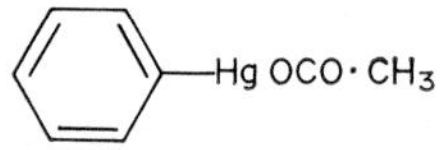

Figure 27.1   Phenylmercury acetate.

Other organo-metallic compounds

Organic compounds containing tin, lead, germanium, arsenic, antimony and bismuth have been tested as fungicides as described by Sijpesteijn *et al.* (1969). Much interest has centred on organo-tin compounds, notably triphenyltin acetate (fentin acetate) and triphenyltin hydroxide (fentin hydroxide). These two fungicides have been used to control potato blight, *Cercospora beticola* on sugarbeet, *Pyricularia oryzae* (rice blast) and coffee berry disease (*Colletotrichum coffeanum*) and are said to be equally effective as copper fungicides at about one-tenth the dose of the latter (Martin, 1968). The toxicity of organo-tin compounds to some plants has limited their use and less phytotoxic compounds are being sought.

Sulphur

Elemental sulphur, used chiefly as a finely divided dust or as a dispersible powder, was one of the earliest fungicides and is particularly effective against powdery mildews. It is, however, toxic to some plants and also to mites. Many explanations of the fungicidal action of sulphur have been proposed, some suggesting that it is reduced to fungitoxic hydrogen sulphide by fungi, others that sulphur dioxide is involved. Present opinion seems to be that sulphur itself is the fungicidal agent, acting as a hydrogen acceptor and thus interfering in the normal processes of hydrogenation and dehydrogenation (Miller, McCallan and Weed, 1953).

As a fungicide sulphur has the advantages of being inexpensive and harmless to man and animals in the amounts normally applied. It is widely used in some areas to destroy smut spores carried by cereal seed and can be quite effective if finely divided. Other fungicides are often more effective and sulphur affords little protection against soil borne pathogens, so that its use as a seed dressing is limited. There are numerous formulations – ground, sublimed, precipitated, wettable and other forms.

Lime sulphur contains chiefly calcium polysulphides and is prepared by boiling lime and sulphur together. It appears to precipitate as a tenacious form of sulphur when applied to plant surfaces but has the disadvantage of causing injury to some plants, bringing about scorching and/or premature abscission of leaves and fruits. Hence its use is limited although it has been used against apple scab, peach leaf curl and powdery mildews on some plants. It is also used against scale insects. Various other formulations of inorganic and organic polysulphides have been produced, as described by Sharvelle (1961). The fungicidal action of sulphur is discussed by McCallan (1964) and Tweedy (1969) who gives an account of sulphur as a fungicide.

Organo-sulphur compounds

Several useful fungicides are derived from dithiocarbamic acid. These fall into three main groups – thiuram disulphides, metallic dithiocarbamates and ethylene bisdithiocarbamates.

Tetramethylthiuram disulphide (TMTD, thiram) (figure 27·2) was developed as a rubber accelerator and was subsequently found to be fungicidal. Thiram is chiefly used as a seed dressing (Arasan, Nomersan, Thiosan) but also finds application as a foliage spray. Although of low toxicity to plants and animals (except possibly hens) it can cause irritation to the skin and mucous membranes. It may taint fruit and so should not be used for fruit destined for canning or deep freezing. Thiram is widely used as a seed treatment, powder or slurry, against *Pythium, Rhizoctonia* and other soil fungi causing damping-off and seedling diseases.

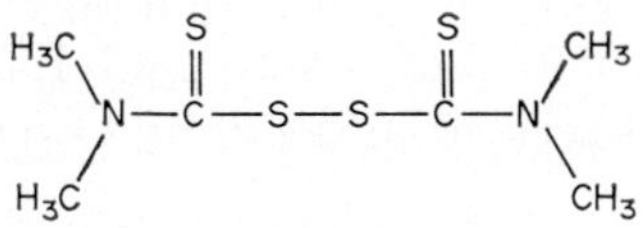

Figure 27.2   Thiram.

Many metallic dithiocarbamates have been developed but only the iron (ferbam) and zinc (ziram) (figure 27·3) dimethyldithiocarbamates appear to have been developed commercially.

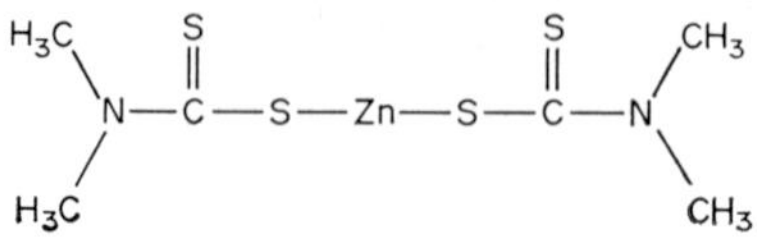

Figure 27.3   Ziram.

These two fungicides are used to control damping-off of seedlings, several foliage and fruit diseases caused chiefly by Ascomycetes and Fungi Imperfecti, and also some rusts and downy mildews. As foliage sprays they are used to correct iron deficiency (ferbam) and zinc deficiency (ziram).

The bisdithiocarbamates are formed by joining two dithiocarbamic acid molecules through the carbon atom as, for example, in zineb (figure 27·4)

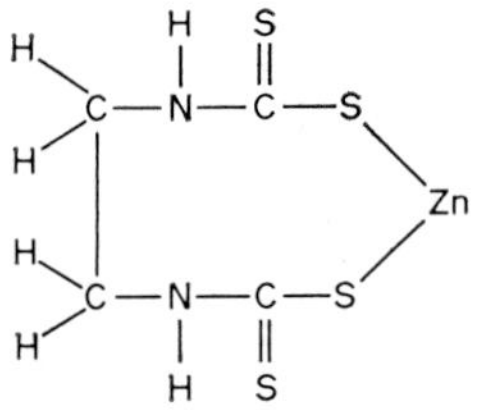

Figure 27.4   Zineb (maneb is similar but with Mn instead of Zn).

Nabam, containing sodium, was the first to be produced but was later replaced by the zinc compound (zineb) which is now widely used against many foliage and flower pathogens. Maneb is the manganese equivalent and a further development is mancozeb, a complex of zinc and maneb containing 20% manganese and 2·5% zinc. These fungicides are in part marketed as various types of dithane and are useful in control of downy mildews, certain rusts, and some Ascomycetes and Fungi Imperfecti which cause leaf and fruit diseases. Dazomet, a dry soil fungicide, is thought to break down to methylaminomethyl dithiocarbamate which in turn yields methyl isothiocyanate. Although phytotoxic it is used as a soil fumigant against *Fusarium, Pythium, Verticillium, Rhizoctonia*, nematodes and other soil pathogens (p. 505). Further information on dithiocarbamates can be obtained from Kerk (1959) and Thorn and Ludwig (1962). Organo-sulphur fungicides are described in detail by Owens (1969).

Heterocyclic nitrogen compounds

The principal fungicides included in this group by Lukens (1969) are glyodin (2-heptadecyl-2-imidazoline acetate), oxine (8-quinolinol, or 8-hydroxyquinoline), Dyrene 2,4-dichloro-6(o-chloroaniline)-1,3,5-triazine

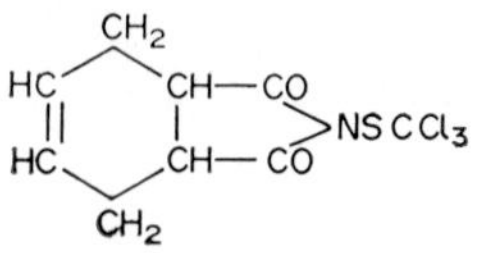

Figure 27.5   Captan.

and captan (N-trichloromethylthio-4-cyclohexene-1,2-dicarboximide) (figure 27·5). Of these captan has proved to be an extemely useful fungicide
since its discovery by Kittleson (1952). It is widely used as a foliage and
fruit protectant, and can be applied to soil or seed or used as a dip for
planting material in control of damping-off. Although a fairly broad
spectrum fungicide it is not generally effective against rusts, powdery

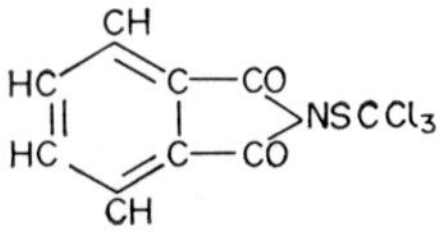

Figure 27.6   Folpet.

mildews and downy mildews. Folpet (Phaltan) (figure 27·6) is N-(tri-
chloromethylthio)phthalimide and is effective against *Sphaerotheca pannosa*
(rose powdery mildew). The activity of captan is attributed to its -SCCl$_3$
group which interferes with vital processes in the fungus involving sulphydryl enzymes (Owens and Novotny, 1959).

Glyodin, a surfactant, has a fairly narrow fungicidal spectrum. It is
effective against *Venturia inaequalis* (apple scab), *Coccomyces hiemalis* (cherry
leaf spot) and *Diplocarpon rosae* (black spot of rose) but is ineffective
against *Podosphaera leucotricha* (apple powdery mildew) and appears to
suppress spore germination. Heterocyclic nitrogen compounds as fungicides are discussed by Lukens (1969).

Quinones

Quinones occur in plants and may be involved in their defence mechanisms against pathogens. Some are highly fungitoxic but only two – chloranil and dichlone – appear to have been developed as fungicides. Chlor-

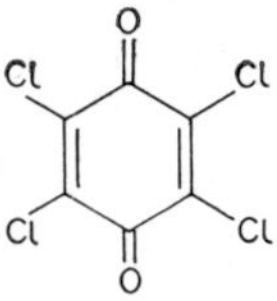

Figure 27.7   Chloranil.

anil (tetrachloro-*p*-benzoquinone, as in Spergon) (figure 27·7) is a useful seed treatment chemical for legumes and vegetables but is of limited value as a foliage fungicide, partly because it decomposes in light. Dichlone (2,3-dichloro-1,4-naphthoquinone, Phygon) (figure 27·8) is also used chiefly as a seed dressing but has been recommended as a foliage fungicide

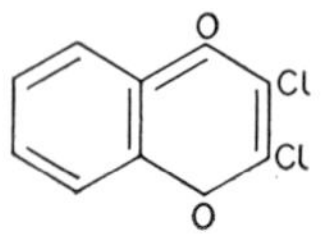

Figure 27.8   Dichlone

against, for example, apple scab. It can, however, be toxic to some plants and is liable to irritate the skin in warm weather. Quinones as fungicides are discussed by McNew and Burchfield (1951) and Rich (1969); dichlone is discussed by Owens and Novotny (1958).

Aromatic compounds

These are discussed by Corden (1969). One of the most useful is dinocap (Karathane, Crotothane), once thought to be 2-(1-methyl-*n*-heptyl)-4,6,dinitrophenyl crotonate but since shown to be a mixture of isomers (figure 27·9). Dinocap was developed as an acaricide and is now extensively used against powdery mildew of apple and other plants. Binapacryl, 2-(1-methyl-*n*-propyl)-4,6-dinitrophenyl 2-methyl crotonate also shows promise against powdery mildews.

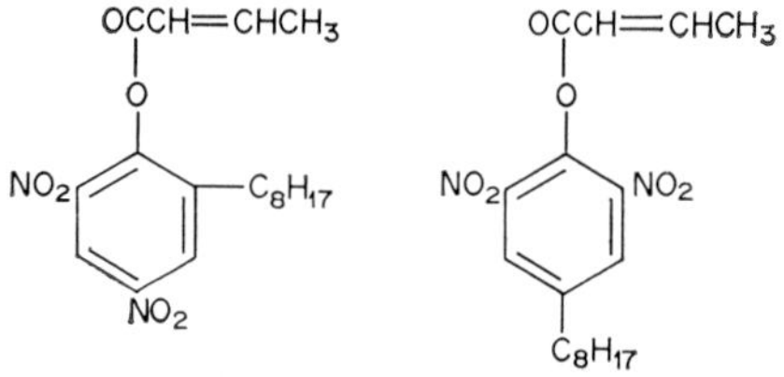

Figure 27.9   Dinocap

Halogenated phenols are often fungicidal but their use in disease control is limited by their phytotoxicity; pentachlorophenol is, however, used as a wood preservative. Other aromatic compounds used as fungicides include hexachlorobenzene (HCB) as a seed treatment against bunt of wheat, pentachloronitrobenzene (PCNB, quintozene) as a soil treatment to control diseases caused by *Corticium solani*, *C. rolfsii*, *Botrytis* and *Sclerotinia* although it is ineffective against *Pythium*, *Phytophthora* and *Fusarium*. Tetrachloronitrobenzene (TCNB, tecnazene) finds application in control of dry rot of potato tubers caused by *Fusarium caeruleum*. Apart from their direct fungicidal effect these chlorinated nitrobenzenes perhaps control diseases by increasing host resistance in some way (Priest and Wood, 1961).

2,6-Dichloro-4-nitroaniline (DCNA, dichloran, Botran) is used for the control of *Botrytis* (grey mould of lettuce) and is effective against some fruit rotting fungi including *Monilinia* and *Rhizopus*. It is also useful as a soil fungicide to control such pathogens as *Sclerotium*, *Sclerotinia* and *Stromatinia*. The use of other aromatics, for example biphenyl and o-phenylphenol, as postharvest fungicides is described elsewhere (p. 507).

Non-aromatic organic compounds

This group includes dodine (Cyprex; *n*-dodecylguanidine acetate), used for control of apple scab and several other diseases caused chiefly by Ascomycetes and Fungi Imperfecti as listed by Byrde (1969). Unfortunately the toxicity of dodine to some crop plants rather limits its usefulness. It is a surface active material which, despite its solubility in water, adheres tenaciously to foliage and has an eradicant action against *Venturia*. It is of interest that some chlorinated hydrocarbon insecticides affect fungi, and soil treatment with aldrin resulted in some reduction in club root of cabbage (Channon and Keyworth, 1960) and take-all of wheat (Slope and Last, 1963).

Other fungicides in this group include chloropicrin, methyl bromide, ethylene dibromide and dichloropropene-dichloropropane (D-D), all used as soil fumigants. Non-aromatic fungicides are described by Byrde (1969).

Antibiotics

Only a few antibiotics are used to control plant diseases. They include streptomycin from *Streptomyces griseus*, marketed as Agrimycin 100 (with oxytetracycline) and Terramycin (oxytetracycline) from *S. rimosus*. These, and particularly Agrimycin, have been used in the treatment of crown gall, fireblight of apple and pear, halo blight of bean, and other bacterial diseases (Sharvelle, 1961) and may find increasing application for this purpose when and if they become cheaper, but medical considerations may restrict their widespread use on food crops.

Antifungal antibiotics have also been used in disease control. Griseofulvin, isolated from *Penicillium griseofulvum* about 30 years ago, and found to be effective against several plant pathogens, notably *Botrytis*, seems not to have lived up to its early promise (Brian, 1960). Cycloheximide (as in Acti-dione), found about 20 years ago in a culture filtrate of *Streptomyces griseus*, is active against a wide range of fungi but its use is restricted by its toxicity to many plants. It can, however, be used at 2 p.p.m. to control cherry leaf spot caused by *Coccomyces hiemalis*, and less phytotoxic derivatives of cycloheximide are being developed (see Ford *et al.*, 1958). It is also used to control several turf grass diseases and some powdery mildews and rusts.

Polyene antibiotics including nystatin, rimocidin, pimaricin, filipin, candicidin and others produced by *Streptomyces* spp. are effective to varying extents against several fungi although results so far have been rather erratic. However, they show high fungitoxicity combined with low phytotoxicity and clearly merit further investigation. Polypeptide antibiotics – subtilin, gramicidin, bacitracin, polymyxin, phytoactin and others mostly produced by species of *Streptomyces* and *Bacillus* – are primarily bactericidal but some are antifungal although tending to be phytotoxic. Several other antibiotics show promise for control of certain fungal diseases of plants, including blasticidin (from *S. griseochromogenes*) against *Pyricularia oryzae*, vancomycin, a readily translocated and relatively non-phytotoxic antibiotic from *S. orientalis*, venturicidin from *Streptomyces* spp. against apple scab (Rhodes *et al.*, 1961), and various others produced chiefly by soil Actinomycetes and particularly by *Streptomyces* spp. These offer a fertile and potentially profitable field of investigation.

Many antibiotics enter roots and stems and may be translocated through the xylem and possibly other tissues (pith and phloem) at varying rates depending on the antibiotic and plant. Some, including griseofulvin, do not readily move from sprayed leaves whereas others (streptothricin and pleocidin: Gray, 1958) are transported, presumably through the phloem, to other parts of the plant and particularly to places of high metabolic activity (including the growing points) in company with food materials from the leaves.

The mode of action of most antifungal antibiotics is obscure. Dekker (1963*a*) points out that they may act, (1) directly on the pathogen at the plant surface, as do many fungicides; (2) on the pathogen within the plant tissues by systemic action; (3) the antibiotic may be transformed into a more active derivative with the tissues, or it might perhaps be similarly inactivated; or (4) some antibiotics can apparently reduce infection by in some way influencing the plant-pathogen interaction in the direction of increased plant resistance. Gottlieb and Shaw (1970), in a detailed discussion on the mechanisms of action of antifungal antibiotics, conclude that these mechanisms include interference with cell wall formation, cell membranes, protein synthesis, nucleic acid synthesis and energy transformation reactions associated with mitochondrial electron transport.

Information on the use of antibiotics in disease control can be obtained from Dekker (1963*a*, 1969), Zaumeyer (1958) and Pramer (1961). Their uptake and translocation by plants are discussed by Goodman (1959), Crowdy (1959), Crowdy *et al.* (1955, 1956), Pramer (1959), and Dimond and Horsfall (1959).

Some angiosperms, ferns, mosses and lichens contain antimicrobial substances ('phytoncides') of various sorts, and the possible use of these substances, including antibiotics from garlic and lichens (usnic acid), in disease control seems worth investigating. Natural antifungal substances occurring in, or produced by, plants are discussed by Fawcett and Spencer (1969, 1970).

Systemic fungicides and systemic compounds

Systemic insecticides have been in use for several years and, after much effort, effective systemic fungicides are now becoming available. A systemic fungicide is one which is taken up and translocated within the plant, as a result of which the latter becomes fungitoxic. Many conventional fungicides probably become systemic to slight extents but not sufficiently to give worthwhile protection. This is particularly true of water soluble chemicals, or those which become soluble in the plant, such as some salts of mercury, zinc and iron, antibiotics, sulphonamides, dithiocarbamates and quinones. Many of these substances are, however, unsuitable in other respects – they may be phytotoxic at fungicidal concentrations, their translocation within the plant may be unduly slow or limited, or they may not persist sufficiently long to give adequate protection.

Some systemic fungicides are fungitoxic *in vitro* and *in vivo* and so may correctly be described as fungicides. Other systemic protectants are fungitoxic only *in vivo*, and are presumably converted into fungitoxic substances within the plant or modify the metabolism of the plant in such a way that it becomes resistant to the pathogen. Substances in the latter category have been termed 'systemic compounds'. The term 'systemic' has been suggested to cover both categories, that is, compounds which, after absorption and subsequent translocation, are able to influence disease development within the plant (Van der Kerk, 1963).

Ideally, systemics should be effective against the pathogen but harmless to the plant and animals, should be readily translocated within the plant and so should preferably be water soluble, should eradicate the fungus within the plant, should be sufficiently persistent within the plant to give an adequate period of protection and should have disappeared by harvest time. They should also be inexpensive, stable, unobjectionable to handle, of low mammalian toxicity and simple to apply.

Methods of application

Systemics are applied to plants in several ways. They can be applied in solution as foliage sprays, although leaves are not well suited to absorption of liquid and the latter may dry up before it is taken in; this can be minimized by using wetting agents and humectants such as glycerol. Application to foliage is likely to be effective against leaf pathogens in that the systemic is thereby brought into close proximity to the pathogen but it is less likely to be effective against fungi which cause root diseases. Application to the soil is likely to be wasteful and hence expensive, unless the systemic can be brought into sufficiently close contact with the roots to encourage its rapid uptake by the plant. This may be possible in irrigated crops, the systemic (preferably in granular form) being placed along two trenches on either side of the row of plants, from whence it is slowly taken up by the roots. Alternatively, the systemic can be placed at the base of the stem as described by Elias *et al.* (1968), who found that one such application of 0·25 g of ethirimol (see below) in 20 ml of water as soon as mildew appeared gave good control of *Sphaerotheca fuliginea* (cucumber powdery mildew) in the glasshouse. The protection lasted for at least 6 weeks and resulted in increased yields, better quality fruit and prolonged life of the plants as compared with those sprayed with standard fungicides. Chemical or microbial breakdown, or physical immobilization of some systemics may occur in soil, and systemic chemicals for use in soil should remain unaltered and available to the plants for as long as possible.

Several systemics have been tested as seed dressings to eliminate seed borne infection. Maude and Kyle (1970) found that Benlate (50% benomyl wettable powder : methyl 1-(butylcarbamoyl)-2-benzimidazole-carbamate) gave complete control of *Ascochyta pisi* infection of pea seeds when used as a dry seed dressing at 1 : 220 and 1 : 300, presumably indicating that benomyl entered the seed. In other cases, the systemic is applied to the seed and is taken up by the seedling during emergence, thereafter protecting the young plant for a variable period of time.

Systemic fungicides have so far given disappointing results when applied to bushes and trees. Apart from woody perennial plants having roots which are more difficult to get at, it seems that systemics are not readily translocated from roots to shoots in woody plants. Foliage sprays or trunk injection may perhaps prove useful in applying systemics to trees and shrubs.

Action of systemic fungicides

Little is known about the ways in which systemic fungicides destroy or inactivate fungi. The possible mechanisms of fungitoxicity include: (1) neutralization of enzymes and/or toxins involved in the invasion and colonization of the plant by the fungus; (2) selective accumulation of the fungicide by the fungus due to greater permeability of the fungal cell wall; (3) damage to the semipermeable membrane of fungal hyphae and infection structures; inhibition of the emergence of germ tubes from powdery mildew spores by systemic pyrimidine fungicides has been described by Bent (1970). Other systemics inhibit or disrupt the formation of appressoria and/or haustoria – for example, 6-azauracil did not inhibit conidial germination or penetration in *Erysiphe cichoracearum* (on cucumber) and *E. graminis* (on wheat), but inhibited these fungi by interfering with their growth during the formation of the first haustorium (Dekker and Oort, 1964); (4) inhibition of fungal enzyme systems, for example, by destroying the sulphydryl bonds of the enzyme.

Systemic fungicides are generally thought to be more specific in their action than are surface fungicides, and this may enable resistance to systemic fungicides to develop more quickly. Indeed it is possible that strains of fungal plant pathogens resistant to some systemic protectants are now appearing, despite the rather short time these chemicals have been in use.

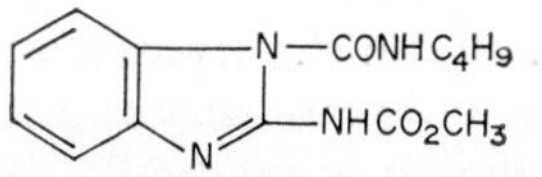

Figure 27.10   Benomyl.

Systemic fungicides

Perhaps the best known is benomyl (methyl-l-(butylcarbamoyl)-2-benzimidazolecarbamate) (figure 27·10), marketed as Benlate. This is effective against a wide range of Ascomycetes, including powdery mildews, some Fungi Imperfecti, has given variable results against Basidiomycetes, and is of little use against Phycomycetes. It has shown promise as a preharvest spray for fruits and is a mite ovicide. Control of many soil pathogens can be obtained provided the roots are confined to the benomyl treated soil. Another benzimidazole derived fungicide is thiabendazole, a thiazolyl compound originally developed as an anthelmintic drug.

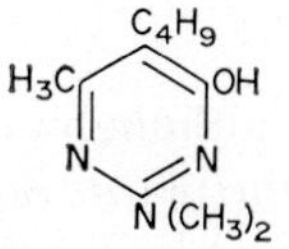

Figure 27.11   Dimethirimol.

The 1,4-oxathiins are systemic fungicides which are particularly effective against Basidiomycetes – smuts, rusts, *Corticium* (*Rhizoctonia*) *solani*. Vitavax (2,3-dihydro-5-carboxanilido-6-methyl-1,4-oxathiin) has been used to free barley seed from *Ustilago nuda* (loose smut) present inside the seed. Plantvax, the sulphone derivative of Vitavax, shows some promise against wheat rusts, seed or soil application giving good control of *Puccinia striiformis* for one month after sowing (Powelson and Shaner, 1966).

Figure 27.12   Ethirimol.

Systemic pyrimidine fungicides have recently been developed, notably dimethirimol (Milcurb) (figure 27·11) which has been successfully used as a seed or soil dressing against powdery mildew (*Sphaerotheca fuliginea*) of cucurbits, and ethirimol (Milstem) (figure 27·12) which is effective as a seed dressing against cereal powdery mildew (*Erysiphe graminis*). These seem to be highly specific – dimethirimol, for example, shows little activity against *Sphaerotheca pannosa* (rose powdery mildew) or *Uncinula necator* (grape powdery mildew). Dimethirimol is in many ways an ideal systemic fungicide as it moves rapidly in the transpiration stream to all the aerial parts of the plant, protects and eradicates at low concentrations, is stable in soil and loosely held so that it is gradually made available to the plant roots. It does not accumulate in the plant tissue, has a low mammalian toxicity, is odourless, does not taint the produce, and there is a wide safety margin between the amount required to kill the fungus and that likely to cause plant damage.

Among other recently developed systemic fungicides are N-tridecyl-2,6-dimethyl-morpholin (tridemorph:Calixin is a 75% w/v. formulation) and o-methylbenzo-acidanilid (mebenil). Tridemorph (Pommer *et al.*, 1969) is used against cereal powdery mildew, one spray application of 0·3 litres in at least 112·5 litres of water being effective for 3–4 weeks. Mebenil is active against a wide range of Basidiomycetes including certain rusts, smuts, *Exobasidium vexans* (blister blight of tea) and *Rhizoctonia*, and for control of rusts is used at 2·5–3·7 kg/ha (Pommer and Kradel, 1969).

Systemic compounds

These are substances which, although not fungicidal *in vitro*, exert a protective effect when applied to the plant. Some are probably converted into fungitoxic derivatives within the plant, others perhaps antidote the toxins produced by some pathogens and so bring about a temporary reduction in symptoms (p. 530). It is possible that some systemic compounds, such as phenylthiourea, act upon polyphenoloxidase enzymes. They thus prevent the oxidation of phenolic compounds which then inhibit the pectolytic enzymes by means of which the pathogen normally colonizes the plant.

Some systemic compounds appear to so modify the metabolism of the plant that it becomes more resistant to the pathogen. Crowdy and Wain (1950) found that certain phenoxyacetic and phenoxy-*iso*-butyric acids reduced infection of broad bean leaves when the seedlings were grown for several weeks in solutions containing 10 p.p.m. of the acids and then inoculated with *Botrytis cinerea*. The fact that lesions formed but did not enlarge in the treated plants suggests that growth of the pathogen in the leaf tissue rather than its initial entry was inhibited. Growth-regulating substances affect the carbohydrate metabolism and hence the sugar balance in leaves, so that high sugar concentrations would tend to make the leaves more susceptible to those pathogens which require much sugar, and more resistant to those which are favoured by low sugar content. Another possibility is that resistance results from a reduced nitrogen concentration in the leaves brought about by growth regulators. Certain amino acids have been reported to increase the plant's resistance to some pathogens; apple leaves whose petioles had been injected with *D*-phenylalanine showed resistance to *Venturia inaequalis* (apple scab) as described by Kuc *et al.* (1957), and other amino acids have shown activity against a range of fungi which attack plants – *Puccinia graminis* and *P. recondita* on wheat, *Phytophthora infestans* on potato tubers, *Erysiphe cichoracearum* on cucumber, *Botrytis fabae* on broad bean, and others listed by Van Andel (1966). Apparently the dextro-rotatory forms of these amino acids are often more effective than the laevo-rotatory forms, whereas the latter generally occur in nature, suggesting perhaps that the former act as antimetabolites, but the mechanisms involved in the increased resistance are obscure. Antimetabolism may also be involved in the activity of fluorophenylalanine, an amino acid not reported to occur in plants, against *Cladosporium cucumerinum* (cucumber gummosis) and *Colletotrichum lagenarium* (cucumber anthracnose) in that this activity was inhibited by phenylalanine *in vitro* (Van Andel, 1962).

Substances which have been detected in shoots after application to roots include antibiotics (cycloheximide, streptomycin), sulphonamides, captan, procaine hydrochloride, 6-azauracil, and others listed by Wain and Carter (1967). Phenobarbitone becomes systemic and controls *Sphaerotheca fuliginea* (powdery mildew) of marrow, but not *Erysiphe graminis* or *Podosphaera leucotricha* (Zaracovitis, 1965; Sijpesteijn and Tempel, 1967). Some of these are no doubt systemic fungicides, others are perhaps systemic compounds and still others have not been investigated in detail.

Systemic fungicides are often regarded as a step forward in plant protection. By comparison with surface fungicides, systemics can move through the plant, destroy established infections, are less liable to loss through weathering, and might be useful for control of systemic pathogens, vascular wilt pathogens and root infecting fungi against which surface fungicides are of little avail. There are, however, possible snags. Some systemic fungicides are effective against only a fairly narrow range of plant pathogens, in some cases a single species of powdery mildew. Hence a mixture of systemics may have to be used to control a mixture of pathogens. Systemics are likely to be more specific than surface fungicides in the way in which they inhibit fungi, and it is possible that the latter may develop resistant strains more rapidly since there may be only one or two mechanisms of fungitoxicity to overcome as compared with several in the case of the less specific surface fungicides. At present, several systemic fungicides active against powdery mildews are known, and there is a need for systemics to control downy mildews, notably *Plasmopara viticola* on grape and *Phytophthora infestans* on potato, and rusts – *Puccinia graminis* on wheat, *Hemileia vastatrix* on coffee and others. Great efforts are being made to find new and more effective systemic fungicides, and it is probably only a matter of time before systemics active against rusts, downy mildews and other pathogens become available. Another possible future development is the use of mixtures of surface and systemic fungicides for disease control, but comparatively few cases of this seem to have been reported as yet.

Disease control by oils

An interesting recent development is the use of oils to control banana leaf spot (Sigatoka disease) caused by *Mycosphaerella musicola* as described by Leach (1962) and Calpouzos (1966). Light viscosity oils atomized into very fine droplets 50–100 μm in diameter seem to be most effective and can apparently stop the growth of the fungus after it has become established inside the leaf. Oils do not prevent the production or germination of the spores of *M. musicola* and it is not known how they control the disease. Other banana leaf spot fungi did not appear to be affected. There is some danger of phytotoxicity but this is slight in sprays applied at 11·25–17·10 litres/ha at 3–4 weekly intervals.

Oil sprays are now widely used for the control of *M. musicola*; nearly 50 million litres are estimated to have been used in Latin America and the Caribbean in 1964 and perhaps another 7·6 million litres in other banana producing areas (Ordish and Mitchell, 1969).

Calpouzos (1966) notes that any hydrophobic fluid of low volatility – for example a chemically inert silicone oil (Calpouzos *et al.*, 1959) – will control *M. musicola*. He suggests that the therapeutic action is perhaps due to the oily physical barrier which interferes with gas exchange in the leaf and so alters its physiology as to stop development of the fungus and there is some evidence that antitranspirants may reduce disease by, for example, inhibiting stomatal penetration (Gale and Pojakoff-Mayber, 1962). Possibly, alterations in the sugar content of the host tissue are involved –

thus *M. musicola* is encouraged by fairly high light intensity which no doubt favours photosynthesis and high sugar concentration. Some high sugar pathogens such as powdery mildews and rusts are apparently susceptible to oils. Further investigation of oils in disease control is clearly needed. They have the advantage of being cheap, of low mammalian toxicity, are effective at low doses (11·25 litres/ha or less in some cases), stick to and spread well over leaves, and are often very effective. However, phytotoxicity may occur with some plants, and oils do not appear to be effective against all pathogens although further investigation of this is needed. Oils have been used successfully against *Cercospora citri-grisea* (greasy spot of citrus) and *C. aleuritidis* (*Mycosphaerella aleuritidis*) which causes angular leaf spot of tung, but are apparently ineffective against *Cercospora* leaf spots of groundnut, tobacco, zinnia and *Panicum* (Calpouzos et al., 1962). Oil sprays have also shown promise against *Septoria apii* on celery, *Puccinia graminis tritici* on wheat and several powdery mildews including *Sphaerotheca pannosa* on rose (McWhorter, 1927). Synthetic oily fluids (polybutenes) are also effective according to Fisher (1959) and Fisher *et al.*, (1960) against *Peronospora tabacina* (blue mould of tobacco), *Plasmopara viticola* on grape and certain viruses, as listed by Calpouzos, (1966). The use of mineral oils in disease control is reviewed by Calpouzos (1969).

Chemotherapy

Chemotherapy is the treatment of infected plants with chemicals to inactivate the pathogen without harming the plant. It has been defined by Dimond *et al.* (1952), as 'the control of plant disease by compounds which, through their effect upon the host or pathogen, reduce or nullify the effect of the pathogen after it has entered the plant'. Systemic fungicides which destroy pathogens without damaging the plant tissue harbouring them are chemotherapeutants. Seed treatment in which the pathogen within the seed is destroyed by heat or chemicals is another example of therapy, as is the application of fungicidal sprays to destroy powdery mildew on the aerial parts of plants or, in a wider sense, the correction of a trace element deficiency by supplying the plant with the deficient element.

Horsfall (1956) distinguishes three main types of chemotherapy: (1) topical chemotherapy (eradication) in which the pathogen is destroyed *in situ*, as in spraying fungicides to control powdery mildews; (2) systemic chemotherapy in which the chemical is applied at one place (possibly to the roots), is translocated through the plant, and destroys a localized infection elsewhere in the plant (for example in the leaves); and (3) systemic chemotherapy in which the chemical is used to treat systemic infections.

Mitigation of the symptoms of some plant diseases can be obtained by applying substances which neutralize the toxins produced by the pathogen, as with quinolinols (oxines) for treatment of Dutch elm disease (Horsfall, 1956). Such treatment does not prevent the fungus from producing further toxin, and the problem may be complicated by several toxins being involved, so that the potentialities of such antidoting substances in disease control are limited. The infected plant is in no sense cured; the symptoms are mitigated but the effect wears off in due course and the pathogen is not killed. p-Dichlorbenzene vapour, although it does not destroy *Peronospora tabacina*, does protect tobacco seedlings until they develop resistance, perhaps by preventing sporulation of the fungus. Antibiotics such as penicillin and streptomycin have been used as chemotherapeutants against several bacterial pathogens with varying degrees of success, and malachite green and other compounds have occasionally been reported to cure virus infected plants. Others, including thiouracil, apparently interfere with virus multiplication and might in their effects be compared with substances which suppress sporulation of fungal plant pathogens.

Chemotherapy is discussed by Howard and Horsfall (1959), Dimond and Horsfall (1959), Dimond (1959), Horsfall (1956), and Byrde and Ainsworth (1958).

Nature of fungicidal action

Fungicides kill fungi in various ways as described by Horsfall (1956), Somers (1962), Woodcock (1959), Owens (1963), Rich (1960), Sisler and Cox (1960), Miller (1968) and in Rich (1963). The ways in which specific fungicides act are discussed by various authors in Torgeson (1969). An understanding of this problem is of great practical importance as it might enable fungicides for specific purposes to be designed rather than discovered. Somers (1962) points out that most of the fungicides in present use have been discovered and developed empirically, often as a result of chance observations, and that the present procedure of testing thousands of chemicals for possible fungicidal properties is wasteful. Nevertheless, our knowledge of the chemical basis of fungitoxicity is at present limited and potentially valuable fungicides are likely to be missed unless the 'blanket' procedure is adopted. It is, in fact, a method widely used in the search for new pesticides in general.

Fungicides are much less toxic than many animal poisons, insecticides, bactericides and herbicides. Whereas toxicity of the latter is often of the order of a few $\mu g/g$, or less, that of many fungicides to fungal spores is often of the order of 85–10,000 μg (Somers, 1962). Further, the metabolic processes of plants and fungi, although different in some respects, are basically similar, so that fungicides are likely to damage both fungus and host plant. There is, however, some degree of selective toxicity although many fungicides are rather unspecific in their toxic action.

Most of the fungicides in use seem to act directly on the fungal cells or spores after entering them. Many are rather insoluble in water but may be sufficiently soluble to inhibit the germination of sensitive spores present in small numbers. Several possible factors bringing about solubilization of fungicides on plant surfaces and in the presence of spores have been suggested – carbon dioxide and ammonia in rain water or dew, guttation fluids and other exudates from the plant, spore exudates, and the ability of spores to accumulate fungicides from very dilute solutions. Much of the work on these aspects has been done with copper fungicides, especially Bordeaux mixture, and other methods of solubilization might occur with other fungicides. Several workers (McCallan and Wilcoxon, 1936; Wain and Wilkinson, 1943, 1946) have shown that exudates from fungal spores increase the toxicity of Bordeaux mixture and this is considered by some to be due to increased solubilization enabling the fungicide to enter the spores in larger amounts. Others believe that molecules of the fungicide diffuse through water to the spore where they are taken up and accumulated: these aspects are discussed by Horsfall (1956).

The uptake of fungicides by spores seems to be a rapid process and their final concentration within the spore may be several thousand times greater than in the ambient fungicidal solution – as mentioned above, many fungicides are effective only at fairly high concentration. The cell wall of many fungi probably offers little resistance to the entry of fungicides of low molecular weight but in others it may prevent certain substances from reaching the protoplast. The cell wall may contain fatty or other substances which reduce its permeability to water and fungicides, or might in some way absorb the latter.

The extent to which the cytoplasmic membrane, generally thought to be lipoprotein in nature, regulates the entry of fungicides into cells is uncertain. Toxicity and lipid solubility are apparently correlated in some cases and the addition of inert lipophilic substituents to the fungicide molecule may increase its fungitoxicity, presumably by facilitating its progress to the fungicide susceptible sites within the cell. The significance of the cytoplasmic membrane as a permeation barrier remains uncertain and there is evidence that in some fungi its ability to reduce the entry of low molecular weight fungicides is limited. Differential permeability of the cytoplasmic membrane, or of the cell wall, might account for the resistance or susceptibility of the fungal cell to fungicides. Rather little is as yet known about the processes which regulate the entry of fungicides into cells, an interesting subject discussed in detail by Miller (1969) and Horsfall (1956).

The killing of cells by chemicals is a complex process which is not well understood, and the following mechanisms may be involved.

Injurious effects on cell walls and cell division

Some fungicides probably exert their harmful effects by damaging cell walls or by interfering with their extension or initiation. These aspects have received relatively little attention. The antibiotic griseofulvin caused swelling and distortion of the growing tip of fungal hyphae, particularly in those thought to have chitinous walls (Brian, 1949), other antibiotics caused lysis of the hyphae of *Glomerella cingulata* (Carter and Lockwood, 1957), and lysozyme (an antibiotic enzyme) lysed the germ tubes of *Stemphylium sarcinaeforme* (Rich, 1960). Some fungicides are thought to reduce the ability of fungi to form new cell walls, probably by interfering with the enzymes involved. Others inhibit nuclear division by interfering with the mitotic spindle or by their effects on the chromosomes, thus resulting in reduced or abnormal growth and sterility. There may be mutagenic effects and some of the mutations are likely to be lethal. Many observers have described the abnormal growth brought about by some fungicides and Horsfall (1956) in his useful account of the subject considers that ketones, phenols and amines inhibit mitosis by combining with sulphydryl, ketone or amino groups in the chromosome proteins. Aromatic hydrocarbons, including chlorinated ones, interfere with the spindle perhaps by dissolving the fatty substances in the spindle fibres, so weakening them that they cannot pull the chromosomes apart.

Effects on the permeability of cell membranes

Several organic compounds of high surface activity (surfactants) have bactericidal and fungicidal properties, as shown by dodine acetate and glyodin. They seem to interfere with the cytoplasmic membrane, thus releasing soluble substances from the cells, but the significance of this in relation to fungitoxicity is uncertain – the spores of some fungi can apparently lose considerable amounts of some constituents and still remain able to germinate (Miller and McCallan, 1957). It may be that the permeability changes are secondary, and glyodin perhaps interferes with the biosynthesis of guanine and xanthine (West and Wolf, 1955). The fungitoxicity of silver is usually attributed to its effect on the permeability of fungal cells, as discussed by Miller (1968). Thus more mercury was taken up by fungal cells which had been pretreated, or simultaneously treated, with silver as compared with those not so treated, suggesting a direct effect of silver on cell permeability leading to release of cell contents.

Extracellular enzymes produced by fungi are presumably formed at the outer surface of the cytoplasmic membrane, and synthesis of cell wall materials probably occurs there. Some fungicides might act by disrupting these and other vital activities occurring at the cell surface although this is difficult to demonstrate convincingly.

Effects on enzymes

Many fungicides act as rather non-specific inhibitors of enzymes. Captan, for example, has been shown to inactive many oxidative enzymes, carboxylases, and enzymes involved in phosphorus metabolism and citrate synthesis. The toxicity of captan, dichlone and probably other fungicides no doubt results from the inactivation of several or many enzymes and coenzymes, particularly those which contain reactive sulphydryl (–SH) groups, which occur frequently in living cells. Metals such as copper and mercury will form covalent bonds with sulphydryl groups to produce mercaptides, but may also inhibit enzymes which are not thought to be dependent on sulphydryl groups for their activity. Enzymes contain several reactive sites including amino groups (–NH_2), imino groups (=NH), hydroxy groups (–OH) and sulphydryl groups (–SH), with which fungicides may react and so inactivate the enzyme. Fungicide molecules which closely resemble those of the normal substrate of the fungus may be incorporated into the latter, thus causing toxic effects.

The fungitoxicity of captan is usually attributed to the –$SCCl_3$ group in its molecule and the biological activity of this group has been investigated by several workers including Hochstein and Cox (1956), Lukens and Sisler (1958) and Owens and Blaak (1960). Lukens and Sisler (1958) consider that the activity of the –$SCCl_3$ group is due to the release of thiophosgene which can then react with free –SH, –NH_2 and possibly –COOH groups in the fungal cells. According to Owens and Blaak (1960), however, captan inhibits many oxidative enzymes and its fungitoxicity may be based on the interaction between the intact captan molecule and free sulphydryl groups. Certain fungicides including ziram, maneb and 8-quinolinol are thought to inhibit the enzyme aconitase, thereby inhibiting the metabolism but not the synthesis of citrate in the Krebs cycle. Others, including thiram, elemental sulphur and ferbam apparently inhibit the synthesis of citrate from acetate, probably by oxidizing coenzyme A, a sulphydryl-containing coenzyme (Owens, 1963). Some fungicides, many of them halogenated compounds, act as alkylating agents as described by the latter author (1963).

Fungicides may also overstimulate certain enzymes of the fungus and so disrupt the normal metabolic processes. Thus, the activity of DPN oxidase from *Monilinia laxa* was greatly stimulated by copper (Byrde et al., 1956). Fungi themselves may act on the fungicide, decreasing or increasing its fungitoxicity – *M. laxa, Botrytis fabae* and *Cladosporium fulvum* are reported to produce esterases which hydrolyse the relatively inactive 2,3-dichloro-1,4-naphthohydroquinone diacetate into its corresponding naphthohydroquinone derivative which is fungitoxic (Byrde and Woodcock, 1953). Further oxidation by a phenol oxidase perhaps results in the formation of the corresponding naphthoquinone as suggested by Horsfall (1956).

Chelation and precipitation

Chelating compounds form stable organic complexes with metals, the latter being held so securely that they are released or exchanged only with difficulty. They include various organic acids, amino acids, enzymes, vitamins and other substances. Chelation as a mechanism of toxicity seems to be established for some fungicides, and many chelating agents have fungitoxic properties but as Horsfall (1956) points out there are objections to the chelation hypothesis. Thus, although the application of metals in appropriate amounts may overcome the fungitoxicity of a chelator this does not always happen. Furthermore, some metal chelates are themselves fungitoxic, as for example, the copper chelate of oxine (8-hydroxyquinoline) which is more toxic than either the metal or the chelator alone. It is possible that this effect in part arises from improved penetration since copper oxinate is more lipoid soluble and therefore probably enters the fungal spore more easily than oxine alone.

Some fungicides, notably those containing sulphur, may precipitate essential metals as insoluble sulphides thus rendering them unavailable to the fungus. Horsfall (1956) suggests that hydrogen sulphide inhibits sporulation of *Pseudoperonospora humuli* by precipitating the metal needed for sporulation.

Antimetabolism

Many highly specific toxicants are antimetabolites, that is they are closely related in structure or chemical reactivity to normal metabolites and interfere with the utilization of such metabolites by taking their place in metabolic processes. These analogues sufficiently resemble normal metabolites to substitute for them but are sufficiently dissimilar to disrupt the metabolic process in which they function. They have been investigated chiefly in medicine but their potentialities as fungicides are now being explored – a useful list is given by Horsfall (1956). The antimetabolite may interfere with a single reaction, or a few reactions, which may in turn have secondary effects on other reactions so that there is a multiple effect. This is likely to be the case when interference takes place in an early stage of a metabolic process but less likely if it occurs at an advanced stage. The harmful effect of an antimetabolite may sometimes be reversed by supplying the appropriate metabolite, as in the well known case of sulphanilamide (p-aminobenzene sulphonamide) replacing p-aminobenzoic acid. Other antimetabolites include pyrithiamine as a competitive inhibitor of the vitamin thiamine, adenosine for cytidine and arginine for lysine.

Antimetabolic action has been suggested for certain fungicides although they perhaps function also in less specific ways. Vitamin K is reported to reverse the fungitoxicity of dichlone, which it resembles, over a limited range of concentration, although it is likely that other mechanisms also play a part (Woolley, 1952). It is possible that antimetabolism is involved in the fungitoxicity of glyodin, captan and sulphur and according to Sisler and Cox (1960) it may be more frequent than at present supposed. Antimetabolites are discussed by Woolley (1952).

Other mechanisms of fungitoxicity

Several other mechanisms have been suggested and yet others doubtless await discovery. Compounds which produce high osmotic pressure tend to prevent growth of microorganisms but are not likely to be of much practical use in disease control. Proteins may be hydrolysed by acids or bases, and other direct interactions between fungicide molecules and vital constituents of cells may lead to toxic reactions which may be irreversible (fungicidal action), or reversible (fungistasis) in which the fungus is inhibited only as long as the fungitoxic substance is present in sufficient concentration. Some fungicides interfere with the synthesis of protein and nucleic acid. Thus, *Botrytis cinerea* which had been treated with DCNA (dichloronitroaniline) showed distortion and bursting of germ tubes and increased amounts of nucleic acid in the mycelium (Sharples, 1962). This fungicide is thought to inhibit protein synthesis and in this respect resembles some antifungal antibiotics (for example cycloheximide), as discussed by Sisler (1969) in his review of the effects of fungicides on protein and nucleic acid synthesis. The effectiveness of Chloroneb (1,4-dichloro-2, 5-dimethoxybenzene) against *Corticium solani* and *C. rolfsii* is ascribed by Hock and Sisler (1969) to direct or indirect inhibition of DNA synthesis at the nucleotide polymerization stage. Much information on these and other aspects of fungicides will be found in the *Contributions from Boyce Thompson Institute for Plant Research*.

Acquired resistance to fungicides

The acquisition of resistance to certain insecticides by insects, to antibiotics by some bacteria and to warfarin by rats is well known, and suggests that fungicide resistant strains of fungi are likely to arise. In the
laboratory it is possible to train some fungi to tolerate increasing concentrations of some fungicides. Examples of this include *Botrytis cinerea*
resistant to copper sulphate, captan, phenylmercuric acetate and ferbam,
but not to mercuric chloride, thiram, ziram or zineb. Attempts to obtain
strains of *Venturia inaequalis* resistant to captan, thiram, ferbam, ziram and
zineb were unsuccessful (Parry and Wood, 1958, 1959) but strains of this
fungus resistant to copper sulphate have been reported by Dunin (1960).
Penicillium notatum, *Sclerotinia fructicola* and *Stemphylium sarcinaeforme* developed resistance to copper sulphate, mercuric chloride, captan and glyodin, but not to phenylmercuric acetate.

The differences in resistance are sometimes very marked. After nine
transfers in 9 months a strain of *Botrytis cinerea* able to grow slowly in a
concentration (12 p.p.m.) of phenylmercuric acetate (PMA) thirty-
two times that (0·375 p.p.m.) tolerated by the original strain was obtained
by Parry and Wood (1958), and there are naturally occurring strains of
Pyrenophora avenae able to tolerate 20 p.p.m. of PMA (Greenaway and
Cowan, 1970). Even greater differences have been reported by Weber
and Ogawa (1965) who found that a sensitive strain of *Rhizopus arrhizus*
was inhibited by 2 p.p.m. of DCNA (2,6-dichloro-4-nitroaniline) whereas
a resistant one withstood 1000 p.p.m.

In his review of the adaptation of fungi to metal toxicants Ashida (1965)
points out that long training periods are apparently needed by fungi to
develop resistance to toxic metallic salts. Yeasts develop resistance against
salts of copper, nickel, manganese, mercury, silver, arsenic, chromium
and other metals, and its seems reasonable to suppose that the fungi and
bacteria which attack plants will also be found to develop resistance – as
noted above, strains of *Botrytis cinerea* resistant to copper and mercury are
known.

Some fungicide resistant strains are reported to lose their resistance
when grown in a fungicide-free medium, as with the increased resistance
of *Sclerotinia fructicola* and *S. laxa* to cycloheximide, dodine and folpet
which was lost after two–five transfers to a fungicide-free medium (Grover
and Moore, 1961). Strains of *Pyrenophora avenae* trained to resist phenylmercuric acetate rapidly lost their resistance when grown on a mercury-
free medium, whereas naturally occurring resistant strains were stable,
and it is probable that the two types of resistance have a different genetic
basis (Greenaway and Cowan, 1970). Strains of *Botrytis cinerea* which had
been trained to tolerate copper sulphate or phenylmercuric acetate were

still resistant after six transfers on fungicide-free media at monthly inter-vals (Parry and Wood, 1958) and were, presumably, genetically stable mutants.

Origin of fungicide resistant strains

How fungicide resistant strains of fungi arise is obscure and little work on the genetics of such strains seems to have been reported. Re-sistance which disappears in the absence of the fungicide could be due to sublethal concentrations of the latter bringing about the formation of a substance or substances which confer resistance, this substance not being formed in the absence of fungicide. Adaptive enzymes whose formation is induced by the fungicide are perhaps involved.

Stable resistant strains presumably arise by some form of mutation which occurs either by chance or – in the case of certain fungicides – is possibly brought about by the fungicide itself. It is perhaps significant that exposure of *Fusarium caeruleum* (potato dry rot) to tetrachloronitrobenzene (TCNB) resulted in the appearance of TCNB resistant mutants (McKee, 1951) and that resistant variants of *Botrytis allii* (onion neck rot) were produced after treatment of the fungus with the vapour of pentachloro-nitrobenzene (Priest and Wood, 1961). Some aromatic hydrocarbons are said to induce gene mutation in fungi, but Harding (1959) who attributed to mutation the resistant strains of *Penicillium italicum* (citrus blue mould) and *P. digitatum* (green mould) which appeared after biphenyl treatment, was not able to distinguish between induced and spontaneous mutation. The fungicide resistance of some fungi, including a few which attack plants, has been shown by genetical analysis to be of chromosomal origin – as in *Hypomyces solani f.sp cucurbitae* (seedling blight and fruit rot of cucurbits) where resistance to TCNB is determined by three independently inherited genes (Georgopoulos, 1962, 1963) – but there is little critical evidence as to whether fungicides can induce fungi mutations in which bring about resistance to fungicides.

Mechanisms of resistance to fungicides

Possible physiological changes in fungi which could result in resistance to fungicides include: (1) the development or increased use by the fungus of an alternative metabolic pathway which bypasses the reaction inhibited by the fungicide; (2) decreased requirement by the fungus of the substance or substances whose formation is disrupted by the fungicide; (3) increased production by the fungus of the metabolites or enzymes which the fungi-

s

cide inhibits; (4) development by the fungus of modified enzymes less vulnerable to the fungicide or better able to compete with the latter for the substrate; (5) production or increased production by the fungus of substances which destroy or otherwise inactivate the fungicide, for example chelators which bind the fungicide and so reduce its toxicity; and (6) reduced permeability of the fungal hyphae or spores to the fungicide.

There is little information on these aspects in fungal plant pathogens except for resistance mechanisms based on reduced permeability, detoxification, and chelation. Kikuchi (1964), cited by Ashida (1965), reported that the mycelium of a copper resistant strain of yeast contained less copper than a copper sensitive strain after both had been cultured in the presence of copper, suggesting that copper entered the resistant strain less easily. Fungicide resistance due to reduced permeability does not seem to have been demonstrated convincingly in fungi which attack plants, most of the results which purport to do so being susceptible to other interpretations as discussed by Ashida (1965) and Georgopoulos and Zaracovitis (1967).

More convincing evidence for fungicide detoxification or chelation is available. Some microorganisms, particularly those in soil, can detoxify fungicides including mercurials (Ashworth and Amin, 1964; Spanis *et al.*, 1962). *Fusarium oxysporum* converts the timber preservative 2,4-dinitrophenol (DNP) into less fungitoxic amino-nitrophenols in culture (Madhosingh, 1961) and pentachlorophenol is detoxified by the enzyme laccase produced by certain wood rotting Basidiomycetes including *Polystictus versicolor* (Lyr, 1963). Rich and Horsfall (1954) have produced evidence for the detoxification of several phenols and quinones by *Stemphylium sarcinaeforme* and *Monilinia fructicola*. *Fusarium oxysporum f.sp. lycopersici* and *f.sp. niveum*, which are rather insensitive to pentachloronitrobenzene (PCNB), converted the fungicide into less fungitoxic substances which were gradually excreted into the medium; *Corticium solani*, on the other hand, accumulated much larger quantities of PCNB and was sensitive to it (Nakanishi and Oku, 1969).

The detoxifications briefly discussed in the preceding paragraph are no doubt brought about largely by enzymes. Toxicants can also be inactivated by fungal metabolites as reviewed by Gottlieb (1957) who distinguishes six types of inactivation, namely chemical combination between toxicant and metabolite, complex formation and chelation of toxicant by metabolite, competitive antagonism between a nutrilite and its analogue, pH effects on ionization of the toxicant, and enzyme action. Of these, chemical combination and the formation of complexes and chelates are particularly relevant when considering the mechanisms of fungicide resistance. Thus, Adam and Powell (1957) found that many metabolic agents, and particularly amino acids, antidoted the toxicity of copper sulphate to *Monilinia fructicola* and *Stemphylium sarcinaeforme*. Spores of these fungi did not germinate in distilled water after exposure to 16 p.p.m. of copper sulphate for 15 and 50 minutes respectively followed by washing, whereas similarly treated spores germinated normally when transferred to water containing 500 p.p.m. of *L*-serine. This treatment was ineffective if the spores were exposed to copper sulphate for 2 or 3 hours respectively, and it was postulated that the detoxification process occurred inside the spore wall.

Fungicides that normally react with sulphydryl (–SH) groups in fungal enzymes can react with similar groups present in some amino acids (cysteine, glutathione) to form less toxic or non-toxic derivatives, and if these amino acids are produced in excessive amounts by the fungus they should confer fungicide resistance on it. Detoxification of this type involves the use of essential metabolites of the fungus and, if prolonged, this might be fatal to it. Perhaps the fact that rather large amounts of fungicides are needed to kill fungal cells is in some way associated with this preliminary defence of the cells by essential metabolites which are, however, limited as to the quantity of fungicide which they are able to detoxify. On this view, fungicide resistant strains are those able to produce the detoxifying metabolite in greater than normal quantities.

It is possible that some fungi have an intracellular 'pool' of non-protein sulphydryl groups which is available for detoxification of fungicides, and Ashworth and Amin (1964) attributed the effectiveness of organo-mercury fungicides against *Corticium solani* and *Pythium ultimum* (seed rot and damping-off) to the absence or inadequacy of such a pool. The ineffectiveness of these fungicides against *Aspergillus niger* (seedling blight of groundnut) was ascribed to this fungus having sufficient non-protein sulphydryl groups to protect its sensitive enzyme systems by forming complexes with the mercury entering the hyphae.

Fungicides that contain sulphydryl groups can be expected to react with fungal metabolites including amino acids, an example of which is the conversion of sodium dimethyldithiocarbamate (NaDDC) to a less toxic aminobutyric acid derivative by various fungi including *Glomerella cingulata*, *Aspergillus niger* and *Cladosporium cucumerinum* (Sijpesteijn *et al.*, 1962, cited by Woodcock, 1967, in his review of microbiological detoxification).

Chelation of metals by amino acids and other substances appears to be involved in some detoxification processes. Several examples of this have been described. For example the toxicity of 8-quinolinol to the spores and mycelium of *Aspergillus niger* and to the mycelium of *Botryosphaeria ribis* (currant die-back) was reversed by casein hydrolysate, *L*-histidine, and especially by *L*-cysteine but not by *L*-methionine, *L*-glycine or *L*-cystine. *L*-cysteine also reversed the toxicity of copper-8-quinolinolate to *A. niger* and *B. ribis*, removing the copper to form a copper-amino acid chelate and free 8-quinolinol. These chelators apparently reverse the fungitoxicity of 8-quinolinol and copper-8-quinolinolate by keeping the copper in the system away from 8-quinolinol or by taking the copper away from the already formed copper-8-quinolinolate (Zentmyer and Rich, 1956).

A correlation between resistance to phenyl mercuric acetate (PMA) and production of red pigments has been reported by Greenaway and Cowan (1970) and Greenaway (1971) in *Pyrenophora avenae* (leaf spot of oats). The pigments (at least two were produced by some isolates of the fungus) are 1,4,5,8-tetrahydroxyanthraquinones which accumulate in mineral oil under which colonies are grown. The pigments in oil solution removed phenyl-Hg^+ ions from aqueous PMA solutions and it seems likely that the binding of these ions by the pigments is the basis of the resistance of *P. avenae* to PMA. It is suggested that the sulphydryl (SH) groups of proteins are protected from PMA by the formation of stable, non-fungitoxic complexes between phenyl-Hg^+ ions and anthraquinone molecules. The close correlation between degree of pigment production and resistance to PMA observed in 124 isolates of *P. avenae* would seem to support this conclusion.

Some wood destroying fungi including *Polyporus vaporarius*, *Merulius lacrymans* (the destructive dry rot fungus), *Fomes annosus* and *Polystictus versicolor* are able to grow on wood treated with a copper fungicide. Rabanus (1939) found that these fungi produced sufficient quantities of oxalic acid to convert the copper carbonate formed on copper sulphate treated telegraph poles into insoluble copper oxalate which was not fungitoxic.

Despite considerable investigation, rather little is known about how fungi develop resistance against the chlorinated nitrobenzene fungicides such as pentachloronitrobenzene (PCNB). These seem to be highly selective fungicides in that they are very effective against some fungi but ineffective, even at high concentration, against others. Resistant strains of some fungi appear as sectors in colonies exposed to these fungicides, and vegetative growth appears to be virtually unaffected by high concentrations of the fungicides although sporulation is often reduced. These strains retain their resistance for long periods of growth in the absence of the fungicide, suggesting that resistance is here genetically stable. Resistance of fungi to the chlorinated nitrobenzenes – and to other organic fungicides – is discussed by Georgopoulos and Zaracovitis (1967).

Doubtless there are other ways in which fungicides are detoxified, and Sijpesteijn and Kaslander (1964) have pointed out that the metabolism of fungicides by plants and microorganisms is only one aspect of the wider problem of the disposal of foreign compounds introduced into plants. These aspects are considered by Sijpesteijn and Kerk (1965), Woodcock

(1964: the microbial degradation of synthetic compounds including fungicides), and Woodcock (1967).

Significance of fungicide resistance

The appearance of biphenyl resistant strains of *Penicillium* spp. and of other fruit-rotting fungi in the U.S.A. and elsewhere has complicated the problem of preventing postharvest losses to citrus fruits. Such strains often develop in packing houses where large populations of fruit-rotting fungi are exposed to fungicides and this inevitably leads to the replacement of fungicide susceptible strains by resistant ones and to serious decay of the fruit during shipment and storage. This is a problem which is likely to intensify with increasing world trade in fruit and vegetables.

The development of fungicide resistance by fungi which cause decay in wood is also becoming a problem, and several wood rotting fungi have developed resistance to fungicides used as wood preservatives. Zinc chloride and copper sulphate, both at 400 p.p.m., significantly increased the rate of decay of Norway Pines caused by *Lentinus lepideus* (Kaufert and Schmitz, 1937) and, as mentioned above, several wood rotting fungi were able to inactivate the copper sulphate used to treat telegraph poles (Rabanus, 1939). *Cladosporium resinae*, the 'kerosene fungus' not only tolerates but metabolizes creosote, a mixture of numerous highly fungi-toxic substances (Christensen *et al.*, 1942; Marsden, 1954). It also grows in kerosene-type aviation fuels and possibly causes corrosion of aluminium as described by Hendey (1964). Apart from these cases, in which fungicide resistant strains of fungi cause considerable damage, the problem of fungicide resistance is not yet acute although it is likely to increase in importance in the future as more highly selective fungicides come into extensive use. Fungicide resistance has been investigated in the laboratory but there is as yet little information as to its significance in the field.

There have been reports of resistant strains of fungi developing in orchards which have been repeatedly sprayed with Bordeaux mixture. The spores of *Physalospora obtusa* (black rot and leaf spot of apple) from apple orchards which had been sprayed with this fungicide for 8 years were found by Taylor (1953) to be more resistant to copper than were the spores from unsprayed orchards. In New York State, dodine (*n*-dodecylguanidine acetate) sprays have given good control of *Venturia inaequalis* (apple scab) for 5–7 years but control became less satisfactory from 1967 onwards. This has been attributed to the appearance of dodine resistant strains of the fungus, and conidia from orchards where control had failed germinated in higher concentrations of dodine than did those from other sources (Szkolnik and Gilpatrick, 1970).

Strains of fungi resistant to thiram, organo-mercurials, copper sulphate, and other fungicides have been reported in the field and in some areas there is a general opinion that potato blight is now less easily controlled by fungicides than hitherto. Reduced effectiveness of hexachlorobenzene against seed borne *Tilletia foetida* (Kuiper, 1965) and of organo-mercurial seed dressings against *Pyrenophora avenae* (Noble *et al.*, 1966; Old, 1968) has been attributed to the development of resistance to these fungicides in the field, and Greenaway and Cowan (1970) have isolated from oat seed strains of *P. avenae* resistant to phenyl mercuric acetate. Chlorinated nitro-benzenes occasionally fail to control *Botrytis cinerea* on lettuce (Way and Keyworth, 1959) and this might be due to resistant strains of the fungus (Priest and Wood, 1961). Isolates of *Sclerotium cepivorum* (onion white rot) from fields treated for a year or more with dichloronitroaniline (DCNA) showed greater resistance to the fungicide in laboratory tests than did isolates from untreated fields, and there was evidence that DCNA was becoming ineffective for control of the disease in the field (Locke, 1969). The increasingly numerous reports of failure of hitherto effective fungi-cides to control diseases are disturbing, and there is little doubt that many such failures are due to the development of fungicide resistant strains of the pathogens involved.

There is little information as to the capacity of fungicide resistant strains of fungi to survive in competition with susceptible strains under natural conditions. Under laboratory conditions Parry and Wood (1959) found that only about 2% of the conidia of a captan resistant strain of *Botrytis cinerea* germinated in 1% sucrose as compared with high germination in the susceptible strain. It was tentatively suggested that captan resistance might be due to reduced permeability of the conidia which also reduced the entry of essential metabolites and so adversely affected germination.

Within limits in the laboratory, resistant strains of fungi generally grow more rapidly in the presence of the fungicide than in its absence, and more slowly than susceptible strains in fungicide-free media. Adaptation to a fungicide would seem to involve changes in the fungus which make it less able to compete with unadapted strains in the absence of fungicide. If this is true, resistant strains can be expected to predominate when fungi-cides are used more or less continuously and to decline in a fungicide-free environment.

Rather few studies seem to have been reported on the pathogenicity of fungicide resistant strains of plant pathogenic fungi. Some workers have reported reduced pathogenicity in such strains, as with three biphenyl resistant strains of *Diplodia natalensis* which attacks oranges (Littauer and Gutter, 1953). Others have found either no differences in pathogenicity between resistant and susceptible strains (as shown by Priest and Wood, 1961, working with *Botrytis allii* and chlorinated nitrobenzenes) or a wide variation in pathogenicity with some resistant strains as pathogenic as non-resistant ones (as found by Georgopoulos, 1963, with chloronitrobenzene resistant strains of *Hypomyces solani f.sp. cucurbitae* on squash seedlings and fruit). The hexachlorobenzene resistant strain of *Tilletia foetida* (Kuiper, 1965) and the mercury resistant strains of *Pyrenophora avenae* (Greenaway and Cowan, 1970) are pathogenic to wheat and oats, respectively, but how they compare in this respect with susceptible strains is not known. One of the few reports of increased pathogenicity in fungicide resistant strains is that of *Corticium solani* on cotton seedlings (Shatla and Sinclair, 1963) in which pathogenicity was to some extent correlated with resistance to pentachloronitrobenzene (PCNB). Maier (1962) was, however, unable to establish such a correlation.

Several possible reasons for the apparently slow development of fungicide resistant strains of fungi in the field have been suggested. It may be that resistant strains of some fungi are less pathogenic or in some other way less fitted to survive than susceptible strains. Resistant strains perhaps arise rather infrequently in the field, possibly because many fungicides appear to be somewhat non-specific in their mode of action in that they probably affect several vital processes of the fungus rather than a single one; hence the appearance of resistant strains is likely to be rather infrequent. Apparent exceptions to this generalization are the strains of fruit rotting fungi resistant to aromatic hydrocarbons, such as biphenyl, which frequently arise in fruit packing stations, and it may be that these fungicides are more specific in their action than many other fungicides.

As more highly specific fungicides, including systemic ones, come into general use so can fungicide resistant strains of fungal plant pathogens be expected to increase and become a major problem in agriculture and horticulture. One way of reducing this potential danger is by using mixtures of fungicides or by using different effective fungicides in successive years, thus, one hopes, avoiding the build up of resistant strains. To do this it is necessary to know the extent to which strains resistant to one fungicide are resistant or susceptible to others. In a general way it can be expected that strains resistant to one fungicide will be resistant to chemically related fungicides, as shown by Priest and Wood (1961) for *Botrytis cinerea* in respect of pentachloronitrobenzene and tetrachloronitrobenzene, but more investigation of 'cross-resistance' to fungicides is clearly needed.

28 Disease control by plant breeding and selection

If plant pathogens were stable entities their control by cultivating varieties of crop plants resistant or, better, immune to them would in many ways be the ideal solution providing such varieties were agronomically and commercially suitable. Unfortunately, many plant pathogens are genetically variable and produce new races with different parasitic capabilities, to which resistant varieties of plants are in time likely to succumb. This is well exemplified in the breeding of varieties of wheat resistant to *Puccinia graminis f.sp. tritici* (black stem rust) in which several hundred races of the fungus have been identified, necessitating a permanent programme of plant breeding to keep ahead of new races of the pathogen as they arise, as described by Stakman and Harrar (1957). The ways in which new races are produced are considered elsewhere (p. 286).

Many plant pathogens comprise races which differ in their cultural characteristics, that is in their characteristics when grown on culture media in the laboratory, and in other respects including pathogenicity. This is well known in such variable pathogens as *Corticium solani*, *Cochliobolus sativus*, *Fusarium oxysporum*, and others. Individual races of a pathogen may differ in their pathogenicity to one variety of the host plant, some causing severe injury and others causing only minor injury. Others show qualitative rather than quantitative differences in pathogenicity, different races attacking a different spectrum of host varieties. The gene-for-gene hypothesis (p. 299) suggests that for each gene in the host capable of mutating to give resistance there exists a gene in the pathogen capable of mutating to overcome that particular resistance, so that any new resistant variety which arises will probably succumb in due course to a new race of the pathogen. How long this can be expected to take will depend on the genetical variability in respect of pathogenicity of the pathogen, and a knowledge of this is clearly essential for rational breeding of resistant varieties. The useful life of new varieties can be very short – about 5 years for oat varieties in the central corn belt of the U.S.A. (Stevens and Scott, 1950).

The likelihood of new races of pathogens arising is one of the great difficulties encountered in controlling disease by resistant varieties, and there are others: (1) There may be considerable sterility in breeding between different species, yet interspecific crosses may be necessary to obtain an adequate level of resistance. (2) Resistance may be closely linked with undesirable characteristics such as susceptibility to other pathogens and pests, inferior quality of the produce for which the crop is grown, lower yielding capacity, and so on. Such linkage can sometimes be broken by prolonged breeding with large populations but this is likely to be expensive. (3) Resistance may be affected by environmental conditions; for example, some varieties of wheat which are resistant to certain races of *Puccinia graminis tritici* at normal temperatures become more susceptible at higher temperatures. (4) There may be no suitable source of resistance among natural plants. In such cases irradiation or some other mutagenic procedure can be applied in an effort to produce mutants, some of which may be resistant.

Despite these very real difficulties, disease resistant varieties of many crop plants have been produced, some of which have proved very successful and have more than repaid the expense of their development. They are of particular value for pathogens which cannot be controlled economically or effectively in other ways, as with root diseases, but they are widely used to control other diseases and, where suitable resistant varieties can be produced, they often offer the best prospect of control. Pathogens which have been successfully combated by resistant varieties include *Synchytrium endobioticum* (potato wart) – but new races of this pathogen have arisen and could be dangerous, as described by (Moore 1957a) – the vascular wilt diseases of cabbage (cabbage yellows) and tomato caused by forms of *Fusarium oxysporum*, and several virus diseases (curly top of beet, bean mosaic, sugarcane mosaic). The growing of resistant varieties is also likely to enhance the effectiveness of other control measures which may be necessary because pathogens develop less rapidly, produce fewer spores and spread more slowly in resistant as compared with susceptible plants, and even moderate resistance can be useful in this respect. The genetical determination of resistance in the plant and virulence in the pathogen is discussed elsewhere although it may be noted here that resistance is frequently dominant to susceptibility and avirulence to virulence.

Immunity and resistance

Crop varieties which are immune to pathogens are clearly the most satisfactory as they do not become infected, so that the pathogen will tend to die out unless it has other hosts on which it survives. In such cases new races of pathogens are not likely to arise but, unfortunately, immune varieties which are also satisfactory in other respects are rarely achieved. There is some confusion in the use of the word immune. It has been defined as 'exempt from infection' (Anon., 1950) but it has also been applied to plants which do not become infected in the field although they may be susceptible when inoculated in the laboratory or greenhouse; this has been described as 'field-immunity'. Plants which are hypersensitive to a pathogen, developing only minute necrotic spots or flecks in which development of the pathogen is inhibited, have also been referred to as immune.

More often the grower has to make do with resistant varieties of plants, the degree of resistance varying considerably. Highly resistant varieties which greatly curtail the multiplication and spread of the pathogen can be satisfactory but resistance, as distinct from immunity, is not an absolute unvarying quality and may be overcome by exposure to massive inoculum under conditions highly favourable to the pathogen. The variability of resistance has been studied in several diseases and such environmental factors as light, moisture, nutrition and (especially) temperature have been shown to alter not only the degree of resistance but also the type of symptoms which develop. The Marquis variety of wheat which is resistant to race 139 of *Puccinia graminis tritici* below about 24°C becomes susceptible at about 30°C (Stakman and Harrar, 1957). With other cereal rusts the reverse may occur, varieties becoming more resistant at higher temperatures.

Vertical and horizontal resistance

Vertical (specific) resistance is effective, usually highly effective, against some races of a pathogen and ineffective against others. Horizontal (generalized, non-specific) resistance operates against all races but usually provides less effective protection. Vertically resistant varieties of plants are likely to succumb when exposed to new races but meantime give greater protection than horizontally resistant varieties which, however, retain their resistance.

In the past, plant breeders have tended to favour vertical resistance as it is often inherited in a fairly simple way (it is often monogenic or oligogenic) and is convenient to work with. The high degree of resistance which it usually confers enables resistant and susceptible plants to be distinguished easily and quickly, thus facilitating the detection and rejection of susceptible plants. Unfortunately, vertically resistant varieties often, but not invariably (see below), succumb to new races of the pathogen when grown on a field scale, so that a more or less permanent and expensive programme of plant breeding becomes necessary to produce varieties resistant to the new races. It is thought that producing vertically resistant varieties reduces their horizontal resistance because the varieties are largely protected from the full pressure of selection from the pathogen. This is the 'Vertifolia' effect (Van der Plank, 1963), so called from Vertifolia, a potato variety selected for its vertical resistance to *Phytophthora infestans* which was subsequently attacked by another race of the fungus and was then found to have only slight horizontal resistance. Breeding for vertical resistance may thus bring about the loss of valuable horizontal resistance, and the present unpopularity of vertical resistance in potato blight control may be associated with this accompanying loss of horizontal resistance.

Despite these disadvantages vertical resistance can sometimes be profitably used. Since it implies resistance to some pathogen races but not to others, more than one genotype of the host plant must clearly be involved; the fact that variety A is vertically resistant indicates that it is being exposed to inoculum from plants of a variety lacking the resistance genes possessed by variety A. There is thus a host–host–pathogen interaction rather than a simple host–pathogen interaction (Van der Plank, 1968). This can be of some practical importance where one variety is exposed to inoculum from a different variety as, for example, when winter varieties of a crop provide the inoculum for spring varieties. This inoculum will be largely ineffective if the spring variety is protected by vertical resistance genes which are effective against most of the races present in the inoculum.

As an example of this Van der Plank (1968) considers the wheat stem rust (*Puccinia graminis f.sp. tritici*) situation in North America. For many years the red spring wheats (largely the variety Selkirk and its derivatives) grown in the northern U.S.A. and Canada have been fairly adequately protected by the resistance gene *Sr6*. This gene protects against most of the races present in the rust inoculum to which the red spring wheats are exposed. The inoculum is chiefly in the form of uredospores produced by infected winter wheat varieties in the south (Mexico, Texas) and most of these winter varieties lack the resistance gene. In the late summer rust uredospores return from the north to the south where the fungus overwinters in the local varieties along with the local races of the rust. Thus the races able to attack spring wheat spend about 2–3 months on spring varieties in the north and 9–10 months on winter varieties lacking the *Sr6* gene in the south. During this long overwintering period it is thought that the races able to attack spring wheats decline. This decline has been ascribed to stabilizing selection (stabilizing pressure) in favour of races which have no unnecessary virulence beyond that required to attack wheat varieties lacking the *Sr6* gene.

That complex races (those with several virulence genes) of a pathogen are not necessarily the best fitted to survive is suggested by evidence that unnecessary virulence can be disadvantageous to obligate and near-obligate parasites which are heavily dependent on their host plants. Thus, in

Mexico, the commonest races of *Phytophthora infestans* on the Criolla varieties of potato – varieties of *Solanum tuberosum* proper without added resistance genes – were found to be those with no unnecessary virulence. The reasons for this are obscure. One suggestion is that vertical resistance genes in some way cause the pathogen to substitute metabolic pathways that are inferior to the normal ones – for example the metabolic changes which enable the pathogen to avoid bringing about hypersensitivity in the infected tissue might handicap it in some way (Van der Plank, 1968).

Whatever the explanation it seems that there is in some cases, some form of stabilizing selection which favours those races of obligate and near-obligate parasites which lack unnecessary virulence. It is possible that the saprophytic phase (in soil or crop residues) of non-obligate parasites exerts a similar stabilizing selection. Many of the non-obligate parasites which attack plants have a fairly extensive non-parasitic phase (the saprophytic medium – host – pathogen interaction of Van der Plank, 1968) in their life cycle which in some way appears to stabilize the races of the pathogen. It is often held that the more specialized a parasite becomes, the less efficient it is likely to be as a saprophyte. If this is true, specialized races of a non-obligate parasite are likely to have reduced saprophytic ability and so to be at a disadvantage when competing with less specialized races during the non-parasitic phase – especially if the latter is prolonged, as with pathogens which attack plants grown as annuals. Thus the resistance of tomato varieties containing a single strong gene for resistance against *Fusarium oxysporum f.sp. lycopersici* (wilt) is apparently effective wherever tomatoes are grown. A race of the pathogen able to attack these varieties is known but has never become prevalent and may have been checked by stabilizing selection.

The foregoing is probably an over-simplified view of the competitive survival of races of pathogens. Apart from virulence genes many factors including, for example, the speed with which the pathogen colonizes the plant and produces propagules, and the ability of the inoculum to survive between successive susceptible crops, influence the fitness of races to persist. In some of the experiments described by Scheifele *et al.* (1968) a race of *Trichometasphaeria turcica* (northern leaf blight of maize) with more virulence genes predominated over one with fewer such genes and Nelson and Scheifele (1970) have subsequently reported that, not only did different races of the fungus have different overwintering ability, but they also showed differing overwintering ability on different host genotypes, suggesting that the nature of the saprophytic overwintering medium plays a part in stabilizing selection. In their experiments a complex race of *T. turcica* appeared to have greater survival ability than a simple race – an apparent exception to the generalization that unnecessary virulence is disadvantageous in the saprophytic phase of a non-obligate parasite.

Exceptions have also been reported for obligate parasites, as by Brown and Sharp (1970) who found that the isolate of *Puccinia striiformis* (yellow rust) having the widest host range and, presumably, the greater number of virulence genes had a greater survival ability on two susceptible wheat varieties than an isolate of narrower host range. In glasshouse experiments and regardless of its proportion in the original inoculum mixture, the race of *P. graminis tritici* with the widest host range became predominant over a race of narrower host range although the latter persisted at low frequency (Ogle and Brown, 1970).

This difference in relative survival ability has been related to differences between the two strains in the frequency of penetration from appressoria, in the rate of uredial growth, in the size of uredia, and in the number of uredospores per uredium (Ogle and Brown, 1971). Three additional exceptions are described by Watson (1970) from Australia, where one of the two most prevalent races of *P. recondita f.sp. tritici* (wheat leaf rust) has few unnecessary virulence genes whereas the other race has two virulence genes which appear to be superfluous. Similarly, races 21 and 34 are the most prevalent races of *P. graminis f.sp. tritici* and each has retained virulence genes which would not seem to be necessary for survival. Unnecessary virulence might also, presumably, be disadvantageous to rusts in their haploid phase. Genes for virulence to *Berberis* and *Thalictrum*, alternate hosts of *P. graminis* and *P. recondita* respectively, are not necessary in the Australia–New Zealand area but only in the case of race 43 of *P. graminis f.sp. tritici* is there any suggestion that an unnecessary gene for virulence has been lost (Watson, 1970). The latter author concludes that, if a gene for virulence has no deleterious effect and is associated with genes for aggressiveness and survival in a well adapted race of a pathogen, it may remain in the population regardless of whether it is necessary or not. More investigation of the relative ability of complex and simple races of a range of plant pathogens to survive under natural conditions is clearly called for.

Heagle and Moore (1970) compared the development of *Puccinia coronata* (crown rust) in moderately resistant and in susceptible varieties of oats and found that infected adult plants of resistant varieties showed fewer infections, retarded hyphal growth of the fungus, delayed production of uredospores and smaller uredia containing fewer spores. In 3 years of tests spread of the rust was much less in moderately resistant varieties than in susceptible ones, indicating that such horizontal resistance is likely to be useful in controlling the disease in the field. The relative yields of maize varieties with polygenic and with monogenic resistance to *Trichometasphaeria turcica* (northern leaf blight) were investigated by Ullstrup (1970). Varieties with polygenic resistance gave greater yield increases over susceptible varieties than did those with monogenic resistance, and showed similar but fewer lesions than did susceptible varieties. Varieties with monogenic resistance developed small necrotic lesions, each of which was surrounded by an extensive chlorotic halo; this, *in toto*, resulted in extensive chlorosis which may have had a debilitating effect on the plant thereby reducing its yield. In this and similar diseases, in which the reaction of vertically resistant plants to the pathogen is such that their growth and yield are adversely affected, it may well be preferable to grow horizontally resistant varieties.

It would seem logical to use vertical resistance for the control of diseases, or in situations in which experience has shown that vertically resistant varieties remain resistant, whatever the reasons, and notably for control of pathogens which produce new races only infrequently or in which such new races are pathogenically ineffective or unlikely to spread quickly.

As mentioned above, horizontal resistance operates against all races of a pathogen but does not generally confer the high degree of protection afforded by vertical resistance. It slows down the spread of the pathogen, frequently by reducing and delaying infection and sporulation. The amount of inoculum at the end of the season is thus reduced and this tends to minimize and delay the outbreak of the disease in the following season.

Before the advent of breeding plants against pathogens there was no doubt some selection of disease resistant or tolerant varieties in the field and such plants would tend to predominate over those severely damaged by disease. Much of the field resistance so selected was probably horizontal (polygenic) and in some cases afforded considerable protection, especially with cross-pollinated plants. Thus Stevens (1939, 1941) concluded that disease was generally less in cross-pollinated (outbred) plants than in self-pollinated (inbred) plants. This may be because the reassortment of genes which occurs in outbreeding brings together and allows the accumulation of resistance genes previously dispersed throughout the plant population: selection pressure would then favour the survival of the more resistant plants. Gene reassortment is less likely to occur in an inbreeding population, so that horizontal resistance has less chance to develop.

Horizontal resistance is often polygenic and difficult to manipulate in plant breeding. The only practicable methods of assessing the horizontal resistance of plant varieties to a pathogen would seem to be: (1) a comparison of the rate of spread of the pathogen in different varieties in the field, or (2) a comparative assessment of the ease with which the pathogen infects and sporulates on plants of different varieties in the greenhouse and laboratory. Further research may enable horizontal resistance to be correlated with some measurable characteristic of the plant, or more refined methods of genetical analysis might enable it to be given a quantitative genetical basis.

It is sometimes difficult to decide whether vertical or horizontal resistance is likely to give the best long term results in disease control. The uses of vertical resistance are discussed above. No hard and fast rules can be laid down but horizontal resistance would seem preferable for the control of very variable pathogens which can spread rapidly, so that any new races produced would be quickly disseminated. The production of new races by such pathogens is likely to cut short the effective life of vertically resistant varieties and in such cases horizontal resistance is likely to prove more useful in the long run.

After considerable preoccupation with vertical resistance plant breeders are now beginning to appreciate the advantages of horizontal resistance and indeed the logical approach would seem to lie in combining the two. Horizontal resistance, besides reinforcing vertical resistance, should also be used in conjunction with other control measures which may be applied. Thus smaller or fewer applications of a fungicide may give adequate disease control in plants of high horizontal resistance as compared with those of lower horizontal resistance. It is a sound general principle to grow plants with the maximum horizontal resistance provided that they are satisfactory in other respects.

Multilines and composite crosses

Multilines are mixtures of individual lines of a plant which are similar agronomically but different in their resistance genes. In the past emphasis has been placed on producing pure lines with uniform agronomic characteristics and of slight genetical variability. The incorporation of vertical resistance into such lines was probably accompanied by a diminution in their horizontal resistance leaving them susceptible to new races of the pathogen to which they were subsequently exposed. A mixture of lines is likely to contain several vertical resistance genes which, provided they are strong enough, reduce the rate of spread of the pathogen because, (1) many of the plants are resistant to one or more of the pathogen races present and so obstruct its spread, and (2) some at least of the pathogen races have unnecessary factors for virulence and, as discussed above, this may be disadvantageous to the pathogen. The resistance shown by multilines is thus similar to horizontal resistance in that, in both, the rate of spread of the pathogen is reduced. If vertical resistance genes are not sufficiently effective for use in multilines it may be possible to combine multiline vertical resistance with horizontal resistance. In Van der Plank's (1968) view multilines, since they act by obstructing the movement of propagules to susceptible tissue, are best suited for small plants, whereas diseases of large perennial plants are best dealt with by using horizontal resistance. In addition to improved disease control multilines are also said to outyield individual lines in the absence of disease (Jensen, 1965).

Composite crosses have been used to develop horizontal resistance in self-pollinated plants (inbreeders) in which gene reassortment is restricted. Several or many varieties containing a range of resistance genes are crossed and selection of promising varieties is carried out on the resulting composite mixture of lines. The use of multilines and composite crosses for disease control is in its early stages although it has been known for many years that crop mixtures buffer against disease loss. It is of interest that a wheat multiline is being used commercially for control of yellow rust (*Puccinia striiformis*) in Columbia as described by Borlaug (1965), and further extension of this promising method of disease control may be expected (see Browning and Frey, 1969).

One of the objections advanced against the use of multilines is that their extensive cultivation might enable individual pathogen races to increase in complexity. Johnson (1961), in his discussion on man-guided evolution in plant rusts, considers that the multiline variety is likely to bring into being simultaneously a considerable variety of pathogen races and thereby increase the diversity of the pathogen's pool of virulence genes. The variety containing all available resistance genes would become susceptible only to a race with a very wide range of pathogenicity, but the danger of encouraging the production of such a 'super' race is obvious. This danger is discounted as unlikely by Browning and Frey (1969) who consider that the extensive use of multiline cultivars would result in a highly heterogeneous pathogen population with biotypes collectively virulent to all components of the multiline, but that a super race would not develop. This view is based on the thesis that complex races with unnecessary virulence are less likely to survive than simple races, an assumption which may not be justified in all cases. These possibilities are discussed by Browning and Frey (1969) who point out that 'a multiline cultivar is a step toward the complete diversity of nature in which a super race has not arisen and predominated in a wild population' and conclude that only extensive cultivation of multilines is likely to provide the answer.

Tolerance and disease escape

Varieties of plants tolerant to pathogens, although susceptible to varying extents, appear to be only slightly damaged. Many wild plants are attacked by pathogens which cause extensive leaf spotting but such plants grow satisfactorily and set seed. Long association between plant and pathogen has led to development of mutual tolerance, plants severely injured by the pathogen being unable to compete with those less severely injured, so that the species as a whole has become tolerant. Tolerance may also arise from imperfect synchronization of pathogen and plant, as in diseases which appear late in the life of the plant. This verges on disease escape, discussed below. Vigorous plants may be able to replace diseased leaves or other organs and so produce a reasonable yield in spite of infection. Some of the minor leaf spot diseases perhaps fall into this category although precise knowledge of the injury they cause is usually lacking and they may be more serious than is generally thought.

Plants tolerant to viruses are often grown containing the virus although these suffer only slight injury. The widespread cultivation of tolerant plants carries with it dangers as they constitute reservoirs of infection for other plants which may not be tolerant, and new races may develop among the large populations of the pathogen involved. Although the presence of the pathogen, especially a virus, in the tolerant plant may to some extent protect against attack by more virulent strains there is also the possibility of a synergistic reaction developing, that is, one in which the two pathogens combined are very much more damaging than either alone. Tolerance is more likely to develop in natural populations of plants in which the less tolerant ones tend to disappear, than in cultivated plants which are artificially kept true to type for horticultural and agricultural purposes. The cultivation of pathogen-tolerant plants, although a potentially dangerous practice, is perhaps permissible if the pathogen has a narrow host range.

Plants escape infection if their susceptible phase happens to come at a time when the pathogen is absent, present in insufficient amount, or when environmental conditions are unfavourable to it. Such disease escape can sometimes be utilized. Early sown potatoes in south-west England, for example, rarely suffer severe blight attack because they are too early for the pathogen.

Methods of obtaining resistant varieties

Resistant varieties of plants can be obtained in several ways. The easiest is to import them from elsewhere but this is not always successful as varieties resistant in one area may be susceptible in others, due to different races of the pathogen or to different climatic conditions or different agricultural practices. The resistance of a variety may be adequate in one area but may prove inadequate in a second where conditions are more favourable to the pathogen and it is advisable to develop resistant varieties in the area where they are to be grown. In this respect a knowledge of the geographical distribution of the races of important plant pathogens is helpful, and the conditions which favour their development and spread need to be thoroughly investigated.

The methods used to produce resistant varieties include selection, hybridization, and induced mutations. Individual plants apparently resistant to certain pathogens can sometimes be found in crop areas and from them it may be possible to develop resistant varieties with satisfactory agronomic and commercial characteristics. Sometimes a single selection is sufficient but more often selection over a number of years is necessary before an acceptable resistant variety finally emerges. This can be a frustrating procedure since the progeny from field resistant plants may show a wide range of resistance, necessitating further selection.

Resistant plants which appear in the field may be unsatisfactory in other respects. They may be unduly susceptible to other pathogens or pests, they may yield poorly, or their produce may be of inferior quality. In such cases a complicated programme of plant breeding may be necessary to obtain satisfactory resistant varieties. This may involve crossing the resistant but otherwise undesirable plants with susceptible but commercially acceptable varieties in an effort to combine resistance and quality. In this a knowledge of the inheritance of resistance and of other desirable characteristics will clearly be very useful, involving cooperation between pathologists and breeders. If the desired characters are inherited independently it may be fairly simple to combine them. If, however, desirable and undesirable characters are linked it will probably be difficult to obtain satisfactory varieties, and large populations of plants may be necessary to achieve this. Various techniques, including back-crossing, are useful in adding genes for resistance to existing successful but susceptible varieties (see Hayes, Immer and Smith, 1955).

Plants with adequate resistance cannot always be found in the field, in which case other sources of resistance have to be used. Resistance genes may be present in wild relatives of crop plants and these have been utilized in breeding against some pathogens. Certain clones of *Solanum demissum*, for example, show considerable resistance to *Phytophthora infestans* and this Mexican weed has been widely used as a source of resistance genes in attempts to breed blight resistant potatoes. It is, of course, necessary to incorporate these genes into commercially satisfactory varieties of potato by appropriate plant breeding methods, and this may prove difficult and time consuming. Wild relatives of other important cultivated plants – sugarbeet, tomato, sugarcane, cotton and others – are likely to contain resistance genes effective against certain pathogens of these plants, and the search for such resistant wild plants is likely to intensify. When these have been found there still remains the problem of transferring the resistance genes to suitable crop varieties. A useful list of sources of resistance to pathogens attacking crop plants has been compiled by Stevenson and Jones (1953).

Genes for resistance to pathogens and pests are likely to be found in regions where the plant in question originated (primary gene centres) or has subsequently been grown (secondary and tertiary gene centres), in that it is in such places that long association between pathogens and plants has occurred with consequent elimination of susceptible plant genotypes through natural selection. Hence resistant material is generally searched for in what are thought to be the gene centres of cultivated plants. The origin and evolution of disease resistance in cultivated plants is discussed by Leppik (1970) who considers that the analysis of available phytogeographic data and the screening of introduced plants for their resistance to pathogens will provide information on the geographical distribution of resistance, which may well be useful in locating the gene centres of the host plants.

Another approach to the problem of finding suitable resistance genes is that of using chemical or physical mutagens to produce mutants, some of which may be resistant to pathogens. Irradiation and chemical mutagens have been used for this purpose although the chances of obtaining resistant mutants would appear to be slight unless very large numbers of plants are so treated. Such mutants may be unsuitable in other respects but might be useful in breeding programmes.

Testing of resistant varieties

Before being released for large scale cultivation, new resistant varieties must be adequately tested in respect of their disease resistance and other characteristics. Such tests should be carried out over several years and over the range of climatic and agricultural conditions which the plants are likely to encounter when grown commercially. Their susceptibility to other pathogens and pests, their inherent yielding capacity, the quality of their produce and other aspects should be assessed and recorded. This can be done in the glasshouse, in field plots, or over larger areas among the commercial crop. There should be sufficient inoculum to ensure that all the plants are exposed to infection, and conditions should be as favourable as possible to the pathogen in order to subject the test plants to rigorous testing. Wherever possible, it is advisable to expose the plants to a mixture of races of the pathogen, particularly to those races which are prevalent in the crop area.

Field trials have the advantage that conditions in them will be similar to those likely to occur in commercial cultivation. Glasshouse testing can be more precisely controlled so that the resistance of the plants under different conditions of temperature, light and humidity can be studied. Their resistance to different races of the pathogen can also be assessed but the final evaluation of resistant varieties must be under field conditions.

Trials in which susceptible and resistant varieties are mixed may give results different from those obtained in the field when the resistant variety is grown alone. In the former case inoculum is likely to be more abundant so that the test is a more severe one, but the latter is more significant in terms of the actual field performance of the resistant variety. In testing for resistance it should be remembered that the reaction of the seedling or young plant is not always a reliable index of that of the mature plant. Neither can it be assumed that because, for example, the leaves are resistant the stems or the fruits will also be resistant. This is well known in potato blight in which the susceptibility of tubers and of foliage can be very different.

The breeding and testing of resistant varieties of crop plants should be carried out on a world-wide basis so that maximum advantage can be taken of resistance genes from as wide an area as possible. This would enable living collections of wild relatives of crop plants to be maintained as a source of genes for resistance to pathogens and pests, and should prove of great value to plant breeders. When a satisfactory resistant variety has been produced it must be 'bulked up' to give sufficient seed for large scale planting. Growth in isolation, often in special propagation areas, may be necessary where cross-pollination is otherwise likely to occur, and annual replenishment of the sowing seed from such areas may be required to ensure uniformity of the variety.

Budding and grafting can sometimes be used to produce resistance. Thus, varieties of *Hevea* rubber resistant to the leaf pathogen *Dothidella ulei* can be budded on high yielding but susceptible rootstocks to produce trees in which high yielding is combined with resistant foliage. Such a tree consists of parts from three individuals – the roots of the rootstock, the trunk of the high yielding clone, and the leaves from the bud inserted into the clone.

With increasing understanding of the genetical basis of resistance to pathogens in plants, and of virulence in pathogens, disease control by the cultivation of resistant varieties will become much more widespread. This will be facilitated by improved breeding and testing techniques and by finding additional sources of resistance for incorporation into crop plants. Some diseases have been satisfactorily controlled in this way for many years but the great variability of plant pathogens should not be underestimated – for some pathogens a more or less continuous programme of plant breeding could be necessary to keep pace with the evolution of new races and in such cases a greater use of horizontal resistance on its own or as an adjunct to other control measures seems logical. The use of multilines and composite crosses in disease control also merit further investigation.

Accounts of disease control by resistant varieties are given by Stakman and Christensen (1960), Walker (1959), Coons (1953), Stevenson and Jones (1953: sources of resistance in crop plants), Walker (1941, 1953, 1965: disease resistance in vegetable crops), and Van der Plank (1968) discusses most aspects of disease resistance in plants. Breeding plants for disease resistance is described by Hayes and Johnston (1971).

29 Disease control by legislation and international cooperation: research and education

Much can be done to minimize the dissemination by man of pathogens and pests, but it is often a compromise between what is desirable and what is possible. Every effort must be made to exclude pathogens – nevertheless, it is unrealistic to assume that none will slip through even the best of quarantine systems. Once introduced it may be possible to eliminate a pathogen by intensive – and expensive – eradication campaigns or, if this is not possible, to contain it within a restricted area, although this is not very satisfactory. Containment may, however, provide time in which a comprehensive eradication campaign can be planned and carried out. Effective and speedy legislation is necessary in such cases.

Plant quarantine

This attempts to prevent the entry of pathogens and pests not already present and in practice must to some extent be selective as it is manifestly impossible to examine all imported plant material. It may operate between different countries or between adjacent states in one country. In agriculturally advanced areas plant quarantine organizations are often large and elaborate whereas they are usually smaller and sometimes virtually non-existent in those which are less advanced. Pathogens are liable to be introduced in or on living plants, seeds, tubers and other planting material, in imported grain, fruit, vegetables and other food-stuffs, in plant material used in industry (for example cotton and other fibres), in plant material used as packing, and in soil or incidental plant débris which may happen to be present.

When importing plants or plant products they should be obtained from areas known to be free from pathogens which might become destructive if introduced. This presupposes a reliable knowledge of the pathogens present in the exporting country – which may or may not be available – and underlines the importance of adequate regional surveys of pathogens and pests. The safest source of supply within the chosen country should obviously be used, and the latter should preferably be one with an efficient quarantine service which will inspect the material before export and certify that it is free from pathogens and pests. Such phytopathological certificates are, unfortunately, not always completely reliable, and imported material should be carefully examined and, if necessary, destroyed or treated to eliminate any pathogens or pests which are present. It is advisable to take such commonsense precautions as importing the minimum quantity of material required and in the form least likely to harbour pathogens; for example seeds are often safer – particularly in respect of viruses – than vegetative propagating material. Special precautions are needed when cultures of pathogenic fungi and bacteria are exchanged for scientific purposes, and the distribution and use of such cultures must be stringently controlled or forbidden. *Cochliobolus victoriae*, for example, causes a serious blight of oats in the U.S.A. and might well prove destructive if let loose in Britain. According to Gram (1960) 'professors are among the worst quarantine breakers'.

When quarantine facilities are limited the emphasis should be on preventing the entry of pathogens, or of new races of pathogens, which are liable to attack plants of economic importance in the importing country. This is particularly true of destructive pathogens but it should be borne in mind that a pathogen which is of only minor significance in one area may become more widespread and damaging in another where climatic or agronomic conditions are more favourable to it, or where the local crop varieties are more susceptible. On this basis it is important to prevent the entry of all pathogens of an important crop plant, even apparently minor ones.

In extreme cases it may become necessary to prohibit the importation of certain plant material or of material from areas where certain specified pathogens occur. Importation may be conditional on the material being substantially free from pathogens as revealed by one or more inspections in the field or at the place of despatch and requests for freedom from specified pathogens may be necessary. Knowledge of these inspection procedures will help prospective importers to decide on the safest source of the plant material which they require. Outport inspection – inspection at the place from where the material is despatched – is useful as a check, especially for small consignments which for some reason may be suspect, but some system of sampling will be required for examining large shipments. The presence of soil or of contaminated packing material can also be detected. If outport inspection reveals the presence of pathogens or pests the material can be destroyed or treated in some way to eliminate them. Some pathogens, however, can develop during transit, especially on sea voyages which last several weeks, so that symptoms which were hardly noticeable on despatch may be conspicuous on arrival at the 'inport'. Prolonged refrigerated storage can be effective in destroying some insect pests, including frit flies, and such treatment may be acceptable to the quarantine authorities.

Effective examination of incoming plant material depends largely on having a sufficient number of adequately trained and experienced inspectors at ports, airports, railway stations and frontier posts through which run the main roads and railways. Although possible in prosperous countries with limited frontiers this presents difficulties in less developed countries with long land frontiers where trained inspectors may be too few for adequate inspection. The phenomenal increase in air travel during recent years also poses problems in plant quarantine, as discussed by Sherman (1957). Unwanted pests and pathogens may be present in fruit, seeds and other planting material brought in by passengers, in provisions picked up by the aircraft at intermediate stops, and even as insects within the aircraft itself. The problem of adequately inspecting several hundred thousand aircraft and millions of passengers each year – as in the U.S.A. – is a formidable one calling for close cooperation between quarantine services, airlines and passengers.

If there is doubt as to whether imported plants or planting material are free from pathogens it may be necessary to grow them under close supervision in isolation after entry (postentry quarantine) and under conditions precluding the escape of any pathogens which may develop. When direct importation is considered too dangerous the material is often quarantined in a third country – intermediate quarantine – and, if free from pathogens, is then sent on to its final destination. This third country should preferably be one in which any pathogens are unlikely to survive should they escape from quarantine. It is sometimes possible to treat plant material before releasing it from quarantine. The methods applied to imported plant material to eliminate pathogens and pests are generally those usually used in crop protection – dusting, spraying, fumigation, dipping, heat treatment – but they must be completely effective. Many fungal and bacterial plant pathogens can be seed borne (a list is given by Noble and Richardson, 1968) and the number of viruses known to be seed transmitted is increasing. Seed which is superficially contaminated with a fungus can often be effectively treated with a fungicide whereas infected seed, although sometimes amenable to heat treatment, may prove impossible to disinfect, in which case it has to be destroyed.

Such diseases as potato blight, apple scab and downy mildew of grape occur in most countries where their host plants are grown, but other important pathogens may be more restricted in their distribution. Coffee rust,* groundnut rosette virus and cotton leaf curl virus are not known to

* Since this was written coffee rust has been reported from Brazil (1970): see p. 364.

occur in the New World whereas Texas root rot (*Phymatotrichum omni-vorum*), milo disease of sorghum caused by *Periconia circinata*, and several other important plant pathogens are apparently restricted to North America. *Xanthomonas stewarti* (maize wilt) and *Exobasidium vexans* (blister blight of tea) are two pathogens which do not appear to have been reported in Africa as yet. Plant quarantine is particularly important in minimizing the spread of pathogens of limited geographical distribution.

An effective quarantine organization with its specialized staff and buildings is costly to set up and maintain. The occasional pathogen or pest slips through even the most efficient quarantine and there is no real uniformity in quarantine procedures between different countries, although it is to be hoped that uniformity will eventually come. These considerations have led some to question the feasibility or even the desirability of plant quarantine. There is little doubt, however, that potentially serious pathogens are intercepted in quarantine inspections, as shown by the lists of intercepted pathogens and pests published by several countries. The damage that these could have caused had they not been intercepted probably more than offsets the cost of the quarantine service. It is sometimes argued that many or most pathogens will in time inevitably slip through quarantine. Even if this is true the delay in the introduction of destructive pathogens and pests may well have been more than worth the effort and expense involved in quarantine. The knowledge that imported plant material is liable to be thoroughly examined will deter those who might otherwise be tempted to import or export material not free from pathogens and pests.

For further information on plant quarantine the book by McCubbin (1954) and papers by Gram (1960) and McCubbin (1946) should be consulted. Sheffield (1958, 1968) discusses practical aspects of quarantine, and much information will be found in the *Plant Protection Bulletin* and *Digests of Plant Quarantine Regulations* published by the Food and Agriculture Organization of the United Nations (for example Ling, 1952). See also the account by Prentice (1971).

Internal legislation on plant pathogens and pests

Quarantine attempts to prevent the entry of new pathogens into an area from elsewhere, but legislation may also be needed to prevent the spread of pathogens within a country. Such legislation takes different forms in different areas. In many countries certain diseases must be notified to the authorities whenever they appear; these diseases are usually very destructive ones of limited distribution and/or infrequent occurrence, such as potato wart (*Synchytrium endobioticum*). Thus the Wart Disease of Potatoes Order, 1958, states that any outbreak of the disease in England and Wales must be notified to the Ministry of Agriculture, Fisheries and Food, that only approved immune varieties of potato may be planted on land known to be contaminated, and that diseased potatoes must be destroyed and may not be offered for sale or planted. Similar notification of outbreaks of newly introduced pathogens or pests may be made compulsory, as in the case of white rust (*Puccinia horiana*) of chrysanthemum in Britain, thus enabling eradication to be attempted; this is, of course, combined with strict quarantine to prevent further introductions of the pathogen.

Destruction of alternate hosts of rusts which attack crop plants, notably barberry as the aecial host of black stem rust of wheat, may be made compulsory in areas where the disease is severe. Legislation to prohibit the sale of planting material infected by certain pathogens may be enacted, as with gooseberry bushes attacked by *Sphaerotheca mors-uvae* (American gooseberry mildew), onions or leeks infected with smut (*Urocystis cepulae*), or brassica plants attacked by *Plasmodiophora brassicae* (club root) in Britain. The planting of trees or bushes which are unduly susceptible to a destructive pathogen may be prohibited by law, as with varieties of pear (Laxton Superb) very susceptible to fire blight (*Erwinia amylovora*) in Britain. Other pathogens legislated against include *Phytophthora fragariae* (red core of strawberry) and *Verticillium albo-atrum* (progressive wilt of hops), many of which are the subjects of advisory leaflets issued by the British Ministry of Agriculture, Fisheries and Food. These leaflets assist farmers and horticulturalists to identify the more important pathogens and pests likely to attack their crops, and also indicate methods of control and any legislation concerning them.

If a pathogen or pest is so destructive as to threaten a crop vitally important to the economic well-being of a country it may become necessary to enforce control measures – often unpopular – by legislation and accompanying inspection. Compulsory destruction of crop residues by a certain date, a ban on unauthorized removal of plant material from the fields, a closed season between crops during which the cultivation of susceptible plants is prohibited, and an obligation to destroy infected alternative host plants are among the measures which may be involved, with appropriate inspection and penalties for non-compliance. In the irrigated Gezira area of the Sudan the valuable cotton crop, the country's most important single export, has for many years been protected against bacterial blight (*Xanthomonas malvacearum*) by seed treatment and intensive sanitation in which the fields are literally swept clean after harvest, the crop residues then being burnt. Similarly it is necessary to pull out the cotton plants, roots and all, to prevent regrowth and accompanying carry-over of the cotton leaf curl virus, and to forbid the cultivation of susceptible malvaceous plants – particularly *Hibiscus esculentus* (okra) a widely grown vegetable – between cotton crops. Not unnaturally such measures are unpopular and should wherever possible be of a temporary nature until other methods of control, including resistant varieties, become available. If considered essential, however, they must be enforced, otherwise serious outbreaks of disease are likely; for example a loss of cotton estimated to be worth at least a million pounds was caused by leaf curl attributed to illegal out-of-season cultivation of okra in the Sudan Gezira (Tarr, 1957).

International aspects of plant pathology

The distribution and activity of plant pathogens and pests depend largely on the presence of susceptible plants and favourable environmental conditions. Pathogens do not respect national frontiers and their control thus involves, or should involve, cooperation between the various countries in which they occur. Much is being done by F.A.O. to foster and emphasize the international aspects of plant pathology, as discussed below, but more could be accomplished if countries would cooperate more closely. Unfortunately cooperation, even in such humanitarian activities as the relief of starvation and malnutrition, is not infrequently ruled out on political grounds, and this is likely to remain so until nations run their affairs more rationally than at present.

There are many aspects of plant pathology in which action on an international scale can fruitfully be undertaken, and specialist organizations have been set up to cover some of them. One of the earliest was the *Phylloxera* Convention of 1881 concerned with the study and control of this insect which attacks the roots of grapevine plants, and many other international bodies dealing with various aspects of plant diseases have been set up, some of which are briefly considered below. Among others, the following would seem to be aspects in which international action could profitably be taken.

(1) Campaigns for the control or eradication of specific pathogens and pests on a regional or continental scale. Eradication of a pathogen in one country is likely to be more permanent if it is also eradicated from adjacent ones which could otherwise act as inoculum sources for further outbreaks. This is particularly relevant for pathogens which multiply rapidly and whose propagules are disseminated by wind to considerable distances, as with the uredospores of some rusts. In some areas outbreaks of black stem rust of wheat apparently originate from air borne uredospores produced by earlier sown infected wheat in other areas, and would be minimized were the disease brought under control in the source areas. Pathogens of limited spread and narrow host range may, however, be eradicated in a country and thereafter excluded by strict quarantine, although the danger of reintroduction is constantly present.

(2) The production, testing and sharing of disease resistant varieties of crop plants. Such varieties are now being selected and bred in many different countries. Although a variety which is resistant to a specific pathogen in one country may be susceptible – or unsuitable in other re-spects – in another, it seems logical to test all such varieties in all areas where they might prove of value and this should be accompanied by a study of the geographical distribution of races of the pathogen. Plant breeders working in different countries may exchange seeds of new varieties but this is a somewhat haphazard process, and organizations concerned with the breeding of specific crops on a world or regional basis, or dealing with specific pathogens, are needed. These are now being developed – for example, the International Rice Commission organized by F.A.O. and the International Wheat Rust Conference for control of wheat rusts in the Americas (see Stakman and Harrar, 1957, for details of others). Collections of plants containing genes for resistance to important pathogens could be maintained and should prove useful to plant breeders engaged in producing resistant varieties.

(3) The setting up of a central organization, possibly with subsidiary regional ones, concerned with the collation and dissemination of infor-mation on plant pathogens, pests and weeds. It would be concerned with the host range, races and economic importance of pathogens, their geo-graphical distribution, climatic requirements, seasonal carry-over, spread, control and other relevant aspects, as well as with outbreaks of new diseases and pests. Monographs summarizing the existing knowledge about important pathogens and pests, and describing those of specific crops, would be issued, also publications of a more general nature concerned with, for example, new crop protection chemicals and new methods of control. The organization would also undertake the identification of plant pathogens and pests, taxonomic studies on them, the building-up of a comprehensive herbarium of plant disease specimens, the maintenance of a culture collection, and the training of pathologists in these and other specialized branches of the subject. Individual pathologists with exper-ience of specific pathogens or of diseases of specific crops would be avail-able on secondment to countries needing their services. Visits and meet-ings of workers studying similar problems would be arranged, and a wider interchange of pathologists would be encouraged. More cooperation between all engaged in investigating plant injury – whether due to patho-gens, pests, or non-parasitic agents – is needed. Exchange of information is greatly facilitated by such events as the periodic International Crop Protection Congresses and the First International Congress of Plant Pathology held in London in 1968, and also through the activities of such bodies as the Federation of British Plant Pathologists and the American Phytopathological Society.

Many of these international aspects of plant diseases and pests are undertaken by the Plant Production and Protection Division of the Food and Agriculture Organization of the United Nations, with headquarters in Rome. The *F.A.O. Plant Protection Bulletin* (successor to the *International Bulletin of Plant Protection*) provides useful information on pests and diseases in most parts of the world and could usefully be expanded. The British Ministry of Overseas Development produces *PANS* (*Pest Articles and News Summaries*), concerned chiefly with crop protection in its widest sense, and several countries publish journals dealing chiefly with field aspects of diseases and pests – *Plant Pathology* (Britain) and the *Plant Disease Reporter* (U.S.A.) are two of these. The Commonwealth Mycological Institute at Kew, England, issues several useful publications including the *Review of Plant Pathology* (previously the *Review of applied Mycology*), *Mycological* and *Phytopathological Papers*, and monographs on the diseases of important crops, in addition to identifying plant pathogens and other fungi and bacteria. The Commonwealth Institute of Entomology and the Commonwealth Bureau of Helminthology perform a similar function in respect of insects and nematodes respectively.

Other bodies concerned with plant pathology include the International Convention of Plant Protection, the International Commission on Chemical Crop Protection, the European Plant Protection Organization (EPPO) and the International Association of Plant Pathology; further details can be obtained from Stakman and Harrar (1957) and Knoll (1957).

An interesting account of national and international phytopathological organizations is given by Chiarappa (1970), from which much of the following information is taken. Of the sixteen national phytopathological societies listed, ten (62%) were founded in 1960 or later, that of the Netherlands being the first-established in 1891, followed by the American Phytopathological Society (1908) and the Phytopathological Society of Japan (1916), the latter two being the best supported with 2440 and 1192 members respectively in 1967. In addition, six associations for applied microbiology and 'phytomedicine' are listed, the oldest of which is the Association of Applied Biologists founded in the United Kingdom in 1904, with a 1967 membership of 980. Eight national plant protection organizations, with substantial interests in plant pathology are listed. Many of these national organizations publish journals, the first of which was the *Netherlands Journal of Plant Pathology* (formerly *Tijdschrift over Planteziekten*) published in 1895 and followed by *Phytopathology* (1910) and the *Annals of Applied Biology* (1914).

International phytopathological organizations include such associations as the Unione Fitopatologica Mediterranea and the Asociacion Latinoamericana de Fitopatologia whose interests are largely regional, specialized study groups concerned with diseases of specific crops or groups of crops (for example the International Organization of Citrus Virologists) and specialized sections of non-phytopathological organizations such as the Committee on Plant Diseases of the International Seed Testing Association.

The number of national organizations concerned wholly or partially with plant pathology varies considerably in different continents, depending partly on the number of countries in the continent, their level of agricultural development, and the number of plant pathologists therein.

There are twelve such organizations in Europe, four in North America but only one in Africa. The setting up of a phytopathological society is justified only if there are sufficient phytopathologists to make it a going concern, and in most countries in Africa this is not so. In such cases, regional organizations embracing several or many countries might be worthwhile.

Experienced plant pathologists, entomologists and nematologists are in short supply whereas the demand for them constantly increases. More must be trained, sufficient not only for the agriculturally developed countries but also – and perhaps more urgently – for those which are less well developed and in which the need is greater. Some countries which are almost completely dependent on agriculture, have no plant pathologists or too few in relation to the total area of arable land and the importance of agriculture in their economy – and it will be many years before this situation can be remedied. This is an urgent problem and requires action at an international level. As Paddock (1967) points out, new methods of training crop protection officers are needed, also new or improved methods of protection suitable for use by fairly unsophisticated cultivators in underdeveloped countries. Too often the control methods successful in temperate, agriculturally advanced areas have been uncritically applied in tropical underdeveloped countries, with little effort to modify them, or devise others, in the light of local conditions. More accurate information on the crop losses due to pathogens and pests is needed, in turn dependent on more precise ways of assessing their incidence over large areas. Such knowledge would indicate the priorities in allocating limited resources in money and trained personnel. This is a difficult problem which is of great practical importance in that some of the published estimates of crop losses are almost certainly exaggerated. This overstatement is harmful in that it is unlikely to be credible to those responsible for the allocation of funds. These and other aspects of plant pathology are worldwide in their implications and should therefore be studied as world problems.

Research and education

The organization of research on plant disease problems varies in different countries. In many it is carried out by staff of the Ministry or Department of Agriculture (particularly field trials associated with advisory work), at research stations which may concentrate on specific crops or groups of crops, by commercial firms interested in crop protection chemicals or in specific crops whose produce they use, and by individual workers in universities and colleges where the emphasis tends to be on more fundamental aspects of plant pathology. There may be specialized units for specific projects and purposes. In England, for example, there are the Plant Pathology Laboratory and the several units set up by the Agricultural Research Council whose 'main functions are to review and facilitate research in progress, promote new research where necessary, and ensure, as far as possible, that manpower and resources are used to the best advantage' (Anon., 1963). Such units include the Systemic Fungicides Unit and the Virus Research Unit. Grants for specified research projects are made by government departments and commercial firms to universities and colleges. Crop Protection Divisions may be set up in some countries, and there are research institutes devoted chiefly to important crops – the Tea Research Institute of Ceylon, the Cocoa Research Institute of Nigeria, the Glasshouse Crops Research Institute at Rustington, Sussex, and many others, most of which have plant pathology and entomology departments.

The need for more research, especially fundamental research, in plant pathology is emphasized by Harrar (1959) who suggests that the limited progress in control of plant diseases as compared with human diseases is due partly to the relatively small amount of money available for phytopathological research and partly to the plant pathologist having to deal with the diseases of numerous species of plants instead of concentrating on one. The scope of phytopathological research has steadily widened and plant physiologists, biochemists, geneticists, cytologists, meteorologists and other scientists now play an increasingly important role, as can be seen by a glance at the contents of the *Annual Review of Phytopathology* for 1968 (see Houten, 1959). More money spent on fundamental research should result in new and more effective methods of controlling plant diseases; understanding of the chemical bases of fungitoxicity should enable fungicides to be designed rather than discovered; knowledge of what makes plants resistant to pathogens should facilitate the production of disease resistant varieties of crop plants, and many other examples of the vital importance of fundamental research could be given. On the other hand, plant pathology is very much concerned with the control of plant disease, and research on the more applied aspects of the subject should obviously not be neglected. On present standards, research in plant pathology requires only relatively modest expenditure and can reduce materially the serious crop losses due to disease all over the world.

Successful research depends on having sufficient trained and experienced scientists of adequate calibre, and the training of plant pathologists is thus a key factor in the expansion of research on plant diseases. Plant pathology is taught to varying extents at undergraduate level in many universities and colleges but it cannot at present be read as a degree subject in British universities. In Britain training in plant pathology often takes the form of a 1-year, mostly instructional, postgraduate course leading to a Master's Degree, or a 2–3 year programme of research on a specific disease problem leading to a doctorate. Both methods have advantages and drawbacks. The former course is shorter and therefore cheaper, and provides a widely based foundation knowledge of plant pathology but relatively little training in research. The 2–3 year course is more expensive and, although providing intensive research training in a specific and often narrow segment of plant pathology, provides little background knowledge of the subject. It would seem desirable to combine the advantages of the two types of training by increasing the research content of the instructional course or by increasing the instructional content of the research training; in the latter case the graduate spending 2–3 years in research on what may be a highly specialized project should acquire an adequate general knowledge of plant pathology which is likely to be useful to him in his subsequent career.

30 Sources of information

The literature on plant pathology is very extensive and only a selection of what are considered to be the more important publications is given below; a fuller list will be found in Ainsworth (1963), in the *Plant Pathologist's Pocketbook* (Commonwealth Mycological Institute, 1968), and in the *Review of Applied Mycology*, **46,** 1, 113 (1967).

Books

General works

Plant Pathology. G. N. Agrios, Academic Press, London and New York, 1969. An introductory text, the first part of which deals with general aspects of infectious diseases of plants and the second part with specific diseases.

Outlines of Plant Pathology. G. A. Strobel and D. E. Mathre, Van Nostrand Reinhold, 1970. A modern introductory text which emphasizes principles rather than specific diseases.

An Introduction to Plant Diseases. B. E. J. Wheeler, Wiley, New York, 1969. The different types of plant disease are described in this interesting and stimulating book.

The Advance of the Fungi. E. C. Large, Jonathan Cape, 1940. A plant pathology 'classic', eminently readable and containing much useful and interesting information on man's early attempts to control plant diseases.

Famine on the Wind. G. L. Carefoot and E. R. Sprott, Angus and Robertson, London, 1969. An account of the impact of plant disease on human history.

Plant Pathology, Problems and Progress, 1908–1958. Edit. by C. S. Holton *et al.*, University of Wisconsin Press, Madison, 1959. An advanced text.

Plant Pathology, an Advanced Treatise. Edit. by J. G. Horsfall and A. E. Dimond, Academic Press, London and New York, Vols **1, 2** and **3,** 1959, 1960.

Plant Pathology, J. C. Walker, McGraw-Hill, New York, 1969. This gives useful accounts of many plant pathogens as well as chapters on general principles.

Principles of Plant Pathology. E. C. Stakman and J. G. Harrar, The Ronald Press, New York, 1957.

T

Principles of Plant Infection. E. Gaumann. English edition edited by W. B. Brierley, Crosby Lockwood, London, 1950.

Diseases in Plants. An Introduction to Agricultural Phytopathology. N. E. Stevens and R. B. Stevens, Chronica Botanica Co., Waltham, Mass., 1952.

Plant Pathology. E. J. Butler and S. G. Jones, Macmillan, London, 1949. The first part of the book is concerned with general principles, the second part describes in some detail the diseases of various groups of cultivated plants in Britain; there are extensive references.

Plant Diseases. F. C. Bawden, Nelson, London, 1948. A good introduction to plant pathology.

Introduction to Plant Pathology. F. D. Heald, McGraw-Hill, New York, 1943.

Fungi and Disease in Plants. E. J. Butler, Thacker Spink and Co., Calcutta and Simla, 1918. Useful for its descriptions of tropical plant pathogens.

British Parasitic Fungi. W. C. Moore, Cambridge University Press, London, 1959. An invaluable guide to the literature on the fungi which attack cultivated plants in Britain, with a useful host index.

The Plant Diseases of Great Britain. G. C. Ainsworth, Chapman and Hall, London, 1937. A bibliography of the early literature.

Plant Diseases. F. T. Brooks, Oxford University Press, London, 1953. Describes many tropical as well as temperate plant pathogens.

Plant Diseases. The Yearbook of Agriculture. United States Department of Agriculture, 1953.

Compendium of Plant Diseases. Rohm and Haas Co., Philadelphia, 1959.

Plant Disease Handbook. C. Westcott, Van Nostrand, Princeton, 1960.

Diseases of Field Crops. J. G. Dickson, McGraw-Hill, New York, 1956.

Plant Diseases in Orchard, Nursery and Garden Crops. E. Gram and A. Weber, Macdonald & Co., London, 1952.

Books in languages other than English

Handbuch der Pflanzenkrankheiten P. Sorauer, Vol 1, Non-Parasitic Diseases; Vol. 2, Virus, Bacterial and Fungal Diseases; Vol. 3, Fungal Diseases, Diseases due to Parasitic Flowering Plants; Vol. 6, Plant Protection, Paul Parey, Berlin, several editions from 1928 onwards.

Krankheiten und schadlinge der Zierpflanzen und ihre bekampfung. H. Pape, Paul Parey, Berlin, 1955.

Phytopathologie und Pflanzenschutz. Edit. by M. Klinkowski, E. Muhle and E. Reinmuth, Vol. 1, (1965), 2 (1966), Akademie-Verlag, Berlin.

Pflanzenschutz in den tropen. G. Frohlich *et al.*, Karl-Marx Universität, Leipzig, 1963.

Les Champignons Parasites des Plantes Cultivées. G. Viennot-Bourgin. Masson et Cie., Paris, 1949.

Phytopathologie des Pays Chauds. L. Roger, Vol. 1 (1951), 2 (1953), 3 (1954), Paul Lechevalier, Paris.

Principes de Pathologie Vegetale. Notions sur les Principales Maladies Parasitaires des Plantes Cultivées. P. Limasset and H. Darpoux, Dunod, Paris, 1951.

Manuale di Patologia Vegetale. R. Ciferri, Vol. 1 (1952), 2 (1955), 3 (1955), Societa Editrice Dante Alighieri, Rome.

Malattie e Parassiti delle Plante Agarie. R. Ciferri and G. Paoli, Società Editrice Dante Alighieri, Rome, 1958.
Manuale di Patologia Vegetale. G. Goidanich, Vol. **1** (1959), **2** (1964), Bologna, Edizioni Agricole.
Tratat de Patologie Vegetala. T. Savulescu and O. Savulescu, Vol. **1,** (1959), Bucharest, Editura Acadamiei Republicii Populaire Romine.
Fitopatologie, E. Radulescu and E. Docea, Bucharest, 1966.

Physiology of plant disease

Physiological Plant Pathology. R. K. S. Wood, Blackwell Scientific Publications, Oxford, 1967. An excellent account of the subject.
The Biochemistry and Physiology of Infectious Plant Disease, R. N Goodman, Z. Kiraly and M. Zeitlin, Van Nostrand, Princeton, 1967.
The Dynamic Role of Molecular Constituents in Plant-parasite Interaction. Edit. by C. J. Mirocha and I. Uritani, American Phytopathological Society, 1967.
Biochemistry and Physiology of Plant Immunity. B. A. Rubin and E. V. Artsikhovskaya, Translated by H. Wareing, Pergamon Press, Oxford, 1963.
Perspectives of Biochemical Plant Pathology. Edit. by S. Rich, *Connecticut Agric. Exp. Sta. Bull.*, 663, 1963.
Phytotoxins in Plant Diseases, Edit. by R. K. S. Wood, A. Ballio and A Graniti, Academic Press, London and New York, 1971.

Epidemiology

Plant Diseases; Epidemics and Control. J. E. Van der Plank, Academic Press, London and New York 1963. A mathematical approach to epidemiology.
Insect Transmission of Plant Diseases. J. G. Leach, McGraw-Hill New York, 1940.
Insects in Relation to Plant Diseases. W. Carter, Interscience, New York, 1962.
The Microbiology of the Atmosphere. P. H. Gregory, Hill, London, 1961.
Airborne Microbes. Edit. by P. H. Gregory and J. L. Monteith, Cambridge University Press, London, 1967.
Biological Aspects of the Transmission of Disease. Edit. by C. Horton-Smith, Oliver and Boyd, Edinburgh, 1957.

Root diseases and soil borne pathogens

Root Disease Fungi. S. D. Garrett, Chronica Botanica Co., Waltham Mass., 1944.
Biology of Root-infecting Fungi. S. D. Garrett, Cambridge University Press, London, 1956.
Pathogenic Root-infecting Fungi. S. D. Garrett, Cambridge University Press, London, 1970.
Ecology of Soil-borne Plant Pathogens. Edit. by K. F. Baker and W. C. Snyder, Murray, London, 1965.
The Ecology of Soil Fungi. Edit. by D. Parkinson and J. S. Waid, Liverpool University Press, Liverpool, 1960.

Disease control

The Scientific Principles of Crop Protection. H. Martin, Arnold, London, 1964.

Plant Diseases: Epidemics and Control. J. E. van der Plank, Academic Press, London and New York, 1963.

The Control of Pests and Diseases in Agricultural and Horticultural Crops. G. L. Hey and K. Marshall, Vinton, London, 1958.

The Nature and Prevention of Plant Diseases. K. S. Chester, The Blakiston Co., New York, 1947.

Principles of Plant and Animal Pest Control. (1) *Plant Disease Development and Control,* 1968, (2) *Weed Control,* 1968, (3) *Insect-pest Management and Control,* 1969, (4) *Control of Plant-parasitic Nematodes,* 1968, (5) *The Vertebrates that are Pests: Problems and Control*; not yet scheduled, (6) *Effects of Pesticides on Fruit and Vegetable Physiology,* 1968. Published by the National Academy of Sciences, Washington, D.C.

The Plant Quarantine Problem. W. A. McCubbin, Ejnar Munksgaard, Copenhagen, 1954.

World Crop Protection. J. H. Stapley and F. C. H. Gayner, Vol. **1, 2** (K. A. Hassal), 1969, Iliffe Books, London.

Fungicides; An advanced Treatise. Edit. by D. C. Torgeson, Vol. **1** (1967); **2** (1969), Academic Press, London and New York.

Guide to the Chemicals used in Crop Protection. E. Y. Spencer, Canada Dept. Agric., Publication 1093, 1968.

Pesticide Manual. Edit. by H. Martin, British Crop Protection Council, 1968.

Plant Diseases and their Chemical Control. E. Evans, Blackwell Scientific Publications, Oxford, 1968.

The Nature and Uses of Modern Fungicides. E. G. Sharvelle, Burgess Publishing Co., Minneapolis, 1961.

Disease Resistance in Plants. J. E. van der Plank, Academic Press, London and New York, 1968.

Decay of Wood and its Prevention. K. S. G. Cartwright and W. P. K. Findlay. H.M.S.O., London, 1958.

Insect, Fungus and Weed Control. E. R. de Ong, Thames and Hudson, London, 1954.

Virus diseases

Plant Viruses and Virus Diseases. F. C. Bawden, Ronald Press, New York, 1964.

A Textbook of Plant Virus Diseases. K. M. Smith, Churchill, London, 1957.

Plant Viruses. K. M. Smith, Methuen, London, 1968.

Plant Virology. Edit. by M. K. Corbett and H. D. Sisler, University of Florida Press, Gainsborough, 1964.

Viruses of Plants. Edit. by A. B. R. Beemster and J. Dijkstra, North Holland Publishing Co., Amsterdam, 1966.

Viruses, Vectors and Vegetation. Edit. by K. Maramorosch, Interscience, New York, 1969.

Plants, Viruses, and Insects. K. Esau, Harvard University Press, Cambridge, 1961.

Plant Viriology. R. E. F. Mathews, Academic Press, London and New York, 1970.

Viruses in Plant Hosts. K. Esau, University of Wisconsin Press, Madison, 1968.

Viruses and Virus Diseases of Plants. M. T. Cook, Burgess Publishing Co., Minneapolis, 1947.

Maladies à Virus des Plantes Cultivées et Méthodes de Lutte. P. Cornuet, Institut National de la Recherche Agronomique, Paris, 1959.

Methods in Virology. Edit. by K. Maramorosch and H. Koprowski, Vol. **1** (1967); **2** (1967); **3** (1967); **4** (1968), Academic Press, London and New York.

Bacterial diseases

Plant Diseases due to Bacteria. W. J. Dowson, Cambridge University Press, London, 1957.

Manual of Bacterial Plant Pathogens. C. Elliott, Chronica Botanica Co., Waltham Mass., 1951.

Bacterial Diseases of Plants. M. V. Gorlenko, Jerusalem, Israel Program for Scientific Translations, 1965.

Bacterial Plant Pathogens. C. Stapp, Oxford University Press, London, 1961.

Parasitic flowering plants

The Biology of Parasitic Flowering Plants. J. Kuijt, University of California Press, 1970.

Mineral deficiency diseases

The Diagnosis of Mineral Deficiencies in Plants. T. Wallace, H.M.S.O., London, 1961.

Trace Elements in Plants. W. Stiles, Cambridge University Press, London, 1961.

Trace Elements in Agriculture. V. Sauchelli, Van Nostrand Reinhold Co., Princeton, 1969.

Trace Elements. Edit. by C. A. Lamb *et al.*, Academic Press, London and New York, 1958.

Trace Elements in Plant Physiology. Various authors, Chronica Botanica, Co. Waltham, Mass., 1950.

Serial publications, journals

These include the following: *C.M.I. Descriptions of Pathogenic Fungi and Bacteria*. Started in 1964, these are published periodically by the Commonwealth Mycological Institute, Kew, and provide excellent descriptions by specialists of some of the more important plant pathogens, together with references. *Descriptions of Plant Viruses* is a comparable series also published by the Commonwealth Mycological Institute. Some fungal pathogens are described in *Iconographia Mycologica* issued from 1959 onwards as part of *Mycopathologia et Mycologia applicata*. Other useful publications include the *Mycological Papers* and *Phytopathological Papers* of the C.M.I., the *Fiches de phytopathologie tropicale* (in *Revue*

Mycol., Suppl. trop.), and the *Phytopathological Monographs* and *Phytopathological Classics* published by the American Phytopathological Society. The *C.M.I. Distribution Maps of Plant Diseases*, the *Bibliography of Systematic Mycology*, and the *Index of Fungi* – all issued by the C.M.I. – contain much useful information on plant pathogens.

Papers on plant pathology are published in many journals (see Ainsworth and Bisby's *Dictionary of the Fungi*, 5th ed., 1963, p. 318), of which the following are a selection: *Phytopathology, Plant Pathology, Annals of applied Biology; Transactions of the British Mycological Society; Mycologia; Plant Disease Reporter; Indian Phytopathology; Annals of the Phytopathological Society of Japan; Netherlands Journal of Plant Pathology; Physiological Plant Pathology; F.A.O. Plant Protection Bulletin; Annales des Epiphyties; Annales de l'Institut phytopathologique Benaki; Revue de Mycologie; Revista di patologia vegetale; Mycopathologia et Mycologia applicata; Sydowia; Phytopathologische Zeitschrift; Zeitschrift für Pflanzenkrankheiten (Pflanzenpathologie) und Pflanzenschutz; Phytopathologia Mediterranea.* Many other journals contain papers of interest to plant pathologists – *Annals of Botany (London); Journal of general Microbiology; Journal of experimental Botany; American Journal of Botany; Canadian Journal of Botany; New Phytologist; Botanical Gazette;* and others.

Useful abstracting and review journals include the invaluable *Review of Plant Pathology* (formerly *Review of applied Mycology*), *Biological Abstracts, Biological Review, Botanical Review, PANS (Pest Articles News Summaries. B. Plant Disease Control)*, and the *Annual Review of Phytopathology, Annual Review of Plant Physiology*, and *Annual Review of Microbiology*.

Diseases of crop plants

Monographs and papers on the diseases of some important crops are listed below. See also *Diseases of Crop Plants*, edit. by J. H. Western (The Macmillan Press, London and Basingstoke, 1971) for diseases of cereals, grasses, herbage and forage legumes, hops, potato, sugarbeet and vegetables.

Banana

Banana Diseases, including Plantains and Abaca, C. W. Wardlaw, Longmans, Green and Co., New York, 1961.

Bean

A monographic study of bean diseases and methods of their control. W. J. Zaumeyer and H. R. Thomas, *Tech. Bull. U.S. Dep. Agric.*, 868, 1957.
Diseases and pests of peas and beans in New Zealand and their control. R. M. Brien *et al., Bull. N.Z. Dep. scient. ind. Res.*, 114, 1955.

Brassicas and other Cruciferae

Diseases of cabbage and related plants. J. C. Walker *et al., Agric. Handb. U.S. Dep. Agric.*, 144, 1958.
Crucifer Diseases in Ireland, R. McKay, Dublin, 1956.

Cacao

The Diseases and Curing of Cacao. H. R. Briton-Jones, Macmillan, London, 1934.
Cacao diseases. S. H. Crowdy and R. S. Elias, *Outl. Agric.*, **1,** 64, 1956.
Cocoa. D. H. Urquhart, Longmans, Green and Co., New York, 1955.
The viruses of cacao. J. M. Thresh and T. W. Tinsley, *Tech. Bull. W. Afr. Cocoa Res. Inst.*, 7, 1959.

Cereals and grasses

Diseases of Cereals and Grasses in North America. R. Sprague, The Ronald Press, New York, 1950.
Cereal Diseases in Ireland. R. McKay, Dublin.
Cereal diseases. W. C. Moore and F. J. Moore, *Bull. Minist. Agric. Fish Fd, Lond.*, 129, 1961.
Diseases of British Grasses and Herbage Legumes. 2nd Ed., K. Sampson and J. H. Western, Cambridge University Press, London, 1954.
Diseases of Turf Grasses. H. B. Couch, Reinhold, New York, 1962.
Fungal Diseases of Turf Grasses. 2nd Ed., J. D. Smith, Bingley Sports Turf Research Institute, 1965.
See also under individual cereals.

Citrus

Citrus Diseases and Their Control. 2nd Ed., H. S. Fawcett, McGraw-Hill, New York, 1936.
Color Handbook of Citrus Diseases. 3rd Ed., L. J. Klotz, University of California Press, Berkeley, 1961.
Le Malattie degli Agrumi. G. Scaramuzzi, Edagricole, Bologna, 1965.

Coffee

An Atlas of Coffee Pests and Diseases. Coffee Board of Kenya, Nairobi, 1961.
Information on coffee diseases is also given by F. L. Wellman in *Coffee, Botany, Cultivation and Utilization*, Leonard Hill, 1961, and in *Plant Diseases, Yearbook of Agriculture*, U.S. Department of Agriculture, pp. 891–896, 1953. See also *Les maladies du Cafeier en Côte d'Ivoire*. M. Meiffren, Abidjan, 1957.

Cotton

There does not appear to be a monograph although one is needed: see *Diseases of Field Crops.* 2nd Ed., J. G. Dickson, McGraw-Hill, New York, 1956 and *Plant Diseases, Yearbook of Agriculture*. U.S. Department of Agriculture, pp. 292–320, 1953.

Flax

The Diseases of the Flax Plant (Linum usitatissimum Linn.). A. E. Muskett and J. Colhoun, W. and G. Baird, Belfast, 1956.

Fruit

Diseases of Fruit and Hops. 3rd Ed., H. Wormald, Crosby, Lockwood and Sons, London, 1955.
Diseases of Fruit Crops. H. W. Anderson, McGraw-Hill, New York, 1956.
Virus diseases of apples and pears. Edit. by A. F. Posnette. *Tech. Commun. Bur. Hort., E. Malling*, 30, 1963.
Krankheiten und Schadlinge im Obstbau und ihre Bekampfung. 3rd Ed., W. Kotta, Paul Parey, Berlin, 1958.
See also under individual fruit crops.

Grapevine

Maladies et Parasites de la Vigne. Vol. **1,** *Maladies cryptogamiques*. J. Lafon *et al.*, J. B. Ballière et fils, Paris, 1959.

Groundnut

Preventing the diseases of peanuts. C. Wilson, *Plant Dis. Yb. Agric. U.S. Dep. Agric.*, pp. 448–454, 1953.
Pest Control in Groundnuts. Edit. by S. D. Feakin, P.A.N.S Manual 2, 1967.

Maize

Corn diseases in the United States and their control. A. J. Ullstrup, *Agric. Handb. U.S. Dep. Agric.*, 199, 1966.

Millets

Diseases of Millets. T. S. Ramakrishnan, I.C.A.R., New Delhi, 1963.
Les champignons parasites des sorghos (*Sorghum vulgare*) et des penicillaires (*Pennisetum typhoideum*) en Afrique Equatoriale française. A. M. Saccas, 1954: *Agron. trop. Nogent*, **9,** 135, 263, 647.

Oil palm

Diseases and Disorders of the Oil Palm in Malaysia. P. D. Turner and R. A. Bull, Kuala Lumpur, 1967.

Onion

Onion diseases and their control. J. C. Walker and R. H. Larson, *Agric. Handb. U.S. Dep. Agric.*, 208, 1961.

Orchids

Orchid diseases. H. C. Burnett, *Bull. Div. Pl. Ind. Fla.*, 1, 1965.

Ornamental plants

Diseases and Pests of Ornamental Plants. 3rd Ed., P. P. Pirone *et al.*, The Ronald Press, New York, 1960.
Diseases of Garden Plants. A. Beaumont, Collingridge, London, 1956.
Diseases of bulbs. W. C. Moore, *Bull. Minist. Agric. Fish. Fd, Lond.*, 117, 1949.
Krankheiten und Schadlinge der Zierpflanzen und ihre Bekampfung. H. Pape and M. Hemer, Paul Parey, Berlin, 1964.
Diseases of ornamental plants. J. L. Forsberg, *Univ. Illinois Coll. Agric. Spec. Pub.*, 3, 1963.

Pea

Pea diseases. W. J. Zaumeyer, *Agric. Handb. U.S. Dep. Agric.*, 228, 1962.

Potato

The Potato in Health and Disease. 3rd Ed., T. Whitehead *et al.*, Oliver and Boyd, Edinburgh, 1953.
Potato Diseases. R. McKay, Dublin, 1955.
Die Wichtigsten Kartoffelkrankheiten und ihre Bekampfung. E. Kohler, DLG-Verlag, Frankfurt, 1962.
Potato blight epidemics throughout the world. A. E. Cox and E C Large, *Agric. Handb. U.S. Dep. Agric.*, 174, 1960.

Rice

Manual of Rice Diseases. G. W. Padwick, C.M.I., Kew, 1950.

Rubber

Diseases and Pests of the Rubber Tree. A. Sharples, Macmillan, London, 1936.
Maladies of Hevea in Malaya. R. N. Hilton, Kuala Lumpur, 1959.

Sorghum

Diseases of Sorghum, Sudan Grass and Broomcorn. S. A. J. Tarr, C.M.I., Kew, 1962.
Le piu importanti malattie del sorgo, con speciale riferimento a quelle sorgo zuccherino. G. Goidanich, *Industr. saccar. Ital.*, **32,** 77, 166.
Sorghum diseases and their control. R. W. Leukel *et al.*, *Fmrs' Bull. U.S. Dep. Agric.* 1959.
Diseases of Sorghum. G. W. Wallace and M. M. Wallace, *Tanganyika Dep. Agric. Pamphlet*, 53, 1953.
Les champignons parasites des sorghos (*Sorghum vulgare*) et des penicillaires (*Pennisetum typhoideum*) en Afrique Equatoriale française. A. M. Saccas, 1954: *Agron. trop. Nogent*, **9,** 135, 263, 647.

Strawberry

Strawberry Diseases. A. G. Plakidas, Louisiana State University Press, Baton Rouge, 1964.

Sugarbeet

Sugar Beet Diseases in Ireland. R. McKay, Dublin, 1952.
Sugar Beet Diseases. R. Hull, *Bull. Minist. Agric. Fish. Fd, Lond.*, 142, 1960.

Sugarcane

Sugarcane and its Diseases. 2nd Ed., C. W. Edgerton, Louisiana State University Press, Baton Rouge, 1958.
Sugarcane Diseases of the World. Vol. **1**, 1961, edit. by J. P. Martin *et al.*, **2,** edit. by C. G. Hughes *et al.*, 1964, Elsevier Publishing Co., Amsterdam.

Sweet potato

Sweet potato diseases. E. M. Hildebrand and H. T. Cook, *Frms' Bull. U.S. Dep. Agric.*, 1059, 1959.

Tea

Tea Pests and Diseases and Their Control. E. Hainsworth, Heffer and Sons, Cambridge, 1952.
Diseases of tea and associated crops in North-East India. K. C. Sarmah, *Mem. Tocklai exp. Stn*, 26, 1960.

Tobacco

Tobacco Diseases. J. C. F. Hopkins, C.M.I., Kew, 1956.
Tobacco Diseases and Decays. 2nd Ed., F. A. Wolf, Duke University Press, North Carolina, 1957.
Diseases of Tobacco. 2nd Ed., G. B. Lucas, the Scarecrow Press, New York, 1965.

Tomato

Tomato Diseases. R. McKay, Dublin, 1949.
Tomato diseases and their control. S. P. Doolittle *et al.*, *Agric. Handb. U.S. Dep. Agric.*, 203, 1961.

Trees

Pathology of Trees and Shrubs. T. R. Peace, Clarendon Press, Oxford, 1962.
Forest Pathology. 3rd Ed., J. S. Boyce McGraw-Hill, New York, 1961.
Pathology in Forest Practice. 2nd Ed., D. V. Baxter, Wiley, New York, 1952.

Pests and Diseases of Forest Plantation Trees. An Annotated List of the Principal Species occurring in the British Commonwealth. F. G. Browne, Clarendon Press, Oxford, 1968.

Decay of Timber and its Prevention. 2nd Ed., K. S. G. Cartwright and W. P. K. Findlay, H.M.S.O., London, 1958.

Vegetables

Vegetable Diseases and their Control. C. Chupp and A. F. Sherf, The Ronald Press, New York, 1960.

Diseases of Vegetable Crops. J. C. Walker, McGraw-Hill, New York, 1952.

Diseases of Vegetables. D. E. Green, Macmillan, London, 1946.

Diseases of vegetables. L. Ogilvie, *Bull. Minist. Agric. Fish. Fd, Lond.*, 123, 1961.

Les Maladies des Plantes maraicheres. C. H. Messiaen and R. Lafon, Vol. **1,** 1963; **2,** 1965: *Inst. nat. Rech. agron., Paris.*

Lists of fungi and plant diseases have been compiled for many countries and are given in detail in Ainsworth and Bisby's *Dictionary of the Fungi*, 5th Ed., 1963, pp. 319–322, in the *Plant Pathologist's Pocketbook*, C.M.I. 1968, and in the *Review of applied Mycology*, **47,** No. 11, 1968 (Africa only).

References

Adam, A. V. (1962). *Pl. Dis. Reptr*, **46,** 366.

Adam, A. V. and Powell, D. (1957). *Phytopathology*, **47,** 1.

Adebayo, A. A. (1969). Ph.D. thesis, University of Exeter.

Ainsworth, G. C. (1963). *Dictionary of the Fungi*, 5th ed. (Commonwealth Mycological Institute, Kew).

Ainsworth, G. C. (1964). *Rep. 6th Commonw. mycol. Conf., 1964*, 19.

Ainsworth, G. C. (1969). *A. Rev. Phytopath.*, **9,** 13.

Ainsworth, G. C. and Cowan, S. T. (1954). *J. gen. Microbiol.*, **10,** 465.

Ainsworth, G. C. and Sneath, P. H. A. (1962). (Eds.), *Microbial Classification* (Cambridge University Press, London).

Ainsworth, G. C. and Sussman, A. S. (1965). (Eds.), *The Fungi*, Vol. **1,** *The Fungal Cell* (Academic Press, London and New York).

Ainsworth, G. C. and Sussman A. S. (1966). *The Fungi*, Vol. **2,** *The Fungal Organism* (Academic Press, London and New York).

Ainsworth, G. C. and Sussman A. S. (1968). *The Fungi*, Vol. **3,** *The Fungal Population* (Academic Press, London and New York).

Aitken, R. A., Eddy, B. P., Ingram, M. and Wearman, C. (1956). *Biochem. J.*, **64,** 63.

Akai, S. (1959). In *Plant Pathology*, Vol. **1,** edit. by Horsfall, J. G. and Dimond, A. E., pp. 391–434 (Academic Press, London and New York).

Albersheim, P., Jones, T. M. and English P. D. (1969). *A. Rev. Phytopath.*, **7,** 171.

Alexander, L. J. (1960). *Phytopathology*, **50,** 627.

Alexopoulos, C. J. (1962). *Introductory Mycology*, 2nd ed. (Wiley, New York).

Allen, E. H. and Kuc, J. (1968). *Phytopathology*, **58,** 776.

Allen, P. J. (1942). *Am. J. Bot.*, **29,** 425.

Allen, P. J. (1954). *A. Rev. Pl. Physiol.*, **5,** 225.

Allen, P. J. (1955). *Phytopathology*, **45,** 259.

Allen, P. J. (1956). *Pl. Physiol., Suppl.* **31,** 29.

Allen, P. J. (1959). In *Plant Pathology, Problems and Progress, 1908–1958*, edit. by Holton, C. S., pp. 119–129 (University of Wisconsin Press, Madison).

Allen, P. J. (1959a). In *Plant Pathology*, Vol. **1,** edit. by Horsfall, J. G. and Dimond, A. E., pp. 435–467 (Academic Press, London and New York).

Allen, P. J. (1965). *A. Rev. Phytopath.*, **3,** 313.

Allen, P. J. (1966). *Phytopathology*, **56,** 255.

Allen, R. F. (1923). *J. agric. Res.*, **21,** 571.

Allen, R. F. (1926). *J. agric. Res.*, **32,** 701.

Anchel, M., Silverman, W. B., Valanju, N. and Rogerson, C. T. (1962). *Mycologia*, **54,** 249.

Andel, O. M. Van (1962). *Nature, Lond.*, **194,** 790.

Andel, O. M. Van (1966). *A. Rev. Phytopath.*, **4,** 349.

Anderson, H. W. and Powell, D. (1950). *Phytopathology*, **40,** 1.

Andreae, W. A. (1952). *Nature, Lond.*, **170,** 83.

Andrews, F. W. (1937). *Emp. J. exp. Agric.*, **5,** 204.

Anon. (1940). *Phytopathology*, **30,** 361.

Anon. (1943). *Phytopathology*, **33,** 627.

Anon. (1947). *Trans. Br. mycol. Soc.*, **31,** 140.

Anon. (1947a). *Phytopathology*, **37,** 354.

Anon. (1950). *Trans. Br. mycol. Soc.*, **33,** 154.

Anon. (1955). *Advis. Leafl. Min. Agric. Fish., Lond.*, 379.

Anon. (1957). *Yb. Agric. U.S. Dep. Agric., 1957.*

Anon. (1963). *The Agricultural Research Service* (Agricultural Research Council).

Anon. (1965). *Estimates of Crop Losses and Disease-control Costs in California, 1963* (Division of Agricultural Sciences, University of California).

Anon. (1968). *Principles of Plant and Animal Pest Control.* (1) *Plant disease development and control;* (2) *Weed control;* (3) *Insect-pest management and control,* 1969; (4) *Control of plant parasitic nematodes;* (5) *The vertebrates that are pests,* (unpublished); (6) *Effects of pesticides on fruit and vegetable physiology* (National Academy of Sciences, Washington, D.C.)

Anon. (1968a). *Neth. J. Pl. Path.*, **74,** 65.

Ark, P. A. (1941). *Phytopathology*, **31,** 956.

Armolik, N. and Dickson, J. G. (1958). *Phytopathology*, **46,** 462.

Arneson, P. A. and Durbin, R. D. (1967). *Phytopathology*, **57,** 1358.

Arneson, P. A. and Durbin, R. D. (1968). *Phytopathology*, **58,** 536.

Arneson, P. A. and Durbin, R. D. (1968a). *Pl. Physiol.*, **43,** 683.

Arnold, M. H. and Brown, S. J. (1968). *J. agric. Sci., Camb.*, **71,** 19.

Arnon, D. I. (1950). *Lotsya*, **3,** 31.

Arnon, D. I. (1956). *A. Rev. Pl. Physiol.*, **7,** 325.

Arny, D. C. and Leben, C. (1954). *Phytopathology*, **44,** 380.

Arsdel, E. P. Van (1965). *Phytopathology*, **55,** 945.

Ashida, J. (1965). *A. Rev. Phytopath.*, **3,** 153.

Ashworth, L. J. and Amin, J. V. (1964). *Phytopathology*, **54,** 1459.

Atanasoff, D. (1964). *Phytopath. Z.*, **50,** 336.

Audus, L. J. (1963). *Plant Growth Substances* (London).

Austen, R. (1957). *A Treatise of Fruit-Trees, shewing the Manner of Grafting, Planting, Pruning, and Ordering of them* . . . p. 54 (London).

Austwick, P. K. C. (1957). In *Biological Aspects of the Transmission of Disease,* edit. by Horton-Smith, C., pp. 73–79 (Oliver and Boyd, Edinburgh).

Babos, P. and Kassanis, B. (1963). *Virology*, **20,** 498.

Bailey, D. L. (1950). *Can. J. Res., C*, **28,** 535.

Bailey, D. L. (1961). (Ed.), *Recent Advances in Botany*, Vols. **1** and **2** (University of Toronto Press, Toronto).

Bailey, J. A. (1969). *Ann. appl. Biol.*, **64**, 315.

Bailey, J. A. and Ingham, J. L. (1971). *Physiol, Pl. Path.*, **1**, 451.

Baker, C. J. (1969). Ph.D. thesis, University of Exeter.

Baker, J. J. (1967). *Pl. Path.*, **16**, 162.

Baker, K. F., Matkin, O. A. and Davis, L. H. (1954). *Phytopathology*, **44**, 39.

Baker, K. F. and Smith, S. H. (1966). *A. Rev. Phytopath.*, **4**, 311.

Baker, K. F. and Snyder, W. C. (1965). (Eds.), *Ecology of Soil-borne Plant Pathogens* (Murray, London).

Baker, R. (1965). In *Ecology of Soil-borne Pathogens*, edit. by Baker, K. F. and Snyder, W. C., pp. 395–403, (Murray, London).

Baker, R. (1968). *A. Rev. Phytopath.*, **6**, 263.

Bald, J. G. (1952). *Am. J. Bot.*, **39**, 97.

Bald, J. G. (1966). *Adv. Virus Res.*, **12**, 103.

Baldacci, E. and Locci, R. (1965). *Riv. Patol. veg.*, *Padvia*, **4**, 5.

Ball, E. M. (1964). In *Plant Virology*, edit. by Corbett, M. K. and Sisler, H. D., pp. 235–252 (University of Florida Press, Gainesville).

Balusubramanian, M. and Rangaswami, G. (1962). *Nature, Lond.*, **194**, 774.

Banfield, W. M. (1941). *J. agric. Res.*, **62**, 637.

Banks, J. (1805). *A Short Account of the Cause of the Disease in Corn* (London).

Barber, D. A. (1968). *A. Rev. Pl. Physiol.*, **19**, 71.

Barger, G. (1931). *Ergot and Ergotism* (Gurney and Jackson, London).

Barnett, H. L. (1959). *A. Rev. Microbiol.*, **13**, 191.

Barnett, H. L. (1963). *A. Rev. Microbiol.*, **17**, 1.

Barnett, J. A. *et al.* (1966). *J. gen. Microbiol.*, **42**, 1.

Barton, R. (1957). *Nature, Lond.*, **180**, 613.

Bary, A. de (1861). *Die gegenwartig herrschende Kartoffelkrankheit, ihre Ursache und ihre Verhutung* (Leipzig).

Bary, A. de (1865). *Mber. dt. Akad. Wiss. Berl.*, 15.

Bary, A. de (1866). *Mber. dt. Akad. Wiss. Berl.*, 205.

Bary, A. de (1886). *Bot. Z.*, **44**, 377.

Bassi, A. (1835). *Phytopath. Class.*, **10**, 1958.

Bateman, D. F. and Beer, S. V. (1965). *Phytopathology*, **55**, 204.

Bateman, D. F. and Lumsden, R. D. (1965). *Phytopathology*, **55**, 734.

Bateman, D. F. and Millar, R. L. (1966). *A. Rev. Phytopath.*, **4**, 119.

Batts, C. C. V. (1955). *Trans. Br. mycol. Soc.*, **38**, 465.

Bawden, F. C. (1939). *Plant Viruses and Virus Diseases* (Chronica Botanica Co., Waltham, Mass.).

Bawden, F. C. (1957). In *Biological Aspects of the Transmission of Disease*, edit. by Horton-Smith, C., pp. 87–93 (Oliver and Boyd, Edinburgh).

Bawden, F. C. (1964). *Plant Viruses and Virus Diseases*, 4th ed. (The Ronald Press, New York).

Bawden, F. C. and Kassanis, B. (1945). *Ann. appl. Biol.*, **32**, 52.

Bawden, F. C. and Kassanis, B. (1947). *Ann. appl. Biol.*, **34**, 127.

Bazzigher, G. (1954). *Phytopath. Z.*, **21**, 105.

Bear, F. E. (1957). In *Yb. Agric. U.S. Dep. Agric.*, *1957*, 165.

Beaumont, A. (1947). *Trans. Br. mycol. Soc.*, **31,** 45.

Beaumont, A. (1954). *Pl. Path.*, **3,** 21.

Beckman, C. H. (1964). *A. Rev. Phytopath.*, **2,** 231.

Beckman, C. H., Kuntz, J. E. and Riker, A. J. (1953). *Phytopathology*, **43,** 441.

Beckman, C. H., Kuntz, J. E., Riker, A. J. and Berbee, J. G. (1953). *Phytopathology*, **43,** 448.

Beemster, A. B. R. and Dijkstra, J. (1966). (Eds.), *Viruses of Plants* (North Holland Publishing Co. Amsterdam).

Beever, D. J. (1970). *Ann. appl. Biol.*, **65,** 85.

Bega, R. (1954). *Phytopathology*, **44,** 482.

Behnke, H. D. (1966). In *Viruses of Plants*, edit. by Beemster, A. B. R. and Dijkstra, J., pp. 28–43 (North Holland Publishing Co. Amsterdam).

Beijerinck, M. W. (1898). *Verh. K. Akad Wet.*, **65,** 3 (*Phytopath. Class.* **7,** 1942).

Bell, A. A. (1969). *Phytopathology*, **59,** 1119.

Bell, A. A. and Daly, J. M. (1962). *Phytopathology*, **52,** 261.

Bell, A. A. and Presley, J. T. (1969). *Phytopathology*, **59,** 1141.

Bell, A. A. and Presley, J. T. (1969a). *Phytopathology*, **59,** 1147.

Bennett, C. W. (1967). *A. Rev. Phytopath.*, **5,** 87.

Bennett, C. W. (1969). *Adv. Virus Res.*, **14,** 221.

Bent, K. J. (1967). *Ann. appl. Biol.*, **60,** 251.

Bent, K. J. (1969). *Endeavour*, **28,** 129.

Bent, K. J. (1970). *Ann. appl. Biol.*, **66,** 103.

Bentley, J. A. (1958). *A. Rev. Pl. Physiol.*, **9,** 47.

Bergdolt, E. (1927). *Ber. dt. bot. Ges.*, **45,** 293, cited by Gaumann (1950).

Berkeley, M. J. (1854–1857). *Gdnrs' Chron.* (1854), **20** *et seq.* (reprinted in part in *Phytopath. Class.*, **8,** 1948).

Berlin, J. D. and Bowen, C. C. (1964). *Am. J. Bot.*, **51,** 445.

Bernstein, L. and Hayward, H. E. (1958). *A. Rev. Pl. Physiol.*, **9,** 25.

Bessey, E. A. (1950). *Morphology and Taxonomy of Fungi* (Constable, London).

Best, R. J. (1968). *Adv. Virus Res.*, **13,** 65.

Bewley, W. F. (1922). *Ann. appl. Biol.*, **9,** 116.

Bhattochayara, P. K., Naylor, J. M. and Shaw, M. (1965). *Science, N. Y.*, **150,** 1605.

Biffen, R. H. (1904). *Jl R. agric. Soc.*, **65,** 337.

Biffen, R. H. (1907). *J. agric. Soc., Camb.*, **2,** 109.

Bisby, G. R. (1953). *An Introduction to the Taxonomy and Nomenclature of Fungi*, 2nd ed. (Commonwealth Mycological Institute, Kew).

Bishop, C. T. and Whitaker, D. R. (1955). *Chemy. Ind.*, Pt. I, 119.

Black, H. S. (1963). *Phytopathology*, **53,** 871.

Black, H. S. and Wheeler, H. (1962). *Phytopathology*, **52,** 725.

Black, L. M. (1943). *Phytopathology*, **33,** 2.

Black, W. (1952). *Proc. R. Soc. Edinb.*, B, **65,** 36.

Black, W., Mastenbroek, C., Mills, W. R. and Petersen, L. C. (1953). *Euphytica*, **2,** 173.

Blackhurst, F. M. (1963). *Ann. appl. Biol.*, **52,** 79.

Blackman, V. H. and Welsford, E. J. (1916). *Ann. Bot.*, **30,** 389.

Block, S. S. (1953). *Appl. Microbiol.*, **1,** 287.

Bollard, E. G. and Butler, G. W. (1966). *A. Rev. Pl. Physiol.*, **17,** 77.

Boller, A. *et al.* (1957). *Helv. chim. Acta*, **90,** 875.

Bonde, R. and Covell, M. (1950). *Phytopathology*, **40,** 161.

Boone, D. M. and Keitt, G. W. (1957). *Phytopathology*, **47,** 403.

Boone, D. M., Kline, D. M. and Keitt, G. W. (1957). *Am. J. Bot.*, **44,** 791.

Boosalis, M. G. (1964). *A. Rev. Phytopath.*, **2,** 363.

Boosalis, M. G. and Mankau, R. (1965). In *Ecology of Soil-borne Plant Pathogens*, edit. by Baker, K. F. and Snyder, W. C., pp. 374–389 (Murray, London).

Borlaug, N. E. (1965). *Phytopathology*, **55,** 1088.

Borner, H. (1960). *Bot. Rev.*, **26,** 393.

Bortels, H. (1947). *Biol. Zentral. Land. Forst. Berlin*, cited by Yarwood (1959).

Bourke, P. M. A. (1953). *Tech. Notes met. Serv. Eire*, 12.

Bourke, P. M. A. (1955). *Tech. Notes Wld met. Org.*, **10,** 1.

Bourke, P. M. A. (1964). *Nature, Lond.*, **203,** 805.

Bourke, P. M. A. (1970). *A. Rev. Phytopath.*, **8,** 345.

Bourke. P. M. A., Arsdel, E. P., Van and Riley, J. A. (1965). *Phytopathology*, 55, 943.

Bowden, J., Gregory, P. H. and Johnson, C. G. (1971). *Nature, Lond.*, **229,** 500.

Boyce, J. S. (1938). *Forest Pathology* (McGraw-Hill, New York).

Boyd, A. E. W. (1952). *Ann. appl. Biol.*, **39,** 339.

Boyd, A. E. W. and Lennard, J. H. (1962). *Pl. Path.*, **11,** 161.

Boyle, L. W. (1956). *Pl. Dis. Reptr*, **40,** 661.

Boynton, D. (1954). *A. Rev. Pl. Physiol.*, **5,** 31.

Bradley, R. H. E. (1964). In *Plant Virology*, edit. by Corbett, M. K. and Sisler, H. D., pp. 148–174 (University of Florida Press, Gainesville).

Bradley, S. G. (1962). *A. Rev. Microbiol.*, **16,** 35.

Brady, B. L. (1960). *Trans. Br. mycol. Soc.*, **43,** 31.

Brandenburg, E. (1950). *NachrBl. dt. PflSchutzdienst, Stuttgart*, **2,** 69.

Brandes, J. (1966). In *Viruses of Plants*, edit. by Beemster, A. B. R. and Dijkstra, J., pp. 218–229 (North Holland Publishing Co., Amsterdam).

Brandes, J. and Bercks, R. (1965). *Adv. Virus Res.*, **11,** 1.

Bratley, C. O. and Wiant, J. S. (1950). *Econ. Bot.*, **4,** 177.

Braun, A. C. (1954). *A. Rev. Pl. Physiol.*, **5,** 133.

Braun, A. C. (1959). In *Plant Pathology*, Vol. **1,** edit. by Horsfall, J. G. and Dimond, A. E., pp. 189–243 (Academic Press, London and New York).

Braun, A. C. (1962). *A. Rev. Pl. Physiol.*, **13,** 533.

Braun, A. C. and Laskaris, T. (1942). *Proc. natn. Acad. Sci. U.S.A.*, **28,** 468.

Braun, A. C. and Pringle, R. B. (1959). In *Plant Pathology, Problems and Progress, 1908–1958*, edit. by Holton, C. S., pp. 88–99 (University of Wisconsin Press, Madison).

Brauns, F. E. (1952). *The Chemistry of Lignin* (Academic Press, London and New York).

Brauns, F. E. and Brauns, D. A. (1960). *The Chemistry of Lignin*. Suppl. Vol. (New York).

Brenchley, G. H. (1968). *A. Rev. Phytopath.*, **6,** 1.

Brian, P. W. (1949). *Ann. Bot.*, **13,** 59.

Brian, P. W. (1955). In *Mechanisms of Microbial Pathogenicity*, edit. by Howie, J. W. and O'Hea, A. J., pp. 294–319 (Cambridge University Press, London).

Brian, P. W. (1957). In *The Biological Action of Growth Substances*, edit. by Porter, H. K., pp. 166–182 (Cambridge University Press, London).

Brian, P. W. (1958). *Outl. Agric.*, **2,** 27.

Brian, P. W. (1958a). *Nature, Lond.*, **181,** 1122.

Brian, P. W. (1960). *Trans. Br. mycol. Soc.*, **43,** 1.

Brian, P. W., Curtis, P. J., Hemming, H. G., Jefferys, E. G., Unwin, C. H. and Wright, J. M. (1951). *J. gen. Microbiol.*, **7,** 619.

Brian, P. W., Curtis, P. J., Hemming, H. G., Unwin, C. H. and Wright, J. M. (1949). *Nature, Lond.*, **164,** 534.

Brian, P. W., Elson, G. W., Hemming, H. G. and Wright, J. M. (1952). *Ann. appl. Biol.*, **39,** 308.

Brian, P. W. and Grove, J. F. (1957). *Endeavour*, **16,** 161.

Brian, P. W. and Hemming, H. G. (1958). *Ann. Bot.*, **22,** 1.

Brinkherhoff, L. A. (1963). *Tech. Bull. Okla. agric. Exp. Stn*, T. 98.

Broadbent, L. (1960). In *Plant Pathology*, Vol. **3,** edit. by Horsfall, J. G. and Dimond, A. E., pp. 97–125 (Academic Press, London and New York).

Broadbent, L. (1964). In *Plant Virology*, edit. by Corbett, M. K. and Sisler, H. D., pp. 330–364 (University of Florida Press, Gainesville).

Broadbent, L. (1965). *Ann. appl. Biol.*, **55,** 67.

Broadbent, L. and Martini, C. (1959). *Adv. Virus Res.*, **6,** 93.

Brodie, H. J. and Gregory, P. H. (1953). *Can. J. Bot.*, **31,** 402.

Brooks, D H. and Dawson, M. G. (1968). *Ann. appl. Biol.*, **61,** 57.

Brooks, F. T. (1908). *Ann. Bot.*, **22,** 479.

Brooks, F. T. (1928). *New Phytol.*, **27,** 85.

Brooks, F. T. and Brenchley, G. H. (1929). *New Phytol.*, **28,** 218.

Brooks, F. T. and Brenchley, G. H. (1931). *J. Pomol.*, **5,** 61.

Brooks, F. T. and Brenchley, G. H. (1931a). *New Phytol.*, **30,** 128.

Brooks, F. T. and Moore, W. C. (1926). *J. Pomol.*, **5,** 61.

Brown, A. and Officer, J. E. (1968). In *Methods in Virology*, Vol. **4,** edit. by Maramorosch, K. and Koprowski, H., pp. 331–364 (Academic Press, London and New York).

Brown, J. C. (1956). *A. Rev. Pl. Physiol.*, **7,** 171.

Brown, J. F. and Sharp, E. L. (1970). *Phytopathology*, **60,** 529.

Brown, R. (1946). *Nature, Lond.*, **157,** 64.

Brown, S. A. (1966). *A. Rev. Pl. Physiol.*, **17,** 223.

Brown, W. (1915). *Ann. Bot.*, **29,** 313.

Brown, W. (1922). *Ann. Bot.*, **36,** 257.

Brown, W. (1922a). *Ann. Bot.*, **36,** 101.

Brown, W. (1934). *Trans. Br. mycol. Soc.*, **19,** 11.

Brown, W. (1936). *Bot. Rev.*, **2,** 236.

Brown, W. (1955). *Ann. appl. Biol.*, **43,** 325.

Brown, W. (1965). *A. Rev. Phytopath.*, **3,** 1.

Brown, W. Brooks, F. T. and Bawden, F. C. (1948). *Proc. R. Soc.*, B, **135,** 171.

Browning, J. A. and Frey, K. J. (1969). *A. Rev. Phytopath.*, **7,** 355.

Broyer, T. C. and Stout, P. R. (1959). *A. Rev. Pl. Physiol.*, **10,** 277.

Bruch, C. W. (1967). In *Airborne Microbes*, edit. by Gregory, P. H. and Monteith, J. L., pp. 345–374 (Cambridge University Press, London).

Bruehl, G. W. (1961). *Barley Yellow Dwarf. Monograph no. 1*, American Phyto-pathological Society.

Buddenhagen, I. and Kelman, A. (1964). *A. Rev. Phytopath.*, **2**, 203.

Burchill, R. T. and Hutton, K. E. (1965). *Ann. appl. Biol.*, **56**, 285.

Burkholder, W. H. (1948). *A. Rev. Microbiol* **2**, 389.

Burnett, J. H. (1968). *Fundamentals of Mycology*, (Arnold, London).

Burrage, S. W. (1970). *Ann. appl. Biol.*, **66**, 429.

Burrows, V. D. (1960). *Nature, Lond.*, **188**, 957.

Burton, G. W. (1954). *Agron. J.*, **46**, 99.

Bussler, W. (1964). *Z. PflErnähr. Düng. Bodenk.*, **105**, 113.

Butler, E. J. (1918). *Fungi and Diseases in Plants* (Thacker, Spink and Co., Calcutta and Simla).

Butler, E. J. (1936). *3rd Cong. int. Path. comp., Athens, 1936.*

Butler, E. J. and Jones, S. G. (1949). *Plant Pathology* (London, Macmillan).

Buxton, E. W. (1956). *J. gen. Microbiol.*, **15**, 133.

Buxton, E. W. (1957). *Trans. Br. mycol. Soc.*, **40**, 145.

Buxton, E. W. (1958). *Nature, Lond.*, **181**, 1222.

Buxton, E. W. (1960). In *Plant Pathology*, Vol. **2**, edit. by Horsfall, J. G. and Dimond, A. E., pp. 359–405 (Academic Press, London and New York).

Buxton, E. W. (1962). *Trans. Br. mycol. Soc.*, **45**, 274.

Buxton, E. W. (1964). In *Microbial Behaviour 'in vivo' and 'in vitro'*, edit. by Smith, H. and Taylor, J., pp. 145–164 (Cambridge University Press, London).

Buxton, E. W. and Perry, D. A. (1959). *Trans. Br. mycol. Soc.*, **42**, 378.

Byrde, R. J. W. (1956). *J. hort. Sci.*, **31**, 188.

Byrde, R. J. W. (1957). *J. hort. Sci.*, **32**, 227.

Byrde, R. J. W. (1963). In *Bull. Conn. agric. Exp. Stn*, 663, 31.

Byrde, R. J. W. (1969). In *Fungicides*, Vol. **2**, edit. by Torgeson, D. C., pp. 531–578 (Academic Press, London and New York).

Byrde, R. J. W. and Ainsworth, G. C. (1958). In *The Strategy of Chemotherapy*, edit. by Cowan, S. T. and Rowatt, E., pp. 309–335 (Cambridge University Press, London).

Byrde, R. J. W. and Fielding, A. H. (1962). *Nature, Lond.*, **196**, 1227.

Byrde, R. J. W. and Fielding, A. H. (1965). *Nature, Lond.*, **205**, 390.

Byrde, R. J. W., Fielding, A. H. and Williams, A. H. (1960). In *Phenolics in Plants in Health and Disease*, edit. by Pridham, J. B., pp. 95–99 (Pergamon Press, Oxford).

Byrde, R. J. W., Martin, J. T. and Nicholas, D. J. D. (1956) *Nature, Lond.*, **178**, 638.

Byrde, R. J. W. and Woodcock, D. (1953). *Ann. appl. Biol.*, **40**, 675.

Cadman, C. H. (1963). *A. Rev. Phytopath.*, **1**, 143.

Caldwell, J. (1952). *Ann. appl. Biol.*, **39**, 98.

Calpouzos, L. (1966). *A. Rev. Phytopath.*, **4**, 369.

Calpouzos, L. (1969). In *Fungicides*, Vol. **2**, edit. by Torgeson, D. C., pp. 367–393 (Academic Press, London and New York).

Calpouzos, L., Colberg, C. and Theis, T. (1962). *Pl. Dis. Reptr*, **46**, 105.

Calpouzos, L., Theis, T., Rivera, C. M. and Colberg, C. (1959). *Phytopathology*, **49,** 119.

Cammack, R. H. (1959). *Trans. Br. mycol. Soc.*, **42,** 27.

Campbell, C. E. and Dimock, A. W. (1955). *Phytopathology*, **45,** 644.

Campbell, R. N. (1962). *Nature, Lond.*, **195,** 675.

Campbell, W. G. (1952). In *Wood Chemistry*, 2nd ed., edit. by Wise, L. E. and Jahn, E. C., pp. 1061–1116 (Reinhold Publishers Corp., New York).

Carefoot, G. L. and Sprott, E. R. (1969). *Famine on the Wind* (Angus and Robertson, London).

Carroll, T. W. and Kosuge, T. (1969). *Phytopathology*, **59,** 953.

Carson, R. (1963). *Silent Spring* (Hamilton, London).

Carter, H. P. and Lockwood, J. L. (1957). *Phytopathology*, **47,** 154.

Carter, W. (1936). *Science, N.Y.*, **83,** 522.

Carter, W. (1939). *Bot. Rev.*, **5,** 273.

Carter, W. (1952). *Bot. Rev.*, **18,** 680.

Carter, W. (1962). *Insects in Relation to Plant Diseases* (Interscience, New York).

Cartwright, K. S. G. and Findlay, W. P. K. (1958). *Decay of Timber and its Prevention*, 2nd Ed. (H.M.S.O., London).

Caspar, D. L. D. (1964). In *Plant Virology*, edit. by Corbett, M. K. and Sisler, H. D., pp. 267–291 (University of Florida Press, Gainesville).

Castano, J. J. and Kernkamp, M. F. (1956). *Phytopathology*, **46,** 326.

Catcheside, D. G. (1951). *The Genetics of Micro-organisms* (Pitman, London).

Caten, C. E. and Jinks, J. L. (1966). *Trans. Br. mycol. Soc.*, **49,** 81.

Cavalli-Sforza, L. L. (1957). *A. Rev. Microbiol.*, **11,** 391.

Chakravarty, D. K. and Srivastava, D. N. (1967). *Ann. Bot.*, **31,** 739.

Chakravarty, T. (1957). *Trans. Br. mycol. Soc.*, **40,** 337.

Chalutz, E. and Stahmann, M. (1969). *Phytopathology*, **59,** 1072.

Chamberlain, A. C. (1967). In *Airborne Microbes*, edit. by Gregory, P. H. and Monteith, J. L., pp. 138–164 (Cambridge University Press, London).

Chamberlain, D. W. and McAlister, D. F. (1954). *Phytopathology*, **44,** 4.

Chamberlain, D. W. and Paxton, J. D. (1968). *Phytopathology*, **58,** 1349.

Channon, A. G. (1970). *Ann. appl. Biol.*, **65,** 481.

Channon, A. G. and Keyworth, W. G. (1960). *Ann. appl. Biol.*, **48,** 1–7.

Chaudhuri, H. (1935). *Proc. natn. Inst. Sci. India*, **1,** 71. Abstract in *Rev. appl. Mycol.*, **14,** 692 (1935).

Cheo, P. C. (1955). *Phytopathology*, **45,** 17.

Chessin, M. (1958). *Proc. 3rd Conf. Potato Virus Dis.*, 80.

Chester, K. S. (1933). *Q. Rev. Biol.*, **8,** 129, 275.

Chester, K. S. (1942). *Pl. Dis. Reptr*, **26,** 213.

Chester, K. S. (1946). *The Nature and Prevention of Cereal Rusts as exemplified in the Leaf Rust of Wheat* (Chronica Botanica Co., Waltham Mass).

Chester, K. S. (1947). *Nature and Prevention of Plant Diseases* (Blakiston, Philadelphia).

Chester, K. S. (1950). *Pl. Dis. Reptr, Suppl.*, 193.

Chester, K. S. (1955). *Ann. appl. Biol.*, **42,** 335,

Chester, K. S. (1959). In *Plant Pathology*, Vol. **1,** edit. by Horsfall, J. G. and Dimond, A. E., pp. 99–142 (Academic Press, London and New York).

Chesters, C. G. C. and Blakeman, J. P. (1966). *Ann. appl. Biol.*, **58,** 291.

Chiarappa, L. (1970). *A. Rev. Phytopath.*, **8,** 419.

Chou, M. C. and Preece, T. F. (1968). *Ann. appl. Biol.*, **62,** 11.

Christensen, C. M. (1957). *Bot. Rev.*, **23,** 108.

Christensen, C. M., Kaufert, F. H., Schmitz, H. and Allison, J. L. (1942). *Am. J. Bot.*, **29,** 552.

Christensen, C. M., Stakman, E. C. and Christensen, J. J. (1947). *A. Rev. Microbiol.*, **1,** 61.

Christensen, J. A. (1969). *Phytopathology*, **59,** 10.

Christensen, J. J. (1963). *Monograph Am. phytopath. Soc.*, 2.

Christie, J. R. and Perry, V. G. (1959). In *Plant Pathology, Problems and Progress, 1908–1958*, edit. by Holton, C. S., pp. 419–426 (University of Wisconsin Press, Madison).

Clayton, C. N. (1942). *Phytopathology*, **32,** 921.

Clinton, P. K. S. (1957). *E. Afr. agric. J.*, **22,** 137.

Cochrane, V. W. (1945). *Phytopathology*, **35,** 458.

Cochrane, V. W. (1958). *Physiology of Fungi* (Wiley, New York).

Cochrane, V. W. (1960). In *Plant Pathology*, Vol. **2,** edit. by Horsfall, J. G. and Dimond, A. E., pp. 167–202 (Academic Press, London and New York).

Cocking, E. C. (1966). *Planta*, **68,** 206.

Cole, M. and Wood, R. K. S. (1961). *Ann. Bot.*, **25,** 435.

Coleman-Cooke, J. (1965). *The Harvest that Kills* (Odhams, London).

Coley-Smith, J. R., King, J. E., Dickinson, D. J. and Holt, R. W. (1967). *Ann. appl. Biol.*, **60,** 109.

Colhoun, J. (1953). *Ann. appl. Biol.*, **40,** 262.

Colhoun, J. (1958). *Phytopath. Pap.*, 3.

Colhoun, J. and Muskett, A. E. (1948). *Ann. appl. Biol.*, **35,** 429.

Conant, G. H. (1927). *Am. J. Bot.*, **14,** 457.

Condon, P. and Kuc, J. (1962). *Phytopathology*, **52,** 182.

Cook, R. J. and Flentje, N. T. (1967). *Phytopathology*, **57,** 178.

Cook, R. J. and Schroth, M. N. (1965). *Phytopathology*, **55,** 254.

Coons, M. K. (1953). *Yb. Agric. U.S. Dep. Agric.*, 1953, 174.

Corbett, M. K. (1964). In *Plant Virology*, edit. by Corbett, M. K. and Sisler, H. D., pp. 1–16 (University of Florida Press, Gainesville).

Corbett, M. K. and Sisler, H. D. (1964). (Eds.), *Plant Virology* (University of Florida Press, Gainesville).

Corden, M. E. (1969). In *Fungicides*, Vol. **2,** edit. by Torgeson, D. C., pp. 477–529 (Academic Press, London and New York).

Corey, R. R. and Starr, M. P. (1957). *J. Bact.*, **74,** 137.

Corey, R. R. and Starr, M. P. (1957a). *J. Bact.*, **74,** 141.

Corke, A. T. K. (1967). *Ann. appl. Biol.*, **60,** 241.

Courshee, R. J. (1967). In *Fungicides*, Vol. **1,** edit. by Torgeson, D. C., pp. 239–286 (Academic Press, London and New York).

Cox, A. E. and Large, E. C. (1960). *Agric. Handb. U.S. Dep. Agric.*, 174.

Cox, P. G. (1969). M.Sc. thesis, University of Exeter.

Cramer, H. H. (1967). *Pflanzenschutz-Nachrichten 'Bayer'*, 20.

Crosier, W. (1934). *Mem. Cornell Univ. agric. Exp. Stn*, **155.**

Crosse, J. E. (1959). *Ann. appl. Biol.*, **47,** 306.

Crosse, J. E. (1966). *A. Rev. Phytopath.*, **4,** 291.

Crosse, J. E. and Pitcher, R. S. (1952). *Ann. appl. Biol.*, **39,** 475.

Crowdy, S. H. (1952). *Ann. appl. Biol.*, **39,** 569.

Crowdy, S. H. (1959). In *Plant Pathology, Problems and Progress, 1908–1958*, edit. by Holton, C. S., pp. 231–238 (University of Wisconsin Press, Madison).

Crowdy, S. H., Gardner, D., Grove, J. F. and Pramer, D. (1955). *J. exp. Bot.*, **6,** 371.

Crowdy, S. H., Grove, J. F., Hemming, H. G. and Robinson, K. C. (1956). *J. exp. Bot.*, **7,** 42.

Crowdy, S. H. and Wain, R. L. (1950). *Nature, Lond.*, **165,** 937.

Croxall, H. E., Gwynne, D. C. and Jenkins, J. E. E. (1952). *Pl. Path.*, **1,** 39, 89.

Cruickshank, I. A. M. (1963). *A. Rev. Phytopath.*, **1,** 351.

Cruickshank, I. A. M. and Mandryk, M. (1960). *J. Aust. Inst. agric. Sci.*, **26,** 369.

Cruickshank, I. A. M. and Perrin, D. R. (1963). *Aust. J. biol. Sci.*, **16,** 111.

Cruickshank, I. A. M. and Perrin, D. R. (1968). *Life Sci.*, **7,** 449.

Cummins, G. B. (1959). *Illustrated Genera of Rust Fungi* (Burgess Publishing Co.)

Curl, E. A. (1963). *Bot. Rev.*, **29,** 413.

Curtis, O. F. and Clark, D. G. (1950). *An Introduction to Plant Physiology* (McGraw-Hill, New York).

Cutter, V. M. (1951). *Trans. N.Y. Acad. Sci.*, **14,** 103.

Cutter, V. M. (1959). *Mycologia*, **51,** 248.

Cutter, V. M. (1960). *Mycologia*, **52,** 726.

Cutter, V. M. (1960a). *A.S.B. Bull.*, 7, 26, cited by C. J. Alexopoulos, *Introductory Mycology*, 2nd ed., Wiley, New York (1962).

Dale, J. L. and Kim, K. S. (1969). *Phytopathology*, **59,** 1765.

Daley, J. M. (1967) In *The Dynamic Role of Molecular Constituents in Plant-Parasite Interaction*, edit. by Mirocha, C. J. and Uritani, I., pp. 144–161 (American Phytopathological Society).

Daley, J. M. and Inman, R. E. (1958). *Phytopathology*, **48,** 91.

Darley, E. F. and Middleton, J. T. (1966). *A. Rev. Phytopath.*, **4,** 103.

Darling, H. M. (1937). *J. agric. Res.*, **54,** 305.

Darlington, C. D. and Mather, K. (1949). *The Elements of Genetics* (Allen & Unwin, London).

Darpoux, H. (1960). In *Plant Pathology*, Vol. **3,** edit. by Horsfall, J. G. and Dimond, A. E., pp. 521–565 (Academic Press, London and New York).

Davies, D. D., Giovanelli, J. and Rees, T. A. (1964). *Plant Biochemistry* (Blackwell, Oxford).

Davies, R. R. (1959). *Nature, Lond.*, **183,** 1695.

Davis, D. and Dimond, A. E. (1954). *Phytopathology*, **44,** 485.

Davis, D., Waggoner, P. E. and Dimond, A. E., (1953). *Nature, Lond.*, **172,** 959.

Davis, R. E. and Whitcomb, R. F. (1969). *Phytopathology*, **59,** 1556.

Davis, R. H. (1966). In *The Fungi*, Vol. **2,** edit. by Ainsworth, G. C. and Sussman, A. S., pp. 567–588 (Academic Press, London and New York).

Davis, W. H. (1935). *Mycologia*, **27,** 527.

Day, P. R. (1957). *Nature, Lond.*, **179**, 1141.
Day, P. R. (1960). *A. Rev. Microbiol.*, **14**, 1.
Day, P. R. (1966). *A. Rev. Phytopath.*, **4**, 245.
Deese, D. C. and Stahmann, M. A. (1962). *Phytopathology*, **52**, 247.
Dekker, J. (1963). *Nature, Lond.*, **197**, 1027.
Dekker, J. (1963a). *A. Rev. Microbiol.*, **17**, 243.
Dekker, J. (1969). In *Fungicides*, Vol. **2**, edit. by Torgeson, D. C., pp. 579–635 (Academic Press, London and New York).
Dekker, J. and Oort, A. J. P. (1964). *Phytopathology*, **54**, 815.
Delacroix, G. (1902, 1908). *Maladies des Plantes Cultivées* (Paris).
Delacroix, G. (1911). *Maladies des Plantes Cultivées dans les Pays Chauds* (Paris).
Delp, C. J. (1954). *Phytopathology*, **44**, 615.
Demain, A. L. and Phaff, H. J. (1957). *Wallerstein Labs. Commun.*, **20**, 119.
Deuel, H. and Stutz, E. (1958). *Adv. Enzymol.*, **20**, 341.
Deverall, B. J. (1964). In *Microbial Behaviour 'in vivo' and 'in vitro'*, edit. by Smith, H. and Taylor, J., pp. 165–186 (Cambridge University Press, London).
Deverall, B. J. (1969). *Fungal Parasitism* (Arnold, London).
Deverall, B. J. and Wood, R. K. S. (1961). *Ann. appl. Biol.*, **49**, 461.
Deverall, B. J. and Wood, R. K. S. (1961a). *Ann. appl. Biol.*, **49**, 473.
Dickinson, S. (1949). *Ann. Bot.*, **13**, 89, 219, 345.
Dickinson, S. (1960). In *Plant Pathology*, Vol. **2**, edit. by Horsfall, J. G. and Dimond, A. E., pp. 203–232 (Academic Press, London and New York).
Diener, T. O. (1963). *A. Rev. Phytopath.*, **1**, 197.
Dimond, A. E. (1955). *A. Rev. Pl. Physiol.*, **6**, 329.
Dimond, A. E. (1959). In *Plant Pathology, Problems and Progress, 1908–1958*, edit. by Holton, C. S., pp. 221–228 (University of Wisconsin Press, Madison).
Dimond, A. E. (1970). *A. Rev. Phytopath.*, **8**, 301.
Dimond, A. E., Davis, D., Chapman, R. A. and Stoddard, E. M. (1952). *Bull. Conn. agric. Exp. Stn.*, 557.
Dimond, A. E. and Horsfall, J. G. (1959). *A. Rev. Pl. Physiol.*, **10**, 257.
Dimond, A. E. and Horsfall, J. G. (1960). In *Plant Pathology*, Vol. **3**, edit. by Horsfall, J. G. and Dimond, A. E., pp. 1–22 (Academic Press, London and New York).
Dimond, A. E. and Horsfall, J. G. (1965). In *Ecology of Soil-borne Plant Pathogens*, edit. by Baker, K. F. and Snyder, W. C., pp. 404–415 (Murray, London).
Dimond, A. E. and Waggoner, P. E. (1953). *Phytopathology*, **43**, 229.
Dixon, G. R. and Pegg, G. F. (1969). *Trans. Br. mycol. Soc.*, **53**, 109.
Dobbs, C. G. and Hinson, W. H. (1953). *Nature, Lond.*, **172**, 197.
Doi, Y., Teranaka, M., Yora, K. and Asuyama, H. (1967). *Ann. phytopath. Soc. Japan*, **33**, 259. Abstract in *Rev. appl. Mycol.*, **47**, 128, 1968.
Domsch, K. H. (1964). *A. Rev. Phytopath.*, **2**, 293.
Dopson, R. N. (1964). *Pl. Dis. Reptr*, **48**, 30.
Doubly, J. A., Flor, H. H. and Clagett, C. D. (1960). *Science, N.Y.*, **131**, 229.
Doupnik, B. and Wheeler, H. (1965). *Phytopathology*, **55**, 1055.
Dowson, W. J. (1922). *Trans. Br. mycol. Soc.*, **7**, 283.
Dowson, W. J. (1923). *Jl R. hort. Soc.*, **48**, 33.
Dowson, W. J. (1949). *Manual of Bacterial Plant Diseases* (Black, London).

Dowson, W. J. (1957). *Plant Diseases due to Bacteria* (Cambridge University Press, London).

Dufrenoy, J. (1936). *Am. J. Bot.*, **23,** 70.

Duggar, B. M. (1909). *Fungus Diseases of Plants* (Boston).

Dunin, M. S. (1960). Abstract in *Rev. appl. Mycol.*, **39,** 664.

Dutta, S. K., Hall, C. V. and Heyne, E. G. (1960). *Bot. Gaz.*, **121,** 166.

Duvdevani, S., Reichert, I. and Palti, J. (1946). *Palest. J. Bot. Rehovot Ser.*, **5,** 127. Abstract in *Rev. appl. Mycol.*, **26,** 477 (1947).

Dye, D. W. (1958). *Nature, Lond.*, **182,** 1813.

Dykstra, T. P. (1961). *Bot. Rev.*, **27,** 445.

Easton, G. D. (1967). *Phytopathology*, **57,** 1004.

Eaton, F. M. (1930). *Phytopathology*, **20,** 967.

Eaton, F. M. and Rigler, N. E. (1946). *J. agric. Res.*, **72,** 137.

Eaton, M. D. (1965). *A. Rev. Microbiol.*, **19,** 379.

Eckert, J. W. (1967). In *Fungicides*, Vol. **1,** edit. by Torgeson, D. C., pp. 287–378 (Academic Press, London and New York).

Eckert, J. W. (1969). *Wld Rev. Pest Control*, **8,** 116.

Eckert, J. W. and Kolbezen, M. J. (1963). *Phytopathology*, **53,** 1053.

Eckert, J. W. and Sommer, N. F. (1967). *A. Rev. Phytopath.*, **5,** 391.

Edwards, H. H. and Allen, P. J. (1970). *Phytopathology*, **60,** 1504.

Eide, C. J. (1955). *A. Rev. Microbiol.*, **9,** 297.

Elias, R. S., Shephard, M. C., Snell, B. K. and Stubbs, J. (1968). *Nature, Lond.*, **219,** 1160.

Ellingboe, A. H. (1968). *A. Rev. Phytopath.*, **6,** 317.

Elliott, C. (1930). *Manual of Bacterial Plant Pathogens* (Baillière, Tindall and Cox, London).

Elliott, C. (1951). *Manual of Bacterial Plant Pathogens*, 2nd ed. (Chronica Botanica Co., Waltham, Mass.).

English, P. D. and Albersheim, P. (1969). *Pl. Physiol.*, **44,** 217.

Esau, K. (1967). *A. Rev. Phytopath.*, **5,** 45.

Etten, H. D. Van and Bateman, D. F. (1969). *Phytopathology*, **59,** 968.

Evans, E. (1968). *Plant Diseases and their Chemical Control* (Blackwell, Oxford).

Evans, E. (1971). In *Diseases of Crop Plants*, edit. by Western, J. H., pp. 45–61 (The Macmillan Press, London and Basingstoke).

Evans, H. J. and Sorger, G. J. (1966). *A. Rev. Pl. Physiol.*, **17,** 47.

Ezekiel, W. N. (1945). *Phytopathology*, **35,** 296.

Farkas, G. L. and Kiraly, Z. (1962). *Phytopath. Z.*, **44,** 105.

Farkas, G. L. and Ledingham, G. A. (1959). *Can. J. Microbiol.*, **5,** 37.

Farkas, G. L. and Lovrekovich, L. (1965). *Phytopathology*, **55,** 519.

Farkas, G. L. and Solymosy, F. (1965). *Phytopath. Z.*, **53,** 85.

Favret, E. A. (1967). *Ciênc. Cult. S. Paulo*, **19,** 179.

Fawcett, C. H. and Spencer, D. M. (1969). In *Fungicides*, Vol. **2,** edit. by Torgeson, D. C., pp. 637–669 (Academic Press, London and New York).

Fawcett, C. H. and Spencer, D. M. (1970). *A. Rev. Phytopath.*, **8,** 403.

Fawcett, C. H., Spencer, D. M. and Wain, R. L. (1957). *Ann. appl. Biol.* **45,** 158.

Feldman, A. W., Caroselli, N. E. and Howard, F. L. (1950). *Phytopathology*, **40,** 341.

Fellows, H. (1928). *J. agric. Res.*, **37,** 647.

Felt, E. P. (1940). *Plant Galls and Gall Makers* (Constable, London).

Fernando, A. M. S., Baker, E. A. and Martin, J. T. (1964). *Ann. appl. Biol.*, **53,** 43.

Ferris, V. R. (1955). *Phytopathology*, **45,** 546.

Fielding, M. J. (1959). *A. Rev. Microbiol.*, **13,** 239.

Fincham, J. R. S. and Day, P. R. (1965). *Fungal Genetics*, 3rd ed. (Blackwell, Oxford).

Findlay, W. P. K. (1951). *Trans. Br. mycol. Soc.*, **34,** 146.

Fink, H. C. (1948). *Phytopathology*, **38,** 9.

Fischer, G. (1953). *Arch. Mikrobiol.*, **18,** 291.

Fischer, G. W. and Holton, C. S. (1957). *Biology and Control of the Smut Fungi* (The Ronald Press, New York).

Fisher, R. W. (1959). *Pl. Dis. Reptr.* **43,** 878.

Fisher, R. W., Chamberlain, G. C. and Kemp, W. G. (1960). *Pl. Dis. Reptr,* **44,** 273.

Flangas, A. L. and Dickson, J. G. (1961). *Am. J. Bot.*, **48,** 275.

Flentje, N. T. (1957). *Trans. Br. mycol. Soc.*, **40,** 322.

Flentje, N. T. (1959). In *Plant Pathology, Problems and Progress, 1908–1958*, edit. by Holton, C. S., pp. 76–87 (University of Wisconsin Press, Madison).

Flentje, N. T. (1965). In *Ecology of Soil-borne Plant Pathogens*, edit. by Baker, K. F. and Snyder, W. C., pp. 255–268 (Murray, London).

Flentje, N. T., Dodman, R. L. and Kerr, A. (1963). *Aust. J. biol. Sci.*, **16,** 784.

Flood, A. E. and Kirkham, D. S. (1960). In *Phenolics in Plants in Health and Disease*, edit. by Pridham, J. B., pp. 81–85 (Pergamon Press, Oxford).

Flor, H. H. (1959). In *Plant Pathology. Problems and Progress, 1908–1958*, edit. by Holton, C. S., pp. 137–144 (University of Wisconsin Press, Madison).

Foister, C. E. (1935). *Bot. Rev.*, **1,** 497.

Foister, C. E. (1946). *Bot. Rev.,* **12,** 548.

Foister, C. E., Wilson, A. R. and Boyd, A. E. W. (1952). *Ann. appl. Biol.*, **39,** 29.

Fontana, F. (1767). *Phytopath. Class.*, **2,** 1932.

Forbes, I. L. (1939). *Phytopathology*, **29,** 659.

Ford, J. H., Klomparens, W. and Hamner, C. L. (1958). *Pl. Dis. Reptr,* **42,** 680.

Fordyce, C. and Green, R. J. (1964). *Phytopathology*, **54,** 795.

Forsyth, F. R. (1955). *Can. J. Bot.*, **33,** 363.

Forsyth, W. (1802). *A Treatise on the Culture and Management of Fruit Trees* (London).

Foster, J. D. (1949). *Chemical Activities of Fungi* (Academic Press, London and New York).

Frank, A. B. (1895–6). *Die Krankheiten der Pflanzen*, Vols. **1, 2** and 3 (Breslau).

Frazer, H. L. (1944). *Ann. appl. Biol.*, **31,** 271.

Frederick, L. and Howard, F. L. (1951). *Phytopathology*, **41,** 12.

Frey-Wyssling, A. (1953). *Sub-microscopic Morphology of Protoplasm and its Derivatives* (Elsevier, Amsterdam).

Frey-Wyssling, A. and Muhlethaler, K. (1965). *Ultrastructural Plant Cytology* (Elsevier, Amsterdam).

Friedman, B. A. and Ceponis, M. J. (1959). *Science, N.Y.*, **129,** 720.

Friend, R. J. (1965). *Trans. Br. mycol. Soc.*, **48,** 371.

Fulton, R. H. (1965). *A. Rev. Phytopath.*, **3,** 175.

Fulton, R. W. (1943). *Phytopathology*, **33,** 674.

Fulton, R. W. (1964). In *Plant Virology*, edit. by Corbett, M. K. and Sisler, H. D., pp. 39–67 (University of Florida Press, Gainesville).

Fulton, R. W. (1966). *A. Rev. Phytopath.*, **4,** 79.

Futrell, M. C. and Kilgore, M. (1969). *Phytopathology*, **59,** 114.

Gale, J. and Pojakoff-Mayber, A. (1962). *Phytopathology*, **52,** 715.

Gallegly, M. E. (1968). *A. Rev. Phytopath.*, **6,** 375.

Gallegly, M. E. and Niederhauser, J. S. (1959). In *Plant Pathology, Problems and Progress, 1908–1958*, edit. by Holton, C. S., pp. 168–182 (University of Wisconsin Press, Madison).

Galston, A. W. and Purves, W. K. (1960). *A. Rev. Pl. Physiol.*, **11,** 239.

Garay, A. S. (1956). *Phys. Pl.*, **9,** 344.

Garber, E. D. (1958). *Am. J. Bot.*, **45,** 523.

Garber, E. D. (1959). *Bot. Gaz.*, **120,** 157.

Garber, E. D. (1961). In *Recent Advances in Botany*, Vol. **2,** edit. by Bailey, D. L., pp. 1004–1007 (University of Toronto Press, Toronto).

Garber, E. D. and Heggestad, H. E. (1958). *Phytopathology*, **48,** 535.

Garber, E. D. and Schaeffer, S. G. (1957). *J. Bact.*, **74,** 392.

Gardner, M. W. and Kendrick, J. B. (1921). *J. agric. Res.*, **21,** 123, cited by Gaumann (1950).

Garrett, S. D. (1944). *Root Disease Fungi* (Chronica Botanica Co., Waltham, Mass.).

Garrett, S. D. (1956). *Biology of Root-Infecting Fungi* (Cambridge University Press, London).

Garrett, S. D. (1959). In *Plant Pathology, Problems and Progress, 1908–1958*, edit. by Holton, C. S., pp. 309–316 (University of Wisconsin Press, Madison).

Garrett, S. D. (1960). In *Plant Pathology*, Vol. **3,** edit. by Horsfall, J. G. and Dimond, A. E., pp. 23–56 (Academic Press, London and New York).

Garrett, S. D. (1965). In *Ecology of Soil-borne Plant Pathogens*, edit. by Baker, K. F. and Snyder, W. C., pp. 4–17 (Murray, London).

Garrett, S. D. (1970). *Pathogenic Root-infecting Fungi* (Cambridge University Press, London).

Garriss, H. R. and Wells, J. C. (1956). *Pl. Dis. Reptr*, **40,** 837.

Gascoigne, J. A. and Gascoigne, M. M. (1960). *Biological Degradation of Cellulose* (Butterworths, London).

Gauch, H. G. (1957). *A. Rev. Pl. Physiol.*, **8,** 31.

Gaumann, E. (1950). *Principles of Plant Infection*, English translation edit. by Brierley, W. B. (Crosby Lockwood, London).

Gaumann, E. (1954). *Endeavour*, **13,** 198.

Gaumann, E. (1958). *Phytopathology*, **48,** 670.

Gaumann, E. and Naef-Roth, S. (1957). *Pflanzenschutz*, **19,** 9.

Gaumann, E. and Obrist, W. (1960). *Phytopath. Z.*, **37,** 145.

Gentile, A. C. (1951). *Physiologia Pl.*, **4**, 370.

Georgopoulos, S. G. (1962). *Nature, Lond.*, **194**, 148.

Georgopoulos, S. G. (1963). *Phytopathology*, **53**, 1081.

Georgopoulos, S. G. and Zaracovitis, C. (1967). *A. Rev. Phytopath.*, **5**, 109.

Gerretsen, F. C. (1937). *Ann. Bot.*, **1**, 207.

Gerwitz, D. L. and Durbin, R. D. (1965). *Phytopathology*, **55**, 57.

Gibbs, A. (1969). *Adv. Virus Res.*, **14**, 263.

Gibbs, A. J., Harrison, B. D., Watson, D. H. and Wildy, P. (1966). *Nature, Lond.*, **209**, 450.

Gibson, I. A. S. (1953). *Trans. Br. mycol. Soc.*, **36**, 198.

Gilchrist, G. G. (1926). *Phytopathology*, **16**, 269.

Gill, L. S. (1953). In *Yb. Agric. U.S. Dep. Agric. 1953*, 73.

Gilpatrick, J. D. and Weintraub, M. (1952). *Science, N.Y.*, **115**, 701.

Gislen, T. (1948). *Biol. Rev.*, **23**, 109.

Godfrey, G. H. and Hoshino, H. M. (1934). *Phytopathology*, **24**, 635.

Goheen, A. C. and Schnathorst, W. C. (1963). *Phytopathology*, **53**, 1139.

Goodman, R. N. (1959). In *Antibiotics, their Chemistry and Non-medical Uses*, edit. by Goldberg, H. S., pp. 323–448 (Van Nostrand, Princeton).

Goodman, R. N. (1960). *Phytopathology*, **50**, 325.

Goodman, R. N., Kiraly, Z. and Zeitlin, M. (1967). *The Biochemistry and Physiology of Infectious Plant Disease* (Van Nostrand, Princeton).

Goodwin, B. C. and Sizer, I. W. (1965). *Science, N.Y.*, **148**, 242.

Goos, R. D. and Tschirch, M. (1963). *Trans. Br. mycol. Soc.*, **46**, 321.

Gordon, F. B. (1950). *A. Rev. Microbiol.*, **4**, 151.

Gorlenko, M. V. (1965). *Bacterial Diseases of Plants*, English translation by Nemchonok, S., (Israel Programme for Scientific Translations, Jerusalem).

Gottlieb, D. (1943). *Phytopathology*, **33**, 126.

Gottlieb, D. (1944). *Phytopathology*, **34**, 41.

Gottlieb, D. (1950). *Bot. Rev.*, **16**, 229.

Gottlieb, D. (1957). *Phytopathology*, **47**, 59.

Gottlieb, D. (1964). *Endeavour*, **23**, 85.

Gottlieb, D. (1966). In *The Fungus Spore*, edit. by Madelin, M. F., pp. 217–234 (Butterworths, London).

Gottlieb, D. and Shaw, P. D. (1970). *A. Rev. Phytopath.*, **8**, 371.

Gottlieb, S. and Pelczar, M. J. (1951). *Bact. Rev.*, **15**, 55.

Graham, D. C. (1964). *A. Rev. Phytopath.*, **2**, 13.

Grainger, J. (1955). *Weather*, **10**, 213.

Grainger, J. (1956). *Phytopathology*, **46**, 445.

Grainger, J. (1959). *Outl. Agric.*, **2**, 114.

Grainger, J. (1962). *Phytopathology*, **52**, 140.

Gram, E. (1960). In *Plant Pathology*, Vol. **3**, edit. by Horsfall, J. G. and Dimond, A. E., pp. 313–356 (Academic Press, London and New York).

Graniti, A. (1962). *Phytopath. Medit.*, **1**, 157.

Gray, R. A. (1958). *Phytopathology*, **48**, 71.

Greathouse, G. A. and Wessel, C. J. (1954). *Deterioration of Materials* (Rheinhold Publishing Corp., New York).

Green, R. J. (1954). *Phytopathology*, **44**, 433.

Green, R. J. (1958). *Phytopathology*, **48,** 575.

Greenaway, W. (1971). *Trans. Br. mycol. Soc.*, **56,** 37.

Greenaway, W. and Cowan, J. W. (1970). *Trans Br. mycol. Soc.*, **54,** 127.

Greenham, C. G. and Hawksworth, F. G. (1964). *FAO/IUFRO Symp. Internationally Dangerous Forest Diseases and Insects*, 1.

Gregory, K. F., Allen, O. N., Riker, A. J. and Patterson, W. H. (1952). *Phytopathology*, **42,** 613.

Gregory, P. H. (1948). *Ann. appl. Biol.*, **35,** 412.

Gregory, P. H. (1952). *Trans. Br. mycol. Soc.*, **35,** 1.

Gregory, P. H. (1958). *Trans. Br. mycol. Soc.*, **41,** 202.

Gregory, P. H. (1960). *Endeavour*, **19,** 223.

Gregory, P. H. (1961). *The Microbiology of the Atmosphere* (Hill, London).

Gregory, P. H. (1965). *Trans Br. mycol. Soc.*, **48,** 157.

Gregory, P. H., Guthrie, E. J. and Bunce, M. E. (1959). *J. gen. Microbiol.*, **20,** 328.

Gregory, P. H. and Monteith, J. L. (1967). (Eds), *Airborne Microbes* (Cambridge University Press, London).

Gregory, P. H. and Stedman, O. F. (1953). *Ann. appl. Biol.*, **40,** 651.

Griffiths, E. and Waller, J. M. (1971). *Ann. appl. Biol.*, **67,** 75.

Grogan, R. G. and Campbell, R. N. (1966). *A. Rev. Phytopath.*, **4,** 29.

Groom, P. and Panisset, T. (1933). *Ann. appl. Biol.*, **20,** 633.

Grover, R. K. and Moore, J. D. (1961). *Phytopathology*, **51,** 399.

Gruem, H. (1959). *A. Rev. Pl. Physiol.*, **10,** 405.

Hadwiger, L. A. and Fulger, S. (1967). *Phytopathology*, **57,** 1005.

Hadwiger, L. A. and Schwochau, M. E. (1969). *Phytopathology*, **59,** 223.

Hafiz, A. (1952). *Phytopathology*, **42,** 422.

Hales, S. (1727). *Vegetable Staticks* (London) (reprinted Scientific Book Guild, 1961).

Halisky, P. M. (1965). *Bot. Rev.*, **31,** 114.

Hall, D. M. and Donaldson, L. A. (1962). *Nature, Lond.*, **194,** 1196.

Halliday, D. J. (1961). *Outl. Agric.*, **3,** 111.

Hallier, E. (1868). *Phytopathologie* (Leipzig.)

Hanchey, P. (1969). *Phytopathology*, **59,** 1060.

Hancock, J. G. (1967). *Phytopathology*, **57,** 203.

Hancock, J. G. and Millar, R. L. (1965). *Phytopathology*, **55,** 356.

Hansford, C. G. (1946). *Mycol. Pap.*, 15.

Hanson, E. W., Milliron, H. E. and Christensen, J. J. (1950). *Phytopathology*, **40,** 527.

Harding, P. R. (1959). *Pl. Dis. Reptr*, **43,** 649.

Harding, P. R. (1968). *Pl. Dis. Reptr*, **52,** 623.

Hardison, J. R. (1948). *Phytopathology*, **38,** 404.

Hare, R. C. (1966). *Bot. Rev.*, **32,** 95.

Hare, W. W. and Lucas, G. B. (1959). *Pl. Dis. Reptr*, **43,** 152.

Harrar, J. G. (1959). In *Plant Pathology, Problems and Progress 1908–1958*, edit. by Holton, C. S., pp. 55–62 (University of Wisconsin Press, Madison).

Harris, H. A. (1940). *Phytopathology*, **30,** 625.

Harrison, B. D. (1960). *Adv. Virus Res.*, **7,** 131.
Harrison, B. D. (1964). In *Plant Virology*, edit. by Corbett, M. K. and Sisler, H. D., pp. 118–147 (University of Florida Press, Gainesville).
Hart, H. (1929). *J. agric. Res.*, **39,** 929.
Hart, H. (1931). *Tech. Bull. U.S. Dep. Agric.*, 266.
Hart, H. (1949). *A. Rev. Microbiol.*, **3,** 289.
Hartig, R. (1882). *Lehrbuch der Baumkrankheiten* (Berlin) (English trans. edit. by Marshall Ward, London, 1894).
Hartman, P. E. and Goodgol, S. H. (1959). *A. Rev. Microbiol.*, **13,** 445.
Harvey, R. (1970). *Trans. Br. mycol. Soc.*, **54,** 251.
Hassall, K. A. (1969). *World Crop Protection.*, Vol. **2,** *Pesticides* (Iliffe Books Ltd., London).
Hastie, A. C. (1962). *J. gen. Microbiol.*, **27,** 373.
Hastie, A. C. (1964). *Genet. Res.*, **5,** 305.
Hattingh, I. D. (1954). *Fmg S. Afr.*, **29,** 316.
Hawker, L. E. (1950). *Physiology of Fungi* (University of London Press).
Hawker, L. E. (1957). *The Physiology of Reproduction in Fungi* (Cambridge University Press, London).
Hawker, L. E. (1960). In *Plant Pathology*, Vol. **2,** edit. by Horsfall, J. G. and Dimond, A. E., pp. 117–165 (Academic Press, London and New York).
Hawkins, L. A. and Harvey, L. B. (1919). *J. agric. Res.*, **18,** 275.
Hawksworth, F. G. (1961). In *Recent Advances in Botany*, Vol. **2,** edit. by Bailey, D. L., pp. 1537–1541 (University of Toronto Press, Toronto).
Hawksworth, F. G. and Wiens, D. (1970). *A. Rev. Phytopath.*, **8,** 187.
Hayes, J. D. and Johnston, T. D. (1971). In *Diseases of Crop Plants*, edit. by Western, J. H., pp. 62–88 (The Macmillan Press, London and Basingstoke).
Haymaker, H. H. (1928). *J. agric. Res.*, **36,** 675.
Hayward, A. C. and Hodgkiss, W. (1961). *J. gen. Microbiol.*, **26,** 133.
Heagle, A. S. and Moore, M. B. (1970). *Phytopathology*, **60,** 461.
Heald, F. D. (1926). *Manual of Plant Diseases* (McGraw-Hill, New York).
Heald, F. D. (1937). *Introduction to Plant Pathology* (McGraw-Hill, New York).
Heald, F. D. and Studhalter, R. A. (1914). *J. agric. Res.*, **2,** 405.
Hebert, T. T. and Kelman, A. (1958). *Phytopathology*, **48,** 101.
Heck, W. H. (1968). *A. Rev. Phytopath.*, **6,** 165.
Heinen, W. and Linskens, H. F. (1961). *Nature, Lond.*, **191,** 1416.
Heitefuss, R. (1966). *A. Rev. Phytopath.*, **4,** 221.
Hendey, N. I. (1964). *Trans. Br. mycol. Soc.*, **47,** 467.
Hendrix, J. W. (1970). *A. Rev. Phytopath.*, **8,** 111.
Hepting, G. H. (1963). *A. Rev. Phytopath.*, **1,** 31.
Hewitt, E. J. (1948). *Nature, Lond.*, **161,** 489.
Hewitt, E. J. (1951). *A. Rev. Pl. Physiol.*, **2,** 25.
Hewitt, E. J. (1958). *Encycl. Pl. Physiol.*, **4,** 427.
Hewitt, W. B. (1953). In *Yb. Agric. U.S. Dep. Agric.*, *1953*, 744.
Hewitt, W. B., Raski, D. J. and Goheen, A. C. (1958). *Phytopathology*, **48,** 586.
Hickman, C. J. and Ho, H. H. (1966). *A. Rev. Phytopath.*, **4,** 195.
Higgins, V. J. and Millar, R. L. (1969). *Phytopathology*, **59,** 1493.
Hilu, H. M. (1965). *Phytopathology*, **55,** 563.

Hiroe, I. (1952). *Ann. Phytopath. Soc. Japan*, **16**, 127. Abstract in *Rev. appl. Mycol.*, **32**, 436 1953.

Hiroe, I. and Aoe, S. (1954). *J. Fac. Agric. Tottori Univ.*, **11**, 1, cited by Pringle and Scheffer (1964).

Hiroe, I. and Nishimura, S. (1956). *Ann. phytopath. Soc. Japan*, **20**, 161. Abstract in *Rev. appl. Mycol.*, **36**, 511, 1957.

Hiroe, I., Nishimura, S. and Sato, M. (1958). *Trans. Tottori Soc. agric. Sci.*, **11**, 291, cited by Pringle and Scheffer (1964).

Hirst, J. M. (1953). *Trans. Br. mycol. Soc.*, **36**, 375.

Hirst, J. M. (1957). *Pl. Path.*, **6**, 57.

Hirst, J. M. (1958). *Outl. Agric.*, **2**, 16.

Hirst, J. M. (1959). In *Plant Pathology, Problems and Progress, 1908–1958*, edit. by Holton, C. S., pp. 529–538 (University of Wisconsin Press, Madison).

Hirst, J. M. (1965). In *Ecology of Soil-borne Plant Pathogens*, edit. by Baker, K. F. and Snyder, W. C., pp. 69–81 (Murray, London).

Hirst, J. M. and Hurst, G. W. (1967). In *Airborne Microbes*, edit. by Gregory, P. H. and Monteith, J. L., pp. 307–344 (Cambridge University Press, London).

Hirst, J. M. and Stedman, O. J. (1963). *J. gen. Microbiol.*, **33**, 335.

Hirst, J. M., Stedman, O. J. and Hogg, W. H. (1967). *J. gen. Microbiol.*, **48**, 329.

Hirst, J. M., Stedman, O. J. and Hurst, G. W. (1967). *J. gen. Microbiol.*, **48**, 357.

Hirumi, H. and Maramorosch, K. (1969). *Phytopathology*, **59**, 399.

Hislop, E. C. (1966). *Ann. appl. Biol.*, **57**, 475.

Hislop, E. C. (1967). *Ann. appl. Biol.*, **60**, 265.

Hislop, E. C. and Cox, T. W. (1969). *Trans. Br. mycol. Soc.*, **52**, 223.

Hitchborn, J. H. and Thomson, A. D. (1960). *Adv. Virus Res.*, **7**, 163.

Hochstein, P. E. and Cox, C. E. (1956). *Am. J. Bot.*, **43**, 437.

Hock, W. K. and Sisler, H. D. (1969). *Phytopathology*, **59**, 627.

Holden, M. (1969). *Bull. Br. mycol. Soc.*, **3**, 19.

Hollings, M. (1965). *A. Rev. Phytopath.*, **3**, 367.

Hollings, M. (1966). In *Viruses of Plants*, edit. by Beemster, A. B. R. and Dijkstra, J., pp. 230–241 (North Holland Publishing Co., Amsterdam).

Holmes, E. (1960). *Outl. Agric.*, **3**, 23.

Holmes, F. O. (1954). *Adv. Virus Res.*, **2**, 1.

Holmes, F. O. (1964). In *Plant Virology*, edit. by Corbett, M. K. and Sisler, H. D., pp. 17–38 (University of Florida Press, Gainesville).

Holmes, F. O. (1965). *Adv. Virus Res.*, **11**, 139.

Holton, C. S. (1943). *Phytopathology*, **33**, 732.

Holton, C. S. (1959). In *Plant Pathology, Problems and Progress 1908–1958*, edit. by Holton, C. S., pp. 145–156 (University of Wisconsin Press, Madison).

Holz, W. (1939). *Angew. Bot.*, **21**, 209, Abstract in *Rev. appl. Mycol.*, **18**, 531, 1939.

Hooke, R. (1665). *Micrographia*, London (reprinted as a Dover paperback).

Horne, R. W. and Wildy, P. (1963). *Adv. Virus Res.*, **10**, 101.

Horsfall, J. G. (1932). *Tech. Bull. N. York State agric. Exp. Stn*, 198.

Horsfall, J. G. (1945). *Fungicides and their Action* (Chronica Botanica Co., Waltham, Mass.).

Horsfall, J. G. (1956). *Principles of Fungicidal Action* (Chronica Botanica Co., Waltham, Mass.).

Horsfall, J. G. and Barratt, R. W. (1945). *Phytopathology*, **35,** 655.

Horsfall, J. G. and Dimond, A. E. (1957). *Z. PflKrankh. PflPath. PflSchutz*, **64,** 415.

Horsfall, J. G. and Dimond, A. E. (1959). In *Plant Pathology*, Vol. **1,** edit. by Horsfall, J. G. and Dimond, A. E., pp. 1–17 (Academic Press, London and New York).

Hosford, R. M. (1967). *Bot. Rev.*, **33,** 387.

Hotson, H. H. and Cutter, V. M. (1951). *Proc. natn. Acad. Sci. U.S.A.*, **37,** 400.

Houten, J. C. ten (1959). In *Plant Pathology*, Vol. **1,** edit. by Horsfall, J. G. and Dimond, A. E., pp. 19–60 (Academic Press, London and New York).

Howard, A. (1940). *An Agricultural Testament* (Oxford University Press, London).

Howard, F. L. and Horsfall, J. G. (1959). In *Plant Pathology*, Vol. **1,** edit. by Horsfall, J. G. and Dimond, A. E., pp. 563–604 (Academic Press, London and New York).

Howell, P. J. and Wood, R. K. S. (1962). *Ann appl. Biol.*, **50,** 723.

Hrushovetz, S. B. (1957). *Phytopathology*, **47,** 261.

Hull, R. (1968). *Pl. Path.*, **17,** 1.

Humphrey, H. B. and Dufrenoy, J. (1944). *Phytopathology*, **34,** 21.

Hunt, P. (1968). *Trans. Br. mycol. Soc.*, **51,** 103.

Hurst, G. W. (1965). *Pl. Path.*, **14,** 47.

Husain, A. (1957). *Phytopathology*, **47,** 17.

Husain, A. and Dimond, A. E. (1958). *Phytopathology*, **48,** 263.

Husain, A. and Dimond, A. E. (1958a). *Phytopathology*, **48,** 263.

Husain, A. and Kelman, A. (1957). *Phytopathology*, **47,** 111.

Husain, A. and Kelman, A. (1958). *Phytopathology*, **48,** 377.

Husain, A. and Kelman, A. (1959). In *Plant Pathology*, Vol. **1,** edit. by Horsfall, J. G. and Dimond, A. E., pp. 143–188 (Academic Press, London and New York).

Hutchinson, C. M. (1913). *Mem. Dep. Agric. India., bact. ser.*, **1,** 67, cited by Wood (1967).

Hutton, K. E. and Burchill, R. T. (1965). *Ann. appl. Biol.*, **56,** 279.

Hyre, R. A. (1957). *Pl. Dis. Reptr*, **41,** 7.

Ingold, C. T. (1953). *Dispersal in Fungi* (Clarendon Press, Oxford).

Ingold, C. T. (1960). In *Plant Pathology*, Vol. **3,** edit. by Horsfall, J. G. and Dimond, A. E., pp. 137–168 (Academic Press, London and New York).

Ingold, C. T. (1964). *Trans. Br. mycol. Soc.*, **47,** 573.

Ingold, C. T. (1965). *Spore Liberation* (Clarendon Press, Oxford).

Ingold, C. T. (1967). In *Airborne Microbes,* edit. by Gregory, P. H. and Monteith, J. L., pp. 105–115 (Cambridge University Press, London).

Ingold, C. T. (1971). *Fungal Spores, their Liberation and Dispersal* (Clarendon Press, Oxford).

Ingold, C. T. and Dann, V. (1968). *Mycologia*, **60,** 285.

Ishiie, T., Doi, Y., Yora, K. and Asuyama, H. (1967). *Ann. phytopath. Soc. Japan*, **33,** 267. Abstract in *Rev. appl. Mycol.*, **47,** 128, 1968.
Ito, K. (1949). *Bull. Gov. Forest. Exp. Stn. Meguro*, **43,** 1.
Ivanowski, D. (1892). *St Peters. Acad. Imp. Sci. Bull. 35* (ser. 4, vol. **3**), 67. English trans. *Phytopath. Class.*, **7,** (1942).

Jackson, R. M. (1957). *Nature, Lond.*, **180,** 96.
Jagger, J. (1958). *Bact. Rev.*, **22,** 99.
James, G. L. (1968). *Ann. appl. Biol.*, **61,** 503.
Jarvis, W. R. (1962). *Trans. Br. mycol. Soc.*, **45,** 549.
Jedlinski, H. (1956). *Phytopathology*, **46,** 673.
Jenkinson, J. G. (1955). *Ann. appl. Biol.*, **43,** 409.
Jennings, P. R. and Ullstrup, A. J. (1957). *Phytopathology*, **47,** 707.
Jensen, N. F. (1965). *Crop Science*, **5,** 566, cited by Van der Plank, 1968.
Jensen, R. E. and Boyle, L. W. (1965). *Pl. Dis. Reptr*, **49,** 976.
Jensen, R. E. and Boyle, L. W. (1966). *Pl. Dis. Reptr*, **50,** 811.
Jepson, W. F. (1956). *Outl. Agric.*, **1,** 59.
Jhooty, J. S. and Yarwood, C. E. (1967). *Phytopathology*, **57,** 148.
Jinks, J. L. (1966). In *The Fungi*, Vol. **2,** edit. by Ainsworth, G. C. and Sussman, A. S., pp. 619–660 (Academic Press, London and New York).
Johnson, G. and Schaal, L. A. (1952). *Science, N.Y.*, **115,** 627.
Johnson, T. (1954). *Can. J. Bot.*, **32,** 506.
Johnson, T. (1960). In *Plant Pathology*, Vol. **2,** edit. by Horsfall, J. G. and Dimond, A. E., pp. 407–459 (Academic Press, London and New York).
Johnson, T. (1961). *Science, N.Y.*, **133,** 357.
Johnson, T. and Newton, M. (1940). *Can. J. Res.*, **C18,** 599.
Johnston, C. O. and Huffman, M. D. (1958). *Phytopathology*, **48,** 69.
Johnston, H. W. and Sproston, T. (1965). *Phytopathology*, **55,** 225.
Joly, P. (1964). *Le Genre Alternaria* (Lechevalier, Paris).
Jones, K. W. (1953). *Emp. J. exp. Agric.*, **21,** 331.
Jones, K. W. (1955). *Emp. J. exp. Agric.*, **23,** 206.
Jones, P. M. (1928). *Arch. Protistenk.*, **62,** 313. Abstract in *Rev. appl. Mycol.*, **8,** 4 (1929).
Jones, R. A. C. and Harrison, B. D. (1969). *Ann. appl. Biol.*, **63,** 1.
Jones, S. G. (1935). *Ann. Bot.*, **49,** 699.
Joslyn, M. A. (1962). *Adv. Food. Res.*, **11,** 1.
Juniper, B. E. (1960). *J. Linn. Soc.*, **56,** 413.

Kassanis, B. (1952). *Ann. appl. Biol.*, **39,** 358.
Kassanis, B. (1957). *Adv. Virus Res.*, **4,** 221.
Kassanis, B. (1963). *Adv. Virus Res.*, **10,** 219.
Kassanis, B. (1968). *Adv. Virus Res.*, **13,** 147.
Kassanis, B., Tinsley, T. W. and Quak, F. (1958). *Ann. appl. Biol.*, **46,** 11.
Katznelson, H. (1965). In *Ecology of Soil-borne Plant Pathogens*, edit. by Baker, K. F. and Snyder, W. C., pp. 187–207 (Murray, London).
Katznelson, H., Lockhead, A. G. and Timonin, M. I. (1948). *Bot. Rev.*, **14,** 543.
Kaufert, F. and Schmitz, H. (1937). *Phytopathology*, **27,** 780.

Kazmaier, H. E. (1960). *Diss. Abstr.*, **21,** 21.
Keen, N. T. and Horton, J. C. (1965). *Phytopathology*, **55,** 1063.
Kefford, N. P. (1959). *J. exp. Bot.*, **10,** 462.
Keitt, G. W., Boone, D. M. and Shay, J. R. (1959). In *Plant Pathology, Problems and Progress, 1908–1958*, edit. by Holton, C. S., pp. 157–167 (University of Wisconsin Press, Madison).
Keitt, G. W. and Langford, M. H. (1941). *Am. J. Bot.*, **28,** 805.
Kendrick, J. B., Middleton, J. T. and Darley, E. F. (1954). *Phytopathology*, **44,** 494.
Kendrick, W. B. and Proctor, J. R. (1964). *Can. J. Bot.*, **42,** 65.
Kennedy, J. S., Day, M. F. and Eastop, V. F. A. (1962). *A Conspectus of Aphids as Vectors of Plant Viruses* (Commonw. Inst. Entom., Lond.).
Kenten, R. H. (1957). *Biochem. J.*, **67,** 300.
Kenten, R. H. (1958). *Biochem. J.*, **68,** 244.
Kerk, G. J. M. Van der (1959). In *Plant Pathology, Problems and Progress, 1908–1958*, edit. by Holton, C. S., pp. 280–292 (University of Wisconsin Press, Madison).
Kerk, G. J. M. Van der (1963). *Wld Rev. Pest Control*, **2,** 29–41.
Kerling, L. C. P. (1952). *Tijdschr. Pl.Ziekt.*, **58,** 29. Abstract in *Rev. appl. Mycol.*, **32,** 163, 1953.
Kerr, A. (1956). *Aust. J. biol. Sci.*, **9,** 45.
Kerr, A. (1963). *Aust. J. biol. Sci.*, **16,** 55.
Kerr, A. and Flentje, N. T. (1957). *Nature, Lond.*, **179,** 204.
Kerr, A. and Rodrigo, W. R. F. (1967). *Trans. Br. mycol. Soc.*, **50,** 49.
Kerr, A. and Rodrigo, W. R. F. (1967a). *Trans. Br. mycol. Soc.*, **50,** 609.
Kertesz, Z. I. (1951). *The Pectin Substances* (Interscience, New York).
Keyworth, W. G. (1942). *Ann. appl. Biol.*, **29,** 346.
Keyworth, W. G. and Dimond, A. E. (1952). *Phytopathology*, **62,** 311.
Kikuchi, T. (1964). *Bot. Mag., Tokyo*, **77,** 395.
King, C. J., Loomis, H. F. and Hope, C. (1931). *J. agric. Res.*, **42,** 827.
King, J. E. and Coley-Smith, J. R. (1968). *Ann. appl. Biol.*, **61,** 407.
Kiraly, Z. and Farkas, G. L. (1959). *Phytopath. Z.*, **34,** 341.
Kiraly, Z., Hammady, M. E. and Pozsar, B. I. (1967). *Phytopathology*, **57,** 93.
Kirkham, D. S. (1957). *J. gen. Microbiol.*, **17,** 120.
Kirkham, D. S. (1957a). *J. gen. Microbiol.*, **17,** 491.
Kirkham, D. S. (1959). In *Plant Pathology, Problems and Progress, 1908–1958*, edit. by Holton, C. S., p. 110–118 (University of Wisconsin Press, Madison).
Kirkham, D. S. and Flood, A. E. (1956). *Nature, Lond.*, **178,** 422.
Kirkham, D. S. and Hignett, R. C. (1966). *Nature, Lond.*, **212,** 211.
Kirschner, O. (1890). *Die Krankheiten und Beschadigungen unserer landwirtschaftlichen Kulturpflanzen* (Stuttgart).
Kittleson, A. R. (1952). *Science, N. Y.*, **115,** 84.
Klein, D. T. and Klein, R. M. (1956). *J. Bact.*, **72,** 308.
Klein, R. M. and Link, G. K. K. (1955). *Q. Rev. Biol.*, **30,** 207.
Klement, Z. and Goodman, R. N. (1967). *A. Rev. Phytopath.*, **5,** 17.
Klement, Z. and Lovrekovich, L. (1962). *Phytopath. Z.*, **45,** 81.
Kline, D. M., Boone, D. M. and Keitt, G. W. (1957). *Am. J. Bot.*, **44,** 797.
Klinkowski, M. (1970). *A. Rev. Phytopath*, **8,** 37.

Knight, C. A. (1964). In *Plant Virology*, edit. by Corbett, M. K. and Sisler, H. D., pp. 292–314 (University of Florida Press, Gainesville).

Knoll, J. G. (1957). *Outl. Agric.*, **1**, 182.

Ko, W. and Lockwood, J. L. (1970). *Phytopathology*, **60**, 148.

Kobel, F., (1951). *Phytopath. Z.*, **18**, 157. Abstract in *Rev. appl. Mycol.*, **32**, 32, 1953.

Kontaxis, D. G. (1962). *Phytopathology*, **52**, 1306.

Koritz, H. G. and Went, F. W. (1953). *Pl. Physiol.*, **28**, 50.

Kosuge, T. (1969). *A. Rev. Phytopath.*, **7**, 195.

Kovacs, A. and Szeoke, E. (1956). *Phytopath. Z.*, **27**, 335. Abstract in *Rev. appl. Mycol.*, **36**, 121, 1957.

Kramer, C. L., Pady, S. M. and Wiley, B. J. (1964). *Trans. Kans. Acad. Sci.*, **67**, 442.

Krasnopoyasovskii, S. I. (1966). Abstract in *Rev. appl. Mycol.*, **46**, 594, 1967.

Kreitlow, K. W. (1945). *Phytopathology*, **35**, 152.

Kremers, R. E. (1959). *A. Rev. Pl. Physiol.*, **10**, 185.

Kreutzer, W. A. (1960). In *Plant Pathology*, Vol. **3**, edit. by Horsfall, J. G. and Dimond, A. E., pp. 431–476 (Academic Press, London and New York).

Krusberg, L. R. (1963). *A. Rev. Phytopath.*, **1**, 219.

Kuc, J. (1962). *Phytopathology*, **52**, 961.

Kuc, J. (1963). In *Bull. Conn. agric. Exp. Stn*, 663, 20.

Kuc, J. (1966). *A. Rev. Microbiol.*, **20**, 337.

Kuc, J., Williams, E. B. and Shay, J. R. (1957). *Phytopathology*, **47**, 21–22.

Kuhlman, E. G. (1969). *Phytopathology*, **59**, 198.

Kuhn, J. (1858). *Die Krankheiten der Kulturgewachse, ihre Ursachen und ihre Verhutung* (Berlin).

Kuijt, J. (1955). *Bot. Rev.*, **21**, 569.

Kuijt, J. (1969). *The Biology of Parasitic Flowering Plants* (University of California Press).

Kuiper, J. (1965). *Nature, Lond.*, **206**, 1219.

Kunkel, L. O. (1915). *J. agric. Res.*, **4**, 265, cited by Gaumann (1950).

Kunkel, L. O. (1936). *Phytopathology*, **26**, 809.

Kunkel, L. O. (1947). *A. Rev. Microbiol.*, **1**, 85.

Kunkel, L. O. (1951). *Phytopathology*, **41**, 22.

Kurosawa, E. (1926). *J. nat. Hist. Soc. Formosa*, **16**, 213. Abstract in *Biol. Abstr.*, **48**, 1066, 1929.

Lackey, C. F. (1946). *Phytopathology*, **36**, 386.

Lamb, C. A., Bentley, O. G., and Beattie, J. M. (1958). *Trace Elements* (Academic Press, London and New York).

Lamphere, W. M. (1934). *Phytopathology*, **24**, 1244.

Lang, A. (1970). *A. Rev. Pl. Physiol.*, **21**, 537.

Langeron, M. and Vanbreuseghem, R. (1952). *Precis de Mycologie* (Masson et Cie, Paris). English translation by Wilkinson, J., *Outline of Mycology* (Pitman, London, 1965).

Large, E. C. (1940). *The Advance of the Fungi* (London, Jonathan Cape).

Large, E. C. (1966). *A. Rev. Phytopath.*, **4**, 9.

U

Large, E. C., Beer, W. J. and Patterson, J. B. E. (1946). *Ann. appl. Biol.*, **33,** 54.

Large, E. C. and Doling, D. A. (1962). *Pl. Path.*, **11,** 47.

Last, F. T. (1955). *Trans. Br. mycol. Soc.*, **38,** 221.

Last, F. T. and Deighton, F. C. (1965). *Trans. Br. mycol. Soc.*, **48,** 83.

Lawson, L. R. and Still, C. N. (1957). *Tappi*, **40,** 58.

Layne, R. E. C. (1967). *Phytopathology*, **57,** 981.

Leach, C. M. (1962). *Can. J. Bot.*, **40,** 151.

Leach, J. G. (1919). *Phytopathology*, **9,** 59.

Leach, J. G. (1923). *Tech. Bull. agric. Exp. Stn Minn. Univ.*, 14.

Leach, J. G. (1940). *Insect Transmission of Plant Diseases* (McGraw-Hill, New York).

Leach, R. (1937). *Proc. R. Soc., B*, **121,** 561.

Leach, R. (1939). *Trans. Br. mycol. Soc.*, **23,** 320.

Leath, K. T. and Rowell, J. B. (1966). *Phytopathology*, **56,** 1305.

Lebeau, J. B. and Dickson, J. G. (1955). *Phytopathology*, **45,** 667.

Leben, C. (1964). *Phytopathology*, **54,** 405.

Leben, C. (1965). *A. Rev. Phytopath.*, **3,** 209.

Leben, C. and Daft, G. C. (1964). *Phytopathology*, **54,** 898.

Leben, C. and Daft, G. C. (1965). *Phytopathology*, **55,** 760.

Leben, C., Scott, R. W. and Arny, D. C. (1956). *Phytopathology*, **46,** 273.

LeClerg, E. L. (1964). *Phytopathology*, **54,** 1309.

Lederberg, J. (1949). *A. Rev. Microbiol.*, **3,** 1.

Ledingham, R. L., Sallans, B. J. and Simmonds, P. M. (1949). *Sci. Agric.*, **29,** 253.

Leeper, G. W. (1952). *A. Rev. Pl. Physiol.*, **3,** 1.

Leigh, J. H. and Matthews, J. W. (1963). *Aust. J. Bot.*, **11,** 62.

Leppik, E. E. (1970). *A. Rev. Phytopath.*, **8,** 323.

Levitt, J. (1951). *A. Rev. Pl. Physiol.*, **2,** 245.

Lewis, B. G. (1964). *Trans. Br. mycol. Soc.*, **47,** 302.

Lewis, R. W. (1953). *Am. Nat.*, **83,** 273.

Lewis, S. and Goodman, R. N. (1962). *Phytopathology*, **52,** 1273.

Lilly, V. G. and Barnett, H. L. (1951). *Physiology of the Fungi* (McGraw-Hill, New York).

Lincoln, R. E. (1940). *J. agric. Res.*, **60,** 217.

Lind, J. (1913). *Danish Fungi as represented in the Herbarium of E. Rostrup* (Copenhagen).

Lindberg, G. D. (1960). *Phytopathology*, **50,** 457.

Linderman, R. G. and Gilbert, R. G. (1969). *Phytopathology*, **59,** 1366.

Linford, M. B. (1931). *Phytopathology*, **21,** 791.

Linford, M. B. (1931a). *Phytopathology*, **21,** 797.

Linford, M. B. (1942). *Phytopathology*, **32,** 580.

Ling, L. (1952). *Dev. Pap., F.A.O.*, 23.

Link, G. K. K. (1933). *Phytopathology*, **23,** 843.

Littauer, F. and Gutter, Y. (1953). *Palest. J. Bot. Rehovot Scr.* (1951–1953), **8,** 185. Abstract in *Rev. appl. Mycol.*, **33,** 349, 1954.

Litzenberger, S. C. (1949). *Phytopathology*, **39,** 300.

Locke, S. B. (1969). *Phytopathology*, **59,** 13.

Lockhead, A. G. (1959). In *Plant Pathology, Problems and Progress, 1908–1958*, edit. by Holton, C. S., pp. 327–338 (University of Wisconsin Press, Madison).

Lockhead, A. G., Timonin, M. I. and West, P. M. (1940). *Sci. Agric.*, **20,** 414.

Lockwood, J. L. (1964). *A. Rev. Phytopath.*, **2,** 341.

Loebenstein, G. (1960). *Nature, Lond.*, **185,** 122.

Loebenstein, G. (1962). *Virology*, **17,** 574.

Loebenstein, G. (1963). *Phytopathology*, **53,** 306.

Loebenstein, G., Rabina, S. and Praagh, T. V. (1966). In *Viruses of Plants*, edit. by Beemster, A. B. R. and Dijkstra, J., pp. 151–157 (North Holland Publishing Co., Amsterdam).

Loo, S. W. (1946). *Am. J. Bot.*, **33,** 295.

Losada, M., Whatley, F. R. and Arnon, D. I. (1961). *Nature, Lond.*, **190,** 606.

Louis, D. (1963). *Annls Epiphyt.*, **14,** 57.

Lovrekovich, L. and Farkas, G. L. (1965). *Nature, Lond.*, **205,** 823.

Lucas, G. B. and von Ramm, C. (1963). *Pl. Dis. Reptr*, **47,** 7.

Ludwig, R. A. (1957). *Can. J. Bot.*, **35,** 291.

Ludwig, R. A. (1960). In *Plant Pathology*, Vol. **2,** edit. by Horsfall, J. G. and Dimond, A. E., pp. 315–357 (Academic Press, London and New York).

Luke, H. H., Warmke, H. E. and Hanchey, P. (1966). *Phytopathology*, **56,** 1178.

Luke, H. H. and Wheeler, H. E. (1955). *Phytopathology*, **45,** 453.

Lukens, R. J. (1969). In *Fungicides*, Vol. **2,** edit. by Torgeson, D. C., pp. 395–445 (Academic Press, London and New York).

Lukens, R. J. and Sisler, H. D. (1957), *Phytopathology*, **47,** 22.

Lukens, R. J. and Sisler, H. D. (1958). *Phytopathology*, **48,** 235.

Lukezic, F. L. and DeVay, J. E. (1964). *Phytopathology*, **54,** 697.

Luttrell, E. S. (1958). *Mycologia*, **50,** 942.

Lyr, H. (1963). *Phytopath. Z.*, **47,** 73. Abstract in *Rev. appl. Mycol.*, **43,** 47, 1964.

Macfarlane, I. (1952). *Ann. appl. Biol.*, **39,** 239.

Machacek, J. E. and Wallace, H. A. H. (1952). *Can. J. Bot.*, **30,** 164.

MacMillan, H. G. (1918). *J. agric. Res.*, **13,** 647.

MacMillan, H. G. (1923). *Phytopathology*, **13,** 376.

Madelin, M. F. (1966). *A. Rev. Entomol.*, **11,** 423.

Madelin, M. F. (1966a). *The Fungus Spore*, edit. by Madelin, M. F. (Butterworths, London).

Madelin, M. F. (1968). In *The Fungi*, Vol. **3,** edit. by Ainsworth, G. C. and Sussman, A. S., pp. 253–269 (Academic Press, London and New York).

Madelin, M. F. (1968a). In *The Fungi*, Vol. **3,** edit. by Ainsworth, G. C. and Sussman, A. S., pp. 227–238 (Academic Press, London and New York).

Madhosingh, C. (1961). *Can. J. Microbiol.*, **7,** 553. Abstract in *Rev. appl. Mycol.*, **41,** 185 (1962).

Maier, C. R. (1962). *Phytopathology*, **52,** 19.

Mandels, M. and Reese, E. T. (1963). *Symp. Advances in Enzymic Hydrolysis of Cellulose and Related Materials*, edit. by Reese, E. T. (Pergamon Press, London).

Mandryk, M. (1960). *Aust. J. agric. Res.*, **11,** 16.

Mandryk, M. (1963). *Aust. J. agric. Res.*, **14,** 318.

Mani, M. S. (1964). *Ecology of Plant Galls* (W. Junk, The Hague).

Mann, B. (1962). *Trans. Br. mycol. Soc.*, **45,** 169.

Manners, J. G. and Gandy, D. G. (1954). *Ann. appl. Biol.*, **41,** 393.

Mantle, P. G. (1962). *Trans. Br. mycol. Soc.*, **45,** 75.

Maramorosch, K. (1957). *Science, N.Y.*, **126,** 651.

Maramorosch, K. (1963). *A. Rev. Entom.*, **8,** 369.

Maramorosch, K. (1964). In *Plant Virology*, edit. by Corbett, M. K. and Sisler, H. D., pp. 175–193 (University of Florida Press, Gainesville).

Maramorosch, K. and Jensen, D. D. (1963). *A. Rev. Microbiol.*, **17,** 495.

Maramorosch, K. and Koprowski, H. (1967). *Methods in Virology*, Vols. **1, 2, 3,** edit. by Maramorosch, K. and Koprowski, H. (Academic Press, London and New York).

Marsden, D. H. (1954). *Mycologia*, **46,** 161.

Marsh, R. W. (1968). *Nature, Lond.*, **218,** 1017.

Marsh, R. W. and Walker, M. M. (1932). *J. Pom. Hort. Sci.*, **10,** 71.

Martin, G. W. (1958). *Mycologia*, **50,** 97.

Martin, H. (1940). *Ann. appl. Biol.*, **27,** 433.

Martin, H. (1963). *Insecticide and Fungicide Handbook*, edit. by Martin, H. (Blackwell, Oxford).

Martin, H. (1964). *The Scientific Principles of Crop Protection*, 5th ed. (London, Arnold).

Martin, H. (1968). *Pesticide Manual*, edit. by Martin, H. (British Crop Protection Council).

Martin, H. (1969). In *Fungicides*, Vol. **2,** edit. by Torgeson, D. C., pp. 101–117 (Academic Press, London and New York).

Martin, J. T. (1964). *A. Rev. Phytopath.*, **2,** 81.

Martin, J. T., Baker, E. A. and Byrde, R. J. W. (1966). *Ann. appl. Biol.*, **57,** 491.

Martin, J. T., Baker, E. A. and Byrde, R. J. W. (1966a). *Ann. appl. Biol.*, **57,** 501.

Martin, J. T., Batt, R. F. and Burchill, R. T. (1957). *Nature, Lond.*, **180,** 796.

Martin, J. T. and Juniper, B. E. (1969). *The Cuticles of Plants* (Arnold, London).

Martyn, E. B. (1968). *Phytopath. Pap.*, 9.

Marx, D. H. (1969). *Phytopathology*, **59,** 153.

Marx, D. H. (1969a). *Phytopathology*, 411.

Marx, D. H. (1970). *Phytopathology*, **60,** 1472.

Marx, D. H. and Davey, C. B. (1969). *Phytopathology*, **59,** 549.

Mason, E. W. (1927). *Trans. Br. mycol. Soc.*, **12,** 152.

Mason, E. W. (1937). *Annot. Acc. Fungi rec. Imp. Bur. Mycol.*, **2,** 3.

Massee, G. (1899). *A Text-Book of Plant Diseases caused by Cryptogamic Parasites* (Duckworth, London).

Massey, R. E. (1931). *Emp. Cott. Gr. Rev.*, **8,** 187.

Massie, L. B. (1971). *Phytopathology*, **61,** 131.

Matsui, C. and Yamaguchi, A. (1966). *Adv. Virus Res.*, **12,** 127.

Matthews, R. E. F. (1953). *Ann. appl. Biol.*, **40,** 377.

Matthews, R. E. F. (1957). *Plant Virus Serology* (Cambridge University Press, London).

Matthews, R. E. F. (1967). In *Methods in Virology*, Vol. **3,** edit. by Maramorosch, K. and Koprowski, H., pp. 199–241 (Academic Press, London and New York).

Matthews, R. E. F. and Smith, J. D. (1955). *Adv. Virus Res.*, **3,** 49.

Maude, R. B. (1966). *Ann. appl. Biol.*, **57,** 83.

Maude, R. B. (1966a). *Ann. appl. Biol.*, **57,** 193.

Maude, R. B. and Kyle, A. M. (1970). *Ann. appl. Biol.*, **66,** 37.

Maude, R. B. and Shuring, C. G. (1969). *Ann. appl. Biol.*, **64,** 259.

Maude, R. B., Vizor, A. N. and Shuring, C. G. (1969). *Ann. appl. Biol.*, **64,** 245.

Maxwell, F. G. (1961). *Diss. Abstr.*, **22,** 948.

Mayer, A. (1886). *Landwirtsch. Vers. Stationen*, **32,** 451. English translation *Phytopath. Class.*, **7,** 1942.

McCain, A. H. (1967). *Phytopathology*, **57,** 1007.

McCalla, D. R., Genthe, M. K. and Hovanitz, W. (1962). *Pl. Physiol.*, **37,** 98.

McCallan, S. E. A. (1946). *Contr. Boyce Thompson Inst. Pl. Res.*, **14,** 108.

McCallan, S. E. A. (1949). *Bot. Rev.*, **15,** 629.

McCallan, S. E. A. (1964). *Agrochimica*, **9,** 15.

McCallan, S. E. A. (1967). In *Fungicides*, Vol. **1,** edit. by Torgeson, D. C., pp.1–37 (Academic Press, London and New York).

McCallan, S. E. A., Hamilton, J. M. and Mills, W. D. (1959). In *Plant Pathology, Problems and Progress, 1908–1958*, edit. by Holton, C. S., pp. 248–261, (University of Wisconsin Press, Madison).

McCallan, S. E. A. and Wilcoxon, F. (1936). *Contr. Boyce Thompson Inst. Pl. Res.*, **8,** 151.

McClellan, W. D. *et al.* (1964). *Phytopathology*, **54,** 1305.

McClure, T. T. (1951). *Phytopathology*, **41,** 72.

McCubbin, W. A. (1946). *Bot. Rev.*, **12,** 101.

McCubbin, W. A. (1954). *The Plant Quarantine Problem* (Ejnar Munksgaard, Copenhagen).

McElroy, W. D. and Glass, B. (1951, 1952). *Phosphorus Metabolism*, edit. by McElroy, W. D., and Glass, B. (Johns Hopkins Press, Baltimore).

McGrath, H. (1964). *P.A.N.S.*, *B*, **11,** 141 (1965), reprinted from *Agric. Chemicals* (1964).

McGrath, H. *et al.* (1957). *U.S. Dep. Agric., agric. Res. Serv. spec. Publication*, 10.

McKee, R. K. (1951). *Nature, Lond.*, **167,** 611.

McKinney, H. H. (1923). *J. agric. Res.*, **26,** 195.

McLean, F. T. (1921). *Bull. Torrey bot. Club*, **48,** 101.

McNew, G. L. (1959). In *Plant Pathology, Problems and Progress, 1908–1958*, edit. by Holton, C. S., pp. 42–54 (University of Wisconsin Press, Madison).

McNew, G. L. (1960). In *Plant Pathology*, Vol. **2,** edit. by Horsfall, J. G. and Dimond, A. E., pp. 19–69 (Academic Press, London and New York).

McNew, G. L. and Burchfield, H. P. (1951). *Contr. Boyce Thompson Inst. Pl. Res.*, **16,** 357.

McWhorter, F. P. (1927). *Phytopathology*, **17,** 201.

McWhorter, F. P. (1965). *A. Rev. Phytopath.*, **3,** 287.

Melander, L. W. and Craigie, J. H. (1927). *Phytopathology*, **17,** 95.

Mellanby, K. (1967). *Pesticides and Pollution*. New Naturalist (Collins, London).

Melville, S. C. and Hawken, R. H. (1967). *Pl. Path.*, **16,** 145.

Menzies, J. D. (1963). *Bot. Rev.*, **29,** 79.

Menzies, J. D. (1963a). *A. Rev. Phytopath.*, **1,** 127.

Meredith, D. S. (1961). *Ann. Bot.*, **25,** 271.

Messieha, M. (1969). *Phytopathology*, **59,** 943.

Metzger, R. J. and Trione, E. J. (1962). *Phytopathology*, **52,** 363.

Meyer, B. S., Anderson, D. B. and Bohning, R. H. (1960). *Introduction to Plant Physiology* (London). (Also Van Nostrand, Princeton, 1963).

Meyer, V. G. (1966). *Bot. Rev.*, **32,** 165.

Micheli, A. (1729). *Nova Plantarum Genera* (Florence).

Middleton, J. T. (1961). *A. Rev. Pl. Physiol.*, **12,** 431.

Middleton, J. T., Kendrick, J. B. and Schwalin, H. W. (1950). *Pl. Dis. Reptr*, **34,** 245.

Milholland, R. D. (1970). *Phytopathology*, **60,** 635.

Millardet, P. M. A. (1885). See *Phytopath. Class.*, **3** (1933).

Miller, C. O. (1961). *A. Rev. Pl. Physiol.*, **12,** 395.

Miller, L. P. (1968). *P.A.N.S.*, *B*, 14, 239–260.

Miller, L. P. (1969). In *Fungicides*, Vol. **2,** edit. by Torgeson, D. C., pp. 1–59 (Academic Press, London and New York).

Miller, L. P. and McCallan, S. E. A. (1957). *Science, N.Y.*, **126,** 1233.

Miller, L. P., McCallan, S. E. A. and Weed, R. M. (1953). *Contr. Boyce Thompson Inst. Pl. Res.*, **17,** 151.

Miller, P. R. (1953). In *Yb. Agric. U.S. Dep. Agric.*, *1953*, 83.

Miller, P. R. (1959). In *Plant Pathology, Problems and Progress, 1908–1958*, edit. by Holton, C. S., pp. 557–565 (University of Wisconsin Press, Madison).

Miller, P. R. and O'Brien, M. J. (1952). *Bot. Rev.*, **18,** 547.

Miller, P. R. and O'Brien, M. J. (1957). *A. Rev. Microbiol.*, **11,** 77.

Millerd, A. and Scott, K. J. (1962). *A. Rev. Pl. Physiol.*, **13,** 559.

Millikan, D. F., Wyllie, T. D. and Pickett, E. E. (1965). *Phytopathology*, **55,** 932.

Mills, W. D. (1944). *Ext. Bull. Cornell agric. Exp. Stn*, 630.

Mills, W. D. and La Plante, A. A. (1954). *Ext. Bull. Cornell. agric. Exp. Stn*, 711, 20.

Mills, W. R. (1940). *Phytopathology*, **30,** 830.

Mirocha, C. J. and Uritani I. (1967). *The Dynamic Role of Molecular Constituents in Plant-Parasite interaction*, edit. by Mirocha, C. J. and Uritani, I. (American Phytopathological Society).

Mirocha, C. J., Vay, J. E. de and Wilson, E. E. (1961). *Phytopathology*, **51,** 851.

Mirocha, C. J. and Wilson, E. E. (1961). *Phytopathology*, **51,** 843.

Miyoshi, M. (1895). *Jahr. Wiss. Bot.*, **28,** 269, cited by Gaumann (1950).

Mode, C. J. (1958). *Evolution*, **12,** 158.

Moore, M. H. (1964). *Ann. appl. Biol.*, **53,** 423.

Moore, R. T. (1965). In *The Fungi*, Vol. **1,** edit. by Ainsworth G. C. and Sussman, A. S., pp. 95–118 (Academic Press, London and New York).

Moore, W. C. (1940). *Trans. Br. mycol. Soc.*, **24,** 264.

Moore, W. C. (1957). In *Biological Aspects of the Transmission of Disease*, edit. by Horton-Smith, C., pp. 135–139 (Oliver and Boyd, Edinburgh).

Moore, W. C. (1957a). *Outl. Agric.*, **1,** 240.

Moore, W. D. (1949). *Phytopathology*, **39,** 920.

Mori, R. (1962). *Lib. Arts J. Tottori Univ.*, **13,** 53, cited by Pringle and Scheffer, 1964.

Moseman, J. G. (1959). *Phytopathology*, **49,** 469.

Moseman, J. G. (1966). *A. Rev. Phytopath.*, **4,** 269.

Moseman, J. G. and Greeley, L. W. (1964). *Phytopathology*, **54**, 618.

Moss, E. H. (1926). *Ann. Bot.*, **48**, 813.

Mulder, E. G. (1950). *A. Rev. Pl. Physiol.*, **1**, 1.

Muller, K. O. (1956). *Phytopath. Z.*, **27**, 237.

Muller, K. O. (1961). In *Recent Advances in Botany*, Vol. **1**, edit. by Bailey, D. L., pp. 396–400 (University of Toronto Press, Toronto).

Muller, K. O. and Borger, H. (1939). *Land. Jb. Berlin*, **87**, 609, cited by Cruickshank, 1963.

Munch, E (1929). *Z. PflKrankh. PflPath. PflSchutz*, **39**, 276.

Mundry, K. W. (1963). *A. Rev. Phytopath.*, **1**, 173.

Murant, A. F. and Wood, R. K. S. (1957). *Ann. appl. Biol.*, **45**, 635.

Muskett, A. E. (1960). In *Plant Pathology*, Vol. **3**, edit. by Horsfall, J. G. and Dimond, A. E., pp. 57–96 (Academic Press, London and New York).

Naef-Roth, S., Gaumann, E. and Albersheim, P. (1961). *Phytopath. Z.*, **40**, 283.

Nakanishi, T. and Oku, H. (1969). *Phytopathology*, **59**, 1761.

Neish, A. C. (1960). *A. Rev. Pl. Physiol.*, **11**, 55.

Nelson, P. E. and Dickey, R. S. (1970). *A. Rev. Phytopath.*, **8**, 259.

Nelson, R. R. (1961). *Phytopathology*, **51**, 736.

Nelson, R. R. (1963). *A. Rev. Microbiol.*, **17**, 31.

Nelson, R. R. and Kline, D. M. (1961). *Pl. Dis. Reptr*, **45**, 644.

Nelson, R. R. and Kline, D. M. (1962). *Phytopathology*, **52**, 1045.

Nelson, R. R. and Kline, D. M. (1963). *Phytopathology*, **53**, 101.

Nelson, R. R. and Scheifele, G. L. (1970). *Phytopathology*, **60**, 369.

Newcombe, M. (1960). *Trans. Br. mycol. Soc.*, **43**, 51.

Newhall, A. G. (1955). *Bot. Rev.*, **21**, 189.

Newton, R. and Anderson, J. A. (1929). *Can. J. Res.*, **1**, 86. Abstract in *Rev. appl. Mycol.*, **9**, 96, 1930.

Newton, R., Lehmann, J. V. and Clarke, A. E. (1929). *Can J. Res.*, **1**, 5. Abstract in *Rev. appl. Mycol.*, **9**, 95, 1930.

Nicholas, D. J. D. (1957). *Ann. Bot.*, **21**, 587.

Nicholas, D. J. D. (1961). *A. Rev. Pl. Physiol.*, **11**, 63.

Nishi, Y. (1969). In *Viruses, Vectors and Vegetation*, edit. by Maramorosch, K., pp. 579–591 (Interscience, New York).

Nishimura, S., Scheffer, R. P. and Nelson, R. R. (1966). *Phytopathology*, **56**, 53.

Noble, M. (1957). In *Biological Aspects of the Transmission of Disease*, edit. by Horton-Smith, C., pp. 81–85 (Oliver and Boyd, Edinburgh).

Noble, M. (1971). In *Diseases of Crop Plants*, edit. by Western, J. H. (Macmillan Press, London).

Noble, M., Macgarvie, Q. D., Hams, A. F. and Leafe, E. L. (1966). *Pl. Path.* **15**, 23.

Noble, M. and Richardson, M. J. (1968). *Phytopath. Pap.*, 8.

Noble, M., Tempe, J. de and Neergaard, P. (1958). *An Annotated List of Seed-borne Diseases* (Commonwealth Mycological Institute, Kew).

Noble, R. J. (1924). *J. agric. Res.*, **27**, 451.

Norkrans, B. (1963). *A. Rev. Phytopath.*, **1**, 325.

Northcote, D. H. (1958). *Biol. Rev.*, **33**, 53.

Nusbaum, C. J. and Keitt, G. W. (1938). *J. agric. Res.*, **56,** 595.

Nutman, F. J. and Roberts, F. M. (1960). *Trans. Br. mycol. Soc.*, **43,** 489.

Nutman, F. J., Roberts, F. M. and Bock, K. R. (1960). *Trans. Br. mycol. Soc.*, **43,** 509.

Nyland, G. and Goheen, A. C. (1969). *A. Rev. Phytopath.*, **7,** 331.

Ogawa, J. M., Hall, D. H. and Koepsell, P. A. (1967). In *Airborne Microbes*, edit. by Gregory, P. H. and Monteith, J. L., pp. 247–267 (Cambridge University Press, London).

Ogle, H. J. and Brown, J. F. (1970). *Ann. appl. Biol.*, **66,** 273.

Ogle, H. J. and Brown, J. F. (1971). *Ann. appl. Biol.*, **67,** 157.

Okabe, N. and Goto, M. (1963). *A. Rev. Phytopath.*, **1,** 397.

Oku, H. (1960). *Phytopath. Z.*, **38,** 342.

Old, K. M. (1968). *Trans. Br. mycol. Soc.*, **51,** 525.

Olive, L. S. (1964). *Science, N.Y.*, **146,** 542.

Oort, A. J. P. (1963). *Neth. J. Pl. Path.*, **69,** 104.

Ordish, G. (1952). *Untaken Harvest* (Constable, London).

Ordish, G. (1964). *Wld Crops*, March 1964.

Ordish, G. and Mitchell, J. F. (1967). In *Fungicides*, Vol. **1,** edit. by Torgeson, D. C., pp. 39–62 (Academic Press, London and New York.).

Orsenigo, M. (1956). *Annali Sper. agr.*, **10,** 1745, 1809.

Orsenigo, M. (1957). *Phytopath. Z.*, **29,** 189.

Oswald, J. W. (1949). *Phytopathology*, **39,** 359.

Overell, B. T. (1952). *Aust. J. Sci.*, **14,** 197.

Owens, R. G. (1963). *A. Rev. Phytopath.*, **1,** 77.

Owens, R. G. (1969). In *Fungicides*, Vol. **2,** edit. by Torgeson, D. C., pp. 147–301 (Academic Press, London and New York).

Owens, R. G. and Blaak, G. (1960). *Contr. Boyce Thompson Inst. Pl. Res.*, **20,** 459. 475.

Owens, R. G. and Novotny, H. M. (1958). *Contr. Boyce Thompson Inst. Pl. Res.*, **19,** 463.

Owens, R. G. and Novotny, H. M. (1959). *Contr. Boyce Thompson Inst. Pl. Res.*, **20,** 171.

Owens, R. G. and Specht, H. N. (1964). *Contr. Boyce Thompson Inst. Pl. Res.*, **22,** 471.

Paddock, W. C. (1953). *Mem. Cornell Univ. agric. Exp. Stn*, 315.

Paddock, W. C. (1967). *A. Rev. Phytopath.*, **5,** 375.

Padwick, G. W. (1956). *Mycol. Pap.*, 1.

Pady, S. M. and Gregory, P. H. (1963). *Trans. Br. mycol. Soc.*, **46,** 609.

Pady, S. M. and Kramer, C. L. (1960). *Mycologia*, **52,** 681.

Page, O. T. (1965). *Phytopathology*, **55,** 259.

Paine, L. A. (1950). *Phytopath. Z.*, **17,** 305.

Paleg, L. G. (1965). *A. Rev. Pl. Physiol.*, **16,** 291.

Park, D. (1963). *A. Rev. Phytopath.*, **1,** 241.

Parmeter, J. R., Snyder, W. C. and Reichle, R. E. (1963). *A. Rev. Phytopath.*, **1,** 51.

Parry, K. E. and Wood, R. K. S. (1958). *Ann. appl. Biol.*, **46,** 446.
Parry, K. E. and Wood, R. K. S. (1959). *Ann. appl. Biol.*, **47,** 1.
Partridge, A. D. and Rich, A. E. (1962). *Phytopathology*, **52,** 1000.
Patil, S. S. and Dimond, A. E. (1967). *Phytopathology*, **57,** 492.
Patil, S. S., Powelson, R. L. and Young, R. A. (1964). *Phytopathology*, **54,** 531.
Patil, S. S., Zucker, M. and Dimond, A. E. (1966). *Phytopathology*, **56,** 971.
Peachey, J. E. and Chapman, M. R. (1966). *Tech. Commun. Commonwealth Bur. Helminthology*, 36.
Peacock, F. C. (1957). *Outl. Agric.*, **1,** 188.
Pearl, I. A. (1967). *The Chemistry of Lignin* (Arnold, London).
Pegg, G. F. and Selman, I. W. (1959). *Ann. appl. Biol.*, **47,** 222.
Pereira, H. G. (1966). *Nature, Lond.*, **210,** 149.
Peries, O. S. (1962). *Ann. appl. Biol.*, **50,** 225.
Perrin, D. R. and Cruickshank, I. A. M. (1965). *Aust. J. biol. Sci.*, **18,** 803.
Perry, D. A. (1959). *Trans. Br. mycol. Soc.*, **42,** 388.
Person, C. (1959). *Can. J. Bot.*, **37,** 1101.
Person, C., Samborski, D. J. and Rohringer, R. (1962). *Nature, Lond.*, **194,** 561.
Person, C. A. (1960). *Can. J. Genet. Physiol.*, **2,** 103.
Peyton, G. I. and Bowen, C. C. (1963). *Am. J. Bot.*, **50,** 787.
Phinney, B. O. and West, C. A. (1960). *A. Rev. Pl. Physiol.*, **11,** 411.
Phinney, B. O. and West, C. A. (1961). *Encycl. Pl. Physiol.*, **14,** 1185.
Pilet, P. E. (1952). *Bull. Soc. bot. Suisse*, **62,** 269.
Pilet, P. E. (1960). *Phytopath. Z.*, **40,** 75.
Pinckard, J. A. (1942). *Phytopathology*, **32,** 505.
Pirson, A. (1955). *A. Rev. Pl. Physiol.*, **6,** 71.
Pitcher, R. S. (1961). In *Recent Advances in Botany*, Vol. **1,** edit. by Bailey, D. L., pp. 477–481 (University of Toronto Press, Toronto).
Pitcher, R. S. (1965). *Helminth. Abstr.*, **34,** 1.
Pitcher, R. S. and Crosse, J. E. (1958). *Nematologica*, **3,** 244.
Pitt, D. (1968). *J. gen. Microbiol.*, **52,** 67.
Pitt, D. and Coombs, C. (1968). *J. gen. Microbiol.*, **53,** 197.
Plank, J. E., Van der (1959). In *Plant Pathology, Problems and Progress, 1908–1958*, edit. by Holton, C. S., pp. 566–573 (University of Wisconsin Press, Madison).
Plank, J. E., Van der (1960). In *Plant Pathology*, Vol. **3,** edit. by Horsfall, J. G. and Dimond, A. E., pp. 229–289 (Academic Press, London and New York).
Plank, J. E., Van der (1963). *Plant Diseases; Epidemics and Control* (Academic Press, London and New York).
Plank, J. E., Van der (1967). In *Airborne Microbes*, edit. by Gregory, P. H. and Monteith, J. L., pp. 227–246 (Cambridge University Press, London).
Plank, J. E., Van der (1967a). In *Fungicides*, Vol. **1,** edit. by Torgeson, D. C., pp. 63–92 (Academic Press, London and New York).
Plank, J. E., Van der (1968). *Disease Resistance in Plants* (Academic Press, London and New York).
Plank, J. E., Van der (1969). *Neth. J. Pl. Path.*, **75,** 45.
Platz, G. A. (1928). *Iowa St. Coll. J. Sci.*, **2,** 137. Abstract in *Rev. appl. Mycol.*, **7,** 440, 1928.
Ploaie, P. and Maramorosch, K. (1969). *Phytopathology*, **59,** 536.

Plowright, C. B. (1889). *A Monograph of the British Uredineae and Ustilagineae* (Kegan Paul, Trench & Co., London).

Pole-Evans, I. B. (1907). *Ann. Bot.*, **21,** 441.

Pommer, E. H. and Kradel, J. (1969). *Proc. 5th Br. Insecticide and Fungicide Conf., 1969*, 563.

Pommer, E. H., Otto, S. and Kradel, J. (1969). *Proc. 5th Br. Insecticide and Fungicide Conf., 1969*, 347.

Pon, D. S., Townsend, C. E., Wessman, G. E., Schmitt, C. G. and Kingsolver, C. H. (1954). *Phytopathology*, **44,** 707.

Pontecorvo, G. (1956). *A. Rev. Microbiol.*, **10,** 393.

Pontecorvo, G., Roper, J. A. and Forbes, E. (1953). *J. gen. Microbiol.*, **8,** 198.

Pontecorvo, G. and Sermonti, G. (1954). *J. gen. Microbiol.*, **11,** 94.

Pool, V. W. and Mackay, M. B. (1916). *J. agric. Res.*, **5,** 1011.

Porter, C. A. (1959). *Adv. Virus Res.*, **6,** 75.

Porter, C. L. and Himelick, E. (1952). *Phytopathology*, **42,** 472.

Posnette, A. F. (1947). *Ann. appl. Biol.*, **34,** 388.

Posnette, A. F. and Todd, J. M. (1955). *Ann. appl. Biol.*, **43,** 433.

Pound, G. S. and Stahmann, M. A. (1951). *Phytopathology*, **41,** 1104.

Powell, N. T. (1963). *Phytopathology*, **53,** 28.

Powell, N. T. and Nusbaum, C. J. (1960). *Phytopathology*, **50,** 899.

Powelson, R. L. and Shaner, G. E. (1966). *Pl. Dis. Reptr*, **50,** 806.

Pozsar, B. I. and Kiraly, Z. (1966). *Phytopath. Z.*, **56,** 297.

Pramer, D. (1959). *Adv. appl. Microbiol.*, **1,** 75.

Pramer, D. (1961). In *Recent Advances in Botany*, Vol. **1,** edit. by Bailey, D. L., pp. 452–456 (University of Toronto Press, Toronto).

Preece, T. F. (1961). *Pl. Path.*, **10,** 52.

Preece, T. F. (1971). In *Diseases of Crop Plants*, edit. by Western, J. H., pp. 8–20 (The Macmillan Press, London and Basingstoke).

Preece, T. F. and Smith, L. P. (1961). *Pl. Path.*, **10,** 43.

Prentice, I. W. (1971). In *Diseases of Crop Plants*, edit. by Western, J. H., pp. 37–47 (The Macmillan Press, London and Basingstoke).

Preston, R. D. (1961). In *Symposium on Macromolecular Complexes, Urbana, Illinois, 1959*, edit. by Edds, M. V., pp. 229–253 (Ronald Press Co., New York).

Prevost, B. (1807). *Memoir on the immediate Cause of Bunt or Smut of Wheat . . .* Translated by Keitt, G. W., *Phytopath. Class.* 6, 1939.

Price, C. A. (1968). *A. Rev. Pl. Physiol.*, **19,** 239.

Price, W. C. (1940). *Q. Rev. Biol.*, **15,** 338.

Price, W. C. (1963). *Adv. Virus Res.*, **10,** 171.

Price, W. C. (1964). In *Plant Virology*, edit. by Corbett, M. K. and Sisler, H. D., pp. 93–117 (University of Florida Press, Gainesville).

Priest, D. and Wood, R. K. S. (1961). *Ann. appl. Biol.*, **49,** 445.

Prillieux, E. (1895–1897). *Maladies des Plantes agricoles et des Arbres fruitiers et forestiers causées par des Parasites Vegetaux*, Vols. 1 and 2.

Pringle, R. B. and Scheffer, R. P. (1963). *Phytopathology*, **53,** 785.

Pringle, R. B. and Scheffer, R. P. (1964). *A. Rev. Phytopath.*, **2,** 133.

Pringle, R. B. and Scheffer, R. P. (1966). *Phytopathology*, **56,** 1149.

Pringle, R. B. and Scheffer, R. P. (1967). *Phytopathology*, **57,** 530.

Pristou, R. and Gallegly, M. E. (1954). *Phytopathology*, **44,** 81.

Pritchard, N. J. (1965). *Phytopathology*, **55,** 505.

Purdy, L. M. (1967). In *Fungicides*, Vol. **1,** edit. by Torgeson, D. C., pp. 195–237 (Academic Press, London and New York).

Quak, F. (1961). *Adv. hort. Sci. Appl.*, **1,** 144. *Proc. 15th int. hort. Congress, Nice*, 1958, edit. by Garnaud, J. C. Abstract in *Rev. appl. Mycol.*, **41,** 760, 1962.

Rabanus, A. (1939). *Mitt. Deut. Forstvereins*, **23,** 77. Abstract in *Rev. appl. Mycol.*, **18,** 426, 1939.

Radley, M. (1961). *Nature, Lond.*, **191,** 684.

Rai, P. V. and Strobel, G. A. (1966). *Phytopathology*, **56,** 1365.

Ramsbottom, J. (1912). *Trans. Br. mycol. Soc.*, **4,** 77.

Rao, A. S. and Brakke, M. K. (1969). *Phytopathology*, **59,** 581.

Raper, J. R. (1940). *Am. J. Bot.*, **22,** 162.

Rathmell, W. G. and Bendall, D. S. (1971). *Physiol. Pl. Path.*, **1,** 351.

Ravin, A. W. (1958). *A. Rev. Microbiol.*, **12,** 309.

Rawlins, T. E. and Parker, K. G. (1934). *Phytopathology*, **24,** 1029.

Ray, P. M. (1958). *A. Rev. Pl. Physiol.*, **9,** 81.

Razin, S. (1969). *A. Rev. Microbiol.*, **23,** 317.

Re, F. (1807). *Saggio Teorico-practico sulle Malattie delle Piante* (Venice). (English translation of 2nd ed., 1817, in *Gdnrs' Chron.*, 1849, 228 *et seq.*)

Reese, E. T. (1956). *Appl. Microbiol.*, **4,** 39.

Regenmortel, M. H. V. Van (1966). *Adv. Virus Res.*, **12,** 207.

Reichert, I. and Palti, J. (1967). *Mycopath. Mycol. appl.*, **32,** 337.

Reuther, W., Embleton, T. W. and Jones, W. W. (1958). *A. Rev. Pl. Physiol.*, **9,** 175.

Rhodes, A., Fantes, K. H., Boothroyd, B., McGonagle, M. P. and Crosse, R. (1961). *Nature, Lond.*, **192,** 952.

Rice, M. A. (1935). *Bot. Rev.*, **1,** 327.

Rice, M. A. (1945). *Bot. Rev.*, **11,** 288.

Rich, A. E. and Richards, M. C. (1959). *Pl. Dis. Reptr*, **43,** 540.

Rich, S. (1960). In *Plant Pathology*, Vol. **2,** edit. by Horsfall, J. G. and Dimond, A. E., pp. 553–602 (Academic Press, London and New York).

Rich, S. (1963). *Bull. Conn. agric. Exp. Stn.*, 663.

Rich, S. (1964). *A. Rev. Phytopath.*, **2,** 253.

Rich, S. (1969). In *Fungicides*, Vol. **2,** edit. by Torgeson, D. C., pp. 447–475 (Academic Press, London and New York).

Rich, S. and Horsfall, J. G. (1954). *Proc. natn. Acad. Sci., U.S.A.*, **40,** 139.

Richardson, D. E. and Saunders, P. J. W. (1968). *J. natn. Inst. agric. Bot.*, **11,** 343.

Riker, A. J. (1951). *Phytopathology*, **41,** 30.

Rishbeth, J. (1950). *Ann. Bot.*, **14,** 365.

Rishbeth, J. (1951). *Ann. Bot.*, **15,** 1, 221.

Rishbeth, J. (1959). *Ann. appl. Biol.*, **47,** 519, 529.

Rishbeth, J. (1963). *Ann. appl. Biol.*, **52,** 63.

Roach, W. A. (1938). *Tech. Commun. Imp. Bur. Hort. Plant. Crops*, 10.

Robb, S. M. (1963). *Ann. appl. Biol.*, **52,** 145.

Robb, S. M. (1964). *Virology*, **32,** 141.

Roberts, E. A., Southwick, M. D. and Palmiter, D. H. (1948). *Pl. Physiol.*, **23,** 557.

Roberts, M. F., Martin, J. T. and Peries, O. S. (1961). *Rep. agric. hort. Res. Stn (Long Ashton) Univ. Bristol, 1960*, 102.

Robinson, P. M. and Park, D. (1966). *Trans. Br. mycol. Soc.*, **49,** 639.

Robinson, P. M., Park, D. and Garrett, M. K. (1968). *Trans. Br. mycol. Soc.*, **51,** 113.

Robinson, R. A. (1969). *Rev. appl. Mycol.*, **48,** 593.

Roelofsen, P. (1959). *The Plant Cell Wall* (Gebruder Borntraeger, Berlin).

Rohringer, R. and Samborski, D. J. (1967). *A. Rev. Phytopath.*, **5,** 77.

Romanko, R. R. (1959). *Phytopathology*, **49,** 32.

Roper, J. A. (1966). In *The Fungi*, Vol. **2,** edit. by Ainsworth, G. C. and Sussman, A. S., pp. 589–617 (Academic Press, London and New York).

Ross, A. F. (1959). In *Plant Pathology, Problems and Progress, 1908–1958*, edit. by Holton, C. S., pp. 511–520 (University of Wisconsin Press, Madison).

Ross, A. F. (1964). In *Plant Virology*, edit. by Corbett, M. K. and Sisler, H. D., pp. 68–92 (University of Florida Press, Gainesville).

Rotem, J. and Cohen, Y. (1966). *Pl. Dis. Reptr*, **50,** 635.

Rotem, J. and Palti, J. (1969). *A. Rev. Phytopath.*, **7,** 267.

Rothman, P. G. (1960). *Phytopathology*, **50,** 914.

Roux, P. M. Le and Dickson, J. G. (1957). *Phytopathology*, **47,** 101.

Rovira, A. D. (1965). In *Ecology of Soil-borne Plant Pathogens*, edit. by Baker, K. F. and Snyder, W. C., pp. 170–184 (Murray, London).

Rowell, J. B. (1955). *Science, N.Y.*, **121,** 304.

Royle, D. J. and Hickman, C. J. (1964). *Can. J. Microbiol.*, **10,** 151, 202.

Rubin, B. A. and Artsikhovskaya, E. V. (1963). *Biochemistry and Physiology of Plant Immunity*, translated by Wareing, H. (Pergamon Press, Oxford).

Rubin, B. A. and Artsikhovskaya, E. V. (1964). *A. Rev. Phytopath.*, **2,** 157.

Rudd, R. L. (1965), *Pesticides and the Living Landscape* (Faber and Faber, London).

Rudolph, K. (1964). *Phytopathology*, **54,** 904.

Ruinen, J. (1956). *Nature, Lond.*, **177,** 220.

Ruinen, J. (1961). *Pl. Soil*, **15,** 81.

Ruinen, J. (1963). *Antonie van Leeuwenhoek*, **29,** 425.

Ruscoe, Q. W. (1967). Ph.D. thesis, University of Exeter.

Russell, R. C. (1961). *Can. J. Bot.*, **39,** 1741.

Sackston, W. E. *et al.* (1968). *Can. Pl. Dis. Surv.*, **48,** 56.

Sadasivan, T. S. (1961). *A. Rev. Pl. Physiol.*, **12,** 449.

Sadasivan, T. S. and Subramanian, D. (1963). *J. Ind. bot. Soc.*, **42A,** 199.

Sallans, B. J., Ledingham, R. J. and Simmonds, P. M. (1949). *Proc. Can. phytopath. Soc.*, **16,** 11.

Salmon, E. S. (1904). *New Phytol.*, **3,** 55.

Salmon, S. C. (1951). *Pl. Dis. Reptr*, **35,** 251.

Samborski, D. J., Forsyth, F. R. and Person, C. (1958). *Can. J. Bot.*, **36,** 591.

Samuel, G. (1927). *Ann. Bot.*, **41,** 375.

Sanderson, K. E. and Srb, A. M. (1965). *Am. J. Bot.*, **52,** 72.

Sanford, G. B. (1959). In *Plant Pathology, Problems and Progress, 1908–1958*, edit. by Holton, C. S., pp. 367–376 (University of Wisconsin Press, Madison).

Sanwal, B. D. (1961). In *Recent Advances in Botany*, Vol. **2,** edit. by Bailey, D. L., pp. 1012–1017 (University of Toronto Press, Toronto).

Saunders, A. R. (1933). *Sci. Bull. Dep. Agric. S. Africa*, 128.

Saunders, P. J. W. (1966). *Ann. appl. Biol.*, **58,** 103.

Saunders, P. J. W. (1967). *Ann. appl. Biol.*, **60,** 129.

Saunders, P. J. W. (1970). *Lichenologist*, **4,** 337.

Savulescu, A. (1960). *Conference on Scientific Problems of Plant Protection, Budapest, 1960*, 83.

Sayre, R. M. (1960). *Nematology, Fundamentals and Recent Advances with Emphasis on Plant Parasitic and Soil Forms*, edit. by Sasser, J. N. and Jenkins, W. R., pp. 427–428 (University of N. Carolina Press, Chapel Hill).

Scardavi, A. (1966). *A. Rev. Phytopath.*, **4,** 335.

Scheffer, R. P. (1961). In *Recent Advances in Botany*, Vol. **2,** edit. by Bailey, D. L., pp. 1007–1012 (University of Toronto Press, Toronto).

Scheffer, R. P. and Pringle, R. B. (1961). *Nature, Lond.*, **191,** 912.

Scheifele, G. L., Nelson, R. R. and Wernham, C. C. (1968). *Pl. Dis. Reptr*, **52,** 427.

Schlegel, D. E. and Smith, S. H. (1966). In *Viruses of Plants*, edit. by Beemster, A. B. R. and Dijkstra, J., pp. 54–65 (North Holland Publishing Co., Amsterdam).

Schnathorst, W. C. (1959). *Phytopathology*, **49,** 562.

Schnathorst, W. C. (1962). *Phytopathology*, **52,** 41.

Schnathorst, W. C. (1965). *A. Rev. Phytopath.*, **3,** 343.

Schnathorst, W. C. (1966). *Phytopathology*, **56,** 151.

Schnathorst, W. C. and Vay, J. E. de (1963). *Phytopathology*, **53,** 1142.

Schneider, I. R. (1965). *Adv. Virus Res.*, **11,** 163.

Schneider, I. R., Diener, T. O. and Safferman, R. S. (1964). *Science, N.Y.*, **144,** 1127.

Schreven, D. A., Van (1948). *Tijdschr. Plantenziekten*, **54,** 149, cited by Sewell, 1965.

Schrodter, H. (1960). In *Plant Pathology*, Vol. **3,** edit. by Horsfall, J. G. and Dimond, A. E., pp. 169–227 (Academic Press, London and New York).

Schrodter, H. and Ullrich, J. (1965). *Phytopath. Z.*, **54,** 87.

Schroth, M. N. and Hildebrand, D. C. (1964). *A. Rev. Phytopath.*, **2,** 101.

Schubert, W. J. and Nord, F. F. (1957). *Adv. Enzymol.*, **18,** 349.

Schwochau, M. E. and Hadwiger, L. A. (1969). *Phytopathology*, **59,** 15.

Scott, F. M. (1965). In *Ecology of Soil-borne Plant Pathogens*, edit. by Baker, K. F. and Snyder, W. C., pp. 145–151 (Murray, London).

Scott, K., Millerd, A. and White, N. H. (1957). *Aust. J. Sci.*, **19,** 207.

Scott, K. J. and Maclean, D. J. (1969). *A. Rev. Phytopath.*, **7,** 123.

Seevers, P. M. and Daly, J. M. (1970). *Phytopathology*, **60,** 1322.

Sela, I. and Applebaum, S. W. (1962). *Virology*, **17,** 543.

Sempio, C. (1950). *Phytopathology*, **40,** 799.

Sequeira, L. (1963). *A. Rev. Phytopath.*, **1,** 5.

Sequeira, L. and Kelman, A. (1962). *Phytopathology*, **52,** 439.

Sequeira, L. and Steeves, T. A. (1954). *Pl. Physiol.*, **29,** 11.

Sewell, G. W. F. (1965). In *Ecology of Soil-borne Plant Pathogens*, edit. by Baker, K. F. and Snyder, W. C. pp. 479–494 (Murray, London).

Shanmuganathan, N. and Arulpragasam, P. V. (1966). *Trans. Br. mycol. Soc.*, **49,** 219.

Shantz, E. M. (1966). *A. Rev. Pl. Physiol.*, **17,** 409.

Sharples, R. O. (1962). *Proc. Br. Insecticide and Fungicide Conf.*, *Brighton, England*, *1961*, 327.

Sharvelle, E. G. (1936). *J. agric. Res.*, **53,** 81.

Sharvelle, E. G. (1961). *The Nature and Uses of Modern Fungicides* (Burgess Publishing Co., Minneapolis, Minn.).

Shatla, M. and Sinclair, J. B. (1963). *Phytopathology*, **53,** 1407.

Shaw, C. G. *et. al.*, (1965). *Phytopathology*, **55,** 819.

Shaw, M. (1963). *A. Rev. Phytopath.*, **1,** 259.

Shaw, M. and Hawkins, A. R. (1958). *Can. J. Bot.*, **36,** 1.

Shea, K. R. (1961). In *Recent Advances in Botany*, Vol. **2,** edit. by Bailey, D. L., pp. 1541–1544 (University of Toronto Press, Toronto).

Sheffield, F. M. L. (1958). *Pl. Prot. Bull.*, *F.A.O.*, **6,** 149.

Sheffield, F. M. L. (1968). *Rev. appl. Mycol.*, **47,** 1.

Shepherd, C. J. (1962). *Aust. J. biol. Sci.*, **15,** 483.

Shepherd, C. J. and Mandryk, M. (1963). *Aust. J. biol. Sci.*, **16,** 77.

Shepherd, R. J., Wakeman, R. J. and Romanko, R. R. (1968). *Virology*, **36,** 150.

Sherman, R. W. (1957). *Pl. Prot. Bull.*, *F.A.O.*, **5,** 89.

Shipton, W. A. (1966). *Adv. Front. Pl. Sci.*, **16,** 189.

Shive, J. W. (1941). *Pl. Physiol.*, **16,** 435.

Siegal, A. (1966). In *Viruses of Plants*, edit. by Beemster, A. B. R. and Dijkstra, J., pp. 3–18 (North Holland Publishing Co., Amsterdam).

Siegel, A. and Zaitlin, M. (1964). *A. Rev. Phytopath.*, **2,** 179.

Sijpesteijn, A. K. (1961). In *Recent Advances in Botany*, Vol. **1,** pp. 457–460, (University of Toronto Press, Madison).

Sijpesteijn, A. S. and Kaslander, J. (1964). *Outl. Agric.*, **4,** 119.

Sijpesteijn, A. K., Kaslander, J. and Kerk, G. J. M., Van der (1962). *Biochim. Biophys. Acta*, **62,** 587, cited by Woodcock, 1967.

Sijpesteijn, A. K. and Kerk, G. J. M. Van der (1965). *A. Rev. Phytopath.*, **3,** 127.

Sijpesteijn, A. K., Luijten, J. G. A. and Kerk, G. J. M., Van der (1969). In *Fungicides*, Vol. **2,** edit. by Torgeson, D. C., pp. 331–366 (Academic Press, London and New York).

Sijpesteijn, A. K. and Tempel, A. (1967). *Nature, Lond.*, **213,** 215.

Silver, W. S., Centifanto, Y. M. and Nicholas, D. J. D. (1963). *Nature, Lond.*, **199,** 396.

Silverman, W. (1960). *Phytopathology*, **50,** 130.

Simmonds, J. H. (1933). *Qd. agric. J.*, **40,** 98. Abstract in *Rev. appl. Mycol.*, **13,** 42, 1934.

Simmonds, J. H. (1963). *Qd. J. agric. Sci.*, **20,** 373. Abstract in *Rev. appl. Mycol.* **43,** 541, 1964.

Simmonds, P. M. (1947). *Sci. Agric.*, **27,** 625.

Sinha, R. C. (1968). *Adv. Virus Res.*, **13,** 181.

Sinha, R. C. and Wood, R. K. S. (1964). *Nature, Lond.*, **202,** 824.

Siradhana, B. S., Schmitthenner, A. F. and Ellett, C. W. (1969). *Phytopathology*, **59,** 405.

Sisler, H. D. (1969). *A. Rev. Phytopath.*, **7,** 311.

Sisler, H. D. and Cox, C. E. (1960). In *Plant Pathology*, Vol. **2,** edit. by Horsfall, J. G. and Dimond, A. E., pp. 507–552 (Academic Press, London and New York).

Siu, R. G. H. (1951). *Microbial Decomposition of Cellulose* (Reinhold, New York).

Siu, R. G. H. and Reese, E. T. (1953). *Bot. Rev.*, **19,** 377.

Siu, R. G. H and Sinden, J. W. (1951). *Am. J. Bot.*, **38,** 284.

Skoog, F. and Armstrong, D. J. (1970). *A. Rev. Pl. Physiol.*, **21,** 359.

Slack, D. A., Powell, N. T., Pitcher, R. S., Raski, D. J. and Hewitt, W. B. (1963). *Phytopathology*, **53,** 27.

Slesinski, R. S. and Ellingboe, A. H. (1969). *Phytopathology*, **59,** 1833.

Slope, D. B. and Last, F. T. (1963). *Pl. Path.*, **12,** 37.

Slykhuis, J. T. (1965). *Adv. Virus Res.*, **11,** 97.

Slykhuis, J. T. (1967). *Rev. appl. Mycol.*, **46,** 401.

Smith, A. L. (1953). In *Yb. Agric. U.S. Dep. Agric. 1953*, 292.

Smith, C. G. (1970). *Trans. Br. mycol. Soc.*, **55,** 355.

Smith, D., Muscatine, L. and Lewis, D. (1969). *Biol. Rev.*, **44,** 17.

Smith, E. F. (1905–1914). *Bacteria in Relation to Plant Diseases*, Vols. **1-3** (Carnegie Institution, Washington).

Smith, E. F. (1920). *Bacterial Diseases of Plants* (Philadelphia).

Smith, K. M. (1937). *A Textbook of Plant Virus Diseases* (Churchill, London).

Smith, K. M. (1957). *A Textbook of Plant Virus Diseases*, 2nd ed. (Churchill, London).

Smith, K. M. (1965). *Adv. Virus Res.*, **11,** 61.

Smith, K. M. (1968). *Plant Viruses*. 4th ed. (Methuen, London).

Smith, O. F. (1938). *J. agric. Res.*, **57,** 671.

Smith, P. F. (1962). *A. Rev. Pl. Physiol.*, **13,** 81.

Smith, R. S. (1966). *Trans. Br. mycol. Soc.*, **49,** 33.

Smith, W. K. (1958). *J. gen. Microbiol.*, **18,** 33.

Smith, W. L. (1962). *Bot. Rev.*, **28,** 411.

Sneath, P. H. A. and Sokal, R. R. (1962). *Nature, Lond.*, **193,** 855.

Snyder, W. C. and Toussoun, T. A. (1965). *Phytopathology*, **55,** 833.

Sokal, R. R. and Sneath, P. H. A. (1963). *Principles of Numerical Taxonomy* (Freeman, San Francisco).

Solomon, S. (1952). *Proc. Ind. Acad. Sci.*, B. **35,** 122.

Somers, E. (1961). *Ann. appl. Biol.*, **49,** 246.

Somers, E. (1962). *Sci. Progr. Lond.*, **50,** 218.

Sorauer, P. C. M. (1874). *Handbuch der Pflanzenkrankheiten* (Berlin).

Sorauer, P. C. M. (1879). *Die Obstbaumkrankheiten* (Berlin).

Spanis, W. C., Munnecke, D. E. and Solberg, R. A. (1962). *Phytopathology*, **52,** 455.

Spencer, E. Y. (1968). *Guide to the Chemicals used in Crop Protection* (5th ed.), Canada Dep. Agric. Publication 1093.

Spikes, J. D. and Stout, M. (1955). *Science, N.Y.*, **122,** 375.

Sprague, R. (1953). In *Yb. Agric. U.S. Dep. Agric.*, *1953*, 667.

Sproston, T. (1957). *Phytopathology*, **47,** 534.

Srivastava, B. I. S., Shaw, M. and Vanterpool, T. C. (1962). *Can. J. Bot.*, **40,** 53.

Stahmann, M. A. (1963). *Bull. Conn. agric. Exp. Stn*, 663, 14.

Stakman, E. C. (1915). *J. agric. Res.*, **4,** 193.

Stakman, E. C. and Christensen, C. M. (1946). *Bot. Rev.*, **12,** 205.

Stakman, E. C. and Christensen, C. M., (1960). In *Plant Pathology*, Vol. **3,** edit. by Horsfall, J. G. and Dimond, A. E., pp. 567–624 (Academic Press, London and New York).

Stakman, E. C. and Harrar, J. G. (1957). *Principles of Plant Pathology* (The Ronald Press, New York).

Stakman, E. C., Levine, M. N. and Loegering, W. Q. (1944). *U.S. Dep. Agric., agric. Res. Admin., Bur. Ent. Pl. Quar., E.* 617. Abstract in *Rev. appl. Mycol.*, **24,** 272, 1945.

Stakman, E. C., Stewart, D. M. and Loegering, W. Q. (1962). *Minnesota agric. Exp. Stn Pap.*, 4691.

Standen, J. H. (1943). *Iowa St. Coll. J. Sci.*, **17**, 263. Abstract in *Rev. appl. Mycol.*, **23,** 383, 1944.

Staples, R. C. and Stahmann, M. A. (1963). *Science, N.Y.*, **140,** 1320.

Staples, R. C. and Stahmann, M. A. (1964). *Phytopathology*, **54,** 760.

Stapley, J. H. and Gayner, F. C. H. (1969). *World Crop Protection*, Vol. **1** (Iliffe Books Ltd., London).

Stapp. C. (1961). *Bacterial Plant Pathogens* (Oxford University Press, London).

Starkey, R. L., Stille, B., Katznelson, H. and Clark, F. E. (1961). In *Recent Advances in Botany*, Vol. **1,** edit. by Bailey, D. L., pp. 601–618 (University of Toronto Press, Toronto).

Starr, M. P. (1959). *A. Rev. Microbiol.*, **13,** 211.

Steere, R. L. (1955). *Phytopathology*, **45,** 196.

Steinberg, R. A. (1947). *J. agric. Res.*, **75,** 199.

Steinberg, R. A. (1951). *Pl. Physiol.*, **26,** 807.

Steinberg, R. A. (1952). *Pl. Physiol.*, **27,** 302.

Stephanov, K. M. (1935). *Bull. Pl. Prot. Lenigr.*, Ser. 2, *Phytopathology*, No. 8, 1, cited by Gregory (1961).

Stevens, N. E. (1939). *Science, N.Y.*, **89,** 339.

Stevens, N. E. (1941). *Science, N.Y.*, **93,** 172.

Stevens, N. E. and Scott, W. V. (1950). *Agron. J.*, **42,** 307.

Stevens, N. E. and Stevens, R. B. (1952). *Disease in Plants* (Chronica Botanica Co. Waltham, Mass.).

Stevens, R. B. (1949). *Science, N.Y.*, **110,** 49.

Stevens, R. B. (1960). In *Plant Pathology*, Vol. **3,** edit. by Horsfall, J. G. and Dimond, A. E., pp. 357–429 (Academic Press, London and New York).

Stevenson, F. J. and Jones, H. A. (1953). In *Yb. Agric. U.S. Dep. Agric.*, *1953*, 192.

Steward, F. C. (1963). *Plant Physiology*, Vol. **3,** edit. by Steward, F. C. (Academic Press, London and New York).

Stewart, R. N. and Schindler, A. F. (1956). *Phytopathology*, **46,** 219.

Stiles, W. (1961). *Trace Elements in Plants*, 3rd ed. (Cambridge University Press, London).

Stolp, H., Starr, M. P. and Baigent, N. L. (1965). *A. Rev. Phytopath.*, **3,** 231.

Stoner, W. N. and Moore, W. D. (1953). *Pl. Dis. Reptr*, **37,** 181.

Stover, R. H. (1953). *Phytopathology*, **43,** 499.

Stover, R. H. (1959). In *Plant Pathology, Problems and Progress, 1908–1958*, edit. by Holton, C. S., pp. 339–355 (University of Wisconsin Press, Madison).

Stowe, B. B. and Yamaki, T. (1957). *A. Rev. Pl. Physiol.*, **8,** 181.

Strobel, G. A. (1963). *Phytopathology*, **53,** 592.

Strobel, G. A. and Sharp, E. L. (1965). *Phytopathology*, **55,** 413.

Stuart, N. W. and Cathey, H. M. (1961). *A. Rev. Pl. Physiol.*, **12,** 369.

Subramanian, D. and Saraswathi-Devi, L. (1959). In *Plant Pathology*, Vol. **1,** edit. by Horsfall, J. G. and Dimond, A. E., pp. 313–348 (Academic Press, London and New York).

Sumere, C. F. Van, Sumere-De Preter C. Van and Ledingham, G. A. (1957). *Can. J. Microbiol.*, **3,** 761.

Sussman, A. S. (1968). In *The Fungi*, Vol. **3,** edit. by Ainsworth, G. C. and Sussman, A. S., pp. 447–486 (Academic Press, London and New York).

Sussman, A. S. and Halvorson, H. O. (1966). *Spores; their Dormancy and Germination* (Harper and Row, New York).

Swenson, K. G. (1968). *A. Rev. Phytopath.*, **6,** 351.

Szkolnik, M. and Gilpatrick, J. D. (1970). *Phytopathology*, **60,** 578.

Talboys, P. W. (1958). *Trans. Br. mycol. Soc.*, **41,** 242.

Talboys, P. W. (1964). *Nature, Lond.*, **202,** 361.

Tamari, K. and Kaji, J. (1954). *Bull. Fac. Agric. Niigata Univ.*, **5,** 33.

Tamari, K. and Kaji, J. (1955). *J. agric. Chem. Soc. Japan*, **29,** 185. Abstract in *Rev. appl. Mycol.*, **35,** 712, 1956.

Tapke, V. F. (1951). *Phytopathology*, **41,** 622.

Tapke, V. F. (1953). *Phytopathology*, **43,** 407.

Tarr, S. A. J. (1951). *Leaf Curl Disease of Cotton* (Commonwealth Mycological Institute, Kew).

Tarr, S. A. J. (1953). *Emp. Cott. Gr. Rev.*, **30,** 19.

Tarr, S. A. J. (1954). *Ann. appl. Biol.*, **41,** 578.

Tarr, S. A. J. (1955). *The Fungi and Plant Diseases of the Sudan* (Commonwealth Mycological Institute, Kew).

Tarr, S. A. J. (1956). *Nature, Lond.*, **178,** 935.

Tarr, S. A. J. (1957). *Pl. Prot. Bull.*, *F.A.O.*, **5,** 85.

Tarr, S. A. J. (1957a). *Nature, Lond.*, **180,** 1143.

Tarr, S. A. J. (1957b). *Emp. J. exp. Agric.*, **25,** 185.

Tarr, S. A. J. (1959). *Outl. Agric.*, **2,** 168.

Tarr, S. A. J. (1959a). *Wld Crops, Nov–Dec., 1959.*

Tarr, S. A. J. (1960). *Wld Crops, Jan. 1960.*

Tarr, S. A. J. (1961). *Emp. Cott. Gr. Rev.*, **38,** 30.

Tarr, S. A. J. (1962). *Diseases of Sorghum, Sudan Grass and Broomcorn* (Commonwealth Mycological Institute, Kew).

Tarr, S. A. J. (1963). *Mycol. Pap.*, 85.

Taubenhaus, J. J. and Ezekiel, W. N. (1936). *Am. J. Bot.*, **23,** 10.

Taylor, C. F., Smoot, J. J., Quinn, D. O., Rhode, R. A. and Elliott, E. E. (1955). *Phytopathology*, **45,** 673.

Taylor, J. (1953). *Phytopathology*, **43,** 268.

Thatcher, F. S. (1939). *Am. J. Bot.*, **26,** 449.

Thatcher, F. S. (1942). *Can. J. Res.*, (*C*), **20,** 283.

Thimann, K. V. (1963). *A. Rev. Pl. Physiol.*, **14,** 1.

Thimann, K. V. and Sachs, T. (1966). *Am. J. Bot.*, **53,** 731.

Thomas, C. A. and Orellana, R. G. (1963). *Science, N.Y.*, **139,** 334.

Thomas, C. A. and Orellana, R. G. (1964). *Phytopath. Z.*, **50,** 359.

Thomas, I. and Vevai, E. J. (1940). *Ann. appl. Biol.*, **27,** 393.

Thomas, M. D. (1951). *A. Rev. Pl. Physiol.*, **2,** 293.

Thomas, M. D. (1961). In *Air Pollution. WHO, Monograph Ser.*, No. **42,** 233.

Thomason, I. J. *et al.* (1970). *Phytopathology*, **60,** 7.

Thompson, J. F. (1967). *A. Rev. Pl. Physiol.*, **18,** 59.

Thomson, A. D. (1956). *Aust. J. agric. Res.*, **7,** 428.

Thorn, G. D. and Ludwig, R. A. (1962). *The Dithiocarbamates and related Compounds* (Elsevier, Amsterdam).

Thorne, G. N. (1966). In *The Growth of Cereals and Grasses*, edit. by Milthorpes F. L. and Ivins, J. D., pp. 88–105 (Butterworths, London).

Thresh, J. M. (1967). *Ann. appl. Biol.*, **60,** 455.

Thrower, L. B. (1965). *Phytopath. Z.*, **52,** 319.

Thrower, L. B. (1966). *Phytopath. Z.*, **56,** 258.

Tillet, M. (1755). *Dissertation on the Cause of the Corruption and Smutting of the Kernels of Wheat*, English translation by William G. Smith, 1789, and Humphrey, H. H. *Phytopath. Class.*, **5,** 1937.

Timonin, M. I. (1940). *Can. J. Res.*, (*C*), **18,** 444.

Timonin, M. I. (1941). *Soil Sci.*, **52,** 395.

Tinline, R. D. (1962). *Can. J. Bot.*, **40,** 425.

Tinline, R. D. and MacNeill, B. H. (1969). *A. Rev. Phytopath.*, **7,** 147.

Tisdale, W. H. (1917). *J. agric. Res.*, **33,** 845.

Todd, J. M. (1958). *Proc. 3rd Conf. Potato Virus Diseases. Lisse-Wageningen*, 132.

Togashi, K. (1949). *Biological Characters of Plant Pathogens; Temperature Relations* (Meibundo Co., Tokyo).

Togashi, K., Ogasawara, N. and Tamari, K. (1960). *Ann. phytopath. Soc. Japan*, **25,** 142. Abstract in *Rev. appl. Mycol.*, **40,** 749, 1961.

Tomiyama, K. (1963). *A. Rev. Phytopath.*, **1,** 295.

Tomlinson, J. A. and Carter, A. L. (1970). *Ann. appl. Biol.*, **66,** 381.

Tomlinson, J. A., Carter, A. L., Dale, W. T. and Simpson, C. J. (1970). *Ann. appl. Biol.*, **66,** 11.

Topps, J. H. and Wain, R. L. (1957). *Nature, Lond.*, **179,** 652.

Torgeson, D. C. (1967). In *Fungicides*, Vol. **1,** edit. by Torgeson, D. C., pp. 93–123 (Academic Press, London and New York).

Torgeson, D. C. (1967a). *Fungicides*, Vol. **1**, edit. by Torgeson, D. C. (Academic Press, London and New York).

Torgeson, D. C. (1969). *Fungicides*, Vol. **2**, edit. by Torgeson, D. C. (Academic Press, London and New York).

Townsend, B. B. (1954). *Trans. Br. mycol. Soc.*, **37**, 222.

Toxopeus, H. J. (1956). *Euphytica*, **5**, 221. Abstract in *Rev. appl. Mycol.*, **36**, 346, 1957.

Toyoda, S. and Suzuki, N. (1957). *Ann. phytopath. Soc. Japan*, **22**, 173. Abstract in *Rev. appl. Mycol.*, **37**, 718–719, 1958.

Toyoda, S. and Suzuki, N. (1960). *Ann. phytopath. Soc. Japan*, **25**, 172. Abstract in *Rev. appl. Mycol.*, **40**, 749, 1961.

Traversi, B. A. (1949). *Rev. Invest. agric., B. Aires*, **3**, 345. Abstract in *Rev. appl. Mycol.*, **30**, 165, 1951.

Trelease, S. F. and Trelease, H. M. (1928). *Bull. Torrey bot. Club*, **55**, 41.

Tribe, H. T. (1955). *Ann. Bot.*, **19**, 351.

Trione, E. J. (1950). *Phytopathology*, **50**, 482.

Troutman, J. L. and Wills, W. H. (1964). *Phytopathology*, **54**, 225.

Tsung-Che Tseng and Bateman, D. F. (1959). *Phytopathology*, **59**, 359.

Tubeuf, K. Von (1895). *Pflanzenkrankheiten durch kryptogame Parasiten verursacht*, (Berlin). English translation by Smith, W. G. (1897).

Turian, G. and Hamilton, R. H. (1960). *Biochim. Biophys. Acta*, **41**, 148.

Turner, E. M. C. (1961). *J. exp. Bot.*, **12**, 169.

Turner, G. J. (1967). *Trans. Br. mycol. Soc.*, **50**, 251.

Turner, J. N. (1959). *Outl. Agric.*, **2**, 229.

Tweedy, B. G. (1969). In *Fungicides*, Vol. **2**, edit. by Torgeson, D. C., pp. 119–145 (Academic Press, London and New York).

Uehara, K. (1959). *Ann. phytopath. Soc. Japan*, **24**, 224. Abstract in *Rev. appl. Mycol.*, **39**, 522, 1960.

Ulfvarson, U. (1969). In *Fungicides*, Vol. **2**, edit. by Torgeson, D. C., pp. 303–329 (Academic Press, London and New York).

Ullrich, J. and Schrodter, H, (1966). *NachrBl. dt. PflSchutzdienst, Stuttgart*, **18**, 33. Abstract in *Rev. appl. Mycol.*, **45** no. 3390, 1966.

Ullstrup, A. J. (1970). *Phytopathology*, **60**, 1597.

Unger, F. (1833). *Die Exantheme der Pflanzen* (Vienna).

Uritani, I. and Akuzawa, T. (1959). In *Plant Pathology*, Vol. **1**, edit. by Horsfall, J. G. and Dimond, A. E., pp. 349–390 (Academic Press, London and New York).

Uttaman, P. (1950). *Proc. Ind. Acad. Sci., B*, **32**, 133.

Vallega, J. and Chiarappa, L. (1964). *Phytopathology*, **54**, 1305.

Vakili, N. G. and Caldwell, R. M. (1957). *Phytopathology*, **47**, 536.

Vanterpol, T. C. (1926). *Phytopathology*, **16**, 311.

Vaughn, J. R. (1948). *Phytopathology*, **38**, 27.

Velsen, R. J., Van (1957). B. Ag. Sc. thesis, University of Adelaide, 1957, cited by Flentje, 1959.

Virtanen, A. I. and Hietala, P. K. (1955). *Acta Chem. Scand.*, **9**, 1543.

Wade, G. C. (1956). *Aust. J. agric. Res.*, **7**, 504.

Waggoner, P. E. (1960). In *Plant Pathology*, Vol. **3**, edit. by Horsfall, J. G. and Dimond, A. E., pp. 291–312 (Academic Press, London and New York).

Waggoner, P. E. (1962). *Phytopathology*, **52**, 1100.

Waggoner, P. E. (1965). *A. Rev. Phytopath.*, **3**, 103.

Waggoner, P. E. and Horsfall, J. G. (1969). *Conn. agric. Exp. Stn Bull.*, 698.

Waggoner, P. E. and Horsfall, J. G. (1969a). *Agric. Sci. Rev.*, **7**, 13.

Wain, R. L. and Carter, G. A. (1967). In *Fungicides*, Vol. **1**, edit. by Torgeson, D. C., pp. 561–611 (Academic Press, London and New York).

Wain, R. L. and Wilkinson, E. H. (1943). *Ann. appl. Biol.*, **30**, 379.

Wain, R. L. and Wilkinson, E. H. (1946). *Ann. appl. Biol.*, **33**, 401.

Wakimoto, S. and Yoshii, H. (1958). *Ann phytopath. Soc. Japan*, **23**, 79. Abstract in *Rev. appl. Mycol.*, **38**, 142, 1959.

Wal, A. F. Van der, Shearer, B. L. and Zadoks, J. C. (1970). *Neth. J. Pl. Path.*, **76**, 261.

Waldee, E. L. (1945). *Iowa St. Coll. J. Sci.*, **19**, 435. Abstract in *Rev. appl. Mycol.*, **27**, 513, 1948.

Walker, J. C. (1941). *Bot. Rev.*, **7**, 458.

Walker, J. C. (1950). *Plant Pathology*, 3rd ed. (McGraw-Hill, New York).

Walker, J. C. (1953). *Bot. Rev.*, **19**, 606.

Walker, J. C. (1959). In *Plant Pathology, Problems and Progress, 1908–1958*, edit. by Holton, C. S., pp. 32–41 (University of Wisconsin Press, Madison).

Walker, J. C. (1965). *Bot. Rev.*, **31**, 331.

Walker, J. C., Link, K. P. and Angell, H. R. (1929). *Proc. nat. Acad. Sci. U.S.A.*, **15**, 845.

Walker, J. C. and Stahmann, M. A. (1955). *A. Rev. Pl. Physiol.*, **6**, 351.

Wallace, H. A. H. (1959). *Can. J. Bot.*, **37**, 509.

Wallace, J. M. (1944). *J. agric. Res.*, **69**, 187.

Wallace, T. (1961). *The Diagnosis of Mineral Deficiences in Plants* (London, H.M.S.O.).

Wallen, V. R. (1955). *Pl. Dis. Reptr*, **39**, 674.

Wallen, V. R. (1964). In *Microbial Behaviour 'in vitro' and 'in vivo'*, edit. by Smith, H. and Taylor, J., pp. 187–212 (Cambridge University Press, London).

Waller, J. M. (1969). *Trans. Br. mycol. Soc.*, **52**, 139.

Wallin, J. R. (1967). In *Ground Level Climatology*, edit. by Shaw, R. H. (American Association for the Advancement of Science, Washington, D.C.).

Ward, H. M. (1903). *Ann. mycol., Berl.*, **1**, 132.

Warren, J. R. (1948). *Mycologia*, **40**, 391.

Watanabe, T., Smith, R. S. and Snyder, W. C. (1967). *Phytopathology*, **57**, 1010.

Waterhouse, W. L. (1921). *Ann. Bot.*, **35**, 557.

Watson, I. A. (1957). *Phytopathology*, **47**, 507.

Watson, I. A. (1957a). *Phytopathology*, **47**, 510.

Watson, I. A. (1970). *A. Rev. Phytopath.*, **8**, 209.

Way, J. M. and Keyworth, W. G. (1959). *Ann. appl. Biol.*, **47**, 685.

Webb, P. C. R. (1949). *Nature, Lond.*, **163**, 608.

Weber, D. J. and Ogawa, J. M. (1965). *Phytopathology*, **55,** 159.

Weber, D. J. and Stahmann, M. A. (1964). *Science, N.Y.*, **146,** 929.

Webster, C. C. (1967). *The Effects of Air Pollution on Plants and Soil* (Agricultural Research Council, London).

Webster, J. (1952). *New Phytol.*, **51,** 229.

Webster, J. (1970). *Introduction to Fungi* (Cambridge University Press, London).

Webster, J. and Lomas, L. (1964). *Trans. Br. mycol. Soc.*, **47,** 535.

Webster, J. M. and Lowe, D. (1966). *Parasitology*, **56,** 313.

Wehnelt, B. (1937). *Nachr. Schadlingsbekampfung, Bayer*, **12,** 45.

Weille, G. A. de (1965). *Agric. Met.*, **2,** 1.

Weindling, R. (1939). *Phytopathology*, **29,** 755.

Weinhold, A. R. and English, H. (1964). *Phytopathology*, **54,** 1409.

Weintraub, M. and Ragetli, H. W. J. (1961). *Phytopathology*, **51,** 215.

Wellensiek, S. J. (1927). *Phytopathology*, **17,** 815.

Wellman, F. L. (1943). *Phytopathology*, **33,** 175.

Wellman, F. L. (1964). *A. Rev. Phytopath.*, **2,** 43.

Wellman, F. L. (1970). *Pl. Dis. Reptr*, **54,** 355, 539.

Wellman, R. H. (1967). In *Fungicides*, Vol. **1,** edit. by Torgeson, D. C., pp. 125–151 (Academic Press, London and New York).

West, B. and Wolf, T. F. (1955). *J. gen. Microbiol.*, **12,** 396.

Weston, W. H. (1923). *J. agric. Res.*, **23,** 239.

Wetter, C. (1965). *A. Rev. Phytopath.*, **3,** 19.

Wheeler, H. (1969). *Phytopathology*, **59,** 119.

Wheeler, H. (1969*a*). *Phytopathology*, **59,** 1093.

Wheeler, H. and Black, H. S. (1962). *Science, N.Y.*, **137,** 983.

Wheeler, H. and Hanchey, P. (1968). *A. Rev. Phytopath.*, **6,** 331.

Wheeler, H. and Luke, H. H. (1963). *A. Rev. Microbiol.*, **17,** 223.

Wheeler, H. and Pirone, T. P. (1969). *Science, N.Y.*, **166,** 1415.

Whetzel, H. H. (1919). *An Outline of the History of Phytopathology* (W. B. Saunders Co., Philadelphia).

Whitaker, D. R. (1953). *Arch. Biochem. Biophys.*, **43,** 253.

Whitaker, D. R. (1957). *Can. J. Biochem. Physiol.*, **35,** 733.

Wickens, G. M. (1956). *Ann. appl. Biol.*, **44,** 129.

Wild, N. (1929). *Phytopath. Z.*, **1,** 367. Abstract in *Rev. appl. Mycol.*, **9,** 264, 1930.

Wilhelm, S. (1950). *Phytopathology*, **40,** 368.

Wilhelm, S. (1955). *Phytopathology*, **45,** 180.

Wilhelm, S. (1956). *Phytopathology*, **46,** 293.

Wilhelm, S. (1959). In *Plant Pathology, Problems and Progress, 1908–1958*, edit. by Holton, C. S., pp. 356–366 (University of Wisconsin Press, Madison).

Wilkinson, J. (1953). *Nature, Lond.*, **171,** 658.

Wilkinson, J. (1960). *Ann. Bot.*, **24,** 516.

Williams, E. B. and Kuc, J. (1969). *A. Rev. Phytopath.*, **7,** 223.

Williams, E. B. and Shay, J. R. (1957). *Genetics*, **42,** 704.

Williams, P. G., Scott, K. J. and Kuhl, J. L. (1966). *Phytopathology*, **56,** 1418.

Williams, P. G., Scott, K. J., Kuhl, J. L. and Maclean, D. J. (1967). *Phytopathology*, **57,** 326.

Wilson, A. R. (1937). *Ann. appl. Biol.*, **24,** 258.
Wilson, A. R. (1963). *Ann. appl. Biol.*, **51,** 171.
Wilson, E. M. (1958). *Phytopathology*, **48,** 595.
Wilson, M. and Henderson, D. M. (1966). *British Rust Fungi* (Cambridge University Press, London).
Wiltshire, S. P. (1915). *Ann. appl. Biol.*, **1,** 335.
Wingard, S. A. (1941). *Bot. Rev.*, **7,** 59.
Wingerberg, F. (1933). Abstract in *Rev. appl. Mycol.*, **13,** 49, 1934.
Winstead, N. N. and Hebert, T. T. (1956). *Phytopathology*, **46,** 229.
Wittwer, S. H. and Teubner, F. G. (1959). *A. Rev. Pl. Physiol.*, **10,** 13.
Wolf, F. A. and Wolf, F. T. (1947). *The Fungi*, Vols. **1** and **2** (Wiley, New York).
Wood, R. K. S. (1951). *Ann. appl. Biol.*, **38,** 203.
Wood, R. K. S. (1955). In *Mechanisms of Microbial Pathogenicity*, edit. by Howie, J. W. and O'Hea, A. J., pp. 263–293 (Cambridge University Press, London).
Wood, R. K. S. (1959). In *Plant Pathology, Problems and Progress, 1908–1958*, edit. by Holton, C. S., pp. 100–109 (University of Wisconsin Press, Madison).
Wood, R. K. S. (1960). In *Plant Pathology*, Vol. **2,** edit. by Horsfall, J. G. and Dimond, A. E., pp. 233–272 (Academic Press, London and New York).
Wood, R. K. S. (1960a). *A. Rev. Pl. Physiol.*, **11,** 299.
Wood, R. K. S. (1967). *Physiological Plant Pathology* (Blackwell, Oxford).
Wood, R. K. S., Ballio, A. and Graniti, A. (1971). *Phytotoxins in Plant Diseases*, edit. by Wood, R. K. S., Ballio, A. and Graniti, A. (Academic Press, London and New York).
Wood, R. K. S. and Tveit, M. (1955). *Bot. Rev.*, **21,** 441.
Woodcock, D. (1959). In *Plant Pathology, Problems and Progress, 1908–1958*, edit. by Holton, C. S., pp. 267–279 (University of Wisconsin Press, Madison).
Woodcock, D. (1964). *A. Rev. Phytopath.*, **2,** 321.
Woodcock, D. (1967). In *Fungicides*, Vol. **1,** edit. by Torgeson, D. C., pp. 613–642 (Academic Press, London and New York).
Woodham-Smith, C. (1962). *The Great Hunger*, London (Reprinted as a Four Square paperback).
Woods, F. W. (1960). *Bot. Rev.* **26,** 546.
Woolley, D. W. (1952). *A Study of Antimetabolites* (Wiley, New York).
Woolley, D. W. (1959). In *Plant Pathology, Problems and Progress, 1908–1958*, edit. by Holton, C. S., pp. 130–134 (University of Wisconsin Press, Madison).

Yarwood, C. E. (1936). *Phytopathology*, **26,** 845.
Yarwood, C. E. (1936a). *J. agric. Res.*, **52,** 645.
Yarwood, C. E. (1939). *Phytopathology*, **29,** 933.
Yarwood, C. E. (1939a). *Phytopathology*, **29,** 288.
Yarwood, C. E. (1950). *Am. J. Bot.*, **37,** 636.
Yarwood, C. E. (1952). *Mycologia*, **44,** 506.
Yarwood, C. E. (1953). *Phytopathology*, **43,** 70.
Yarwood, C. E. (1956). *A. Rev. Pl. Physiol.*, **7,** 115.
Yarwood, C. E. (1956a). *Phytopathology*, **46,** 523.
Yarwood, C. E. (1956b). *Phytopathology*, **46,** 540.
Yarwood, C. E. (1956c). *Pl. Dis. Reptr*, **40,** 318.

Yarwood, C. E. (1957). *Adv. Virus Res.*, **4**, 243.

Yarwood, C. E. (1957a). *Bot. Rev.* **23**, 235.

Yarwood, C. E. (1959). In *Plant Pathology*, Vol. **1**, edit. by Horsfall, J. G. and Dimond, A. E., pp. 521–562 (Academic Press, London and New York).

Yarwood, C. E. (1959a). In *Plant Pathology, Problems and Progress, 1908–1958*, edit. by Holton, C. S., pp. 548–556 (University of Wisconsin Press, Madison).

Yarwood, C. E. (1964). *Nature, Lond.*, **203**, 426.

Yarwood, C. E. (1964a). *Phytopathology*, **54**, 936.

Yarwood, C. E. (1967). *A. Rev. Pl. Physiol.*, **18**, 419.

Yarwood, C. E. and Middleton, J. T. (1954). *Pl. Physiol.*, **29**, 393.

Yarwood, C. E. Resconich, E. C., Ark, P. R., Schlegel, D. E. and Smith, K. M. (1961). *Pl. Dis. Reptr*, **45**, 85.

Yarwood, C. E. and Sylvester, E. S. (1959). *Pl. Dis. Reptr*, **43**, 125.

Yoshii, H. (1936). *Ann. phytopath. Soc. Japan*, **6**, 199. Abstract in *Rev. appl. Mycol.*, **16**, 339, 1937.

Yoshii, H. (1941). *Bull. Sci. Fak. Terkult. Kyushu imp. Univ. Fukuoka Japan*, **9**, 277, cited by Wood, 1967.

Yoshii, H. (1948). *Ann. phytopath. Soc. Japan*, **13**, 14.

Young, P. A. (1926). *Bot. Gaz.*, **81**, 258.

Yu, P. K. and Viglierchio, D. R. (1964). *Exp. Parasitol.*, **15**, 242.

Zaag, D. E., Van der (1956). *Tijdschr. Plantenziekten*, **62**, 89.

Zadoks, J. C. (1965). *Pl. Prot. Bull.*, *F.A.O.*, **13**, 1.

Zak, B. (1964). *A. Rev. Phytopath.*, **2**, 377.

Zakon, S. J. and Benedek, T. (1944). *Bull. Hist. Med.*, **16**, 155.

Zallinger, J. B. (1773). *De morbis plantarum cognoscendis et curandis dissertation exphaenominis deducta* (Innsbruck).

Zaracovitis, C. (1965). *Nature, Lond.*, **206**, 954.

Zaumeyer, W. J. (1958). *A. Rev. Microbiol.*, **12**, 415.

Zaumeyer, W. J. and Harter, L. L. (1943). *J. agric. Res.*, **67**, 305.

Zentmyer, G. A. (1961). *Science, N.Y.*, **133**, 1595.

Zentmyer, G. A. and Rich, S. (1956). *Phytopathology*, **46**, 33.

Ziegler, H. (1962). *Encycl. Pl. Physiol.*, **17**, 484.

Zimmer, D. E. (1965). *Phytopathology*, **55**, 296.

Zimmerman, W. A. (1936). *Z. Bot.*, **30**, 209, cited by Wood, 1967.

Acknowledgements

The author acknowledges with thanks the courtesy of all who have kindly given permission for the reproduction of the following illustrations.

Figure 2.1. From Orlob, G. B., 'The Concepts of Etiology in the History of Plant Pathology', in *Höfchenbr. Bayer Pflschutz-Nachr.* **17** (1964), figure 7.

Figure 10.1. From Butler, E. J. and Jones, S. G., *Plant Pathology*, Macmillan, London (1949), figure 103.

Figure 10.2. From Butler, E. J. and Jones, S. G., *Plant Pathology*, Macmillan, London (1949), figure 108.

Figure 10.3. From Butler, E. J. and Jones, S. G., *Plant Pathology*, Macmillan, London (1949), figure 111.

Figure 10.4. From Gäumann, Ernst, *Principles of Plant Infection*, Crosby Lockwood, London (1950), figure 4.

Figure 11.3. From Hawker, L. E., *Physiology of Fungi*, University of London Press (1950), figure 7.

Figure 11.4. From Peyton, G. I. and Bowen, C. C., *Am. J. Bot.*, **50** (1963), figure 11, p. 792.

Figure 15.1. From Plank, J. E. Van der, *Plant Diseases*, Academic Press, London and New York (1963), figure 14.1.

Figure 15.2. From Hadwiger, L. A. and Schwochau, M. E., *Phytopathology*, **59** (1969), table 1, p. 225.

Figure 17.5. From Zadoks, J. C., *Pl. Prot. Bull. F.A.O.*, **13** (1965), figure 1, p. 7.

Figure 18.1. From Bessey, E. A., *Morphology and Taxonomy of Fungi* (1950), figure 135A. (c) McGraw-Hill, New York.

Figure 18.3. After CMI Distribution Maps of Plant Diseases, No. 237.

Figure 19.1. From Rotem, J. and Palti, J., *Ann. Rev. Phytopath.*, **7** (1969), figure 3, p. 280.

Figure 22.1. From Large, E. C. and Honey, J. K., *Plant Pathology*, **4**, (1955), figure 1, p. 2, reproduced by permission of H.M. Stationery Office.

From James, W. C., Jenkins, J. E. E. and Jemmett, J. L., *Ann. appl. Biol.*, **62**, figure 8, p. 288, by permission of the Editor.

Keys (c), (d), and (e) are included by permission of the Plant Pathology Laboratory of the Ministry of Agriculture, Fisheries and Food.

Figure 23.1. From Sharvelle, E. G., *The Nature and Uses of Modern Fungicides*, Burgess, Minneapolis (1961), figure 2.

Index

Diatretynes, in disease resistance, 321
Dichlone, fungicide, 520
Dichloran, fungicide, 508
Dichloropropane-dichloropropene (D-D), fungicide, 521
Dimethirimol, fungicide, 526
Dinocap, fungicide, 520
Disease complexes, 460
Disease-pest complexes, 461
Disease incidence, assessment of, 434
  disease assessment diagrams and scales, 437
  methods used in, 435
Dispersal of plant pathogens by
  hyphal fragments, 351
  insects, 369
  man, 376
  mites, 374
  nematodes, 374
  other animals, 375
  spores, air borne
    deposition, 361
    dispersal, 359
    liberation, 354
    long-distance dissemination, 362
    production, 353
    splash-dispersed, 366
    water, 368
Dispersing agents, use with fungicides, 494
Dodine, fungicide, 521
Dyrene, fungicide, 518

Emulsifying agents, use with fungicides, 494
Endodermis, as a barrier against plant pathogens, 252
Endoparasitic pathogens, 175
Entry of pathogens into plants through
  buds, 167
  cuticle (direct), 157, 161
  flowers, 167
  hydathodes, 156
  lenticels, 156
  lesions of other pathogens, 151
  root hairs, 166
  seedlings, 166
  stomata, 152
  wounds due to climatic factors, 150
  wounds due to insects, 150
  wounds due to man, 150
wounds due to nematodes, 150
Entry by hyphae, 168
Entry by mycelial strands, 168
Entry by rhizomorphs, 168
Enzymes
  cellulases, 225
  cuticle degrading, 217

hemicellulases, 228
  lignin degrading, 228
pectic enzymes
  in leaf spots, 222
  in soft rots, 222
  in vascular wilts, 223
pectic glycosidases, 220
pectic lyases, 220
pectinesterases, 220
phosphatidases, 229
polygalacturonases, 220
proteolytic, 229
protopectinase, 221
Epidemiological patterns
  compound interest pathogens, 380
  in rusts, 393
  in seed borne pathogens, 393
  simple interest pathogens, 380
Epiphytotics
  characteristics of, 387
  conditions favouring, 390
  rapid, 389
  simulation of, by computer, 412
  slow, 388
Eradication of alternate hosts of rusts, 476
Eradication of alternative hosts of plant pathogens, 476
Eradication of plant pathogens, 475
Ethirimol, fungicide, 526
Ethylene damage to plants, 22
Ethylene dibromide, fungicide, 521

Ferbam, fungicide, 517
Filipin, antifungal antibiotic, 522
Flooding, destruction of diseased plant tissue by, 473
Floral abnormalities caused by pathogens, 206
Forecasting of plant diseases
  apple scab (*Venturia inaequalis*), 425
  bean stem blight (*Macrophomina phaseoli*), 427
  beet root rot (*Aphanomyces cochlioides*), 426
  club root (*Plasmodiophora brassicae*) of brassica crops, 426
  cucurbit downy mildew (*Pseudoperonospora cubensis*), 423
  empirical methods, 428
  fundamental methods, 428
  grape downy mildew (*Plasmopara viticola*), 423
  groundnut leaf spots (*Mycosphaerella arachidicola*, *M. berkeleyi*), 424
  Lima bean downy mildew (*Phytophthora phaseoli*), 423
  maize bacterial wilt ((*Xanthomonas stewarti*), 419